D0671156

THEORETICAL GENETICS

RICHARD B. GOLDSCHMIDT

THEORETICAL GENETICS

UNIVERSITY OF CALIFORNIA PRESS
BERKELEY AND LOS ANGELES 1958

UNIVERSITY OF CALIFORNIA PRESS
BERKELEY AND LOS ANGELES

CAMBRIDGE UNIVERSITY PRESS
LONDON, ENGLAND

SECOND PRINTING, 1958

LIBRARY OF CONGRESS CATALOG CARD NUMBER: 55-9881
PRINTED IN THE UNITED STATES OF AMERICA

DESIGNED BY JOHN B. GOETZ

PREFACE

The introduction to this book contains all the information on its scope and intentions, remarks which might have been used in a preface. Thus only the statement is added here that I have tried to the best of my ability to keep the facts up to date to the very moment of going into print.

I should not have been able to finish the manuscript during a time of severe personal handicaps but for the devoted and unselfish help given me by Dr. Leonie Kellen Piternick. I have no words to express my feelings of gratitude for everything she did, voluntarily, efficiently, and graciously. Thanks are due to Dr. Sarah Bedichek Pipkin for her help with the editing of the manuscript.

This book was written while I had the privilege of a Guggenheim fellowship, graciously offered by Dr. Henry Allan Moe. I do not need to emphasize gratefully how much this meant to me.

My thanks are offered finally to the University of California Press for the traditionally fine publishing job.

Richard B. Goldschmidt
Professor of Zoölogy Emeritus

Berkeley, California, 1955

CONTENTS

PART III:

THE ACTION OF THE GENETIC MATERIAL

PART IV:

GENETICS OF SEX DETERMINATION

INTRODUCTION

Zuwachs an Kentnis ist Zuwachs an Unruhe.
Goethe, *Aus meinem Leben,* 8. Buch

Our doubts are traitors
And make us lose the good we oft might win
By fearing to attempt.
Shakespeare, *Measure for Measure*

The division of physics into experimental and theoretical physics is generally accepted. The meaning of this subdivision is well expressed in the British name for theoretical physics: Natural Philosophy. It means that philosophical features are abstracted from the descriptive and experimental facts and formulated in a general way. In physics the obvious method of doing so is with the help of advanced mathematical treatment.

There is no reason why biological disciplines should not proceed in the same way. But actually theoretical biology has, in most instances, tried to consider biological facts in terms of abstract philosophy, if not metaphysics, while the general elaboration of laws and rules has been intricately interwoven with the diverse types of factual study. Abstract concepts such as mechanism, vitalism, teleology, holism, creative evolution, and psycholamarckism are the topics of discussion in theoretical biology; but the theoretical aspects, say, of evolution or development are usually discussed with the factual presentations as an integral part of the special knowledge. Many biologists are suspicious of generalizations which are not part and parcel, actually a small part, of descriptive or experimental studies. There is even a school of biologists which frowns upon any general ideas beyond the limited topic of the special study. These workers would consider the non-existence of a theoretical biology, comparable to theoretical physics, a very laudable condition. This proves that biology has not yet progressed to the same level as physics, besides not being intrinsically able to generalize in terms of mathematical functions, except in limited, special fields. It may be appropriate to insert a telling quotation from a theoretical physicist (Whittaker, 1952).

"At this point it may be observed that there is a notable difference between theoretical Physics on the one hand and Pure Mathematics and Experimental Physics on the other, in respect of the enduring validity of the advances that are made. A theorem of Pure Mathematics, once discovered, is true forever; all the pure mathematics that Archimedes knew more than 2000 years ago is taught without essential change to our students today. And the results of Experimental Physics, so far as they are simply the expression in mathematical language of the unchangeable brute facts of experience, have the same character of permanence. The situation is different with an intellectual adventure such as Theoretical Physics: it is built round conceptions and the progress of the subject consists very largely in replacing these conceptions by other conceptions, which transcend, or even contradict, them. At the beginning of the century the two theories which seemed most firmly established were that which represented gravitation in terms of action at a distance, and that which represented light as a motion of waves: and we have seen the one in a certain sense supplanted by General Relativity and the other trying to make the best of an uneasy conjunction with Quantum-mechanics. The fame of a theoretical physicist rests on the part that his ideas have played in the history of the science; it does not necessarily detract from his importance if none of them survive into the physics of his remote successors."

Genetics, younger than other biological fields, has not reached the level at which theoretical genetics can be established as a recognized discipline. Generalizing and theorizing in genetics is still a part, and a minor one, of the factual attack upon individual problems, though it seems that the tendency is increasingly to extend specific generalizations to a wider field, which would amount to the emergence of a theoretical genetics. Thus my endeavor to sketch an outline of a future theoretical genetics is not outside the trends of the time. Speaking for myself, it is actually a further development of a personal inclination which has been at the back of about forty-five years of genetical work. Though I had the good fortune to contribute a large and diversified mass of factual data in many separate fields of our science, I always made the effort to draw general conclusions and to extend these to as many groups of facts as I could muster. To satisfy my own need for unified thought, I tried to work generalized, all-embracing ideas into a unified and coördinated system which might be called genetical theory or theoretical genetics. In my first book of this kind (1920*a*), which is probably unknown to present-day geneticists, I started with the facts derived from the discovery of intersexuality and its genetical and developmental analysis, which led me to present definite ideas about the gene and its action, and to bring together genetics, development, and evolution on the basis of a simple generalization. Ever since, I have felt constrained to review the accumulating facts, my own as well as those of other investigators, with the intention of building up a general theory of heredity which would unify and explain the welter of facts. Thus, while my experimental, factual work remained always in the foreground I indulged from time to time in the dangerous pleasure of looking over the whole and trying to explore the possibilities for broad general conceptions. The major steps in this development were my books of 1920*a*, 1927, 1938*a*, and 1940, and such general discussions as those of 1934*b*, 1938*d*, 1944, 1946*b*, 1948*c*, 1951*a*, 1952*a*, and 1954.

Sewall Wright's work approached the same goal during the same time, and many points of contact as well as divergence exist.

I consider the time ripe for a review of the basic features of genetics so far as they contribute to the emergence of a theoretical genetics. It is not my intention to present a complete review and discussion of the facts and all the ideas which have been offered to explain them. I propose, rather, to select the salient facts and ideas, and to present them as I see them in their meaning for the general theory of genetics. Hence this study will not be a text or a review, but rather an intimate and personal report, a dialogue with others of a similar or a different mental attitude, a dialogue in which (as is true of all good dialogues) I endeavor to convince my interlocutors of the correctness of my own point of view. But I realize that it is rather unimportant whether I succeed in this or not, so long as I and perhaps a few others may derive satisfaction from a well-rounded synthesis.

Theoretical genetics comprises all the problems connected with the following questions: (1) What is the nature of the genetic material? (2) How does the genetic material act in controlling specific development? (3) How do the nature and action of the genetic material account for evolution? These three major problems of genetics are closely interconnected, for the answer to one affects the answer to the others. Since these problems cover the entire body of genetical facts, their analysis will have to touch upon numerous individual phases of genetics, including the disciplines upon which genetics rests, such as cytology and experimental embryology, but also many other border fields. Since the present work is neither a textbook nor a review, it is assumed that the reader has advanced knowledge of genetics as well as of general biology.

It is obvious that some more or less arbitrary decisions have had to be made in regard to the inclusion of topics. To include every topic on which theoretical discussions are possible or have been made would be a hopeless undertaking. I tried to make it a rule not to enter in detail into problems which, though interesting in themselves, do not contribute much to the general theory of genetics. Hence, for example, the theory of crossing over is mentioned only briefly because it is considered to be a special problem. For general genetic theory it is very important that crossing over occurs. But whether Janssens' or Belling's or Darlington's or any other theory is correct does not affect the theory of the gene and its action. The aspects of this problem that bear upon general theory will be mentioned, but the specific theories will not be taken up. This does not mean, however, that one day a new solution of the problem may change this situation completely and make it focal for genetic theory. This type of limitation will occur with many individual topics, and I suggest that a reader who misses a topic in which he is interested ask himself whether I did not omit it for the reason indicated above. In a number of cases he will find that I discussed the topic in my other writings, but decided that it does not belong here. Of course, another author would probably have different ideas and make different selections.

PART I THE NATURE OF THE GENETIC MATERIAL

1

THE CHROMOSOME AND ITS DIVISION

An inquiry into the nature of the genetic material must start with the following basic facts. (1) The chromosomes are the structural elements which from bacteria to man are in control of the major features of heredity. (2) All chromosomes are similar in structure and behavior. (3) On the morphological as well as the genetical level, chromosomes are largely constant within a given species. This includes their "individuality," meaning their actual continuity through all phases of cell life. (4) Chromosomes are able to duplicate and the two duplicates are normally identical, morphologically and genetically. (5) Chromosomes in diploid organisms, or diploid stages of organisms, consist of two sets of identical partners. (6) These homologues are endowed with the ability to synapse, undergo meiosis, and exchange segments at definite stages of the cellular cycle. (7) Chromosomes have in addition to their visible structure a genetical structure, which is strictly polarized: this linear differentiation is completely orderly from point to point in a definite and constant pattern, which duplicates exactly in division. On the morphological level this is often visible as a constant arrangement of different segments or chromomeres and also as the typical point by point synapsis in meiosis. On the genetical level it is expressed in the well-known arrangement of genetic loci or genes on the chromosome map. (8) Chemically, chromosomes are always a combination of proteins, only a few of which are known, and desoxyribonucleic acid (DNA), both together being the chromatin of the cytologist. A varying amount of ribonucleic acid (RNA) is also present. (9) There is a chemical interaction between chromosomes and cytoplasm involving the nucleic acids, especially RNA. (10) The chromosomes are capable of abnormal behavior: breakage, abnormal distribution, and so on. The genetic consequences are always those expected on the basis of the known genetic, polarized structure. All the facts of classic genetics may thus be described as a result of the distribution of the chromosomes and their parts, which is an expression of the statistical consequences of chromosomal behavior in meiosis and fertilization. (11) The cytoplasm must play a role in heredity, since no nucleus without cytoplasm exists. Whether cytoplasmic heredity is independent of the chromosomes and, if so, how it compares with chromosomal heredity are special questions. (12) The genic material within the chromosomes is self-duplicating and capable of mutating into a new and again self-duplicating condition, and if genetic material exists in the cytoplasm it must have the same characteristics.

It is not difficult to derive a theory of the genetic material which accounts for most of the basic facts in a formal way. In the classic theory of the gene, a chromosome is a string of discrete bodies, the genes, arranged in linear order within the framework of the chromosome. These genes are endowed with the power of self-duplication as well as of specific attraction to their likes and repulsion to unlikes, and they interact in some way with the cytoplasm as determiners of reactions. It is the first problem of theoretical genetics to scrutinize the details of chromosomal behavior which underlie these basic facts, and to see whether the theory of the gene in its classic formulation is a satisfactory description and a logical explanation of the facts, or whether it will have to be replaced by a more comprehensive idea which accounts for more of the special facts. Thus we must scrutinize the details of the cytological and genetical facts pertinent to the formulation of a general theory to see whether they point to a general principle which might or might not be the classic theory of the gene. In doing so we shall have to touch upon many facts without trying to catalogue them, but with the intention of not missing any really relevant information.

The first question is whether the known structure, chemistry, and behavior of the chromosome shed any light upon its genetic organization. Clearly, the basic fact of genetics is the ability of the chromosome to reduplicate. If there were no genetic material to be duplicated, the old description of the chromosome splitting into longitudinal halves would suffice. The more recent additional details, namely, the dividing of the centromere and the appearance of the two coiled chromonemata, would not change the simple picture of a more or less amorphic material growing to double size and just being divided up. But this simple picture is no longer accurate when we think of the genetic material in the chromosome. Whatever its chemical composition, an exact replica is required by the facts of genetic constancy.

Biochemists seem to be generally of the opinion that a large molecule of the type probably constituting the genic material is not synthesized independently in innumerable synthetic steps by the respective enzymes, but is molded by a template process involving the surface of the molecule to be reduplicated. For the details of this concept on a molecular basis see Pauling and Delbrück (1940) and Friedrich-Freksa (1940); for its application to the genetic material see also S. Emerson (1945). The idea requires the interimistic production of a negative. Recently Watson and Crick (1953*a,b;* Crick, 1954) have proposed for the first time a molecular structure which makes possible an understanding of how the template idea works. We shall present the details later in our discussion. A variant of the template ideas proposed by Haldane (1954) will be mentioned below when discussing crossing over.

Assuming the genetic material in the chromosome to consist of a series of individual gene molecules, it would not be difficult to visualize such a scheme of duplication if the old idea were true that the chromosome disintegrates in the resting nucleus and is reassembled at the time of division. The gene molecule floating in the nuclear sap could proceed with re-creating its likeness as indicated. The non-genic part of the chromosome could divide by real fission and afterward adsorb the genes in their proper place, say by means of specific haptenes comparable to those assumed to act in immunity reactions. (If I am not mistaken, I first used such a scheme when I tried a since disproved and discarded alternative explanation for crossing over; Goldschmidt, 1917*b*.)

All the more recent developments of cytology point, however, in the direction of a chromosome which remains more or less, if not completely, intact in the interphase nucleus. Chromosomes have been isolated by grinding up resting nuclei, even of cells like erythrocytes, which do not divide further; as far as can be judged, the structure and biochemistry of these chromosomes are normal (Claude and Potter, 1943; Mirsky and Ris, 1947*a,b,* 1951). (But doubts still exist in regard to the chromosomal nature of the isolates; see Alfert's review, 1954.) Moreover, a number of cell types are known, like gland cells of waterbugs (Geitler, 1940*a,* 1954) and tissue cells of Diptera, in which the chromosomes in resting nuclei are visible, with their normal structural details, because of polyteny and (or) giant size. Though the visibility of the structural details seems to be an unusual feature of these giant chromosomes, the presence of intact chromosomes may be safely assumed for all interphase nuclei. It has been observed many times that telophase chromosomes may double before restoration of the daughter nucleus. Thus it may be considered certain that whatever the genic material is, it divides or reduplicates with and within the chromosome. The biochemist interested in these problems easily forgets that the genetical problems are on the chromosomal level and that facts relating to molecules, even large ones, must be integrated into the structure of the chromosome.

These facts raise great difficulties for the assumption of individual gene molecules which duplicate by re-creation of their like. Whatever the genic material, it is an integral part of the entire chromosome. This means it is a part of a rather complicated structure which is capable of exact reduplication. Though chromosomes, especially those of different size, may vary in structural details, we may safely assume that all chromosomes have in common these elements: (1) a chromonema which is able to change its length by visible coiling and uncoiling, and also able in special cases to undergo molecular uncoiling; (2) a nucleoprotein or chromatin which is part of the chromonema but tends to accumulate at about equal distances along the chromonema as chromomeres of different and typical size which are visible when the chromonema is much uncoiled, as in prepachytene chromosomes, or extremely stretched, as in giant chromosomes; (3) some kind of ground substance between the coils of the chromonema, sometimes called kalymma, which may form an actual membrane that seems to appear and disappear easily; (4) a centromere, which is certainly a differentiation of or within the chromonema that may or may not be comparable to other parts of the chromonema (to call it a gene, as some geneticists do, is rather confusing); (5) nucleolus-forming regions, which again are part of the chromonema structurally, though in some way different from both centromeres and chromomeres.

This complex structure has the mechanical and optical properties of a visible fiber and therefore must be built of micellae of parallel chain molecules (Schmidt, 1937, 1941). Unlike an ordinary fiber these micellae cannot be simple polymerized chains of one kind, and they must be integrated somehow into the complicated structure of the whole. A chromosome, therefore, is an organism rather than a fiber, though it has a fibrous structure and is doubly refringent at certain stages. Hence its division can hardly be the fission of bundles of identical micellae or the re-creation of individual molecules at the surface of old ones. The genic material, whatever it is, cannot individually duplicate by re-creation, but its duplication must be an integral part of the duplication of the entire chromosome. The alluring picture of the template theory meets, therefore, with tremendous difficulties when we try to apply it to the real chromosome and not to an ideal gene molecule, except when we assume that the chromosome is a single immensely long and thoroughly coiled molecule.

There is no doubt that the centromere with the spindle-fiber attachment plays a decisive role in the division of the chromosome, for fragments without a centromere are doomed. This may be a mechanical feature, meaning that the centromere alone is capable of sprouting a spindle fiber or of making the connection with one, whatever theory of spindle formation turns out to be true, under the assumption that only the centromere-spindle mechanism can separate the two split halves. There is some reason to assume that centromeres and centrioles are identical elements, since Pollister's (1943) work has shown that in the atypical sperm of *Paludina* the centromeres of discarded chromosomes behave subsequently like centrioles. If this is true, the centromere is completely different from the other constituents of the chromosome, though it remains a body endowed primarily with the ability of self-duplication just like the centriole. This would mean also that its location within the series of chromomeres could hardly be used as evidence that it is a special kind of chromomere (e.g., a piece of heterochromatin). It is more comparable to the cytoplasmic centrioles and "kineties." The position of the centromere as an apparent member of the chromomeric series would be indicative of a mechanical cause: the function of the centromere in division requires its being anchored in the chromonema, in analogy but not in homology with the chromomeres.

The centromere, like the centriole, seems to have two main properties: the ability to divide; and, after Pollister's (1943) work and Carothers' (1936) observations on grasshopper spermatocytes, the ability to sprout an axial fiber. Whether the latter is due to molecular unfolding, as some work on flagella indicates, or to polymerization is not known. Thus the centromere becomes a non-genic, non-chromatic differentiation of the chromonema, which nevertheless has the property of self-duplication. There is a strong suspicion that two centromeres may unite, two sister centromeres in preleptotene and two homologous centromeres in diakinesis. Though an origin of a centromere *de novo* has never been proved, and though the acquisition of a centromere by a separating chromosome arm may be due to translocation or abnormal duplication of the centromeric region, an origin *de novo* cannot be called impossible; in parthenogenetic sea urchin eggs centrioles may be formed *de novo* (if Wilson's old observations still stand), which, in view of the interchangeability of the two organelles, may likewise be a capacity of the centromere. There remains the rather enigmatic diffuse centromere which Schrader (1953) finds in coccids and scorpions. Since this would mean a stretching of the centromere the entire length of the chromosome, it would exclude any relation to the series of chromomeres in the chromonema and demand a self-duplication which occurs completely in harmony with the processes for the entire chromosome. However, the possibility cannot be excluded that the diffuse centromere is a repeating member of the chromomeric series, pushed together in the metaphase chromosome by the extreme coiling.

This leads us to Lwoff's and Chatton's brilliant studies and generalizations based upon the division of the infusorian body (see Lwoff, 1950*b*). The equivalent of a centriole in a dividing cell or in a flagellate or sperm and, therefore, of a centromere is, in Infusoria, a kinetosome. This body can produce different structures according to its position in the cell or the time within the life cycle. It can divide into two kinetosomes; it can sprout a fiber or a cilium; it can grow into a trichocyst, a tubular structure which can be protruded; also a trichite, a stiff hair. The decisive feature is that the kinetosome cannot be formed *de novo*, but is a self-duplicating elementary structure. This means that a new kinetosome cannot be produced without the participation of the old one, serving as a template or autocatalytic agent. In this respect the kinetosome would be comparable to the genic material, but it should be emphasized, in view of Watson and Crick's work on the template structure of the DNA molecule, that no nucleic acid is present in these structures, just as there is none in centrioles and centromeres. The comparison could also be extended to the kinetosome's ability to produce the forementioned products dependent upon its chemical surroundings and to change its functions by "mutation." One important point must be added, or, rather, specified. When a kinetosome divides and one of the products develops irreversibly into a trichocyst, this may be called an unequal division. However, it may also happen that one of the products of unequal division does not transform directly into a trichocyst, but first divides repeatedly before each descendant becomes a trichocyst.

As already stated, there is every reason to assume that the centromere in the chromosome is equivalent to the centriole and also to the kinetosome. Thus it may be concluded, on the basis of Lwoff's analysis, that the centromere is basically a self-duplicating body just as any genic material within the chromosome or any self-duplicating material within the cytoplasm. Compared with the kinetosome, however, the potencies of the centromere are limited to the formation (or participation in the formation) of the spindle fiber and, in special cases, as in the *Paludina* sperm, an axial fiber. Therefore the centromere would not be different from the genic material if self-duplication alone were considered to be the characteristic of genic material. But it would be very different in regard to functional potencies. It is important to keep this in mind when discussing self-duplication as the main characteristic of genetic material. There is a whole school willing to call any self-duplicating material a gene. This attitude forces the facts into a scheme which does violence to clear notions.

Returning to the phenomenon of chromosome division, another point from Lwoff's work must be mentioned. At a given time of the ciliate cycle, all kinetosomes may divide simultaneously. This means, to Lwoff, the interaction of the kinetosome with a specific substance. Applying this fact and interpretation to the chromosome, it could be concluded that the appearance of such a hypothetical substance within the chromosome (all chromosomes) would start the division of all self-duplicating parts of the chromosome, centromere as well as genic material. If this is so, the chromosome becomes a still more complicated organism. In certain divisions (meiosis of the lepidopteran egg) large amounts of RNA are sloughed off the chromosome, which must have been present somewhere outside the chromonema itself. This underscores the danger of drawing conclusions about processes on the chromosomal level from molecular models.

Do these facts and interpretations shed light upon the division of the chromosome as a whole? We see two possibilities. The first is that no further problem is involved. Just as a kinetosome duplicates as a whole, with an organization far above the molecular level, the much more complicated chromosome may duplicate in all its parts and the resulting daughter parts separate. This means that the old naïve description of the chromosome being split in two is literally true, with the addition that some essential parts are self-duplicating after the manner required by the template theory. This leaves us where we were, unable to understand such a procedure in a micellar, fibrous body only part of which, the genic material (and perhaps also the centromere), is supposed to be self-duplicating on the molecular level.

The second possibility is that we do not compare the chromosome to the kinetosome or to a string of kinetosomes but to the entire protozoan organism, of course only by analogy, not by homology. We consider the chromosome as a unit containing systems of self-duplicating subunits, arranged according to a pattern under the influence of forces within the whole, which may be called "field forces." These subunits, further, are controlled in their duplication by a "substance" or field action working over the whole; they are subject also to a polarized force or gradient originating in the centromere or its surroundings. This would mean that the division of the chromosome is not simply the sum of the divisions of the self-duplicating genic units, but is a feature of the entire chromosomal unit, involving fields and gradients in addition to the self-duplicating parts. This again means that a ground substance, a kalymma or whatever it may be called, must be present which, in analogy to the cytoplasm of the ciliate, is the seat of the coördinating substances, fields, and gradients. This non-genic part of the chromosome contains only one self-duplicating part, the centromere. The rest may be considered as growing by accretion and dividing by fission.

It is obvious that this discussion has a considerable bearing upon the problem of what the genic material is in the chromosome and what its organization is. It clearly points to an over-all organization of the chromosome in which the self-duplicating genic parts are not independent of the whole, as opposed to the genic string of the classic theory. The only alternative would be that the chromosome is a single immensely folded and coiled molecule, a simplification which could hardly meet the facts of cytology. Again we must warn against making the leap from a DNA molecule to the whole chromosome too lightheartedly. We shall return to this point below, when studying Watson and Crick's model of the structure of nucleic acid, revealing a new type of template-like self-duplication and its relation to genic material and chromosomes.

The argument will become still more cogent if we add a few more relevant facts in regard to Lwoff's findings on the self-duplicating kinetosomes and the organelles derived from them. There are a few more important facts to be added which relate to the field action already mentioned. First (Lwoff), the realization of the potencies of the kinetosomes of the ciliates depends upon their localization within the proper cytoplasm, that is, their respective chemical surroundings. Second, the behavior of the differentiations of the ciliate body during division involves: (1) the formation of two morphogenetic fields within the cytoplasmic body which control subsequent processes; (2) the destruction of all differentiations based upon the products of the kinetosomes; (3) the division of one or a few kinetosomes and the distribution of the daughter granules (or fibers) in the two fields; (4) the formation of "anarchic fields" of kinetosomes, and finally their

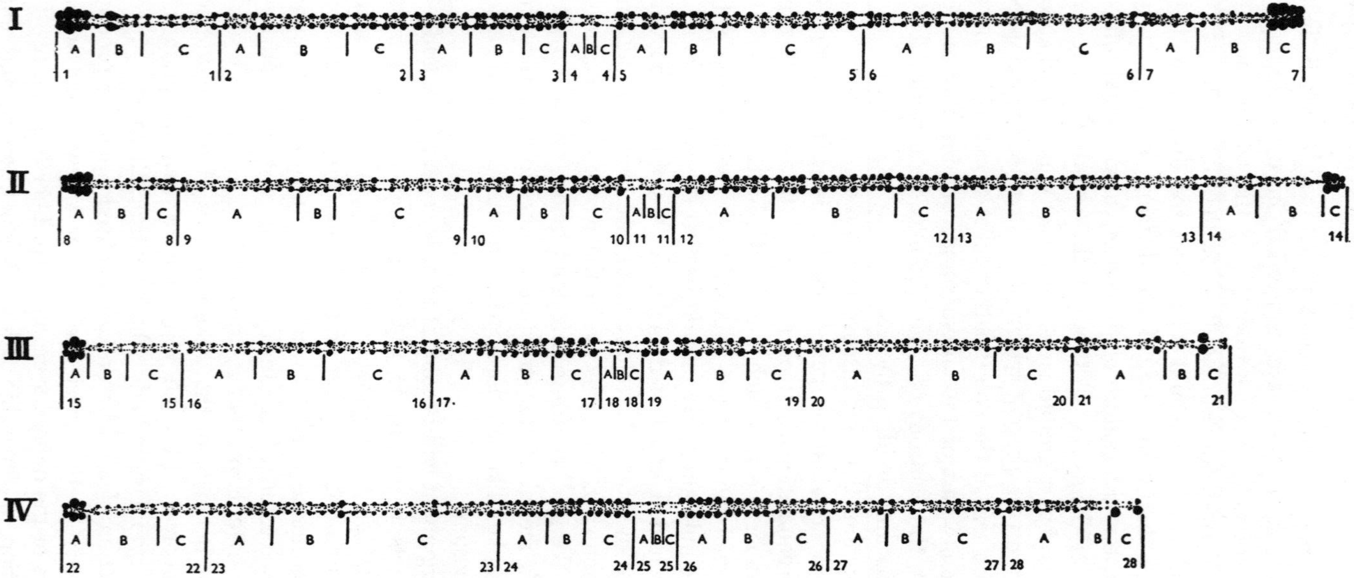

I
A B C A B C A B C A B C A B C A B C A B C
1 1 2 2 3 3 4 4 5 5 6 6 7 7
II
A B C A B C A B C A B C A B C A B C A B C
8 8 9 9 10 10 11 11 12 12 13 13 14 14
III
A B C A B C A B C A B C A B C A B C A B C
15 15 16 16 17 17 18 18 19 19 20 20 21 21
IV
A B C A B C A B C A B C A B C A B C A B C
22 22 23 23 24 24 25 25 26 26 27 27 28 28

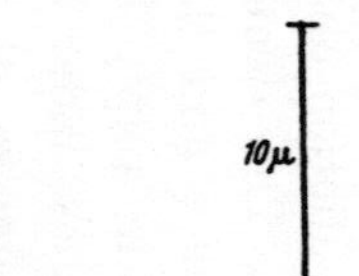

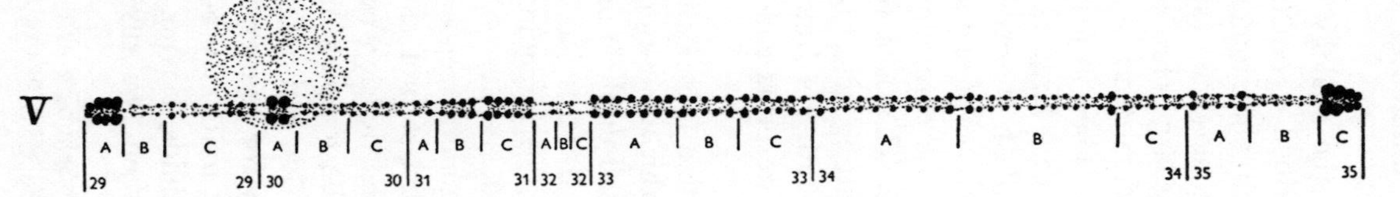

Fig. 1. The seven chromosomes and standard fragment of *Secale cereale* at pachytene, showing the chromomeres in a reference map. (From **Lima-de-Faria,** 1952.)

orderly reorganization in the proper pattern and differentiation under the influence of the specific cytoplasmic environment. This demonstrates that the complicated pattern of the kinetosomes and their products (e.g., the oral, stomatal spirals) does not divide simply, but is built up anew from individual self-duplicating bodies under the influence of field forces, gradients, and specific differences of the environment.*

Another interesting fact brings us back from the analogy to the actual chromosomes. Lima-de-Faria (1952) described a remarkable structural rule in the chromosomes of rye. The chromomeres in pachytene show a strange size gradient in all chromosomes (see fig. 1). On both sides of the centromere a particularly large chromomere is located. From here on the size of the chromomere decreases with complete regularity toward the ends of the chromosome in a typical gradient. Near the end is a knob formation with very large chromomeres; if there are any beyond, they are the smallest. It seems that knob formation and length of the chromosomal arm control the rate of this size gradient, which shows that the size of the chromomere is controlled by its position within the chromosome. This is a further proof that the dividing chromosome is not a gene string held together for purposes of the mechanics of division, but is rather a functional and structural unit in which the parts are in some respects controlled by the configuration of the whole.

This conclusion is based upon the assumption that it is possible to compare the division of the chromosome, not to the separation of a string of independent genic units after individual self-duplication, but rather to the division of a differentiated organism. If we try to derive a general picture of chromosomal division from the foregoing discussions the following hypothetical picture emerges:

1. The centromere is self-duplicating in a general sense. This means that its substance must be divided as the first step of chromosome division. It does not necessarily mean that the division consists in a re-creation of a twin molecule according to the template model. Since the only potencies of the centromere are division and outgrowth of a fiber, the exact molecular duplication necessary for genic material is not needed. A micellar bundle of self-duplicating units may be split approximately under the influence of two arising fields, leaving aside the moot question of how the body grows between two divisions.

---

* In principle this was anticipated a long time ago by Schuberg as opposed to R. Hertwig. Both were partially wrong, but Schuberg came nearer to the truth.

Since kinetosomes of ciliates may grow into fibers which break up into subunits, and since the centromere also is endowed with the faculty of growing into a fiber, the simple breakage into two of a growing centromere is quite possible, though Lwoff's work is more in favor of assuming that strict self-duplication is a basic property of the centromere and all its equivalents.

2. The important point is the relation of the exactly self-duplicating genic material to the rest of the chromosome, which is difficult to visualize in the complicated micellar organization of the chromosome, as opposed to a simple string of chain molecules, an ideal abstraction not actually representing the chromosome. It is, however, asserted that at one stage the oöcyte chromosome is a single molecular chain. (See below a discussion of lampbrush chromosomes, but these are not directly comparable to mitotic chromosomes.) If we compare the chromosome, by analogy, to an organism containing self-duplicating and simply growing parts, we can conceive a process of division very much like that of a ciliate (without the nucleus). This would mean that the cytologically visible division would be actually a simple fission after growth of the chromosome as a cylindrical, fiber-like body. The self-duplicating genic material, however, would behave like the kinetosomes in Infusoria: all micellae except a single molecular string would degenerate, and these molecules would duplicate according to the template model. We could imagine that in the so-called resting nucleus these things take place and the chromosome is stripped down to a single molecular chain of a nucleoprotein. If this were so, chromosome doubling in telophase should not be possible except where telophasic karyomeres have already produced the resting nucleus condition for each individual chromosome. I do not know whether any unassailable cases of chromosome splitting in late anaphase without karyomeres have been established.

In mitotic chromosomal division, a field-forming gradient starting from the divided centromere would produce two fields into which the duplicated molecules are drawn and arranged in their proper way by the same type of polarized field forces which produce the regular pattern of the ciliate kinetosomes after the "anarchic pattern" following division. The reproduction of the chromosome, then, requires the following: real division of the amorphic centromere; disintegration of the genic structural elements into units of molecular size; duplication of these units all within the intact amorphic, non-genic material of the chromosome; formation of two fields along the chromosome, and distribution of the duplicates to the fields with proper polarization;

and separation of the contents of the two fields by simple fission of the amorphic part of the chromosome. In such a scheme the chromosome would split and not split, it would keep its morphological individuality and nevertheless disintegrate, it would re-create (self-duplication) but also divide (growth and fission), and it would lose and reconstruct its intimate structure while remaining a unit. Up to this point it does not make any difference what ideas we have about the actual structure of the genic material. The theory of gene molecules and the more modern ideas dispensing with corpuscular genes fit equally well into the picture at the level of our present discussion. On the contrary, it is possible that the genic material never has a micellar structure but remains always an immense single-chain molecule, connected somehow with the rest of the chromosomal material of which it strips itself when dividing and afterward reassembling the whole. Biochemically, this is the simpler assumption but otherwise the less probable one. It is of course the old idea of the gene string, the genonema of Koltzoff (see 1928, 1939).

2

GENIC AND NON-GENIC PARTS OF THE CHROMOSOME

Thus far we have dealt only in a general way with genic and non-genic parts of the chromosome in relation to chromosome division. The next basic problem is to find out whether these two elements can be distinguished morphologically, chemically, or by genetical experiment.

A. CONCLUSIONS FROM MORPHOLOGY

It seems at once obvious that in this connection the centromere, the nucleolus, the ground substance, or kalymma, and, where found, the chromosomal membrane may be ruled out. The centromere may be morphologically equivalent to parts for which the problem "genetic or not genetic" exists. Normally it has morphological continuity, which may be termed genetic. We must assume, in explanation of the cytological and cytogenetic facts discussed above, that the centromere may multiply apart from chromosomal division or even be formed *de novo;* also, that two centromeres may unite. The centromere is clearly not concerned with what we understand as genic functions, that is, with control of hereditary characters. In the same way the nucleolus is not genic, although it is formed from a constant and self-perpetuating part of a chromosome, and may play an important role in the action of the genic material. A chromosomal membrane said to exist in some ordinary chromosomes (Hirschler, 1942) and certainly present in salivary gland chromosomes (Kodani, 1942) cannot be called genic. The ground substance, or kalymma, filling the spaces between the chromosomal spirals—not generally accepted as existing—is ruled out. There remain the chromonema proper with its visible differentiations, the non-chromatic or little chromatic thread, and the chromatic knots, knobs, and accretions generally called chromomeres and separated into euchromatic and heterochromatic sections.

There is no morphological differentiation between the chromomeres that could supply a clue to the genic or non-genic function of the chromonema. Physically it is fibrous and more or less spiralized according to the condition of the chromosome. Whether the chromonema ever appears completely stretched is unknown. Even in a very much stretched condition, as in the salivary chromosomes and in the lampbrush chromosomes, it can still be stretched further experimentally (Duryee, 1937), which might reach into the level of molecular unfolding. Only in the lampbrush chromosomes of the vertebrate germinal vesicle, the longest chromosomes known (Gall, 1954), does the chromonema seem maximally stretched; the single strand of the synapsed homologues has the diameter of a large chain molecule. But the electron microscope (Guyénot and Danon, 1953; Guyénot *et al.*, 1950) reveals the presence of two strands! As far as we know, the chromonema between the chromomeres is chemically not different from the chromomeral section, at least qualitatively; in the lampbrush chromosomes it contains diffuse DNA. Caspersson (1940) once maintained that different proteins are contained in the two sections, but we have not heard much about this recently. Microscopically, it may appear achromatic, but both nucleic acids are found microchemically, which may signify only a quantitative difference from the chromomeres; and even none, if the chromomeres are not an accumulation of DNA but chromonema whorls, which is not probable. Only one important difference is visible: wherever spontaneous or experimental breaks of the chromosomes can be seen microscopically (in salivary chromosomes and some pachytene chromosomes) they are located between the chromomeres. This shows that the processes leading to a break and to reunion of broken ends are confined (or at least more easily accomplished) between the chromomeres, or perhaps are visible only between the chromomeres. (Actually we have reason to believe that breaks within single salivary bands may occur, though the microscope does not reveal them.) The visible occurrence of breaks between the chromomeres does not necessarily mean that the chromonema has here a different function. It might be a purely mechanical cause which keeps chromonema incrusted with much DNA or coiled into a tight whorl (in the chromomeres) from being easily broken.

We have very little information on the visible relation of chromonema and chromomere. Salivary gland chromosomes after treatment with alkali change their structure so as to reveal within the chromomere what looks like a coil of the chromonema to which droplets of chromatin are attached (Kodani, 1942; Goldschmidt and Kodani, 1942). However, it is very difficult to say what is normal and what is an artifact in this remarkable aspect. Bauer's (1952*b*) statement that it is simply an artifact is categorical but difficult to prove. He forgets that an experiment consists in production of a controlled artifact from which to draw conclusions about the normal condition. In the present case the "artifact" is a typical, orderly structure, always produced identically with the same treatment. This must somehow be based upon a definite structural condition, which has to be analyzed.

It is possible to interpret the characteristic structure of the lampbrush chromosomes in the vertebrate oöcyte similarly. Attached to the chromomeres is a ring or rosette of fine loops of the thin chromonema (which accounts for the name "lampbrush" chromosomes; Rückert, 1892). If they were attached to a fine chromonemal coil (which cannot be seen) and incrusted with DNA (which in this stage is not the case), the same structure as in treated salivary chromosomes would be present. (See Duryee, 1941 ff.; Dodson, 1948; Guyénot *et al.*, 1950; Callan, 1952; Gall, 1954; Alfert, 1954.) Ris (1945) maintains that the chromomeres are loops of the chromonema. Thus it is rather probable that the chromonema, containing only small amounts of nucleic acid, is structurally and chemically continuous, but makes periodically tight coils to which large amounts of DNA are attached in quantities and configurations typical for the individual chromomere. Since these accumulations of DNA (fig. 1) may be controlled by a gradient centered in the centromere, the typical differences of these chromomeres are not a function of their individual chemical or physical constitution but a function of their position in the chromosome. Is the naked chromonema non-genic and the chromonema coil (if existing) plus nucleic acid or the nucleic acid alone genic? The facts reported on structure hardly permit us to draw a conclusion. Actually, they show that the whole question is wrongly put, a question which is derived from the a priori idea of the gene string. Later discussions will revert to this point and suggest a solution of the difficulties. At the present stage of our discussion it might suffice to point out that it is, in my opinion, impossible to assert that definite parts of the chromonema play the role of the string in a string of beads, while the beads themselves are alone the important factors, that is, the genic material or individual genes. However, it remains a fact that whatever complication of morphological structure is found in the chromosomes has to do with the chromomeres. Therefore, in our search for the genic material, we must scrutinize more carefully these structural elements.

The term "chromomeres" was first applied to the structure of leptotene and pachytene chromosomes, which were assumed to be fully stretched chromosomes. However, when speaking of chromomeres in a comparative way, we must always specify which chromomeres are meant. Actually, chromomeres are found at different levels of spiralization of the chromosome and are therefore not strictly comparable. At one end of the series are the large chromomeres seen in diakinesis of large chromosomes and found to be constant in a given chromosome. Their number is small, say in the neighborhood of ten. These are clearly not the same chromomeres that are typical in the leptotene and pachytene stages of animals and plants. These are again individually constant and synapse point by point, thus showing their specificity. Their number is about a hundred. Therefore the diakinetic chromomeres are compounds of the pachytene ones in the order of magnitude of ten per package. This must be the result of denser spiralization, which, however, is so exactly alike in the two homologues that the chromomere-by-chromomere synapsis still holds. The salivary gland chromosomes (with transitions in chromosomes of other dipteran tissues) are on a different level. There is no doubt that the bands or discs of these chromosomes are chromomeres (more correctly, sets of chromomeres), just as typically different and specific as the others, and that each one synapses with its homologue. The number is roughly a thousand for a large chromosome arm. Clearly, still more despiralizing must be involved. There is no reason to assume that the series has reached its end here. Kodani (1947) has shown that under certain conditions a number of small bands may contract into a single thicker band. Hence the opposite might be expected, namely, the despiralization of individual bands into still smaller units—in the present discussion, chromomeres of fourth grade. The limits of microscopic visibility are reached here, but there is no reason why this subdivision could not continue to the submicroscopic and finally the molecular level.

At this point some genetic facts must be taken into account. The technique of the salivary gland chromosomes sometimes allows a localization of a definite mutant locus within a single visible band. For example, the absence, deficiency, of a single band produces the mutant effect or the typical effect of a deficiency for the locus in question. Some optimistic geneticists do not hesitate to identify the bands with the genes of classic genetics. We shall later see why this is not possible. Here I shall mention only two facts: first, the mutant effect can be produced also by a rearrangement break between two chromomeres (position effect); second, it can be produced, too, by the complete absence of a band, as in homozygous yellow deficiency. The fact remains that the chromomeres must be of some importance in the genic function of the chromosome, even if they are not the genes themselves. A newer and more helpful theory of the genic material as related to the morphology of the chromosome will be presented later.

The chromomeres contain the major part of DNA. In the lampbrush chromosomes of the vertebrate oöcyte, which may have a diameter of only about 150–200 Å (reports vary from 150 to 1,000) and may thus be single molecular chains, Feulgen positive chromomeres are present in definite intervals, and the loops are attached to them. Nevertheless, between the chromomeres the chromonema probably also contains DNA, but so scattered that the Feulgen reaction does not always show it. These chromosomes certainly look very different from those of cleavage cells or tissue cells, but the constancy of the DNA content holds for these nuclei as for all others. It is very difficult to imagine this, if the variable visible structure indicates a really different charge or incrustation with DNA locally. It is expected, instead, that DNA is present along the entire chromonema in equal amounts and that the chromomere is therefore a kind of knot in the chromonema (loop, according to Ris, 1945), which appears more "chromatic" because of the many layers of DNA in a whorl-like structure. I still believe that the very regular artifacts produced by Kodani (1947) in salivary chromosomes are indicative of a real structure. A decision is difficult in view of the fact that one author finds only four strands in the *Drosophila* salivary chromosomes, another sixteen, and still another one thousand! All these data and claims must be brought into line if we are to derive insight into the genic properties of the visible structures from morphological work.

The synaptic attraction chromomere by chromomere is one of the major riddles of cytology. Many geneticists and biophysicists (Muller, 1947; Friedrich-Freksa, 1940; Jehle, 1952; Delbrück, 1941) have proposed explanations for the attractive forces, which seem to be beyond a physical explanation. For our present discussion we ask only whether a solution of the physical problem helps our understanding of which part of the chromosome is endowed with genic properties. Certainly synapsis is one of the basic features of genetics, without which Mendelian inheritance and crossing over would not be possible. There is no indication thus far whether the genetic material has anything to do with the phenomenon, whether it occurs on the all-chromosomal level or whether only the centromeres or other parts of the chromosome are decisive. Though the microscope reveals a synapsis chromomere by chromomere, the ignorance of what a chromomere is makes it impossible to decide whether the attraction is only between two extremely folded stretches of a macromolecule or anything else, and, further, why it is present or absent in the different stages of the chromosomal cycle but partly present in somatic cells of Diptera. No primary problem of cytogenetics is more obscure than the processes at synapsis and crossing over. The brilliant theory of Darlington (1937) amounts, at close sight, to a restatement of the observed facts in terms of unknown forces. Even the purely morphological processes at the time of crossing over (including the time itself) are unknown and the subject of dissension. Thus a more detailed discussion would hardly help our present understanding of the genic material in the chromosome. But some remarkable trends may be pointed out.

Practically all geneticists are convinced that crossing over involves breakage of chromatids and reunion. There are powerful facts in favor of this, apart from the cytological details, which still, after all the work of devoted specialists, permit such different explanations as those of Matsuura, Belling, and Darlington. But according to the well-known experiments of Stern and McClintock and Creighton, described in all textbooks, a segmental exchange, involving two breaks, seems to be a necessity for crossing over, whatever the details, causes, and forces may be. The same conclusion follows from unequal crossing over of the Bar segment, also of Beadex (Green, 1953*b*). The two attempts at explaining crossing over without exchange of segments are generally regarded as antiquated. This is true of my own theory (1917*b*) that individual genes are assembled to the chromosome after the manner of antigen-antibody fixation, with a variable force providing for the numerical rules. Another large-scale attempt at explaining crossing over without chiasmatype was made by Winkler (1930) in his conversion theory (hardly noticed until recently) of direct change of individual alleles into each other.

It is rather remarkable that elements from these older theories have been revived in a recent biochemical theory of Haldane (1954), which, however, is not worked out in detail to include the numerical aspect of crossing over. He assumes that a chromosome is copied into a different structure, related like antigen and antibody. This is a template, or negative, which is recopied into two positives. It is further assumed that original and negative are nucleic acid and protein, respectively. "It is intelligible, that each [of the copies] should be a mixed copy of maternal and paternal material. If this is correct, crossing over, in the sense of chromosome breakage and subsequent reunion, never occurs." Thinking in chemical terms, Haldane compares the non-mechanical exchange with transpeptidization, and proposes to consider the process of crossing over, as far as proteins are concerned, as a series of simultaneous transpeptidizations. I quote these views as a sign that the theory of crossing over is, after almost fifty years, still or again in the stage of uneasy discussion, even of its elementary aspects. But I may add, with due caution, that there are indications that duplication of genetic material occurs—at least in meiosis—independently of chromosome duplication. Thus it may be possible to discern genic and non-genic parts on this level: genic parts duplicated by a template mechanism, non-genic parts dividing simply so as to assemble the new genic parts into a new chromatid. Belling's old theory of crossing over led to such a view, which again may find support in recent tests for Belling's theory. This hints at the possibility that a real understanding of crossing over may also reflect upon our views on chromosomal constitution and division, and thus on the nature of the genic material (see Schwartz, 1954).

B. CONCLUSIONS FROM BIOCHEMISTRY

a. Chemistry of the chromosome

At this point we turn to biochemistry for more information. It is rather disconcerting that in the chromosomes, which should have a very complicated and diversified chemical structure, only a few components have thus far been isolated that are the same in chromosomes of the most diversified forms of animals and plants. This is in contrast to our knowledge of other active stuffs, which, though differing in different groups, seem to be within the groups always derivatives of a single chemical type: many hormones are sterols; many vitamins are amino acids; all the dubitable sex stuffs of Kuhn and Moewus were said to be derived from crocin; all enzymes are probably proteins. But the few types of proteins which have been found in chromosomes do not give us much information. The claim that different parts of the chromosome contain varying fractions of these proteins does not seem to be generally accepted. Thus the statement that the chromosomes contain chain molecules of proteins does not convey much genetical insight and does not set apart the chromosomes from other cell structures.

A different situation exists with the nucleic acids. Though only the two, DNA and RNA, have been isolated, we have at least one important fact: DNA is a typical constituent of the chromosomes which is hardly found outside the chromosomes, though it occurs sometimes in mitochondria and sometimes in the cytoplasm. RNA, however, is predominantly at home in the nucleolus, the nucleus outside the chromosomes, and in the cytoplasm. Thus DNA has established a predominant claim either to be the genetic material or to be necessary for the function of the genetic material, while RNA cannot be genetic material *sensu strictu*. This does not mean that RNA is unrelated to the function of the chromosome and, eventually, to its genic functions in some indirect way. RNA might be used in synthesis of DNA, or DNA might be the source of formation of RNA; neither theory thus far can be checked. But one thing is certain: DNA is constant in the chromosomes, while RNA is produced and again removed. The most convincing case (apart from the behavior of the nucleolus and the removal of RNA through the nuclear membrane) is that of the so-called elimination chromatin in Lepidoptera. Seiler (1914) found that in the lepidopteran egg during meiosis a considerable amount of "chromatin" is sloughed off all chromosomes and remains visible for a long time in the egg without an apparent function. It was thought at first that this might somehow parallel chromatin diminution in *Ascaris*. But it turned out that the elimination material was Feulgen negative, and recent work (Ris and Kleinfeld, 1952) proved it to be RNA. Thus RNA can accumulate on the chromosomes during oögenesis for an unknown purpose and be thrown off when not needed any more. Ris assumes that the same process might occur in other objects, but without visible removal in a body. This shows that there must be room within the structure of the chromosome for large amounts of non-genic material which can be stored and removed. The chromosome thus cannot be a single immense DNA polymer.

The present knowledge of the chemistry of the chromosome does not help much in understanding the genic material. There is always the objection that we have knowledge only—or almost only—of the chemistry of previously destroyed structures and that conclusions upon the living condition are dangerous. This does not apply, however, to the optical analysis of the chromosome by Caspersson (1939 ff.), and it does not apply (or not completely) to results of digestion with different enzymes and direct staining reactions, though such methods are rather crude from the point of view of pure chemistry.

We shall consider briefly the meaning of biochemical information for the understanding of chromosomal duplication and for the problem of the genic material in the chromosomes. With the arginine reaction the presence of large amounts of basic protein can be proved after complete removal of DNA by nuclease. This is present in the chromonema within as well as between the chromomeres. The reaction for basic protein increases with the increase of DNA in the contracting chromosome, and it is weakest when the chromosome is devoid of DNA. This conclusion from a staining reaction is, however, not safe; the result may be caused optically by the coiling of the chromonema, as in the lampbrush chromosomes. Serra (1950) states that in the salivary chromosomes the arginine content is high in the bands and low between them, which is in favor of a coupling of DNA and basic protein. In addition to protamine, histones and chromosomin have been found in the chromosomes, and a differential distribution of histones has sometimes been claimed. It would be surprising if other proteins were not present, but it seems that present techniques do not permit going beyond such crude facts as these; moreover, the chemical analysis of extracts has not gone farther. It is possible to digest DNA and the basic protein as well as RNA and the residual protein (chromosomin) without destroying the structure of the chromosome (see Mazia, 1952). However, Serra claims that the decomposition of salivary chromosomes in alkali proves that a continuous core of non-basic proteins is present in the chromonema and thus also in the chromomeres. It is the basic protein which is supposed to be linked by salt links with the DNA in the chromomeres. Serra calls this the "peripheric nucleoprotein" and considers it as identical with the kalymma of the morphologists; he concludes that only the chromonema (with its mostly non-basic protein) is responsible for genic activities, while the peripheric nucleoprotein is important in cell physiology. Thus, on the basis of a chemical investigation of the chromosome, he arrives at conclusions which are rather different from those of most cytologists and geneticists. This is partially compensated because he thinks that, at the time of reduplication of the genes, the nucleic acid surrounds the genic chromonema and produces a passing nucleoproteinic structure of the genic material. This interpretation can be easily brought into line with the results of our former discussion, based upon chromosomal morphology. The same is true of Serra's (1947) statement that it is expected, in view of the diversity of genic actions, that the pure chromonemata consist of many proteins and polypeptides. The extraction of only one protein, say chromosomin, means that this is no more than an oversimplification owing to the absence of more refined technique. (Further, not very helpful details can be found in the reviews by Mazia, 1952, and Alfert, 1954.)

From such chemical and positional facts, Serra derives further ideas on the physicochemistry of the chromonema, though the direct attack has not provided much information. The chromonema can be stretched immensely in the already stretched salivary and lampbrush chromosomes (Duryee, 1937; Buck, 1942), up to three to five times its length, which must involve molecular unfolding. The chromosome as a whole is a special kind of fiber in which the proteins are disposed as if they were semiglobular and semifibrous units, in a sequence similar to that of the genes. The proteins are folded in a visible helix (spiralization), and more or less similar foldings exist also at submicroscopic levels, down to the molecular looping which must be similar to the folding of globular proteins rather than to the more or less straight disposition of the polypeptide chains in fibrous proteins (Serra, 1947). A chromonema, however, is not a single protein chain but a bundle composed of from 10^4 to 10^5 individual chains, according to Serra's calculation.

The recent work on lampbrush chromosomes (see I 2 A) makes it probable that in the growing oöcyte the chromonema may be reduced to a single-chain molecule, probably of nucleoprotein, and there is cause to assume that the same is true of the preleptotene chromosome. The reason is that it was found (Callan and others) that the lampbrush chromonema, which (as part of a tetrad) should consist of two chromatids, is single, showing that two chromonemata may unite secondarily into one. If the one is actually a single-chain molecule, remarkable conditions must prevail here at the molecular level. Now it has been maintained by Kuwada (1940)—and there are many facts in his favor—that a preleptotene chromosome can be double (two chromatids and chromonemata) but afterward become single again by union of the two chromonemata. Such facts will have to be correlated (apart from their meaning for meiotic phenomena) with the possible micellar structure of the chromosome at other stages of its cycle. According to Guyénot and Danon (1953), the electron microscope reveals that the single strand of the lampbrush chromosome contains two parallel threads; these are clearly seen in the photos. Are these threads the molecular backbones of the two united chromatids? Or could they possibly be related to the two parallel chains of the Watson-Crick model of DNA? A diameter of 100–150 Å is given for one such "chromonema." The situation is not made clearer by what Guyénot sees in the chromomeres and loops. In the electron microscope the loops seem to consist of folding chains of rods. It is assumed that they are surrounded by fibrous protein. Only in the chromomeres—one per loop, called a "chromiole"—is DNA attached on the outside. The fact (see Duryee, 1941; and Serra, 1947) that all DNA and RNA can be removed from these chromosomes by nucleases without disturbing their coherence shows that the strands seen in the electron microscope cannot consist of nucleic acid alone. Guyénot, if I understand him correctly, considers the loops as products of the activity of the genes which take part in the metabolic processes of the oöcyte. Gall (1954) is of this opinion also. Dodson (1948) showed that the loops start as Feulgen positive hairs and later become DNA free loops. Since they can be dissolved without damage to the chromosome (Gall), they are clearly different from the chromonema and not loops of the chromonema as Ris assumed. The lampbrush chromosomes still present many riddles (see Alfert's review, 1954) and all our conclusions must be considered tentative. But we may say at least that the facts thus far do not support the idea of DNA as exclusive genic material.

Only one more discussion of the same problem from the biochemical point of view will be mentioned here, though we shall return to it below. Mazia (1952) states correctly that every constituent of the nucleus merits examination as the potential carrier of genetic specificity. He refers to the work of Marshak (1950) on nucleic acids showing that the RNA in the nucleus is chemically different from that in the cytoplasm, and further to the lack of knowledge of whether the RNA of the nucleoli is different from that of the chromosomes (analytical work by Mirsky, Kauffman, and others). Mazia emphasizes that protamine is probably specific for fish sperm with little room left for other proteins; the residual protein (chromosomin of the Stedmans, 1943, 1947) is found in variable amount, as is the case for the basic histones and a few others. In regard to the quantities of all these, he remarks that it is not very relevant to our problem, since the requirements of genetics are satisfied by quantities below the limit of present analysis. "The chromosomes consist of two major blocks of material; the DNA-basic protein fraction and the 'residual' fraction containing the insoluble residual proteins and RNA." (I refer here to the later discussions—in the chapter on genic action—of the old ideas, now reappearing, on idio- and trophochromatin.) Mazia continues, "The former may, in some types of nuclei, be extracted by means of salt solutions, leaving a structurally identifiable residual chromosome [Mirsky and Ris, 1947]. The latter may be digested by pepsin, leaving behind the DNA and at least some of the basic protein, again as a continuous structure retaining the structural characteristics of the chromosome" (Mazia, 1941, 1952). The association of DNA with one fraction and of RNA with the other is readily demonstrated by staining and by analytic methods. The relative quantity of the two fractions varies from tissue to tissue within one species. The intermolecular associations of the two fractions as well as of nucleic acid with protein are not clear, since the famous association by salt links does not correspond to the natural condition. Though some chemical suggestions can be made, no real knowledge exists about the natural associations both of DNA and protein and the two main fractions. This is not very encouraging to the geneticist, looking for genetic material with the help of the biochemist.

Another problem is the seat of the enzymes within the nucleus. Mirsky (1947) found that the phosphatase activity remains with the residual fraction when the DNA-histone fraction is removed, which might mean that the nucleoprotein considered to be genic is full of this enzyme. But later work did not lead to such simple results (see discussion by Chèvremont and Firket, 1953). Also, a DNAase was located in the nucleus (but also in the cytoplasm), which again is not very helpful.

Mazia's conclusions about the problem which is foremost in the mind of the geneticist, the nature of the genetical material in a biochemical sense, are as follows: "The 'physical basis of heredity' is something in the chromosome which may or may not be DNA, but which follows DNA for all the practical purposes of cytogenetics. We cannot be sure that the question 'what is the genetic constituent of the chromosome?' is a meaningful one. The structure of the chromosome as a whole is so astonishingly reproducible that the skillful cytologist can always recognize a given one . . . The regularities of chromosome structure may reflect regularities of intermolecular relationships so decisive that it may prove to be misleading to think in terms of molecules at all. . . . The fractions that we isolate may be extremely artificial entities, telling us a little about the weak points in the fabric but nothing about the associations as they actually function."

Mazia discusses the possibility that an unknown fraction (other than the known basic protein) may be combined with DNA for genic function and finds that the quantities needed would easily escape analysis. However, it remains a fact (according to studies with tagged P and N) that DNA is very stable and incorporates these atoms only during mitosis. After reviewing the biochemical evidence, Mazia concludes: "It would then seem that DNA meets a number of our specifications for genetic material. However, it must be remembered that the specifications themselves were necessarily extremely crude, simply because we are not yet able to formulate in chemical language the more sophisticated questions that the science of genetics asks of the gene. If we recall how poorly characterized are the chemical constituents of the nucleus and their associations, we will admit that we are scarcely in a position to formulate the alternatives, much less to propose that one of the known fractions is the genetic fraction."

It is not probable that these conclusions will have to be changed after Mazia's new work (1954). He succeeded in breaking up the sperm-head chromosomes into tiny segments of nucleoprotein, each about 4,000 Å in size. This was done without splitting peptide bonds, rather by treatment with agents (versene or citric acid and distilled water) which do not break ordinary bonds but separate units held together by electric forces, by binding calcium or magnesium ions. It is concluded that the chromosome consists of macromolecular complexes of nucleoprotein, linked by bridges of divalent ions (Ca, Mg, or both) as well as by the interactions making for insolubility at moderate ionic strengths. We do not think that these findings change anything in our discussion of the genic material.

The insight gained into the nature of the genic material in the chromosome from direct biochemical study is virtually nil thus far, and we must rely on indirect information from morphology, genetics, and general cytology. Most of such work deals with the theory that DNA is the genuine genic material (as opposed to the proteinic chromonema or genonema). Thus we must consider critically the data in favor of DNA.

b. DNA as genic material

The first and main support of the claim that DNA is the exclusive genic material is the constancy of the quantity of DNA in the nuclei of cells of a given species and its absolute dependence upon the number of chromosomes within the species. The development of more (Caspersson, 1939 ff.; see 1950) or less (Pollister and Ris, 1947) complicated methods of measuring this quantity by light absorption has led to remarkable information (work initiated by Boivin, 1947, and Mirsky and Ris, 1947, followed by Pollister, Schrader, Leuchtenberger, Alfert, and Swift; see review by Swift, 1953).

aa. Quantitative constancy of DNA

The work started from experiments with bacterial transformation in which a specific DNA supplied in the medium seems to become incorporated into the genetic system. On the theory that a genic constituent should show the same quantitative relationship per nucleus as does the chromosome number, Boivin (1947) determined the amount of DNA in tissue nuclei. The amount was found to be constant, and the amount in haploid sperm cells approximately half of it. Boivin as well as Mirsky and Ris worked this out in great detail for a variety of cells with the same result, but there were some discrepancies which could not be accounted for, because these measurements were made by chemical analysis of millions of cells. The introduction of optical methods permitting measurement of single nuclei showed the cause of the discrepancies.

Such measurements by these and other authors revealed that the quantity of DNA in many nuclei approximated a 1:2:4 ratio. Jacobj

(1925) had already shown that tissue nuclei are found in sizes of 1:2:4, and had concluded that nuclei grow by endogenous polyploidy (polyteny), that is, chromosomal division without cell division from the diploid to the tetraploid and octoploid condition. Mirsky and Ris and Boivin corroborated this conclusion and simultaneously demonstrated the constancy of the amount of DNA per chromosome set. Table 1 illustrates the fact well.

TABLE 1

AVERAGE AMOUNT OF DNA IN SOMATIC TISSUES OF MICE, IN OPTICAL MEASUREMENTS FROM FEULGEN SLIDES EXPRESSED IN ARBITRARY UNITS
(From H. Swift, 1953)

Cell type	*Subgroup*	*DNA (units)*	*Ploidy*
Liver	1	3.34	2
	2	6.77	4
	3	13.20	8
Pancreas	1	3.10	2
	2	6.36	4
	3	12.40	8
Thymus	1	3.28	2
	2	6.17	4
Lymphocytes	1	3.20	2
	2	6.00	4
Sertoli cells	1	3.00	2
	2	6.40	4
Kidney tubule		3.14	2
Intestinal epithelium		2.97	2
Spleen		3.12	2
Ganglion cells		3.14	2
Testis interstitium		3.05	2
Spermatids		1.68	1

This rule has since been confirmed many times for many types of cells. A very convincing example is illustrated in figure 2; the measurements were made in somatic cells of maize, which are basically diploid, and also in basically triploid endosperm cells, so that a clear series of sizes of 2:4:8:16 and 3:6:12:24 was obtained. The range of variation is, by the way, a good indication of the reliability of the method; another very good example is found in figure 3, *a* and *b*.

It is important for our problem to know the quantity relations of DNA in dividing cells. The measurements showed that between telophase and early prophase this quantity doubles, as it would be expected to do if the synthesis for the following division takes place at this stage and not during mitosis. This is also confirmed by the fact that radioactive phosphorus is taken into the nucleus on a large scale only at this time. For other material it is maintained that the doubling of DNA by synthesis occurs at another time. Since the visible doubling of the chromosomes seems to occur at different stages in different cells, sometimes as early as telophase, such varia-

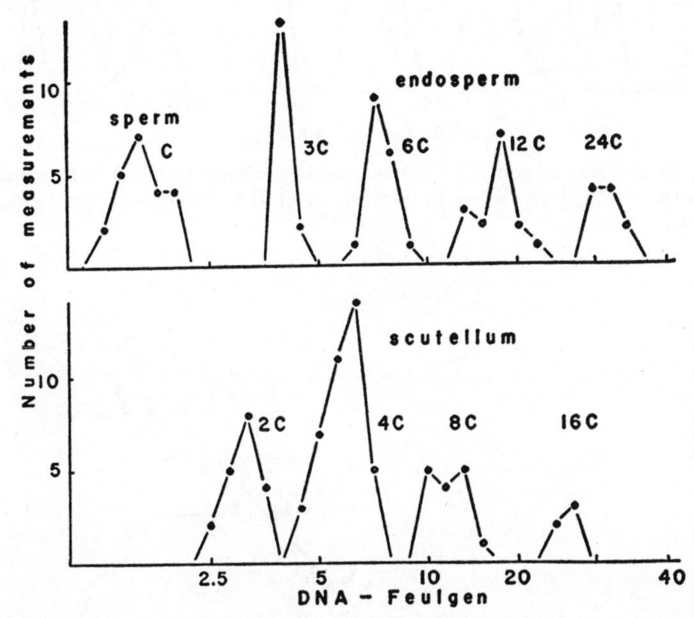

Fig. 2. Relative amounts of DNA in nuclei of maize kernel and mature pollen. A 2:4:8:16 series is evident in the scutellum, and a 3:6:12:24 series in the triploid endosperm. (From Swift, 1953; reproduced by permission of the author and the Academic Press, Inc.)

tion appears quite possible. In meiosis, synthesis of DNA for all four division products occurs before leptotene, with subsequent distribution to first and second cytes and spermatids (ova) in a ratio of 4:2:1, a fact which closely parallels the visible behavior of the tetrads.

The authors who did most of this work seem to be unanimous in their assumptions (Swift, 1953): "DNA is the one constituent of chromosomes showing the quantitative behavior that might be expected from a carrier of genetic specificity . . . RNA [as opposed to DNA] apparently shows some variability between malignant and

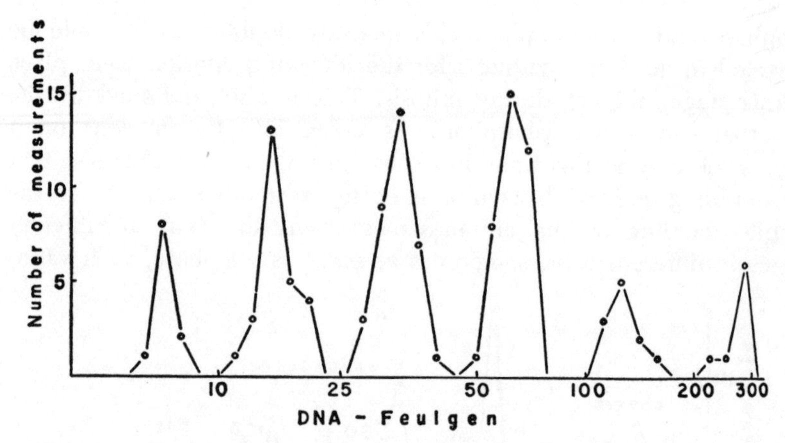

Fig. 3*a*. Relative amounts of DNA in nuclei of salivary gland of *Helix pomatia*. (From Swift, 1953; reproduced by permission of the author and the Academic Press, Inc.)

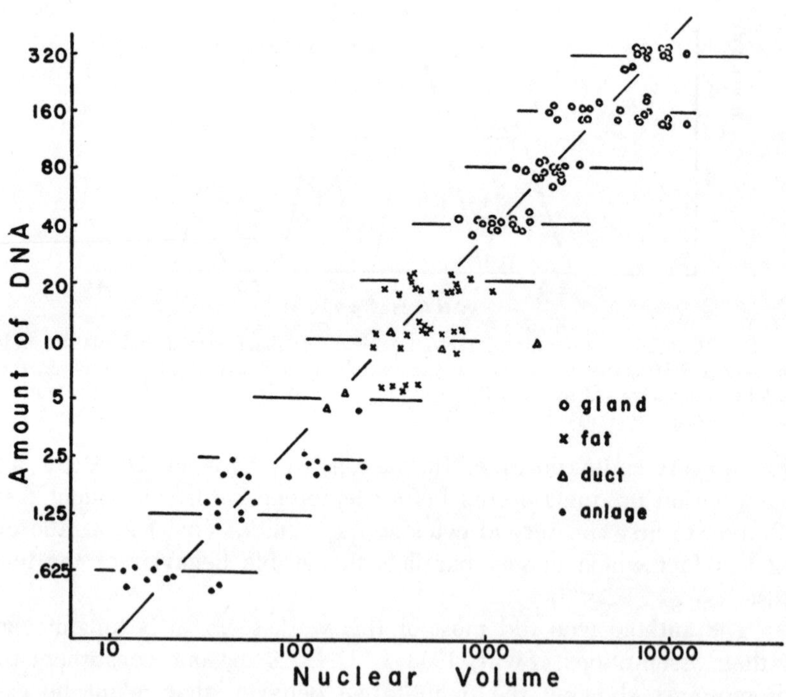

Fig. 3*b*. Amount of DNA plotted against size of different polytene cell types of *Drosophila*. (From Alfert, 1954; reproduced by permission of the author and the Academic Press, Inc.)

normal cells, but more work is needed to clarify this point. Histones are altered or lost during sperm formation in some animals, and residual protein varies from tissue to tissue in the same organism. Other protein fractions have not been studied in more than a few tissues. It is quite possible that one of these may also show a quantitative constancy." Swift's words "carrier of genetic specificity" are not identical with "genic material," though I think that he meant to say "are the genic material." We shall see that it is quite possible (even probable) that DNA has much to do with the specificity of the genic material without being it.

bb. Information derived from the structure of the nucleic acid molecule

While the importance of nucleic acid, both in quality and quantity, for the function of the chromosome cannot be denied, the geneticist cannot help feeling that this does not necessarily mean that DNA is the genetic material. It might mean that it is a necessary chemical cog in the structural stability of the chromosome or in the self-duplication of the genic material and the entire chromosome, and (or) as an energy producer for the actions in the chromosome. Actually, all these views have been derived from the chemistry of DNA, though the most recent developments favor or seem to favor the genic nature of DNA. In the main the following formula or a similar one had been accepted until recently. The molecule is a straight chain formed by the polymerization of nucleotides each of which consists of a purine or pyrimidine base and the phosphate of the desoxyribose sugar. There are four different bases in definite proportions, adenine, thymine, guanine, and cytosine, which seem to be attached platelike at a right angle. We shall consider first some consequences of these older molecular formulae.

Much has been made of the fact that Astbury's (1939) X-ray analysis revealed that these flat rings of the bases are piled on each other at a distance of 3.4 Å from one to the next, because this is also about the distance between the amino acid residues in a protein chain molecule (protamine), to which the nucleic acid is presumably joined in the chromosome, either always, or only, before reproduction, as discussed in the chapter on biochemistry of the chromosome. An important property of the molecule is the unusual viscosity in solutions. This is explained by the assumption that the molecule is a stiff rod and that in solutions these rods stick together in a network, perhaps via hydrogen bonds. It is assumed that under certain conditions and after breakage of the hydrogen bonds the molecule can fold up into a more compact form. Of course nobody knows whether these properties apply also to the molecule within the chromosome alone.

From these basic and many additional facts, conclusions have been drawn in regard to the role of the DNA molecule in the chromosome, apart from simply identifying it with the gene. It has been suggested that it acts as a template on which the peptide

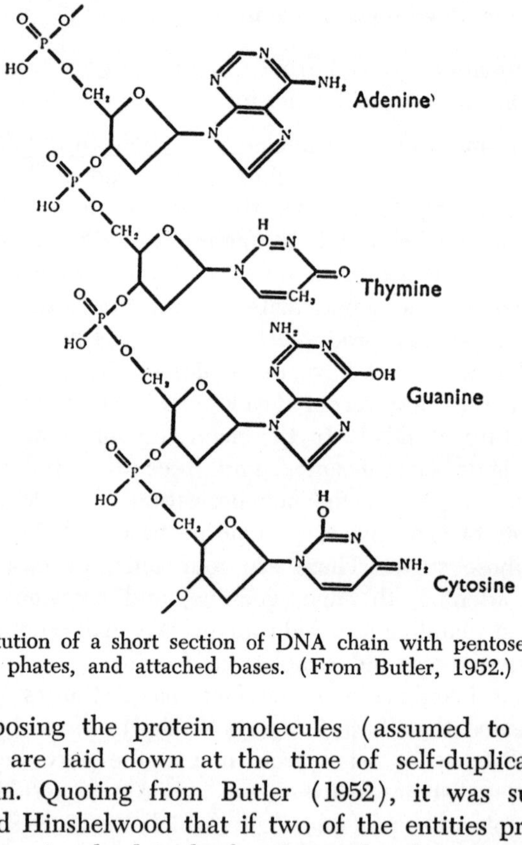

Fig. 4. Constitution of a short section of DNA chain with pentose sugars, phosphates, and attached bases. (From Butler, 1952.)

chains composing the protein molecules (assumed to be the real genic part) are laid down at the time of self-duplication of the protein chain. Quoting from Butler (1952), it was suggested by Caldwell and Hinshelwood that if two of the entities present in the nucleic acid are involved in the formation of each amino acid residue, the permutations and combinations of four bases and one sugar taken two at a time provide the necessary number of possibilities. The general idea is that the DNA is not the self-duplicating unit of heredity but only a support for the proteins, which are the actual self-duplicating units, though the DNA scaffolding seems indispensable for it. The stiffness of the DNA molecule and the presence of energy-rich P-bonds may be additional properties in this relation to the protein. The "stiffness" may serve to hold the peptide chains in an extended form while they are being copied (meaning while a second chain is laid down by a process akin to crystallization). A nice detail, according to Butler, is that in the zigzag arrangement of the phosphate groups there are two parallel rows. If a peptide chain were held to one row, it may be supposed that a copy could be laid down on the second: the function of the phosphate groups would be to anchor the peptide, while the amino and hydroxyl groups of the bases would keep the nucleic acids in a particular configuration and so control the configuration of the protein. I shall refer later to this general idea as the idea of the "scaffolding" function of the DNA molecule, though in a certain sense it might also be joined to the template concept. In view of the constancy of DNA, it should be realized that this "scaffolding" process requires a constant quantity of DNA to work with a definite amount and arrangement of proteins, which have the actual genic functions, though the nucleoprotein combination is an unavoidable prerequisite of genic duplication.

Two new structural formulae have recently been proposed for the nucleic acid molecule, both of which have a considerable bearing on our subject. The first is that by Pauling and Corey (1953). Basically the model is similar to the one used above, but the axis of the molecule consists of three helices of closely packed phosphoric acid tetrahedras held together by chains of ribose and the attached pyrimidine and purine rings. This results in a very closely packed, cylindrical, highly polymeric molecule of over a million molecular weight. The geneticist, though awed, has difficulty in seeing how this could be the structure of the self-duplicating genic material, and is inclined (while confessing his standing as a biochemical layman) to conclude that he does not receive much help for his quest for the genic material, either *pro* or *contra* DNA.

Recently, however, a very ingenious and, as it seems, experimentally well founded new structure for the DNA molecule has been proposed by Watson and Crick (1953; see also Crick, 1954) which at first sight seems to shift the scales very much in favor of DNA as the genetic material. As the facts are rather exciting, they should be clearly stated before trying to evaluate their genetic meaning. Watson and Crick prepared fibers of a salt of DNA, which they consider to be no artifacts because similar ones were obtained from sperm heads and bacteriophage by Wilkins and Call. X-ray analysis showed the presence of long chains, the backbone of which consists of alternate phosphate and sugar groups (fig. 4). To each sugar is attached a nitrogenous base which can be the purines adenine and guanine and the pyrimidines thymine and cytosine. The sequence of these bases along the chain is irregular. The individual monomere (the nucleotide) consists of phosphate, sugar, and base. The important new point is that the molecule consists of two such helical chains,

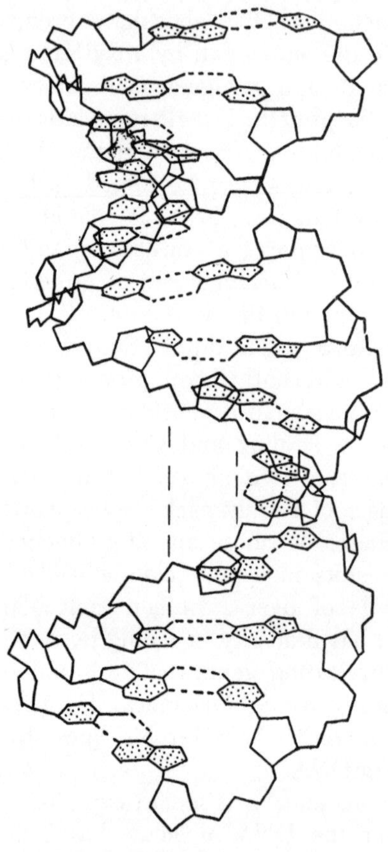

Fig. 5. Watson and Cricks model of DNA molecule with two chains arranged in helices consisting of sugars (pentagons) and phosphates in between (not marked especially), connected by a stack of bases, one purine, one pyrimidine on each level, with hydrogen bonds between the pair of bases. (From Crick, 1954; redrawn from photo of wire model in *Scientific American*, by permission of the author and the publisher.)

coiled around a common axis (fig. 5). They are held together by H-bonds between the bases; thus the bases are joined in pairs. Only certain pairs of bases will fit into this structure. One must be a purine; the other, a pyrimidine: adenine must join with thymine and guanine with cytosine, independently of their position in one or the other chain (fig. 5). The backbone of the molecule is regular, but *any* sequence of the pairs of bases fits into the structure. This means that in a long molecule many permutations are possible, and (quoting) "it therefore seems likely that the precise sequence of the bases is the code which carries the genetical information."

In a semipopular paper (1954) Crick explains it thus: "Such an arrangement can carry an enormous amount of information. If we imagine that the pairs of bases correspond to the dots and dashes of the Morse code, there is enough DNA in a single cell of the human body to encode about a thousand large textbooks. What we want to know, however, is just how this is done in terms of atoms and molecules. In particular, what precisely is it a code for? As we have seen the three components of living matter—protein, RNA and DNA—are probably all based on the same general plan. Their backbones are regular and the variety comes from the sequence of the side groups. It is therefore very natural to suggest that the sequence of the bases of the DNA is in some way a code for the sequence of the amino acids in the polypeptide chains of the proteins which the cell must produce."

It follows that if the order of bases in one chain is given, that on the other chain is obligatory, and complementary. This makes it possible that each single chain if separated from its partner can act as a template (two complementary templates), thus supplying for the first time a model of a template in terms of atoms and residues. In detail, the hydrogen bonds are broken, the two chains uncoil and separate, each chain serves as a template to the companion chain, producing two identical new molecules (without the need of a negative and positive, as in the old template concept). It is supposed that after the H-bond breakage, the single chain takes up a helical configuration. If free nucleotides are available in quantity from time to time, the base of a free nucleotide will join one of the bases already formed on the chain. A polymerization of the monomeres to form a new chain is possible only if the resulting chain can accomplish the correct structure. A special enzyme may mediate the polymerization, or the single chain may act as an enzyme. This is clearly a molecular structure capable of self-duplication, and, if self-duplication is the main characteristic of the genic material, we may conclude that the DNA molecule is the genic material. Watson and Crick clearly think so and adduce further facts and deliberations.

It can be calculated that the two molecular chains twist in 34 Å distances and accomplish about 150 turns per million molecular weights. The visible coiling of the chromonema may reflect similar processes on a molecular level. "Although it is difficult at the moment to see how these processes occur without everything getting tangled, we do not feel that this objection will be insuperable." (I suggest that the weakest link in the reasoning is the transition from molecule to chromosome. We shall return to this important point.)

According to Watson and Crick, the new structure of the DNA molecule is an open one. Between the coupled chains, room is left for polypeptide chains to wind around the same helical axis. The distance of 7.1 Å between adjacent P-atoms is close to the repeat of a fully extended polypeptide chain (Astbury, 1939). "The function of the protein might well be to control the coiling and uncoiling, to assist in holding a single nucleotide chain in a helical configuration or some other non-specific function." Thus the new theory clearly attributes to the DNA the specific, that is, the genetic, function and to the protein moiety a secondary, non-genetic one, that is, the opposite of what many geneticists assume. The protein now becomes the first product of the genic DNA. This is the conclusion which must be weighed against all the cytological and genetic evidence.

So much work is in progress on this subject that almost every month new facts and ideas come to light. Gamow (1954) has begun to develop a mathematical theory of how amino acids are assembled at the surface of the bases in a definite order. Dekker and Schachmann (1954) propose that the two helical strands are composed of fairly large molecules with alternate interruptions which permit the formation of a long chain. Much interest is concentrated also upon the derivation of RNA from DNA; the importance of this problem will become apparent in a subsequent chapter.

These are certainly far-reaching and exciting facts, and it will be important to see whether further biochemical work will confirm the correctness of the basic assumptions. The geneticist, who is anxiously waiting for the biochemist to explain some of his difficulties, will grasp these new ideas, though he is rarely prepared to weigh the biochemical evidence. However, he will not be content to accept a fine explanation of self-duplication as proof that the substance in question, DNA, is the genic material. Such a proof requires agreement with the entire body of biochemical, genetical, and cytological facts discussed in this chapter, and the exclusion of alternative interpretations.

It is at once clear that there should be no difficulty in reversing the theory and concluding that the DNA molecule is the scaffold which keeps the proteinic genic material in place for its reduplication, which might be coincident or not with the DNA duplication as described. Such a function of the stiff DNA fiber was frequently assumed for former models of this material. It includes as a corollary the idea that self-duplication is a property of the nucleoprotein combination. An explanation of how it occurs for the nucleic acid moiety can therefore be made to include self-duplication of the proteinic molecule working together with its DNA scaffolding. Thus we are still left without a proof that DNA is the genic material, alluring as the new model is.

Now we come to the decisive point, which Watson and Crick more or less wave aside, namely, how to bridge the gap between the DNA molecule and the self-duplicating chromosome with all its constituent parts, visible and biochemical. If DNA is the genic material because the structure of the molecule permits self-duplication, we see only two possibilities: (1) either the entire chromosome is a single giant DNA molecule to which proteins are attached and passively divided with the DNA chain or temporarily removed and attached again in some way, which is not relevant for the actual genic material; or (2) the DNA molecule is the gene in a chromomere which duplicates in the proposed way, leaving us to explain how the entire chromosome duplicates (perhaps in a haphazard way by accretion and fission?). Either way, there is no possibility of genic function of the DNA molecule unless it serves as a template for the primary gene products, which may be RNA in part but certainly also enzymes (i.e., proteins). Thus nothing is gained by the assumption of genic properties of DNA, compared with its acting as a scaffold for the duplication of protein molecules, with which DNA is always associated. It is certain that the self-duplicating double structure goes far toward satisfying our requirements for the nature of the genic material. But the beauty of the concept should not obscure the fact that, when seeking to determine the relative role of DNA within the whole of the chromosome, we are confronted again with the DNA-protein combination and the probability that the self-duplicating DNA is only the prop for the real, proteinic genic material, though the integral prop. Further, it should be emphasized that there are many self-duplicating structures which are certainly free of DNA: centrioles, kineties, and all the specific protein molecules in the cell. It is unknown whether, at the moment of their duplication, RNA is present. Brachet's work intimates that RNA may actually be needed for all cytoplasmic syntheses. Such ideas are some of the reasons why all the self-duplicating elements in the cell are frequently called genes (e.g., plasmagenes). These are problems for later discussion, but, since all our ideas are closely interwoven, the points that can be used, as far as I can see, either for or against the DNA monopoly as genic material should be mentioned here. In my opinion the whole body of facts concerning RNA in the cytoplasm is in favor of a scaffolding function of both nucleic acids for self-duplication of proteins and (or) as templates of protein synthesis.

In my view of the genic material, there is no corpuscular gene but only a definite pattern in the chromonema the changes of which are the mutations. I have repeatedly pointed out (1946*b*, 1952*a*) that we are waiting for details concerning the supermolecules, the polymerized combinations of different individual molecules, the pattern of which alone accounts for genic activities and changes. In those discussions I might have used Watson and Crick's statement, if it had been available then, that the arrangement of the bases in the DNA molecule is "the code in which the genetic specificity is spelled." I have sometimes used as examples combinations of the same four or five letters that contain a different sense: fowl, flow, wolf; tame, team, meat. Though this is somewhat different from Watson's code, the underlying idea of specific patterns formed by the same elements is similar. My simile is more nearly comparable to the idea of stereoisomeres (though of course not literally), while Watson's code means, if I understand correctly, an unending series of different DNA's based upon sequence and permutation of the bases: a pattern of four nonobligatory units within the monomere and thus a still more complicated pattern in the polymer. Thus it would not be difficult to work out my thesis of the hierarchy of genic material (see I 3 C *c* ff.) with Watson and Crick's formula of the DNA molecule and without recourse to genes. Again we face the same situation: if DNA is the scaffolding for the genic proteins, it is possible to work the same scheme for the pattern of duplicating amino acid residues, peptides, and polypeptides. The answer to the question, "What is the genic material?" might still be, "the chromosome." All the facts relating to the chromosome and its structure, behavior, chemistry, and physics must be integrated when we are looking for the genic material and not merely for the chemistry of one part.

The arrangement and behavior of the chromomeres are important features of the chromosome, which has a complicated micellar structure. A spatial configuration that would permit the duplication of the genic part of the chromosome according to schemes based upon molecular structure alone would be very difficult to conceive. We would therefore have to turn to the idea developed previously that at the time of reduplication the genic material is reduced to the single molecule (of each kind) level to be reassembled consecutively in the chromosome. Even then the arrangement of the DNA in the chromomeres of the non-dividing chromosome remains a riddle. A large chromomere must contain a huge number of molecules of DNA. If they were attached to the protein, according to Astbury, an extremely complicated globular arrangement would result, an equal division (re-creation) of which is difficult to imagine, though we have already mentioned one possibility, a whorl structure of the chromomere which could be unfolded at the time of duplication. It is very difficult to fit this into the cytological facts. In the lampbrush chromosomes we have just the opposite situation. They are possibly of the nature of a single immense molecule, but this has nothing to do with chromosomal division. Quite the contrary, the two chromatids have united! (Callan and others). We might conclude that the chromomeric configuration has quite a different meaning, as also the strange size law reported above indicated. This can only have to do with the function of the genic material within the chromosome. Even if we assume the correctness of the classic theory of the gene which practically identifies chromomeres and genes, the difficulties are not solved. Actually they are increased as we now have the problem of self-duplication of the DNA-rich chromomeres and the DNA-poor interspaces.

In the lampbrush chromosomes of the vertebrate oöcytes the chromomeres sprout the petal-like arrangement of long loops attached to the chromonema. There is no generally accepted interpretation of the meaning of this configuration (I 2 A; see Gall, 1954; and Alfert, 1954). Ris considers the loops to be coils of the chromonema; Duryee, Dodson, Guyénot, and Gall assume that they are products of the chromomeres, functional elements which have nothing to do with chromosomal structure, but with chromosomal function in the growing oöcyte. Their development and independent solubility are in favor of such a view. However this may be, the actual chromonema is about thirty times as long as the mitotic chromosome and, possibly, of the diameter of a large chain molecule (Gall, Callan, Guyénot). This may represent an almost maximally stretched molecular chain of nucleoprotein. In some materials the Feulgen method reveals only a few irregular concretions (Dodson); in other materials, chromomeres are arranged in a typical way and have been described as appearing in the center of the whorl of loops and even with one chromiole (Guyénot) for each loop. It seems that the DNA, here at least, is partly diffusely attached to the chromonema, which means in a single parallel molecular layer, according to Astbury's scheme, and therefore too diluted to be optically visible. We know now, first, that genic reduplication is not involved at this stage (actually the opposite); second, that extrusion of RNA into the cytoplasm probably takes place on a large scale for participation in the cytoplasmic growth; and third, that genic functions are performed in connection with the differentiation of the cytoplasm into zones of different prospective fate (predetermination). The immense stretching of the chromonema must have something to do with these functions (see also Guyénot). Since the stretching produces a maximum of active surface which should favor the elaboration of the products of genic action, whatever these are, it sounds reasonable to conclude that these characteristic features are an indication of the genic function of the chromonema. The chromomeres with their accumulation of DNA would then be either a structural feature based upon the conglomeration of the folding chromonema into a whorl, held together by the DNA, or involved somehow in the mechanics of the chromosome, not in its genic function. Much remains to be learned about these processes, but already they make very improbable the idea that the chromomeres either are the "genes" or contain them (which goes back to Belling) and with this also the idea that DNA alone is the genic material. It must be realized, however, that the law of DNA constancy holds also for the amphibian oöcyte. The complicated configurations of the lampbrush chromosome and the visible status of the Feulgen positive material do not change anything quantitatively. It is very difficult at present to put all these facts together in a convincing way without succumbing to one or the other dogmatism.

There is still the possibility that the real situation is just the reverse, namely, a proteinic skeleton of the chromosome forming its mechanical backbone to which the real genetic material, the DNA, is attached. This opinion is obviously favored by students of the DNA constancy and by the recent biochemical work. There are more relevant facts which thus far have not been mentioned. Schultz (1941) maintains that with Caspersson's optical method a difference in quantity of DNA can be observed in the salivary band supposed to contain the white locus when the normal form is compared with the white mutant. Most geneticists have been very cautious in accepting this claim, I being one of them, though it must be added that none of the critics worked with Caspersson's method. Recently Schultz (Rudkin, Temin, and Schultz, 1953) returned to the subject and stated, "The cytological difference between the white mutant and wild type, confirmed in this material, is thus not accompanied by a quantitative difference in ultra-violet absorbing material," which is DNA. This does not help us very much in our discussion.

A completely different attack upon the same problem has been made by analyzing the action of chemical mutagens. Clark (1953) comes to the conclusion that pyronine produces its mutagenic effect by combining directly with nucleic acid. He thinks there is a possibility that the mutagenic action might result from combination with depolymerized DNA during its synthesis. But he considers also the possibility of primary action on RNA in the cytoplasm which is later incorporated into the nucleus. Whatever these processes may be, they could both be interpreted in favor of DNA as genic material or as a template. In the first possibility, the combination with the dye would produce alterations in the spatial arrangement of nucleotides characteristic for a given locus. In the second, the chemical would prevent the DNA from maintaining the protein in the expanded state (the scaffolding function). This type of attack on our problem ends again in a *non liquet*.

The geneticist, taking cognizance of this group of facts, can hardly doubt that DNA must play an important role in the makeup of the genic material. This, however, does not necessarily mean that it *is* the genic material. The chemical extraction of a few proteins from the chromosome does not convey much information on the actual chemical composition of the continuous chromonema to which the DNA seems to be attached by salt links in identically spaced groups (Astbury, 1939). If we are looking for individual genes, the molecules of DNA may be the answer, though it raises all the problems just discussed. However, if we abandon the idea of the corpuscular gene, it appears more probable that the genic action resides in the combination of the proteinic chromonema with the attached DNA, and many facts to be discussed still favor such a view. But it will be good to realize how much semantics is involved in this discussion. If the DNA is the necessary scaffolding for the duplication of protein molecules and therefore must be kept constant in quantity, spacing, and so on in order to act specifically, we might call it the primary genetic material, even if it were not the active one, or we might call it the auxiliary to the genuine one; or we might stress the interdependence of the two, as I prefer to do.

At the end of this discussion a fact should be mentioned briefly to which we shall return below when discussing the theory of the gene. This is the fact that mutagenic ultraviolet rays act maximally at the wave length of absorption for DNA. This is an undisputed proof that DNA is involved in the genic functions. But it does not prove that DNA is the genic material, for the fact would also agree with other interpretations (e.g., that DNA is the necessary scaffolding). Here again the facts present the same level of information as all the others, with different and equally good possibilities of interpretation, an equilibrium which can be shifted only if all groups of relevant facts are taken together and weighed coolly.

Returning to the Watson-Crick model of DNA structure, I cannot help proposing what looks like a rather wild idea, based upon the assumption that the structure is as claimed. It is independent of the alternative interpretation of DNA function as genic material per se or as a scaffolding for the proteinic genic material because both DNA and protein will remain together somehow during chromosomal maneuvers. If the two chains of the molecule can become independent and re-create their respective partners, it might be assumed that under special conditions they may remain separate or unite again. As only hydrogen bonds are assumed to be involved, this should be a fair assumption. The "wild idea" is that such a separation happens in the preleptotene or postleptotene chromosome, with all other ingredients of the chromosome following the stiff DNA scaffolding. The two chromatids of the synapsing chromosomes would then differ from two ordinary mitotic split halves in containing only the single chains of DNA. Not much imagination is needed to realize that such a fact would at once solve all the major riddles of synapsis including crossing over. It would also explain such atypical features as preleptotene doubleness followed by fusion (Kuwada, 1940) and absence of double chromatids in the tetrad lampbrush chromosome. As anybody can draw the detailed consequences of such a "wild idea," this short statement may suffice.

One indirect contribution to our problem presents some rather remarkable facts. S. Hughes-Schrader (1953) found in mantids two species which are phenotypically indistinguishable but have a completely different karyotype: males have $2n = 21$ and $2n = 17$, respectively. But in the first species the amount of DNA per nucleus is one and a half times that of the other species. Another species with 23 chromosomes has one and a half times as much DNA as a similar one with 33 chromosomes. The conclusion is drawn that DNA cannot be simply the genetic material.

cc. Conclusions from bacterial transformation and transduction

The most potent claim for the genic nature of DNA is derived from the amazing phenomenon of bacterial transformation (Griffith, 1928; Avery, MacLeod, and McCarty, 1944; and many others since), to which recently the phenomenon of transduction has been added by Lederberg (see Lederberg, 1952; Lederberg and Tatum, 1953; Zinder and Lederberg, 1952; Zinder, 1953). Unencapsulated pneumococci could be made to transform into an encapsulated type as an inherited change under the influence of a substance derived from a capsulated strain, which turned out to be DNA. Boivin *et al.* (1945) found similar results for *Escherischia coli,* but not with the same regularity. Alexander and Leidy (1953) found the same in a very different bacterium, *Hemophilus influenzae,* another parasitic bacterium, where the transforming agent comes from streptomycin-resistant strains. Since the first discovery, it has been shown in pneumococcus that several different kinds of transformation can be performed, each through the action of a particular nucleic acid from a particular mutant strain.

One character involved is the capsule (a shell of polysaccharides secreted around the bacterium), which may appear rough or smooth. It is known that one is derived from the other by mutation, but transformation can produce either type according to the origin of the transforming agent. Intermediate types are produced by quantitative mutation, depending on the amount of the secreted polysaccharides. The nucleic acid extracts of these intermediate types transform rough strains into exactly the same phenotype of intermediaries. The intermediate mutants are thus based upon a mutation (= production of an allele) of the normal capsular agent. No mutation of one intermediate type into another has been found and no two such specific types simultaneously. (The geneticist drawing parallels with higher forms might say—assuming bacteria to be haploid—that this is a set of multiple alleles which have been produced directly from the original rough form.)

Another cell character has been described as extreme rough (Taylor, 1950; see also Ephrussi-Taylor, 1951), arisen by mutation from rough. This can be transformed to rough by nucleic acid extracts from both rough and smooth strains. In reverse the extracts from extreme rough can transform rough into extreme rough. Thus, by mutation, an extreme rough agent has arisen, which can be extracted for production of transformation. As a complication, some strains of extreme rough have been found (Taylor) which cannot be transformed into encapsulated (smooth), while others permit this transformation.

Other pneumococcus transformations have been reported by Hotchkiss (1951). He found the same type of action as described for the capsule in antigenic specificities and in resistance to streptomycin, penicillin, and sulfa drugs. Again the specific DNA from donor cells is required, and a number of experimental conditions. In addition, only a small percentage of the treated cells transform. The resistant donor cells are, in the case of streptomycin resistance (as well as in the cases mentioned above), simple mutants. The penicillin-resistant strain was, however, obtained by long selection and would therefore be considered in Mendelian terms as polygenic. It is remarkable that here the transformation does not succeed at once but occurs in three distinct steps after three exposures, each producing only a certain level of resistance. Table 2 summarizes these facts.

TABLE 2

PROBABLE DISTRIBUTION OF VARIOUS TRANSFORMING AGENTS AMONG DIFFERENT KINDS OF STRAINS OF PNEUMOCOCCI USED IN TRANSFORMATION STUDIES
(From H. Ephrussi-Taylor, 1951)

	Smooth strains				*Rough strains*		
Transforming agents	*Sensitive*	*P-resistant mutant*	*Str-resistant mutant*	*Intermed. smooth str.*	*Sensitive*	*P-resistant mutant*	*Extreme rough strains*
Capsular....	+	+	+	+ (mutated)			
Rough......	+	[+]	[+]	+	+	[+]	+ (mutated)
M protein...	+	[+]	[+]	[+]	[+]	[+]	[+]
P resistance							
1°........		+				+	
2°........		+				+	
3°........		+				+	
Str resistance			+				

Brackets = presence indirectly proved
P = penicillin, Str = streptomycin

Since, in all these cases, specific extracted DNA is the transforming agent, the supreme importance for the problem of the genic nature of DNA is obvious. Ephrussi-Taylor rather understates it as follows: "We have here the beginnings of a very unique system of genetical analysis. It is a system in which, as yet, no bridge can be seen leading over into classical genetics, but which is promising enough to be an end in itself." The simple and consistent facts reported thus far are not the only ones known. Ephrussi-Taylor has worked with cases in which the transformation produces a third type, different from both the treated and the treating types. An explanation of the entire phenomenon must take such facts into account.

Lederberg (1952; Cavalli and Lederberg, 1953; Lederberg and Tatum, 1953) has introduced the term "transduction" to include bacterial transformation of the pneumococcus type as well as a remarkable new type. Zinder and Lederberg (1952) described how the transfer of antigenic properties in the bacterium *Salmonella typhimurium* from bacterium to bacterium can be effected by a non-killing bacteriophage. The phage must pull out some genetic particle from its host and deposit it in another host as a genic property. Lederberg thinks that the process—also the one in pneumococcus—amounts to a hybridization which involves not whole cells (i.e., their germ plasm) but only parts of the genic system (therefore only a single character can be transduced in one experiment).

These amazing facts raise the question whether bacterial genetics is not based upon an at least partly different principle. If a virus-like body is used to transfer bodily what might be called a single locus, we could speak of a kind of fertilization-ersatz with features completely different from those in the standard type of zygote formation. If this is true, bacterial transformation might be a part of this completely different genetic system or, in the terminology of Lederberg, transformation and transduction would be essentially the same thing. This conclusion, at which we hinted above, has been emphasized by Zinder (1953). The greatest similarity is in the effect: namely, a stable new character brought about by the incorporation of its causative agent into the genome by a process involving the replacement of the homologous material. But the agents which bring this about are dissimilar: specific DNA-tes in transformation, and a virus or phage of unknown properties in the transduction. It seems that in both cases any bacterial character can be transferred, though usually only singly; and it seems certain also that they replace already present materials and are not just added to the existing material (i.e., they are incorporated into a chromosome). There are also instances, in both transformation and transduction, in which linked properties are transferred together. In transformation, then, the genetic material is isolated by the extraction process and enters directly the bacterium which it transforms. In transduction the transferable material is isolated by partial lysis due to phage, is then incorporated into or attached to the phage, and is transduced with it. Since closely linked properties, involving related reactions, are transferred in both cases, Zinder is ready to compare this situation to pseudoallelic conditions in *Drosophila*.

The facts and interpretations amount to the claim that genes or genic material are transduced; it might then be asserted that the DNA in the pneumococcus transformation is a piece of genic material, assuming that the method of its extraction excludes the presence of attached protein. The reported facts may be described as the replacement of the nucleic acid component of a genetic structure in the cell (because of its mutability) by an introduced, external, and different though closely related nucleic acid, extracted from a different organism for which it is characteristic. It is reported as certain, so far as experimentation goes, that the transforming agent is a pure polymerized DNA, although different kinds of molecules of DNA are present in the extracts, and it is rather tempting to consider them to be genes. Hotchkiss and Marmur (1954) found recently that in bacterial transformation one DNA extract could transfer two different genetic properties simultaneously. This is compared directly with linked genes. If these conclusions were unavoidable, the nucleic acid nature of the genetic material would be proved.

But it is far from certain that the interpretation is so simple, apart from the variations of the results reported above. All modern information tends to show that bacteria have regular chromosomes (Robinow, De Lamater; see De Lamater, 1951) and that crossing over occurs according to the classical scheme (Lederberg and Tatum, and others). If this is true also for the organisms in which transformation has been found (actually *E. coli* is one of them), and if the transforming agent is genic, transformation should be described thus: the DNA extracts used for transforming contain molecules of different specific DNA's, and are of the nature of genes. These are taken into the treated bacterium, where they push out of the chromosomes the homologous gene present and assume its place for good; or, what amounts to the same, they force the homologous gene to change its molecular structure into that of the intruder. Since genic material is self-reproducing, the last assumption is not very commendable; and the first one appears at present beyond the limit of what we can safely believe. The geneticist who approaches these facts with an open mind will be loath to accept such an explanation as final and to consider transformation a proof of the nucleic acid nature of the genic material. He will expect that further work may lead to a more plausible explanation.

If the idea promoted by some chemists is true—that the nucleic acids are not themselves self-reproducing units but act as templates or scaffolds which keep the self-duplicating protein molecules in place and shape during this process—one corollary would be that the nucleic acids are synthesized and augmented outside the chromosomes and become attached to the protein chain secondarily by formation of salt links. The action of the transforming DNA extract could then mean that the rich source of DNA offered in the extract is not used via breakage and resynthesis of the molecule but enters as such into the bacterial nucleus, where at the time of chromosomal growth and division it replaces similar molecules simply by being available in larger quantities. Transformation, then, would introduce somewhat different templates; this means that DNA is not the genic material but one indispensable for the reproduction of genic material. Though not too satisfactory in detail, such a type of interpretation may open the way for a different experimental attack.

The new model of the DNA molecule proposed by Watson and Crick (see I 2 B *b bb*) may support such an interpretation or a similar one. The self-duplication of the two half-molecules proposed by these authors takes place by the addition of nucleotide monomeres which are assumed to be plentiful in the surroundings. In the adaptation experiment there might be available within the organism many times more of the introduced and depolymerized DNA than the amount of the available genuine DNA monomeres synthesized in the bacterial cell. Just as tagged atoms are built into the molecules of different kinds in organisms, these introduced monomeres could be built into the duplicates of the half-molecules. Since this would happen in subsequent duplications in a compound-interest sequence, the new DNA would soon replace the old one completely. Whether this applies to the entire polymere or only to definite macromeres needed for the mutant character cannot be decided, though the result would be the same in either case. (The fact that in vitro depolymerized DNA does not produce transformations may or may not reflect upon what happens within the cell.) If some such scheme is accepted—and I think this worthy of serious consideration—we find ourselves at the same *non liquet* situation reached at the end of the last section: the facts may be interpreted in terms of DNA either as the genic material or as the scaffolding for the assemblage of the proper protein molecules. Such an interpretation of the transformation could suggest more decisive experiments, to be made with forms which at present do not give 100 per cent clear results, experiments which might also settle the biochemical details of the assumed substitutions. Consult at this point the facts relating to the transfer and use of DNA from one nucleus to another one in growing egg cells, mentioned in the next section.

Further information comes from the behavior of bacteriophage inside the bacterium, which somewhat parallels the basic features of bacterial transformation. It is known (see review by Doermann, 1953) that the phage entering the bacterium is stripped of its protein and enters a vegetative phase, in which the phenomena of recombination occur in one or another way. Hershey (see 1953) showed that during this period of vegetative (non-infectious) multiplication of the virus particle the genic apparatus of the bacterium is obliterated, though in the beginning the bacterial DNA is in excess 100 times over that of the initial content of the phage. The increase of phage DNA then follows exactly the rules of phage particles increase until their maturation. Thus DNA is again at the center of the whole process. But Hershey, who has done so much work in this entire field, does not conclude that this proves DNA to be the genetic material. He says, "My own guess is that DNA will not prove to be the unique determiner of genetic specificity, but that contributions to the question will be made in the near future only by persons willing to entertain the contrary view."

Another possibility should not be disregarded, though it is rather vague. The work on phenocopies in many organisms has shown that the phenotype of any mutant may be produced as a non-hereditary effect by treatment at the normal developmental stages with various agents. For the present discussion the important fact is Rapoport's discovery (confirmed by a number of workers) that certain chemicals produce specifically phenocopies of one definite mutant. It is obvious that here something is introduced which acts in development in the same way as the mutant action does, directly or indirectly. If, for example, a metal ion inhibits or slows a definite enzymatic reaction, it may be assumed that both the mutant action and the phenocopic action of the ion succeed in changing the phenotype by inhibiting the same enzyme function. Let us assume that the transformer acts as a phenocopic agent upon the bacterian cell, which implies that the genic material is not involved. (One might speak of *Dauermodifikation;* see discussion below.) The first prerequisite of such a process would be that the effect be visible only within a clone (which corresponds to a multicellular organism) and end with a sexual phase. It may be said that no sexual phase is known in pneumococci; in *E. coli,* where the assumption of a sexual phase is unavoidable, the transformation experiments gave "irregular" results (Boivin, 1945), facts which might provide some clue. The important point is that the DNA extract produces the phenotype of its own origin, while the action of a metal ion in phenocopy experiments has no relation to the origin of the agent. If in the bacterium the mutant effect consisted in an effect upon a certain enzyme action (as in *Drosophila*), and if this effect were produced by some derivative of a certain DNA, the introduction of the same DNA into a cell could lead to a specific phenocopic action. The fact that depolymerization of DNA in vitro prevents the transformation action may or may not militate against this possibility. I think that this type of argument which can be put to experimental test should not be overlooked, whatever the difficulties at the present moment and however vague it appears thus far.

In view of the caution we adopted in the interpretation of the important facts we may now quote some more optimistic views. Haldane (1954), after a calculation of the molecular species supposed to be present in a bacteriophage and available for chemical isolation, declares: "On the other hand, the purification of a transforming principle may be simpler. But it is perhaps in these simple organisms that the material basis of inheritance will first be specifiable in chemical terms." But on the next page we read: "There is no reason to expect a priori that the general principles of genetics should hold for bacteria. If some of them do so, that is very satisfying, but it seems equally unwise to argue, except in the most tentative way, from bacterial mutations to mutations in other organisms, or from non-Mendelian behavior in bacteria against Mendelian behavior in other organisms."

dd. Some additional relevant facts

It is known that RNA is somehow produced by the DNA in the chromosomes, deposited in the nucleolus (see, however, Hämmerling), and transferred into the cytoplasm of cells in which protein synthesis is taking place. RNA, therefore, is considered to be important mainly for protein synthesis. It occurs in the chromosomes also, which might mean that it is itself synthesized there. Its quantity is not constant. (See, above, the "elimination chromatin.") However, there are many indications that DNA is derived only from former DNA. There is a huge body of facts in the older literature showing that growing oöcytes will assimilate other nuclei. That this means mainly DNA is demonstrated by such cases as that discovered in some Bryozoa by Bonnevie (1907). Here the growing oöcyte is inseminated by many spermatozoa which are dissolved in the cytoplasm obviously serving as source of DNA. In archiannelids (*Dinophilus;* see Shen, 1936) and some oligochaetes (Oschmann, 1914, and others), nurse cells are phagocyted by the growing oöcyte, and a series of nuclei (i.e., their DNA) enter the cytoplasm of the oöcyte. In obligatory polyspermy (Lepidoptera, *Selachia*), there is at least a suspicion that the introduced extra nucleic acid is used up in some way, which might mean as source material for DNA in the nuclei. Though biochemical work has not yet been done on all these cases, the facts are highly suggestive.

Nurse cells which are not incorporated into the ovum but become loaded with DNA by endomitosis have been described for the insect ovary by Painter and Reindorp (1939) and for tapetum cells of anthers by Brown (1949). In these examples, as well as some in which no polyteny is known, it has been observed that DNA is liberated from the nurse cell nuclei and enters the cytoplasm of the egg cell with the nutrient stream (Schrader, 1951, for insects; Konopacki, 1936, for the ascidian egg). Still more important is the observation by Cooper (1952) that DNA granules leave the tapetum cells of the anthers and enter bodily the nuclei of the microsporocytes during the synaptic stages with polar orientation of the chromosomes, and spread over the chromosomes from their ends. In the light of these results some of the old material, in which nucleo-cytoplasmic exchanges during the bouquet stage have been claimed or doubted (*Blatta* spermatocyte, axolotl oöcyte), should be checked again after more than forty years.

In this connection, also, the changing views on cytoplasmic DNA should be recorded. It used to be a dogma that DNA does not occur in the cytoplasm. Hoff-Jørgensen and Zeuthen (1952) and Elson and Chargaff (1952), among others, found enough DNA in the cytoplasm of sea urchin eggs to take care of the needs of the embryonic nuclei.

This may mean that actually DNA could be used from nucleus to nucleus. It is difficult to reconcile such facts with the genic nature of DNA as well as the genic nature of bacterial transformations. We shall return to this problem repeatedly. (See the previous discussion on bacterial transduction via phage, which is on a similar level.)

Another group of relevant facts relates to the basic proteins in the chromosome. A distinction has been made between structural proteins which keep the chromosome together and are not easily dissolved, and the simpler protamines which can be removed without changing the chromosomal structure (Mirsky). These proteins are not found in constant quantity from cell to cell. It is maintained that sperm heads, consisting of closely packed chromosomes, are formed mostly of DNA, with only a small portion of protamine added, which would seem to favor DNA as genic material. But in all these deliberations it should be kept in mind that we are not dealing with the original substances *in situ,* which might be very different from the extracts in vitro; and, further, that the quantity of protein needed is probably below that accessible analytically. However, work in these fields progresses so fast that it is unwise to draw more than preliminary conclusions.

A last group of facts favoring DNA as the genic material comes from virus studies. Some viruses consist mainly or totally of nucleic acids, even crystallizable, without losing their infective power. A more special fact is that when a particle of the bacteriophage T2 attaches itself to a bacterium, most of the DNA of the phage enters the cell, and most of the sulfur-containing protein remains outside (Hershey, 1953; Hershey and Chase, 1951). It is, however, not known whether sulfur-free protein enters the cell and whether this is incorporated in the phage progeny, and further whether the DNA (or its constituents) is directly or indirectly taken into the phage progeny. Thus the authors conclude that a separation of the phage into genetic and non-genetic parts is possible, but they are not willing to say which is the genetic part. We have mentioned that another powerful argument against the genic nature of DNA is to be derived from polytenic chromosomes which multiply their DNA immensely while assuming extreme non-genic functions. The discussion of this will be taken up in a later chapter, where the facts will be interpreted as excluding the genic nature of DNA.

c. General conclusions

In summarizing what is known about the location and nature of the genic material in the chromosomes, we must keep in mind that the nucleus not only has genetic functions but also controls the physiological activity of the cell in an exchange of materials. If we find, therefore, chemical differences in protein content between nuclei of differently functioning cells, we cannot draw conclusions in regard to the genic material.

The biochemists at present are in favor of the idea that DNA is the genic material in the chromosomes. In favor of this view are (1) the constancy of the amount of DNA in all cells of a species, whereas the protein contents of the chromosomes vary; (2) the location of concentrations of DNA at points of the chromosome which the experiment reveals to be genic (the bands in the salivary gland chromosomes); (3) the facts of bacterial transformation via specific DNA and transduction via phage; (4) the role of the nucleic acids in viruses; (5) the structure of the DNA molecule which permits visualizing self-duplication.

But it must be realized that many of the detailed features of chromosomal behavior and structure fit better into the opinion of some chemists and many geneticists that the nucleic acids are needed as templates of protein synthesis, or as scaffolding to keep the duplicating protein molecules in position (Haurowitz, 1950). It is, furthermore, so much more probable that the genic functions are based upon an enzymatic nature of the genic material, and enzymes are proteins. A powerful argument against the genic nature of DNA can be derived from the group of facts which show that DNA prepared and sometimes mass-fabricated in certain nuclei (nurse cells, tapetum cells, and nurse cells and sperm phagocyted by oöcytes) can be transferred to the cytoplasm of an egg cell where it may be used directly in building up the DNA of the embryonic nuclei, and, in addition, may probably be used in cytoplasmic protein synthesis as well. The negative fact that no quantitative constancy has been found for any nuclear constituent but DNA should be used with caution, because the optical methods based upon the Feulgen reaction allow such measurements for DNA; while a comparative direct method for the intact protein in the chromosome does not exist. If DNA is the scaffolding for protein synthesis, its constancy is to be expected.

We conclude that a final decision has not been reached and that it cannot be stated as a dogma or as a proved fact that DNA is the genic material. My conclusion from the facts available today is that the protein of the chromonema is the genic material proper, but that it requires the linked DNA molecules for self-duplication. Thus the combination of both is the basis for genic action. We shall have to return many times to this basic and intriguing problem.

C. HETEROCHROMATIN

In the search for the genic material of the chromosome we have neglected thus far two other constituents of the chromosome. One is the nucleolus, a structure for which nobody would claim genic properties. It is cyclically destroyed and rebuilt and is quantitatively more variable than could be assumed for genic material. Thus there are chromosomes without a nucleolus, which is formed only in one or two pairs of a genome. There are also chromosomes (amphibian oöcyte) in which numerous nucleoli are imbedded. The major part of the nucleoli consists of ribonucleic acid, and it is generally assumed that this has to do with protein synthesis in the cytoplasm. Thus nucleoli are chromosomal structures concerned with the non-genic functions of the chromosomes. They will be taken up again in the discussion of the relation between nucleus and cytoplasm.

That part of the chromosome which is called heterochromatin shows a number of very remarkable properties. There is a large literature on the subject, both in cytological and genetic work (good reviews: Pontecorvo, 1944; Hannah, 1951; Barigozzi, 1950*a*; cytological details: White, 1945; Smith, 1952; genetical study: Goldschmidt, Hannah, and Piternick, 1951). Not all the numerous facts known fit together, and contradictions are frequent. It is hardly possible yet to develop a completely satisfactory theory of heterochromatin. However, one thing may be said with certainty: heterochromatin must play a considerable role in the history of the chromosomes and in their function, and an important but unorthodox genetic role is expected. In order to reach more specific conclusions we shall group the genetic and cytological facts so that their individual meaning comes out before we attempt a synthesis of all the facts. In doing so we shall not emphasize difficulties and discrepancies, but rather shall try to elaborate the positive, constructive parts of our knowledge.

a. The cytological aspect

The original meaning of the term "heterochromatin" was purely cytological (Heitz, 1929). It meant the existence of chromosomal regions differing from the others by their staining, according to the amount or concentration of DNA in the chromomeres. (Darlington speaks of the charge with DNA; see Darlington and La Cour, 1940.) These differences are specific at different times of the mitotic cycle. In interphase, when the chromosomes (i.e., their euchromatic regions) become invisible through disintegration (scattering or swelling by hydration, not chemical disintegration) of the chromomeric material, heterochromatin is highly stainable and is condensed into a block, called a chromocenter if it is a single mass, or chromocentric blocks if there are many. This phenomenon is called heteropyknosis (Gutherz, 1907). At other stages of the mitotic cycle when the euchromatin is very dense, the heterochromatin stains differently. This phase difference (also called positive and negative heteropyknosis), based upon the minute arrangement of the chromomeres, is called allocycly (Darlington and La Cour, 1940). It involves dense coiling and chromomeres of rather large size. These are the two most distinctive properties of heterochromatin on the cytological level, but there are innumerable additional details and variants: the structural differences in the salivary gland chromosomes of Diptera, the specific features of the sex chromosomes, and of course all the facts relating to genetics.

Let us first view the purely cytological features and, without going into all the variations, mention the salient facts which we consider of importance for the theoretical analysis in special cases. Heterochromatin is essentially a cytological concept based upon heteropyknosis and allocycly. If these criteria alone are used, it is hardly possible to give a description which fits all cells. White (1951) actually speaks of a continuous spectrum between the extremes, euchromatin and heterochromatin. (For details see the reviews by Resende, 1945, and Barigozzi, 1950*a*; also Darlington and La Cour, 1947.) Resting nuclei may show chromocentral accumulations or none at all, even within the same organism. In the same way, mitotic chromosomes may have allocyclic segments or not. The observable quantity of heterochromatin may be very different in nearly related species (White, 1945) or even within the same chromosome after treatment at different temperatures. White (1945) speaks of microheterochromatic species with allocycly of only the sex chromosomes, and megaheterochromatic species with much allocyclic material in the autosomes. Virkki (1951) has tabulated these conditions for a large number of scarabaeids (Coleoptera) and discussed other cases; Smith (1952) has done the same for tenebrionid beetles. This is a good illustration of the cytological variability of the phenomenon, which, though incomprehensible, nevertheless indicates a unified importance of heterochromatin.

Specific features of heterochromatin are observed also in pathological cells (cancer cells), but without any definite rule. The structure of chromocenters is highly variable. Some appear to be structureless deep-staining matter; others, lighter staining groups of granules. Certainly, none are dense spiralizations, as one theory requires. Within the chromosomes, heterochromatic sections may appear only as larger or clumped chromomeres with normal spiralization of the chromonema; or spiralization may seem to be absent and the heterochromatic portions show an irregular structure. Some authors insist on a definition based upon spiralization, others, upon DNA metabolism. Some consider all transitions between eu- and heterochromatin possible, and even interpret the size differences of the chromomeres as a transition to heterochromatization (Pontecorvo, 1944; White, 1945; Virkki, 1951). Another opinion is that heterochromatin is phylogenetically degenerated euchromatin. These great variations both in resting nuclei and in mitotic chromosomes make it very difficult to give a general description or definition of heterochromatin. It cannot even be said that it is ubiquitous, because, in view of its great changeability, it might be present even when not seen; furthermore, structures may be called heterochromatic without any certainty that they are homologous to others that have been similarly labeled. This confusion is made worse by the concept of heterochromatization, meaning the change of euchromatic into heterochromatic sections. This is frequently claimed in cytogenetic work in *Drosophila* (Hannah, 1951; and especially the papers of Belgovsky, 1938, 1944, 1946; Prokofyeva-Belgovskaya, 1947). Sometimes it is based upon alleged changes in the stainability of sections of salivary chromosomes; sometimes it is inferred from aberrant genetic behavior; and, I dare say, it is always a vague, slippery subject which cannot be accepted as proved or disproved. Unified theoretical considerations are possible only on the basis of indisputable material. Aberrant and queer data may one day become of the greatest significance. However, if it is not possible today to absorb them into the major body of established facts, the pragmatic attitude is to note their existence but leave them aside for the time being. (We shall return to the idea of heterochromatization when discussing the mottling position effect in the presence of heterochromatic breaks and again when discussing the theories of position effect.)

Unfortunately, there is no chemical definition. Some heterochromatin is clearly very rich in DNA; in other cases it is reported to be composed mainly of RNA. The facts are so contradictory that it is not worth while to quote them. Actually, it seems probable that heterochromatin is the seat of chemical processes which change its composition constantly, processes which most cytologists assume to be connected with protein synthesis, apart from genic protein. In favor of this is the fact that the nucleolus is frequently in a heterochromatic section. Heterochromatin is so elusive a structure that it would be better not to attempt a theoretical discussion, were it not that we know a number of interesting features which in the cells where they are found are perfectly clear and straightforward. Therefore it seems advisable—we have already called it the pragmatic attitude—not to dwell upon what we do *not* know of heterochromatin but to pass in review the available positive and invariable facts. There are purely cytological facts as well as cytogenetic features around which a fruitful discussion can be built; these show that heterochromatin, whether we can define it or not, must have important functions in the cell.

The most conspicuous group of facts is the one relating to entire heterochromatic chromosomes and their fate. These facts stand somewhat apart from those generally found, in which heterochromatic sections of the chromosomes show the different types of allocycly. The completely heterochromatic chromosome may be considered the extreme end of a series of conditions which are more widely spread but do not give such clear information. In detail we refer to three somewhat different types: (1) one in which heterochromatic chromosomes are preserved only in the cells of the germ track; (2) one in which heterochromatin is not organized into chromosomes and reserved for a special type of cells; and (3) a type involving the existence of heterochromatic chromosomes which are not complete chromosomes, the so-called supernumeraries, but, nevertheless, show some preferential distribution upon specialized cells.

b. Chromatin diminution and related phenomena

The first group contains the different cases of so-called chromatin diminution. The classic case is that of *Ascaris* (Boveri), now called *Parascaris equorum.* It is a little complicated by the fact that the chromosomes in the sex cells are collective chromosomes joined to each other end by end and having many centromeres and spindle fibers. This condition is not easily explained, but it has been found that frequently chromosomes tend to such more or less irregular associations immediately before the meiotic prophase (Lepidoptera: Seiler, 1914; Goldschmidt, 1923*b*; some plants: Thomas, and Revell, 1946). One interpretation is that this is a heterochromatic association, meaning that heterochromatic sections of chromosomes tend to unite under some conditions in the nucleus. This would, then, involve the same type of unspecific attraction between heterochromatic sections which sometimes produces chromocenters. Whether this interpretation applies to *Ascaris* or not is difficult to decide. Actually, the non-heterochromatic individual chromosomes assembled into the collective chromosome contain hardly any chromatin (Lin, 1954). The fact remains that these collective chromosomes keep together only in the germ cells but break apart in the somatic cells. Assuming that the collective chromosome is based upon heterochromatic association, the breaking up might be caused by removal of the last interchromosomal vestiges of heterochromatin, which, however, are not visible.

These long collective chromosomes have heavy, deeply staining distal ends which were proved (Goldschmidt and Lin, 1947; details in Lin, 1954) to be heterochromatic (fig. 6). In the nuclei of the meiotic prophase they unite into an unusually large chromocenter, and in diplotene this breaks up so that the chromosome ends appear as separate chromocentric blocks (Lin, 1954). Boveri showed that these chromosome ends, which we must consider now as the heterochromatic partners of the individual chromosomes within the collective chromosome, are broken off in the mitosis of prospective somatic cells and are dissolved in the cytoplasm, while the collective chromosome breaks up into its constituents. We may say now that these heterochromatic ends do not have a centromere of their own, as is also visible in the division configuration of the collective chromosome, and therefore are removed from mitotic distribution once the collective chromosome breaks up into the many somatic chromosomes. Before that time and in all germ-track cells in which no diminution takes place, the heterochromatic ends show the heteropyknosis and allocycly (and staining reactions) of heterochromatin. The lack of a centromere puts these individual partners of the somatic chromosomes within the collective chromosomes in the same category as supernumeraries, but with much more regularized, orderly behavior because of their inclusion in the collective chromosome. The final effect of this heterochromatic behavior in *Ascaris* is the conservation of all heterochromatin in the germ-track cells and its removal from all somatic cells.

Conditions, in the end identical with these though in detail very

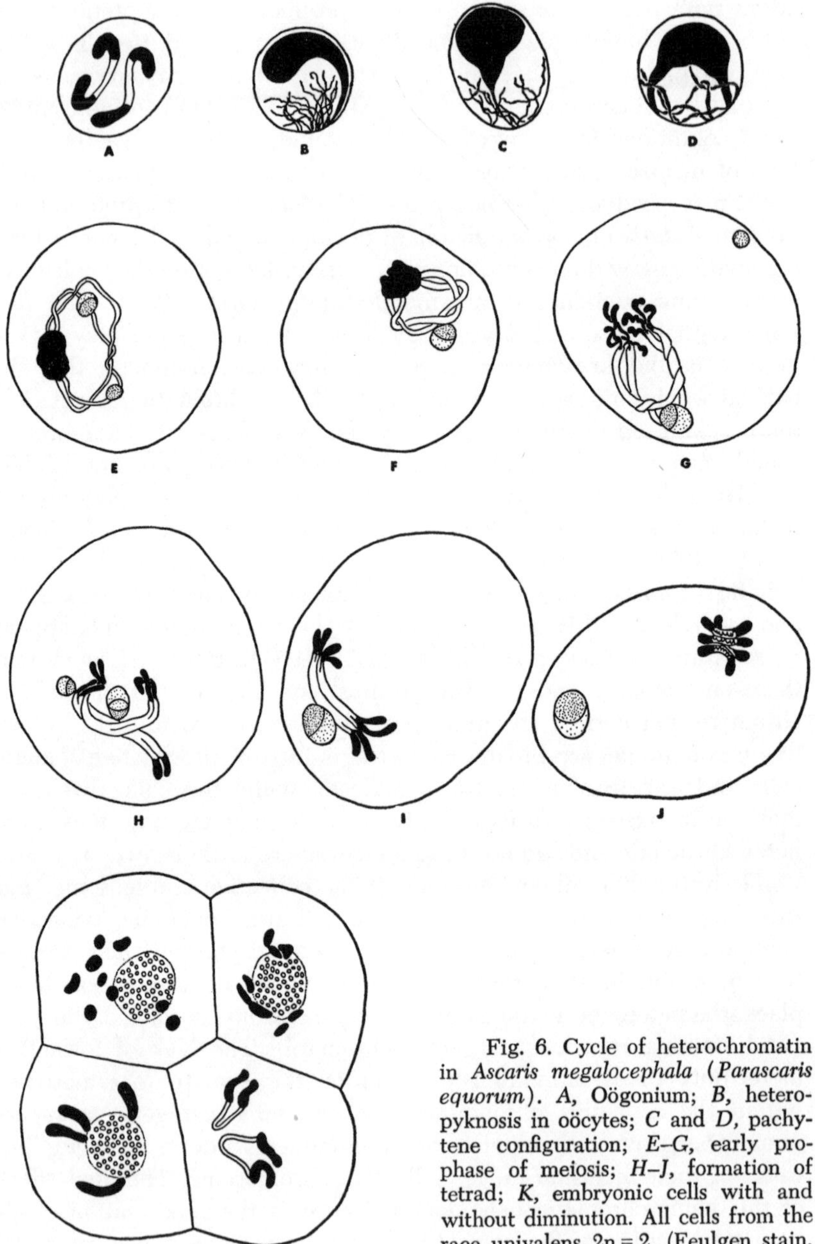

Fig. 6. Cycle of heterochromatin in *Ascaris megalocephala* (*Parascaris equorum*). *A*, Oögonium; *B*, heteropyknosis in oöcytes; *C* and *D*, pachytene configuration; *E–G*, early prophase of meiosis; *H–J*, formation of tetrad; *K*, embryonic cells with and without diminution. All cells from the race univalens 2n = 2. (Feulgen stain, redrawn from Lin, 1954.)

different, are found in a few Diptera. The most extreme and complicated type is that of the manure fly *Sciara.* Without entering into all details of the chromosomal cycle (see fig. 7), the following facts have been described (Metz, Dubois, and others; see Metz, 1938). All germ-track cells have three pairs of autosomes, one (male) or two (female) X-chromosomes and two very large "sex-limited" chromosomes, actually two completely heterochromatic chromosomes, comparable to the chromosomal ends in *Ascaris,* but provided with centromeres and thus dividing normally in the germ-track cells. All somatic cells are devoid of these two heterochromatic elements. The heterochromatic element (not present in all species) shows also heteropyknosis. There are some strange complications in chromosome numbers which are rectified during development (shown in the diagram, but not of interest in our present discussion). The main point is that in development these large heterochromatic chromosomes are removed from the nuclei of the somatic cells in a manner strictly parallel to the situation in *Ascaris.* One suspects that something is wrong with the centromere of these chromosomes.

Another variant is found in the gallflies (Kahle and many successors; see White's book, 1945, and White, 1950). Here again the germ-track cells have different chromosome complements from the somatic cells. In the same way as before, a diminution takes place in early development, when germ cells and somatic cells are segregated, but here a clear cytological distinction between heterochromatic and other chromosomes has not been possible. The microscopic picture shows many (64 in one case) chromosomes in the fertilized egg and in the cells of the germ track. When diminution takes place in the cleavage cells of the embryo, the majority of these chromosomes (in one case, all but 10) are removed in one or two divisions by remaining in the equator of the spindle and being excluded from the daughter nuclei. Again something must have happened in the centromeric apparatus under the influence of the segregated cytoplasm of the potential somatic cells, something which does not happen in the cytoplasm of the germ-track cells (known to be cytoplasmically different; this is true also of *Ascaris,* as Boveri has already emphasized). The facts are similar to those discussed for Infusoria: a cytoplasmic gradient or field controls happenings in the self-duplicating organelles of division, the kinetosomes there, the centromeres here. So far, no proof of the heterochromatic nature of the diminished chromosomes has been found (heteropyknosis), but I cannot see how we can escape the conclusion that we are dealing with the same thing. Actually

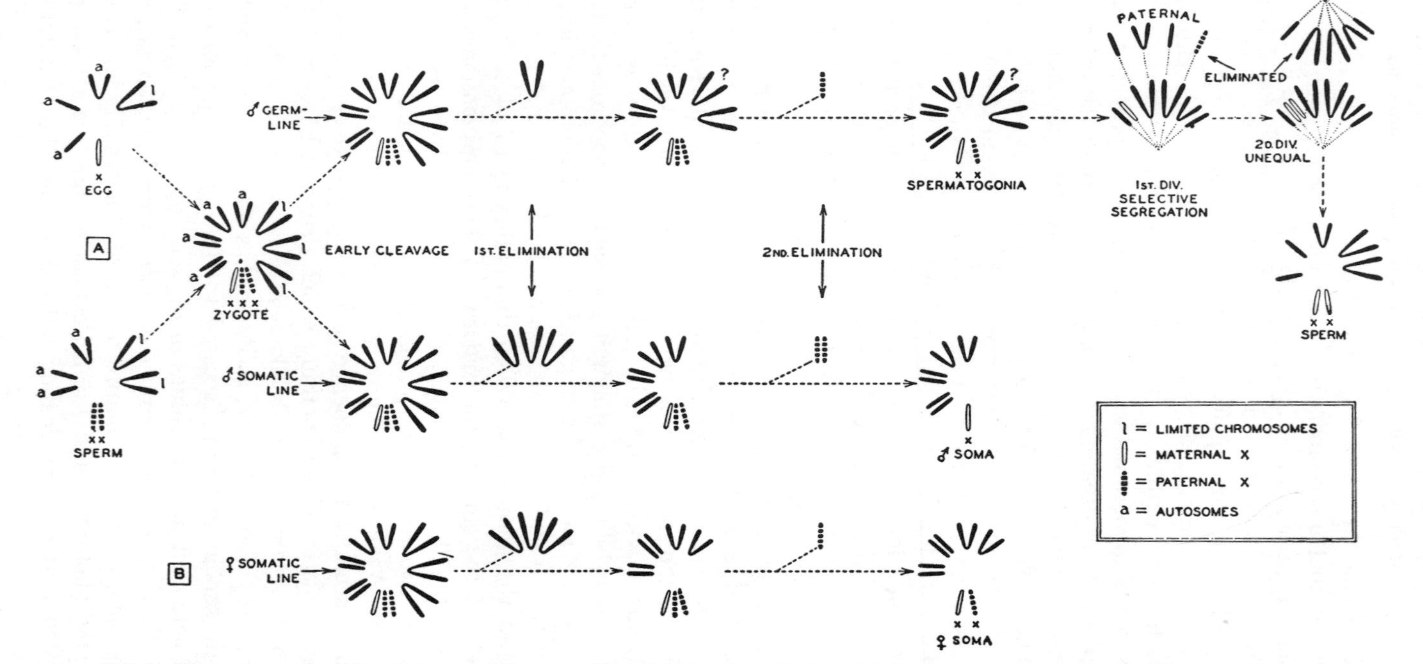

Fig. 7. Chromosomal cycle of *Sciara*. The complicated behavior of the X-chromosomes is not studied here. See only the large heterochromatic "limited" chromosomes (l) and their elimination in female and male somatic line, marked "first elimination" and retention in germ line (top row). (From Metz, 1938.)

Bauer and Beermann (1952) have described a similar case in the chironomid group Orthocladiinae, though the details are somewhat different. Thus the gallflies do not stand alone.

In the same category, though the details are not so concise and regular as in the typical chromatin diminution, are the facts concerning the supernumerary chromosomes in plant cells. (For details see Darlington and Upcott, 1941; Darlington and Thomas, 1941; Resende, 1945.) These small, centromereless chromosomes are frequently found in pollen cells in different, not constant, sometimes large numbers.

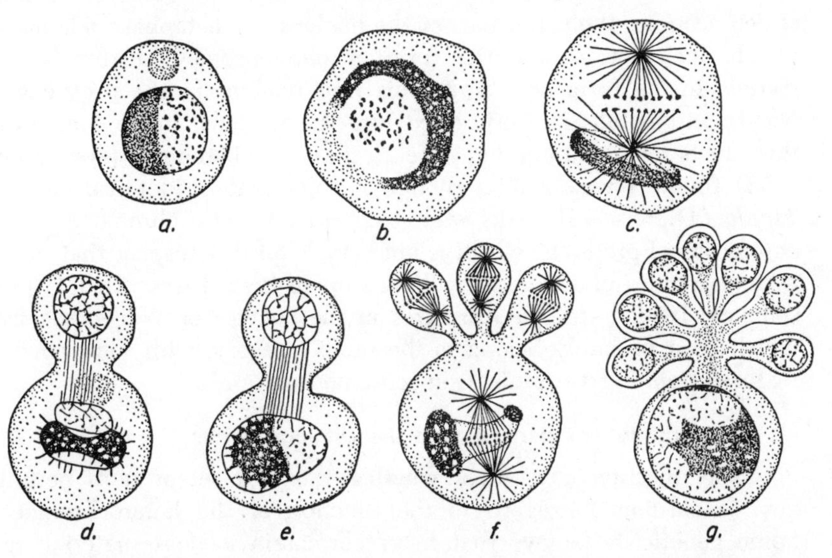

Fig. 8. Giardina ring (heterochromatin) in ovogenesis of *Dyticus* and its retention in ovocyte in divisions separating egg and follicle cells. Note its mass compared with that of small chromosomes. (Combined from Giardina, Günthert, and Korschelt.)

Theoretically, they should disappear after many mitoses, as they are passively distributed in the cytoplasm during division. Actually they remain, as a whole, rather constant and even accumulate in the cells of the germinal layer, which may be compared to a germ track. It is generally recognized that these supernumerary chromosomes are heterochromatic. Obviously they take some active part in divisions in spite of the absence of the centromere, as otherwise they could not keep their own in the germ cells. This must amount to some control of their movements by a differentiated cytoplasm. I think that the most remarkable fact found thus far is Darlington and Thomas' (1941) statement that pollen grains with an accumulation of supernumeraries may undergo some extra divisions.

An apparently completely different set of facts seems to me to continue the line of variations thus far mentioned, though the difference between germ cells and somatic cells is not involved in the same way. This is the remarkable unequal division discovered by Giardina (1901) in the ovary of water beetles (*Dyticus*) (fig. 8). Here the young egg cell undergoes four unequal divisions in which fifteen nurse cells are separated from the oöcyte. In the prophase of these divisions the heterochromatin is assembled into a huge chromocenter which occupies the major part of the nucleus. In metaphase this mass, which does not assume the form of chromosomes, surrounds the spindle in the form of a ring. This ring remains in the prospective oöcyte and is again incorporated into the nucleus. For a long time these facts remained unique. Recently Bauer and students (see Bauer, 1952) found a very similar though not completely identical case in *Tipula* (Diptera). He calls what I consider to be a chromocenter "a chromosomal product," which is not very helpful. I suspect that many other examples of this type will turn up in time. I described (Goldschmidt, 1950*a*) strange structures in the oöcytes of a deep sea fish which most probably belong to the same category, with some special features pointing to origin from chromosome ends.

c. Interpretations derived from the cytological facts

The question now arises whether this first set of facts permits any conclusions in regard to the function of the heterochromatin. Some geneticists believe that heterochromatin is inert material and that it is possible that heterochromatic chromosomes are functionless and frequently lost in phylogeny, but the facts concerning diminution of heterochromatin certainly do not agree with such a point of view. The individual processes are so precise and constant where they are found that they must have a definite meaning. Even the simple cytological aspect militates against such a view. In figure 6 of *Ascaris* oöcytes, the heterochromatic chromocenter contains most of the formed material of the nucleus; in *Sciara* the heterochromatic chromosomes are unusually large; and in the cecidomyids they are five-sixths of the chromosomal material. However, there is also a diametrically opposed interpretation: White (1950) thinks that the somatic chromosomes of the gall midges are the heterochromatic ones! Now in all the other animal material, heterochromatin in the form of chromosomes or chromosome parts is kept intact in the germ cells and removed from the nucleus in prospective somatic cells. With Boveri we can safely assume (as is experimentally proved in *Ascaris* and clear from the morphological facts of the early separation of germ-line material in the egg) that the kind of cytoplasm in which the nuclei lie controls that nuclear process. It may be safely assumed also that the absence or weakening of the centromere in the heterochromatic chromosomes plays the decisive role in the mechanics of diminution. In the comparable plant case (Darlington and Upcott, 1941; Darlington and Thomas, 1941) it can be stated that there is at least a great similarity to diminution in animals, as far as the difference between germinal and somatic cells is involved. Hence the function of the heterochromatin must be involved in the differences between somatic and germinal cells. We can visualize at present three major possibilities:

1. Heterochromatin is a substance which is needed in the synthetic processes of development and therefore reserved for the sex cells. This view encounters serious difficulties. Both in *Ascaris* and in insects the few sex cells (two primary ones in *Ascaris*) are separated early in development and start forming gonads only much later, while all the features of development are concentrated in the somatic cells. The idea under discussion could apply only to the processes taking place in the egg in the next generation, that is, the growth and organization of the oöcyte, a time at which great visible changes do occur in the nucleus and in its relations with the cytoplasm. We could object that this would not apply to the sperm cells, but since we know that one and the same primordial sex cell can develop into an egg or a sperm and this actually happens in insects (*Lymantria*), we should not expect differences between female and male cells in this respect. If this idea were correct we should expect to find diminution in all animals with large organized eggs (predetermined eggs, in the language of the experimental embryologist). *Ascaris* could only partly belong to this group, but all insects and amphibia would. It would be hard to understand why it is found only in *Sciara* (not even in all species!), the cecidomyids, and the chironomid family, though here White claims heterochromasy for the somatic cells. The *Dyticus* case could be interpreted in this way without difficulty, and it is always possible to account for the rarity of such events by saying that the process actually occurs in all eggs or large eggs but is not visible because the heterochromatin is finely divided. This does not appear to be a very happy solution, and it does not fit the supernumeraries of plants at all.

2. Another interpretation is derived from *Ascaris,* in which an important and remarkable difference between germinal and somatic cells does indeed exist. Nematodes are cell-constant animals (Goldschmidt, 1903–1908; see Martini, 1924). This means that growth and differentiation take place largely without cell division. Thus only about eight divisions of one cell are needed to produce all central ganglion cells (162) of the animal (Goldschmidt, 1908). (The details are a little more complicated and variable than this brief statement indicates, but it is essentially correct. See the most recent contribution to the subject by Wessing, 1953, who also found 162 ganglion cells in a completely different nematode.) The sex cells, however, divide indefinitely. Thus we could conclude that heterochromatin is needed for continuous cell division. Actually this conclusion already had been reached from other deliberations (Darlington), and it was even pointed out that accumulation of heterochromatin beyond the normal may be the cause of malignancy. Let us assume that this explanation of diminution (Goldschmidt and Lin, 1947) is correct for *Ascaris.* Why, then, does diminution take place in *Sciara* and the cecidomyids? Neither is cell-constant in the sense of the nematodes, though some organs like salivary glands, epidermis, and oenocytes seem to be cell-constant in Diptera. And, of course, the problem comes up again, why only the few species show the phenomenon. It should be added that Darlington and Thomas' (1941) observation of extra divisions in the pollen in the presence of extraheterochromatin is generally in harmony with what *Ascaris* seems to teach.

3. There is a third possibility, almost the opposite of the second. One of the differences between sexual and somatic cells in the animals under consideration is this (again pointing to White's aberrant claim for the gall midges): the germinal cells are early separated and then do not divide for a long time. The formation of a gonad with intensively dividing sex cells occurs only late in development after all the rest of the body is well differentiated. From this we could conclude that heterochromatin in bulk is a hindrance to quick division and is therefore removed from the quickly dividing cells. We could bring this into agreement with the facts of cell constancy. Both nematodes and insects have a great tendency to endomitosis, meaning a duplication of the chromosomes within the nucleus up to a high polyploidy. In cell-constant animals and organs of otherwise not cell-constant animals this endomitosis seems to play a considerable role in differentiation. Thus we might conclude that heterochromatin is also a hindrance to endomitosis. This third hypothesis recognizes, like

the second, a role of heterochromatin in cell division, but runs in the opposite direction from the second hypothesis. It would permit the inclusion of the *Dyticus* case, because the egg cell is one which for a long time grows without division. It would also permit an explanation why insects and especially cecidomyids are so conspicuous: their development is an extraordinarily fast one, meaning very quick division of the somatic cells (see, however, White, 1950). But here as before remains the question why only the few examples are known. It is hardly imaginable that such a complicated and conspicuous cytological feature is meaningless. It is also impossible that an important process takes place, say, in one species of *Sciara* and not in another. We are almost forced to assume that comparable processes are ubiquitous but only rarely organized on the level of microscopic visibility. At present I prefer this explanation (no. 3) to our former one (no. 2). Both have their good points and their difficulties.

4. A variant of the interpretation just discussed was proposed earlier by Painter (1945). He starts from the fact that RNA plays a role in the functions of the cytoplasm as a source of protein synthesis and of synthesis of DNA for the nuclei. Therefore, quickly dividing cells, the somatic cells in development, have a greater need for RNA which is being satisfied by the eliminated heterochromatin; the latter, as genetically inert, is not needed in the nuclei. This point of view does not emphasize presence or absence of heterochromatin after diminution, but the diminished material itself as a source of RNA for use in cell propagation. The presence of supernumeraries in plant root cells is considered to have the same meaning. In favor of such an idea is a strange phenomenon (discussed I 2 B *a*), the sloughing off of chromosomal material in the meiotic divisions of lepidopteran eggs, discovered by Seiler (1914). It is known now that this material is RNA. But there are difficulties for a comparison with real chromatin diminution. There is no heterochromatin involved; the time of the happening is too late for a role in egg organization and too early for a role in development; further, the crosslike mass of sloughed-off RNA can be seen unchanged for a considerable time and does not seem to contribute anything to development, which is also true of the sloughed-off heterochromatin in *Ascaris*.

5. There is still another interpretation of heterochromatin which does not consider all the remarkable facts discussed above but deals only with the general aspects of heterochromatin distribution in the chromosomes and its relation to chromosome structure. We have discussed (in I 2 B *a*) Serra's views of the intimate structure of the chro-

mosome. He also tried to fit heterochromatin into his scheme. He concludes that heterochromatic regions (and chromosomes) differ from euchromatic ones in retaining the peripheric nucleoproteins while those in euchromatic regions are disintegrating, and this applies especially to the part closely bound to the chromonemata. The reason is the non-functioning of these regions from a genetic point of view. Heterochromasy may be permanent or transitory and does not play a great role. An excess of heterochromatin represents a charge for the cell, because heterochromatic regions are slower in dividing and pairing, and many heterochromatic chromosomes have a tendency to be lost. "Heterochromatic regions are maintained by a balance between their usefulness in mechanisms of sex determination, in rendering inert certain duplicated or unbalanced fractions of the genotype, and in making stable certain special zones of the chromosomes like terminal regions and those adjacent to the centromere in many species, on one side—and on the other, their detrimental properties upon the mechanisms of division and pairing. Natural selection acts upon the net result of this balance and maintains or rejects heterochromatic chromosomes."

This interpretation fails completely to explain the facts discussed thus far and also those to be discussed below. It practically denies a functional role on the basis of morphological observations in plant cells and makes use of the equivocal concept of inert material. Thus it represents a rather negative point of view, which, I think, the facts do not require.

It seems that an explanation cannot be given which fits all the remarkable and conspicuous facts. However, in a general way we may accept the view that heterochromatin is involved in rapid cell division, either preventing it from taking place if retained in the chromosomes or encouraging it if removed into the cytoplasm. A further role in the production of cell constancy and endomitosis is probable. It is not known why the distribution of and happenings to the heterochromatin are so conspicuous in some organisms, while in others nothing of the kind is seen but must be supposed to occur on a submicroscopic level, as must also be assumed for the sloughing off of RNA, visible only in Lepidoptera.

d. Cytology and genetics of heterochromatin in Drosophila

A remarkable body of knowledge on heterochromatin is derived from the study of *Drosophila,* in which cytology and genetic experimentation can collaborate. Though much is still obscure even in this favorable material, a rather large number of important facts are available for theoretical analysis. I shall arrange these facts according to the way I interpret their interrelations. I consider as the first decisive fact, both for cytological description and genetic interpretation, the distinction between chromocentral and intercalary heterochromatin. In a general way this means heterochromatin all of which enters into the framework of the chromosomes during mitosis, but which during interphase as well as meiotic prophase, and also in nuclei that have ceased to divide, shows its two different types. The first type, chromocentral heterochromatin, is removed from its place in the chromosomes and combined in a single chromatic mass, the chromocenter. It is contained in the mitotic chromosomes in large blocks and may even constitute an entire chromosome, as in the Y-chromosome in *D. melanogaster* (and also the cases mentioned in the preceding chapter). The other type of heterochromatin is found in smaller sections over the length of the individual chromosomes. This intercalary heterochromatin is structurally and quantitatively different from the chromocentral type and, in addition, shows different cytological affinities and genetic significance. We would be completely justified in restricting the name "heterochromatin" to the chromocentral type and in using a special term for the intercalary.

In the discussions of the preceding chapter this distinction was not made. In *Ascaris* we dealt with chromocentral heterochromatin, in some of the discussions (e.g., Serra's theory) mostly with intercalary. The following analysis will shed light also on the former material.

aa. Chromocentric and Y-chromosomal heterochromatin

The chromocentric heterochromatin of *D. melanogaster* consists of three parts (see fig. 9): (1) rather large blocks surrounding the centromere in the second and third chromosomes, probably also in the fourth; (2) one large block at the spindle fiber end of the X-chromosome, containing the nucleolus-organizing region; (3) the entire Y-chromosome, also with a nucleolar organizer. All these parts were distinguished by Heitz (1933) in the mitotic metaphase by distinctive staining. They show their nature in many interphase nuclei by combining in a chromocenter (fig. 10). This is best known from the salivary gland nuclei, in which all these sections, including the entire Y, are united in a chromocenter to which the chromosomal loops are attached. The salivary gland chromosomes are indicated in figure 9; the lines showing identical points in mitotic and salivary chromo-

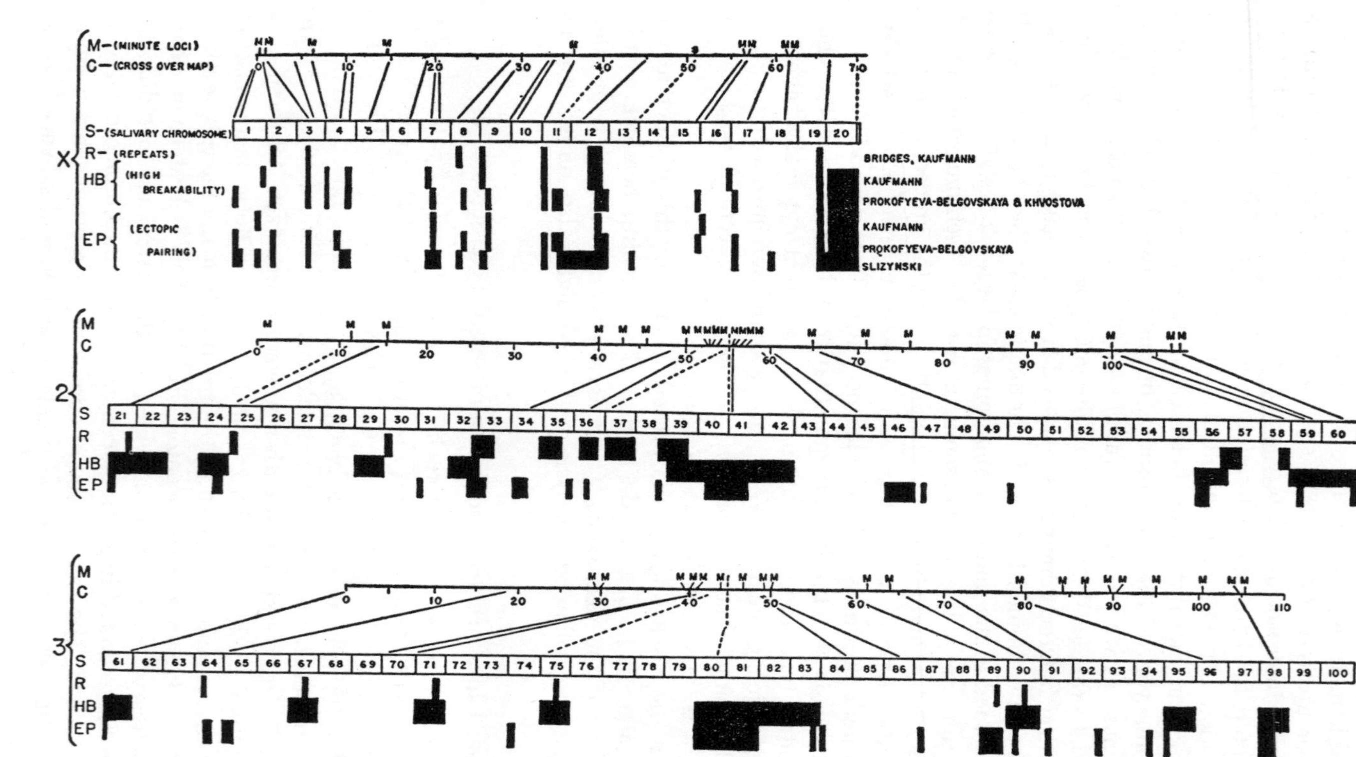

Fig. 9. Delineation of heterochromatic regions in first, second, and third salivary chromosomes of *Drosophila melanogaster* as determined by high breakage (HB), ectopic pairing (EP), and compared with repeats (R) and Minutes (M), and related to genetic map distance (C) and salivary chromosome structure (S). (From Hannah, 1951.)

somes indicate the absence of the heterochromatic regions. It is irrelevant for the present discussion that the big block in the X-chromosome is represented in the salivaries by a single band, which might mean that a tiny euchromatic section is present in the block

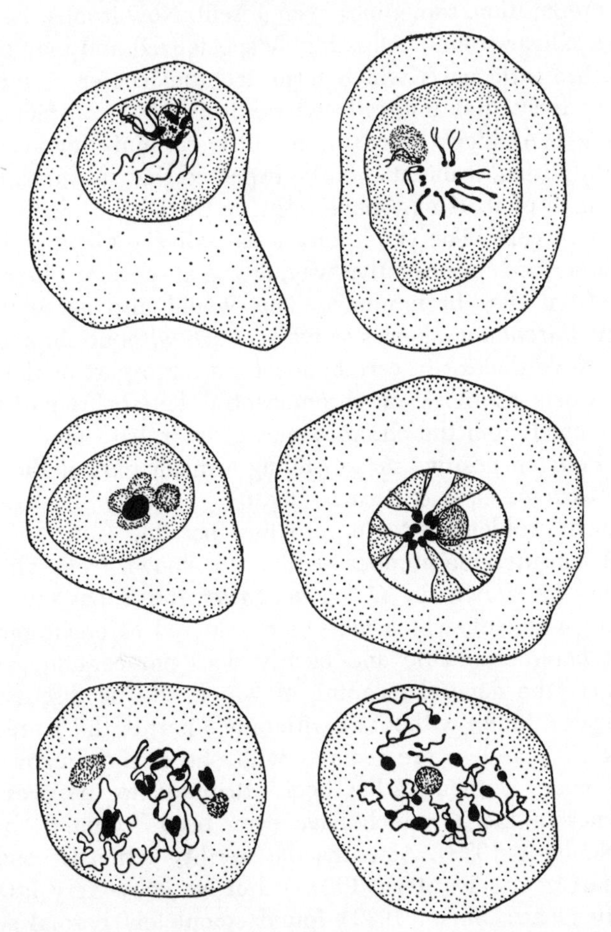

Fig. 10. Different prophases of neurocytes of *Drosophila virilis* larvae, showing large amount of heterochromatin in heteropyknosis in form of chromocenters or individual blocks. (From Makino.)

(Muller's description of this band as a gene which organizes the heterochromatic block does not appeal to me; it actually seems dangerous, because it suggests an explanation while being only a way of terminology). It has been claimed (Prokofyeva, 1935) that within the chromocenter the Y-chromosome can still be recognized as a few weak bands. But the Y-chromosome contains a small pairing section (in the bobbed region) which, if visible, does not affect our ideas about the chromocenter. The chromocenter usually appears as an unorganized, granular, or even degenerating mass, which is easily broken in preparation, sometimes even absent. Now it must be kept in mind that a salivary gland cell is highly specialized and may not need the heterochromatic parts which form a chromocenter in interphase nuclei of actively dividing cells where it is very conspicuous and deeply stained. As block heterochromatin is certainly involved somehow in cell division, it might even be expected that salivary nuclei do not show much of it. It may have been destroyed during the growth phase of these cells. The condition in the salivary gland cells might better be described in a negative way, as the absence of block heterochromatin from the chromosomes. This would also agree with the fact that in *Chironomus* species salivary nuclei without chromocenters are found. Nevertheless, in certain species a large part of the heterochromatin exists as block or chromocentral heterochromatin which may be removed from the chromosomes in interphase and assembled into huge Feulgen positive masses filling a major part of the nucleus in such an extreme case as *Ascaris* (fig. 6).

The next problem is to inquire into possible functions of this material. A considerable number of facts are known from which conclusions may be drawn. In *D. melanogaster* the Y has only a very small pairing segment, which may be considered as euchromatic. All the rest is heterochromatic and clearly does not contain sex-determining units (the general meaning of which will be discussed in a chapter on sex). Males without or with only a part of the Y are normal (though sterile) and so are females with one or more extra Y. The sterility of males without Y has been attributed to the presence of fertility genes in the Y, which have even been "counted" by some authors (Neuhaus, 1939). Actually, the sterility action is confined to a certain part of the Y (Stern, 1929*b*), but we know very little what this sterility means. Shen (1932) found completely normal spermiogenesis in males without a Y; but when the spermatozoa reach a certain part of the vas deferens they are immobilized (see also Stern and Hadorn, 1938). Now we know, at least for Lepidoptera, that the motility of the spermatozoa is dependent upon secretions in the female bursa copulatrix (Klatt, 1919). Thus we may suppose that the immotility of the sperm in the absence of the Y-chromosome may be caused by some small chemical change in the secretion of the vas deferens. From this we may conclude that the absence of certain parts of Y heterochromatin changes some feature of chemical physiology, preventing definite cells from producing their proper secretion. This would mean some, though very slight, participation of heterochromatin in rather restricted chemical actions of some cells. If this conclusion is correct, it involves a genetic diversity of different sections of the Y heterochromatin, which, however, is probably very different from what are usually called genes. The meaning of this will be discussed below. (Though we are dealing here only with *Drosophila,* it might be pointed out that in the Y of plants different sections of action have been claimed by Knapp, Warmke, Westergaard. However, here the Y contains parts affecting sex determination, as will be discussed in detail; the relations to heterochromatin are not yet clear.)

Much better information comes from experiments in which the amount of Y heterochromatin was not decreased but increased. Mather (1941) was the first to find that the addition of an extra Y-chromosome enhanced the expression of a trait assumed to be under polygenic control. He concluded from this that the so-called polygenes were also heterochromatic in character, a problem to which we shall return. The best examples known were found for the so-called podoptera mutants (Goldschmidt, Hannah, and Piternick, 1951). The extremest case is that of pod K, in which only males show the mutant character. However, if an extra Y is introduced into the female, the same phenotype is realized. In other mutants rather variable effects of extra Y's were found. In some XXY combinations penetrance was decreased; in the XYY male it was increased. These facts are comparable to those found by Mather, who stated that Y-chromosomes of different origin exert a specific, though rather small, influence upon the number of chetae, some in the minus, some in the plus direction. The effect is even smaller than that of some environmental influences. From this Mather concluded that the Y heterochromatin also contains polygenes. (We shall discuss the concept of polygenes later.) A comparable fact has been found by Barigozzi (1949, 1950*b*): the amount of Y heterochromatin affects the size of wing cells and eye facets, which means an influence upon cell division. Differences of effect in regard to the origin of the Y were found also. This agrees well with facts and interpretations to be studied below. Barigozzi is inclined to explain the results in terms of polygenes, maintaining that heterochromatin is made up of genes all acting on cell size and similar characters of the cell (see Barigozzi and Pasquale, 1953).

It is certain that the amount of extra heterochromatin influences certain developmental features which control the expression of some mutants of *Drosophila.* In the two cases mentioned it was suspected that the mutants themselves were of heterochromatic nature somehow controlled by properties of intercalary heterochromatic blocks, though the detailed interpretations of Mather and Goldschmidt are rather different. Actually, it seems that some rule is hidden behind these facts. Thus it is known that the expression of Minute mutants, much suspected to be of heterochromatic nature, is strongly influenced by the absence of a Y-chromosome. Another case is that of the mutant "sparkling" in the fourth chromosome (L. V. Morgan, 1947), which produces irregularities in eye structure that may be called a variegation. No position effect is involved, but there is a suspicion that the locus is heterochromatic. The phenotype is strongly influenced by the quantity of heterochromatin. More heterochromatin produces a decrease of the effect; less heterochromatin, an increase of mutant action, according to detailed studies. In this case both Y-chromosomal and X-chromosomal heterochromatin were tested.

This group of facts suggests a specific influence of the quantity of chromocentral heterochromatin upon development of mutant characters suspected of being based upon heterochromatic loci or euchromatic ones imbedded in heterochromatic sections.

In a general way non-Y-chromosomal block heterochromatin acts like Y heterochromatin (see L. V. Morgan, 1947). Besides the Y-chromosome, the major heterochromatic, chromocentral block is the big block near the proximal end of the X-chromosome. It was supposed that its absence or duplication was without genetic effect (inert region of Muller and Painter). But it has been shown since that duplications of the heterochromatic block in the X-chromosome act like an extra Y (Noujdin, 1936); further, that deficiencies of the same region (Khwostova, 1939) enhance the variegation position effect. Heterochromatic regions in other chromosomes, especially the second, have been tested, and it was found that their deficiency has the same action as the absence of Y (see Morgan, Schultz, and Curry, 1940, 1941). The facts of rather different type agree well in a general way, though, thus far, it is not clear what type of action is involved. Nevertheless, it is possible to derive some notion from the variegated position effect. Here extra Y's in normal flies make the eye color mottled. In chromosome rearrangements with variegated effect, addition or subtraction of the Y or its parts affects the degree of variegation. In general (see Schultz, 1947) we may say that the more heterochromatin the less variegation and vice versa. Further examples of the action of chromocentral heterochromatin upon developmental features can be found in the reviews and papers quoted.

bb. Genetic functions? Chromosomal breaks and heterochromatin

In order to derive general conclusions from this array of mixed facts we return to the podoptera case. Here a few more facts are known which can further an interpretation. The most important are the following (Goldschmidt *et al.*, 1951, 1952*b*). The mutant Beaded (Bd) in the third chromosome enhances the action of the pod factors. One allele at the Bd locus was found which enhances the penetrance of tetraltera (belonging to the podoptera group) almost thirtyfold. In pod K only males show the phenotype, and females only when they have an extra Y (L. Kellen Piternick in Goldschmidt *et al.*, 1951, 1952*b*), but Beaded is able to replace completely the extra Y in pod K females! The situation here can only be that the pod action is very narrowly timed in regard to the developmental processes. (This can be expressed also in terms of a very narrow threshold zone for determinative action.) In the male developmental system the proper threshold is surpassed. In the very different female developmental system (actually different in timing and speed of many developmental processes) the threshold is not reached. Beaded, an otherwise known enhancer of podoptera penetrance, acts upon this system in the female by pushing the decisive determinative processes above the threshold of action. Y heterochromatin has the same effect, which, however, may vary quantitatively and even in direction with different Y's and different genotypes of podoptera, which includes, then, enhancement or inhibition. In a general way, these effects must act as steering specific mutually attuned or balanced growth processes, which result in reaching, not reaching, reaching only partly, or more than sufficiently reaching, the threshold level. Differential growth processes are ordinarily linked to the speed of cell division. Thus the genetic facts known about chromocentral chromatin lead to the same result as the cytological study of heterochromatin in chromatin diminution: they show an influence upon cell division and cell growth. (Other generalized chemical effects were mentioned above when studying the sterility factors in the Y-chromosome.)

These conclusions emphasize a genetic function of the heterochromatin which is different from that of the euchromatin with its specific mutant loci. We might call it a generalized function, not affecting a definite, local determination process but a general feature of development like speed of cell division. This conclusion replaces the old, no longer tenable idea of Muller and Painter (1932) that block heterochromatin, especially the Y, is genetically inert. Of course, if this were so, it would be hard to understand why the inert material would be conserved in phylogeny. In a general way our conclusions agree with those of Caspersson (1947) and Darlington (1942), who make the more specific biochemical claim (which is very difficult to prove by the facts thus far known) that the heterochromatin controls cell metabolism and especially the nucleic acid synthesis.

The idea of inert heterochromatin in my opinion is much abused, especially in speculations of a phylogenetic type. Evolution of different chromosome numbers in nearly related species (e.g., *Crepis:* Babcock, 1947 *a,b*; Tobgy, 1943) is explained by one or more chromosomes becoming, in some way, heterochromatic, and, since this is assumed to mean genetically inert, such an element is supposed to become useless and be removed by selection. The same idea has been used to explain differences of evolutionary significance in chromosome arms or sections (see Smith, 1952). It seems to me that we should be very cautious about such speculations. They are all based upon Muller's proof that deletion of the large block of chromocentral heterochromatin in the X-chromosome of *Drosophila* does not influence the phenotype. Since that time so many cases—mentioned or to be recorded—have been found in which addition or subtraction of heterochromatin (including the X-chromosome block) influenced the phenotype that the idea of "inertness" must be regarded as disproved.

Most of these speculations deal with loss of chromosomes via inertness. But they have also been extended to the gain of chromosomes in genera in which the oldest species is supposed to have the lowest number of the group. As an example of what in my opinion is a perverted way of looking at the problems of heterochromatin, I mention the work of Kushnir (1952) on the chromosomes of *Gryllotalpa* species. She speaks of heterochromatic polysomy which led from a form with 15 chromosomes to a form with 19 and 23. The idea is that "the heterochromatic content of these chromosomes which, on one hand, was responsible for their multiplication through irregular segregation enabled them, on the other hand, to survive in larger numbers without upsetting the genic balance of their bearers. While such an addition of heterochromatin must have entailed immediate effects on the metabolism of the animals, it also prepared the ground for a multitude of mutations, which gradually established themselves in the new chromosomes. Through the accumulation of such mutations changing polygenes into major genes, some of the heterochromatin may have become transformed into euchromatin. It is also possible that from the crowd of identical polysomes distinct pairs may have become differentiated." I do not think that this type of phylogenetic speculation is very different from that of Haeckel's day.

One more group of facts should be interpreted similarly, namely, the mottling position effect of heterochromatic breaks. Position effect will be discussed later. Here it suffices to say that a rearrangement break near a known locus produces the phenotype of a mutant of that locus, the position effect. If the rearrangement contains a break within chromocentric heterochromatin which thus becomes adjacent to a euchromatic section, the position effect does not reproduce the complete phenotype of a nearby mutant but only a part of it spatially so that a mottled condition appears. If it is a position effect for the locus of the normal allele of white, the eye is not white but white and wild color (also other colors) mottled. The detailed facts have been reviewed by Hannah (1951) and Lewis (1950); the original discovery was made by Muller (1930). If such a heterochromatic rearrangement is found near a number of closely located loci, all of them may show the mottling (variegation, mosaic). The grade of this variegation is influenced by addition or subtraction of block heterochromatin, and it is affected also by neighboring intercalary heterochromatin. Another agent affecting the grade of mottling is a rearrangement with heterochromatic breaks which are independent of the locus of position effect (Schultz, 1941). However, these and other comparable features are more or less expected, as it is generally known (Goldschmidt and Gardner, 1942; Gardner, 1942) that rearrangements can affect the phenotype of independent mutants. Also, temperature affects the variegation in a rather irregular way (E. Sutton Gersh, 1949), which again is expected. (Many other details will be mentioned below.)

The question arising from these facts is: Why does the presence of block heterochromatin adjacent to a position effect break produce mottling? A number of authors since Demerec and Slizynska (1937) have assumed that here the meaning of position effect is revealed, namely, the production of mutation near the break. Other purely genetic interpretations have been tried. Cytological interpretations also have been suggested, based upon the "heterochromatization" of euchromatic parts (Prokofyeva-Belgovskaya, 1947; also accepted by

Serra, 1949). Prokofyeva-Belgovskaya maintains that in a series of mottled position effects it can be seen that the euchromatic bands adjacent to the heterochromatin become heterochromatinized. This means that instead of clear salivary bands one finds a diffuse chromatic "network" of the kind seen in the chromocenter. The idea is that the function of the euchromatic loci is impeded by this heterochromatization, all of which sounds to me rather crude. Other investigators, however, could find no such cytological changes, which cannot be accepted as established. Serra is more cautious: he does not think of euchromatic bands changing into heterochromatin, but of heterochromatin enveloping the euchromatin and hindering its function. This whole heterochromatization, even if it were a fact, does not help us to understand why the result is mottling rather than normalcy, or why euchromatic rearrangements do not result in mottling.

I have never doubted (see Goldschmidt, 1946*b*) that the mottling is a developmental and not a genetic or cytological phenomenon. If an ordinary (euchromatic) position effect means that a locus near a rearrangement break acts as if it had mutated, the mottled effect could only mean that in the presence of heterochromatin the changed action is not perfect. This means that the action is not completely penetrant in all cells. If the white eye mutant is involved, some of the ommatidial cells show the effect above its threshold of action and are free of pigment (white). In others the threshold is not surpassed and they are pigmented. Still others may react near the threshold and form variable small quantities of pigment, depending upon the breadth of the threshold zone. My conclusion was that the neighboring heterochromatin simply weakens the effect of breakage, which, because of the developmental features of pigmentation, results in a mosaic action, a type which is otherwise well known in mutants with varying penetrance. Recent work by E. Sutton Gersh (1952) on the development of mottled eyes completely confirms this point of view. Apart from the problem of position effect, this shows again a generalized, quantitative action of heterochromatin upon cellular processes, well in conformity with our former conclusions on the function of block heterochromatin.

These deliberations seem to be so important that a few more detailed facts should be discussed. I have already mentioned that loci adjacent to the euchromatic break may show more or less variegation. It seems (literature in Lewis, 1950, and Hannah, 1951) that there is a correlation between the distance of a locus from the break and its variegation, so that the effect decreases with the distance from the break. This applies as much to variegation as such (i.e., penetrance) as it does to the degree of variegation (i.e., expressivity, meaning, e.g., for the white locus more white facets if the break is nearer to white). This can only mean that something emanates from the block heterochromatin with a diminishing gradient which affects the threshold of the position-effect action in development. We see two things at work: first, the position effect of the break, making a locus nearby act as if it were mutated; and second, an action of heterochromatin influencing the penetrance and expressivity of the action of the break during development with narrow threshold conditions, which by the inherent variability of action above and below the threshold produce the mosaic effect. We also find the breakage effect acting with a gradient, decreasing with distance. Not all loci clearly show this distance relation and, further, differences in the effect have been observed, when the heterochromatin adjacent to the break was derived from different blocks of chromocentral heterochromatin, which might be caused by qualitative or only quantitative differences.

In maize, conditions are known which affect the variegation (McClintock's Ac and Rhoades' Dt). The latter is described as a dominant locus within a heterochromatic block. We do not know what this means, but the action parallels that of extra heterochromatin in *Drosophila*. It is quite possible that in plants heterochromatic conditions exist—symbolized as Dt—which, morphologically, are different from those in *Drosophila* and do not necessarily have to be additions or subtractions of substance. (More details on maize variegation in a later chapter.)

The facts discussed thus far relate to euchromatic loci as influenced by adjacent heterochromatin. The last example refers to euchromatic loci within heterochromatic blocks. The experiment with variegation should give information. On the side of the break in the euchromatin, euchromatic loci are located. If there are euchromatic loci within the heterochromatic block, they would be put into the neighborhood of euchromatin via the heterochromatic break (each rearrangement requiring two breaks). A heterochromatic locus should also show variegation, provided that variegation, generally, is the result of abnormal union of eu- and heterochromatin on both sides of a break. Actually, many such cases have been described (Sutton, 1941) for loci in different chromosomes, like bobbed, light, pink, radius incompletus, all of which have been localized in heterochromatic regions genetically as well as in the salivary chromosomes, as far as possible. Now all these mutants behave like any other mutant; hence the conclusion could be drawn that heterochromatin differs from euchromatin genetically only in containing very few mutant loci (genes). This is not very satisfactory in view of all the special features recorded for chromocentric heterochromatin.

One may be inclined to assume that all these loci are small sections of euchromatin intercalated into the heterochromatin. In favor of this assumption is the fact that the heterochromatic block of the X-chromosome is represented by one regular band in the salivary X (see, above, Muller; I 2 *C d aa*) and, further, that the Y may be represented by a few bands attached to the chromocenter, which must contain a bobbed allele, bobbed being such a "heterochromatic locus." It is maintained (see the reviews, work mostly by Schultz) that such heterochromatic loci react differently to extra heterochromatin (an additional Y) as follows: while variegation of euchromatic loci is reduced by an extra Y, this is not true for some heterochromatic loci. It is claimed that this is what is expected, though I am not convinced of the logic of the argument.

Actually, we know that in podoptera an extra Y may act as an enhancer or as a reducer of penetrance in different genotypes, including the two sexes, and the influence of an extra Y on mottling is clearly the same thing as its influence upon penetrance in podoptera, requiring the same explanation. As so-called heterochromatic mutants also are known for which an intermediate action of extra heterochromatin is claimed, it seems to me that there are no heterochromatic loci in the strict sense of the term, but only euchromatic loci surrounded by heterochromatin, which, like other such loci, may react in different directions upon extra heterochromatin, as well as upon breaks in the heterochromatin. This agrees also with the general interpretation of heterochromatic function given above. If heterochromatin exercises a general, quantitative action upon developmental and cellular processes, there is no reason why this must always go in one direction. It is more probable that it may be positive, negative, or anything in between according to the specific genetic milieu in which it acts.

Recent work by Baker (1953) seems to agree very well with these conclusions. He studied a variegated position effect for the peach locus in *Drosophila virilis,* which is located within chromocentral heterochromatin near the centromere of the fifth chromosome. Variegation is produced (in a large material) by placing foreign heterochromatin distal to the peach locus, or proximal to this locus; or by placing euchromatin either distal or proximal to the locus. This shows clearly that the cause of the variegated position effect is simply the disruption of heterochromatin by a break. This means that it is a break, a change of pattern, which produces the position effect: Lewis' (1950) artificial distinction in principle between variegated and other position effect is not necessary, and is actually mistaken. The variegation in the presence of the heterochromatic break is, I think, to be explained here in the same way as above: the heterochromatin affects the penetrance and expressivity of the mutant-like action of the break (i.e., position effect) during development by lifting the developmental processes above a threshold or not (this includes chemical syntheses in the case of eye colors). Baker himself gives an interpretation in the currently popular terms of interaction between necessary substrates of gene and heterochromatin, but he adds that he is aware that such a model is only one of many possible schemes. I prefer the one presented in this chapter. (We shall not go into further details at this point, since only heterochromatic function is under discussion, not the theory of position effect, which will be discussed below.)

As far as our present discussion of the function of heterochromatin is concerned, all the different facts show in the end that chromocentral heterochromatin has a generalized function connected with rates of cell division and quantitative features of intracellular metabolism.

cc. Intercalary heterochromatin

The other type of heterochromatin, the intercalary one, was also discovered by Heitz, who found that mitotic chromosomes of *Drosophila* had at certain stages a beaded appearance, showing a number of more darkly staining blocks. Kodani (1942) proved later for the X-chromosome that Heitz's heterochromatic segments correspond closely to those he could delineate by specific reaction to urea-alkali. Similar observations were made in other animals and plants. Darlington and La Cour (1938) showed the alternation of eu- and heterochromatic segments in the chromosomes of *Fritillaria*. Later they found that cold treatment reduced the stainability of these chromosomes in segments, which closely corresponded to those seen in pachytene chromosomes and therefore are heterochromatic (their so-called chromatin starvation). In other chromosomes (see fig. 10) intercalary heterochromatin appears in the form of larger and condensed chromomeres, a kind of heteropyknosis. White (1945) actually defines (all) heterochromatin as those chromosomal regions which become heteropyknotic at some time during the chromosomal cycle.

The best information on intercalary heterochromatin again comes from the salivary gland chromosomes in *Drosophila*. On a purely morphological basis, it is difficult to define the intercalary heterochromatic segments. In a general way they show less stainability and differentiation of dark bands, features which, however, are not equally clear in all regions, but are just the opposite of the behavior in metaphase and prophase chromosomes where heterochromatin is highly chromatic. However, there are a group of criteria which permit a fair delineation of these segments. The first is the tendency of heterochromatic segments to get attached to other heterochromatin in the same or other chromosomes. By checking carefully the bands which show this unspecific attraction (so-called ectopic pairing), as opposed to the specific band-by-band attraction of euchromatin, Prokofyeva (1939) could map the distribution of intercalary heterochromatin. A less exact method was found by Kodani (1942), who showed that heterochromatic segments are more quickly dissolved in alkali-urea and can thus be delineated approximately if inversions are used as markers. As far as this goes the results agree with Prokofyeva's and similar studies by Kaufmann (1946, 1948*a*). A third method is based upon the property of the heterochromatic segments of being more easily broken by X rays or spontaneously. By mapping easily broken sections, Prokofyeva (1939), Slizynski (1945), and Kaufmann (1946) again localized the heterochromatic sectors. The results of these studies are well summarized in Hannah's (1951) scheme (fig. 10) for the first, second, and third chromosome. It does not include Kodani's data, but includes for the X-chromosome so-called repeats, assumed to be heterochromatic, and the location of the Minutes, which are suspected to be heterochromatic. The salivary chromosome is represented with the numbered sections as laid down in Bridges' maps, and the crossover maps are added for comparison. The rather good fit of the different checks is apparent.

A word should be added about repeats and Minutes, which are represented in figure 9. Bridges described many places in the salivary chromosomes which look as if the same band or bands had been repeated by some process of doubling. Much theoretical interest is attached to these. At this point we are concerned only with the idea that repeats are heterochromatic. It cannot be said that this is actually proved, though the localization points to it. One idea deserves to be mentioned (Pontecorvo, 1944), that heterochromatin generally is the result of duplications of chromomeres resulting in an aggregation of chromomeres of similar function (an idea which could also be paralleled by Mather's blocks of polygenes). Thus far such notions can only be registered. The Minutes, however, are very special occurrences. Many dozens of Minutes are known (see Schultz, 1929), distributed over all chromosomes with a predilection for chromocentric regions. All of them are dominant, homozygous lethal mutants with similar pleiotropic effects upon bristles, body size, wing structure, and genitalia. Many of them are known to be deficiencies and are also known to react to extra quantities of Y-chromosome. In addition, they interact specifically with the Beaded locus (Goldschmidt, 1949*a*), making Bd 100 per cent dominant instead of plus or minus 5 per cent. It is known (Goldschmidt, Hannah, Piternick, 1951) that Bd is able to replace the action of Y-chromosome material. From such facts we derive the suspicion that Minutes are changes, actually quantity changes within the intercalary heterochromatin, all of which have a similar effect because of the generalized action of heterochromatin. It is very difficult to prove such an interpretation, which thus remains a hypothesis.

dd. Genetic function of intercalary heterochromatin

The decisive question is now, Does intercalary heterochromatin have a genetic effect? This would be demonstrated if it is found capable of changes that can be compared to euchromatic mutation, though less typical. The first question would be whether heterochromatic mutation is altogether an erroneous assumption based on overlooking the fact that heterochromatic sections contain standard mutants of the same type as those in euchromatic sections. While discussing the chromocentric heterochromatin, we have emphasized the possibility of standard mutants within block heterochromatin. We came to the conclusion that such loci as were proved to be present in heterochromatic sections are to be regarded as small intercalated euchromatic sections. Naturally the same thing might also occur within intercalary heterochromatin, though it would be difficult to prove on account of the difficulty of exact delineation of the intercalary sections. If the Minutes are heterochromatic mutants, they demonstrate that such mutants are rather different from euchromatic ones, since all Minutes have approximately the same effects, which in a general way may be described as interference with growth processes.

It does not seem that the existence of standard mutants within intercalary heterochromatin has been demonstrated (or can be demonstrated). There are indications (Griffen and Stone, 1940) that intercalary heterochromatin breaks producing position effects lead to variegation just as do breaks involving block heterochromatin. If this is confirmed, the intercalary would have one important feature in common with the chromocentric heterochromatin. We have already mentioned the greater breakability of this heterochromatin which must result in more deficiencies and also more position effects in the neighborhood of heterochromatic blocks. This would make eventual heterochromatic mutants suspect. At present it is safe to say that intercalary heterochromatin is genetically different from euchromatin and also from block heterochromatin, with which it has, however, some features in common.

The first to ascribe a special genetic function to the intercalary heterochromatin was Mather (1941), who derived his conclusions from selection experiments with the number of abdominal bristles in *Drosophila*. From the way the successful selection was running, especially the sudden jumps after periods of constancy, he concluded that the multiple factors controlling the character are present not only in a balanced condition which permits plus and minus shifts, but that they are packed tightly in blocks, which he called polygenic blocks, within which crossing over can occur, leading to a sudden change in balance. These polygenic blocks are spread over all chromosomes and are important as an always available source of adaptive selection.

Looking for an explanation of these assumed polygenic blocks, Mather reasoned in the following way: supernumerary chromosomes in plants are not entirely dispensable, as they remain in the cells, though theoretically they should be sorted out during cycles of division. They must, therefore, betray a kind of balanced condition favored by selection. This means, he thinks, that they take part in a balance of polygenic action. They do not contain major genes and are considered to be heterochromatic. Because they are, nevertheless, partly dispensable, genes with similar action must be contained in the ordinary chromosomes. These latter contain, as derived above, groups or blocks of polygenes, balanced to insure both genetical stability and flexibility, the balanced polygenic blocks. By analogy with the supernumeraries, also subject to polymeric balance, it may be assumed that these polygenic blocks are located in the heterochromatic sections. Therefore the phenotype (abdominal chaetae) supposed to be controlled by these blocks was checked in the presence or absence of Y and extra Y material. As I mentioned previously, Y-chromosomes of different origin exert a specific, rather small influence upon the number of chaetae, some in the minus, some in the plus direction. This effect is continuous and rather small in comparison with that of environmental factors. The action "must" depend upon a number of genes, according to Mather. Since it is assumed that the polygenic blocks in different chromosomes have a similar effect, it is assumed also that the heterochromatic Y-chromosome has all the properties of a polygenic setup: quantitative action depending upon a number of genes with similar small quantitative effects, balance of its polygenic blocks, and possibility of new combinations via crossing over. Reasoning backward, therefore, the polygenic blocks are heterochromatic, or all heterochromatin contains polygenes.

It can be understood that this analysis has not met with general approval. This applies to the conclusion of the existence of polygenic blocks as well as to their connection with heterochromatin. Here we are interested only in the second part, which was the first attempt to assign a definite genetic function to heterochromatin. It has been argued, since, that duplication of genes could be a method of producing such polygenic blocks. The facts are insufficient for a convincing proof of the existence of the polygenic blocks and of their heterochromatic nature, though some of the conclusions concerning the action of heterochromatin, apart from the polygene concept, agree with those we derive from different facts.

Rather different conclusions about the genetic function of intercalary heterochromatin have been derived by Goldschmidt (1949*c*) and Goldschmidt, Hannah, and Piternick (1951) from their study of the podoptera mutants of *D. melanogaster*. The very large and complicated body of facts may be summarized thus: podoptera (and the similar tetraltera) is a group of homoeotic mutants in which the wing is changed in a characteristic way into a leglike (sometimes haltere-like) structure; furthermore, other wing parts (i.e., their embryonic material) are transformed into thorax. A considerable number of such known podoptera types are genetically and phenotypically somewhat different. They are no simple mutants, but the phenotype is based upon a number of mutant loci with different quantitative effect, collaborating in a definite way. We speak, therefore, of the podoptera effect, not of simple pod mutants. Genetically, pod factors are known in all chromosomes. If isolated, some have very little effect; others, large effects; and together they produce a penetrance of the effect that varies from less than 1 per cent to 100 per cent. Selection experiments (see 1951; and Goldschmidt, 1953*b*) show a considerable similarity to the ones reported by Mather, though they deal with penetrance (and partly correlated expressivity) of a single though variable phenotype, not with a numerical variation of a character. Selection, as a rule, does not lead very far, though it shows the not unusual availability of minor modifiers. However, selection from less than 1 per cent to 100 per cent penetrance can be accomplished in a few major jumps. Some of these sudden jumps were shown to be due to the introduction of major enhancers; others must have been based upon the liberation of recessive enhancers by crossing over from a balanced condition. But there is no reason whatever to assume special balanced blocks of polygenes. Individual enhancers, balanced by association with lethals, suffice.

A number of special features distinguish the podoptera effect from ordinary mutant effects. In their totality, these special features suggest that we are dealing not with the ordinary type of mutants, but possibly with mutated conditions, whatever that may mean, of the intercalary heterochromatin. There is no reason to compare such conditions of the heterochromatin with standard point mutants. I am inclined to think of a difference in quantity, without any proof for such an interpretation other than the comparison with the effect of quantities of block heterochromatin. These distinctive features of the pod effect are as follows. (1) Genetic factors for the pod effect are ubiquitous, and can be found in any *Drosophila* line which has been properly tested. (2) The effect varies down to such a low penetrance and expressivity that there is practically no limit between a low effect and normality. (3) Pod factors are known in all chromosomes and have different effectiveness. Their exact localization is difficult except for one or two major ones in the first and second chromosome. (4) These factors control definite and different phenotypes within the general pod effect in different selected lines. (5) Within each line these multiple factors collaborate in an additive or multiplicative total effect, the details being rather complicated. (6) The pod factors of different lines do not replace each other, are not allelic. (7) Nevertheless, there is some interaction between these non-allelic factors, as their simultaneous, heterozygous presence gives a little pod effect. We may therefore speak of a weak false allelism (a "false" allelism because the term "pseudoallelism" already has a different meaning), which is not confined to factors in the same chromosome. (8) The degree of dominance of some dominants is influenced by the presence of pod factors. (9) We have mentioned the remarkable effects of the Y-chromosome upon the pod effect: in one line, pod K, the females do not show the effect except when they have an extra Y. In all lines the addition of an extra Y or part of one changes penetrance and expressivity, usually in different directions in the two sexes. (10) There are remarkable relations to dominant Beaded: ordinary Bd does not enhance pod, but one allele, Bd^P, enhances one pod type greatly. Also, the presence of pod increases the penetrance of Bd itself; the strangest interaction of all is that in which Bd replaces the action of an extra Y in pod K (point 9). (11) Another strange feature is that in a pod line, pod H, the main pod factor simultaneously causes a high incidence of chromosome elimination. The same factor has also a maternal effect; that is, it acts upon the egg cytoplasm before fertilization. (12) An unusually high incidence of pod factors was found in the Minutes, themselves suspected of being heterochromatic.

All these facts lead us to the conclusion that we are dealing with heterochromatic heredity. It seems rather remarkable that one of the features, the false allelism of the pod factors in different chromosomes, parallels the cytological behavior of intercalary heterochromatin, namely, its unspecific attraction. The essential sameness of mutant effects, their false allelism, their ubiquity, their interrelations with Y heterochromatin, and their affecting early embryonic differentiation suggest their being a part of an indispensable, integrated, somehow generalized part of the genetical material, all of which points to the intercalary heterochromatin. Needless to say, this conclusion is based upon circumstantial evidence. A direct proof or a decisive test is not yet available.

There is some remarkable, though not completely clear, work by Mampell (1945, 1946) with *D. persimilis* which shows some interesting parallels to our podoptera work. He describes a recessive "mutator," a locus in the second chromosome, which produces somatic mosaics mostly of the Minute type. Sometimes the germ cells are affected, and hereditary Minutes over all the chromosomes result which are mostly deficiencies; also chromosome elimination is observed, both very much like the pod action in pod H, and similar in percentage. Females do not show the effect, but addition of an extra Y makes it appear, again, a close parallel to pod K. Mampell, therefore, thinks of a heterochromatic action, though he overlooks the intercalary heterochromatin. It cannot be doubted that all the facts reported thus far together make a strong argument, though there is much still left to be cleared before our hypothesis may be considered as proved.

ee. Heterochromatin and the genetics of sex

One more group of facts is strongly suggestive and has been used (Goldschmidt, 1949*c*) in presenting the hypothesis that heterochromatic heredity is involved. Some discussion by Pontecorvo (1943) could be considered as foreshadowing this idea. One type of heredity, the heredity of sex, is completely different from all others. A single hereditary difference, working, as a first approximation, like a Mendelian backcross, determines maximally a difference affecting the entire organism, actually every single cell. This is the most generalized genetic action known; in many instances it produces phenotypic differences of the entire body or of one or many individual parts, which, purely quantitatively, are of the order of specific, generic, and still higher differences. If, for example, we were to consider the highly different genital armatures as two individual organisms, these would appear as different as if they belonged to different taxonomic classes. Furthermore, the genetic differences between the sexes in higher diploid organisms like insects exhibit a type otherwise unknown in genetics. It is well known what this is: (1) the differentiation of a special pair of chromosomes, the X-chromosomes, which play the decisive role by a kind of backcross mechanism which takes care that half of the fertilized eggs normally receive two, and the other half one X-chromosome; (2) the establishment of genetic factors for the control of one of the sexes (e.g., the male in *Lymantria*, the female in *Drosophila*) located within the X-chromosomes; (3) the provision of genetic factors for the control of the other sex outside the X-chromosomes (in some the Y-chromosome or autosomes or both); (4) the control of the sexual alternative, that is, of the entire female or male phenotype with all its differences by a simple quantitative ratio or balance: one dose X-chromosomal determiners inferior, two doses superior, to the identical (homozygous) action of the determiners outside the X-chromosomes. This genetic mechanism, which works at least in all diploid, genuinely dioecious organisms, is an old specific feature different from the usual interplay of Mendelizing standard loci. It is at once suggestive that the seat of these genetic factors (I purposely use this general terminology) are the two chromosomes which are known to be the richest in heterochromatin and to exhibit most prominently all the characteristic features of heteropyknosis and allocycly, so well known to cytology.

We might summarize (details will be analyzed in a later chapter) the genetic facts which seem to fall in line with the special cytology of the sex chromosomes. In *Drosophila* a very thorough search for the genetic sex factors in the X-chromosomes could be made since Dobzhansky and Schultz (1934) introduced the method of adding or subtracting broken fragments of the X to the normal 2X of triploid intersexes and measuring the feminizing or masculinizing effect by the grade of intersexuality. The most detailed work was done by S. Bedichek Pipkin (1940, 1942, 1947). The first unequivocal result is that no single female sex gene could be located. In a general way the feminizing effect of extra sections is proportional to the size of the fragment. From this the conclusion was drawn that multiple female sex "genes" are spread over the X-chromosome. But there are some significant details. The most important one is (Pipkin) that the part of the X-chromosome to the left of section 17 has more feminizing influence than that to the right. Actually, almost all intercalary heterochromatin is found in that left section with rather equal distribution. Though no exact localization is possible in these experiments, there are no facts which would be opposed to the location of the female determining action in the series of intercalary heterochromatic blocks. With this, however, we do not mean multiple "genes" like other Mendelizing loci. We mean general actions of heterochromatin blocks, without any need for special genes located therein, actions upon generalized processes of early development that decide the growth properties of the cells, which after all make up the morphological sex differences. The genetics of sex determination, the balance and detailed genetic setup, are not under discussion here, but solely the facts pointing to heterochromatin.

A number of detailed facts agree with such a conclusion, which would of course have to be applied also to the male determining sections outside the X-chromosome (in *Drosophila*). In *Lymantria*, where the female determiners are located outside the X-chromosomes, they were found in the Y-chromosome and thus inherited from mother to daughter. Cytologically the Y could not be distinguished, and therefore its heterochromaticity is not known. Also in *Bombyx mori* the Y-chromosome contains the female factors (Tazima, 1943), in this case very powerful ones which are not suppressed by a multiplicity of male X factors. In addition to the main female determiners in the Y-chromosome, autosomal modifiers are known, but again no information about heterochromatin in the autosomes is available except the fact of prophasic association mentioned above (Goldschmidt, 1923*b*), which indicates at least the presence of heterochromatin. In *Drosophila* it was originally assumed that all autosomes carry male determiners (Bridges, 1922). But the fourth chromosome is ruled out because haplo- or triplo-IV does not affect sex. A careful check of the second chromosome made by S. Bedichek Pipkin (1947) with the translocation and triploid method failed to find any major sex determiners, which, then, must be located in the third chromosome. Some geneticists consider all mutant loci which can produce a shift in sex (different types of intersexuality, abnormal genitalia, sterility) as sex determiners, and such loci are found also in the second chromosome. But a comparison with the facts in *Lymantria* as well as Pipkin's results show that we must distinguish between sex determiners responsible for the F/M balance and modifiers affecting special developmental processes (to be discussed in a later chapter). Thus far, no facts are available which would permit localizing the male factors with certainty in intercalary heterochromatin of the third chromosome. But it is at least significant that the transformer locus (tra, 3.43–45.5), which in homozygous condition transforms genetic females into almost males (extreme female intersexes) is located in a region with an accumulation of Minutes, and in or near heterochromatic sections (fig. 9). Lebedeff's (1939) powerful intersexuality factor in *D. virilis* has a similar localization.

Moreover, there are a number of indirect signs indicating the heterochromatic nature of the autosomal male determiners. We remember that there is a strong suspicion that the Minutes are heterochromatic mutants (deficiencies). One of the characteristics of these mutants is a tendency to change the male genital armature, which has to be interpreted as beginning intersexuality, that is, weakening of the male determiners (details in Goldschmidt, 1949*a*, 1951*b*). We remember further that the mutant Beaded shows heterochromatic features, being able to replace the action of Y heterochromatin in pod K. Bd and the Minutes interact strongly so far as all Minutes enhance the penetrance (and expressivity) of Bd from a small percentage in Bd/+ to 100 per cent. The combination of Bd with some Minutes produces a peculiar low-grade and characteristic type of intersexuality in males (Goldschmidt, 1949*a*). All this taken together suggests strongly the heterochromatic nature of the male determiners.

In the same experiments was found (Goldschmidt, 1951*b*) another feature that adds to the indirect evidence. It could be shown that the genetic control of intersexuality by the Bd-M combination, the weakening of the action of the male determiners, takes place in the egg before maturation (so-called maternal effect). Now we know that in *Lymantria* the Y-chromosomal sex determiners act in the same way; we know further that some of the podoptera factors act in the same way, and that some of the podoptera factors assumed to be heterochromatic (in pod H) also show the maternal effect. In addition, it is known (Sturtevant, 1946) that intersexuality produced in species (geographic "species" or subspecies) crosses of members of the *Drosophila repleta* group is based upon an autosomal dominant acting upon the egg cytoplasm before fertilization, a maternal effect. Finally, such a maternal effect in sex determination has been found also in plants (*Streptocarpus:* Oehlkers, 1938, 1940, 1941) in which a close parallel to the analysis of intersexuality in *Lymantria* was established (further details, and differences, to be discussed in a later chapter). Hence no doubt can exist that we are dealing here with a phenomenon of basic importance. All this adds up to a rather strong argument in favor of our conclusion that sex determination is actually a function of intercalary heterochromatin, a generalized function, not capable of being dissolved into sets of multiple genes with special actions.

One more very powerful argument is worth consideration. (See discussion in Goldschmidt, 1950*b*.) We remember the mottled position effect which is produced by heterochromatic breaks in the general vicinity of a known locus. Now position effect alone means that a non-mutated locus acts like a mutant when the chromosomal pattern near it is shuffled. The additional mottling in the special cases means that the mutation imitating position effect is not pushed above the threshold of action in a number of cells (which remain wild type). The number of such cells as well as their distribution can be influenced by additional heterochromatin. Altogether, the lesion of a segment of intercalary heterochromatin affects a quantitative feature of development so as to reach or not to reach a threshold value. (Similar facts are contained in McClintock's work, as analyzed in my paper, 1950*b*.) The facts known in regard to sex determination may be considered as being of the same general type. Intersexuality in *Lymantria* and other organisms with a comparable genetic method of sex determination (e.g., *Drosophila*) means that, as a result of disturbed balance of the female and male sex determiners, development starts with the chromosomal sex but continues after a definite time, the turning point, with the opposite sex. In many cases this is a simple all-or-none affair, and all development after the turning point is of the opposite sex. But in certain cases, as in *Lymantria* males and in females of special genetic constitution, a mosaic effect is observed (see Goldschmidt and Poppelbaum, 1914, and Poppelbaum, 1914). In the extreme this occurs in the triploid intersexes of *Solenobia* (Seiler; see his final discussion, 1949) in which all (?) the intersexual development is of the mosaic type. This means that each cell has only the alternative female or male (as also in the non-mosaic type) but that the decision of this alternative at the time of the turning point requires a threshold condition, which in the mosaic type is not reached in all cells. The consequence is that a more or less large number of cells remain as they were, while the others change their sexual development, closely parallel to the mottled eyes of *Drosophila.* The fact is best seen in wings of intersexual *Lymantria* males (or females of special genetic composition) in which some groups of scales remain male while others turn female; or in the genital ducts of intersexual *Solenobia* (Seiler) in which a mosaic of patches of the very different female and male type epithelium appears. In both cases the amount of mosaic spots with the changed sex character increases with intersexuality (i.e., earlier turning point). The parallel effect in *Drosophila* is increase of white spots when the quantity of heterochromatin changes. It is very tempting to parallel the two sets of facts by saying that the different potencies of sex determiners in diploid intersexuality (*Lymantria*) which control the amount of mottling and the different quantities (via numbers of chromosomes) in triploid intersexuality (*Solenobia*) are in fact differences in heterochromatin. This means that the sex determiners involved are blocks of heterochromatin. I consider these facts and their analysis to be a very important asset to the view presented here.

3

CHROMOSOMES AND GENES

The morphology and the biochemistry of the chromosome have taught us a number of important facts. But they have failed thus far to give a clear answer to the question: What is the genic material in the chromosome? Perhaps the question itself was based upon a wrong, preconceived idea. Saturated as we are with the clear, unassailable facts of Mendelian inheritance, we are conditioned to thinking in terms of discrete units which can be shifted and recombined like dice in a throw, never losing their identity in a kind of splendid isolation. Therefore, it is a kind of natural instinct to look in a chromosome for these discrete units, the genes, and this desire prompted our question about the genic part of the chromosome.

Optimistic observers more than once have claimed to have seen the genes. About twenty years ago Belling, a brilliant observer and a keen thinker, took me with solemn ceremony to his microscope to show me the gene. He had succeeded in staining distinctly within some big chromomeres a tiny but clearly visible central dot which he considered to be the gene finally made visible. The number of geneticists is not small who talk of the bands in the salivary chromosomes as genes and obviously are convinced that these are the real, visible genes of classic Mendelism, though numerous facts already mentioned or still to be mentioned are opposed to such oversimplification. Recently much smaller structures have been seen in the bands with the electron microscope and have been hailed as the real genes.

If we try to forget this instinctive quest for the visible hereditary unit and face the facts described in the search for the genic material in the chromosomes in an unprejudiced way, we cannot help feeling that the facts point in another direction. They seem to indicate that the chromosome is not an assembly of independent units but a kind of microörganism in which all parts are needed and interacting in some way, so that the entire chromosome, not definite parts, has to be called the genic material. Just as the theory of the separate units, the genes, was not derived from cytological facts but from genetic analysis, the ideas of a different type are based upon genetic facts, though it seems to me that the morphology and the biochemistry of the chromosomes are pointing in the same direction.

A. THE THEORY OF THE GENE

The theory of the gene goes back to the desire, visible in all pre-Mendelian speculations of the epigenetic type, to explain heredity by proper hereditary corpuscles in the cells which could be moved around in the proper way to meet the needs of the respective theory. With the discovery of mitosis these corpuscles were put in linear order into the chromosomes (Roux, 1883), and Mendelian genetics revived them as genes (Johannsen's term). The experimental underpinning of these speculations begins with Boveri-Sutton's proof that Mendelian segregation and recombination is the consequence of the location of Mendelizing factors within a pair of homologous chromosomes. It reaches its climax with the crossing-over studies of the Morgan group, which proved the exact order, linear arrangement, and localization of Mendelizing alleles in the chromosomes; and it ends with the proof (Painter) that the visible arrangement of structures of the salivary gland chromosomes agrees exactly with the results of genetic localization. In the minds of geneticists and nongeneticists alike, this established the gene as the unit of heredity, even the unit of life, being corpuscular, individual, independent, self-duplicating, but capable of mutational change, beadlike, as in a string of beads and imbedded in the chromosome.

Though this was and is clearly the idea of a gene, its definition, as derived from experiments by the Morgan group, was less concrete. By definition the gene was the smallest section of a chromosome within which no crossover break can occur. But this definition does not make much sense, for it is based upon a criterion which cannot be stated in absolute terms. The distance between two genes is measured by the percentage incidence of a crossover break between them. The smaller the distance the more improbable a break and the larger the number of individuals needed to discover a break. It is well known that a number of apparently unitary loci have been separated by breaks when sufficiently large numbers were used and the tendency for crossover breaks increased by proper experimentation. Where is the limit for this? Since this question cannot be answered, the crossover definition of the gene is not possible. It is important to realize this fact, because this very definition has frequently been used to avoid the consequences of modern discoveries for the classic theory of the gene.

The difference between the classic definition and recent views has been put very well in a discussion between Whiting and Lewis (see Lewis, 1951) in which Lewis defends the classic point of view and Whiting breaks a lance in my behalf. I quote:

"*Whiting:* The speaker has defined the gene as the unit within which there is no crossing over. Three years ago I questioned the existence of genes [P. W. Whiting, *Biol. Bull.*, 95:257] as units of hereditary transmission, pointing out that ideologically the gene is the lineal descendant of the subcellular units of past philosophies—micellae, pangenes, etc.—and that we have no evidence that crossing over does not occur in the homozygote within that portion of the chromosome acting as a unit in the heterozygote. The 13 sex alleles found by Goldschmidt in the Z-chromosome of *Lymantria* and the 8 in the W-chromosome act as units in the hybrids, but there may well be intragenic crossing over in the pure races. Similarly in *Drosophila,* the sex gene is diffuse, scattered throughout the active portion of the X. This acts as a unit segregating from the Y or the lack of X in the sex-heterozygote, the male, but it is not a unit in the sex-homozygote, the female, as shown by the localized sex-linked genes for which the female may be heterozygous. The germ plasm is genic material but it does not consist of genes. It produces genes by such structural reorganizations as may subsequently Mendelize with the original condition."

"*Lewis:* The speaker's remark about the definition of the term, gene, was given as a very brief aside to the main paper. Since there are conflicting viewpoints on the matter of this definition, we will amplify here our reasons for employing the crossing over process as an essential part of a working definition of the gene. The definition of any particulate unit must be in terms of its indestructibility by some breakage or splitting process. The crossing over process and any which leads to chromosomal arrangements are the only yet known processes of this kind which can be used in defining the unit of heredity. The point we wish to emphasize is that the discovery of what we have called position pseudoallelism relegates the rearrangement process to second place. Thus, if a chromosomal rearrangement separates units which must lie close together in order to function normally, then the effect of that rearrangement will be to cause an apparent destruction of one or more of the units which are acting physiologically as one. In practice, we would conclude nothing in such a case until we knew the behavior of the physiological unit following an exact reversal of the rearrangement to the original condition, or following a recovery of that unit in its original arrangement as the result of crossing over. Actually it has never been possible to effect either of these reversals (except in the case of position effects involving the heterochromatic regions, where the issue has been one of deciding whether the gene has changed by virtue of its being next to heterochromatin as opposed to euchromatin). Crossing over, on the other hand, is the unique process which results in recombinations of chromosomal parts without altering the physical distance between genes. It is therefore capable of leading and has led in the examples cited in this paper, to the recognition of smaller units within a portion of the chromosome acting as a physiological unit. These smaller units we still call genes."

We shall discuss below in detail the factual material underlying this discussion and its possible explanations. Here I point out only that Lewis' discussion starts with "the definition of any particulate unit," which to me means that the classic dogma of the particulate gene is accepted a priori in its totality. Hence all further conclusions are only a reflection of this basic dogma, which I shall try to criticize and to destroy.

Actually, the idea of the particulate gene makes sense only in what I may call its naïve formulation. There is no way of talking about a gene if no mutant is known which can be distinguished (see Whiting's happy formulation that the mutation creates the gene). If this mutant locus formed with the non-mutated locus a pair of Mendelizing alleles, the conclusion was drawn that at the original locus of the chromosome a gene was located which had changed by mutation into its allele. It is surprising how many geneticists speak about genes, finding new genes, and so on, without realizing that they mean a mutant locus, from the existence of which they extrapolate upon the normal gene without knowing anything of its reality.

It is remarkable how many geneticists are unable to concur in this simple conclusion, stating, for example, that if something mutates, the original something is the normal gene, though we know only that a change has occurred at a point of the chromosome which altered its function. The change at a point does not mean that this point contains a separate corpuscle of unitary action. However this may be, we cannot define a gene, even assuming the correctness of the classic idea of the particulate gene, by the breakability of the chromosome (crossover). The definition must contain the characterization of the gene itself, and that is its ability to mutate into one or more alleles.

We must ask which facts can be said to prove the existence of the corpuscular, individual gene within the chromosome, the existence of which was extrapolated from the mutant locus. If we carefully survey the facts of genetics, we notice with surprise how few facts demand the existence of the gene. Let me make the meaning of this clear. The corpuscular gene as used in standard genetics must be one or more molecules of a definite substance, different from that of the next gene and the others which are held together in a definite order by some structure or links comparable to the string in a string of beads, or by chemical links, or by electric ones. But it is conceivable that the chromosome is a genetic whole with a complicated structure which changes from point to point as the prosthetic groups do in a protein molecule. In such a structure, that is, a chain molecule, as well as a supermolecule built of individual linked molecules, there are no independent or separate bodies but innumerable points, loci, in which something can change in a chemical or physical sense (i.e., structure or pattern) though leaving the changed group or radical or side chain or part molecule still a part of the whole. The model of this on the unimolecular level would be the stereoisomere. It would certainly be farfetched to call such a sterically displaced group of atoms an independent body, a kind of gene.

Mazia's (1954) experiments (mentioned in I 2 B *a*) resulted in breaking up the naked chromosomes of the sperm head into particles of macromolecular size, which are supposed to be held together by metal ions. There is no reason to assume that the particles represent genes. The facts as far as they go may be considered to be a demonstration of the supermolecular nature of the chromosome. If the interpretation is correct, it would mean that supermolecules are built from macromolecules not by utilizing the same bonds which keep the macromolecule together but by different links. This may result in larger functional units, just as well as if other chemical bonds or links were used. Thus Mazia's results do not affect the theory of the genic material one way or the other. We still have to decide whether genetic facts are available which exclude our view of the loci and mutant loci in the chromosome as patterns in a whole and demand the corpuscular, separate, imbedded gene.

I can find only a single group of facts which might supply decisive information. The effect of a deficiency for a definite locus is canceled by the presence of a chromosomal segment containing the normal locus. Further, a mutant locus contained in a chromosome fragment acts, as far as known, in the same way as if it were included in a normal chromosome. Finally, in the majority of cases in which a homozygous recessive contains an additional fragment with the normal locus, the normal phenotype appears, though in a number of cases the recessive action remains. We can express both situations by saying that usually one dominant dominates two recessives, but sometimes the two recessives are dominant (or part dominant) over one dominant. This group of facts certainly demonstrates that a locus plus its next neighborhood (the smallest extra fragments are still relatively large) can have the specific action of one allele or a pair of alleles independently of the rest of the chromosome, and thus may be considered as a separate entity, the gene. However, no systematic quantitative study of this problem has yet been made. The question to be solved is whether this group of facts means that all genetic actions are based upon particulate genes.

B. THE THEORY OF THE GENE MOLECULE

a. Treffer theory

It was emphasized repeatedly that "the gene" is known only through a change, the mutant condition; or, more correctly, is an extrapolation from the mutant locus. From this it follows that we should know what a gene is, if it can be realized what the mutational change means. An experimental attack upon this problem became possible after Muller (1928) discovered the production of mutation by ionizing radiations; and the dosage law of this effect was added by Oliver (1932), Hanson and Heys (1928), Stadler (1928), and others. The first theoretical analysis of the meaning of the facts for the theory of the gene was made by Delbrück in Timoféeff-Ressovsky, Zimmer, and Delbrück (1935). The argument consists of two parts. The first is the so-called Treffer (target) theory, introduced by Crowther and Dessauer (see in Dessauer, 1954) as a general theory of the action of ionizing radiation upon biological systems. The idea is that a single hit produces a pair of ions which is responsible for all effects. Applied to radiation-produced mutation, the law of proportionality of mutations can be expressed in a general empirical equation. This is compared with the general equation covering all cases of effect by a definite dose upon x out of n possible areas.

These two equations are found to be identical if the number of hits is one.

These deliberations led to the construction of a model. It is supposed that the gene is a very stable molecule, a combination of atoms with definite positions and electronic conditions. Such a system might be changed in different ways, the most important of which is the dissipation of energy of excitation. This leads to an ionization in the neighborhood, a rearrangement of the atomic complex by a single elementary process. A comparison of the energy requirements with certain facts of mutation shows a qualitative agreement.

The latter comparison is based upon the facts of spontaneous mutation. Changes within a molecule may be produced not only by external energy, like radiations, but also by the statistical variation of the temperature oscillations between the atoms. The speed of such changes is known to be dependent upon temperature and energy of activation for the start of the reaction. The temperature relations are expressed in the rule of Arrhenius-vant'Hoff, which establishes a relation between energy of activation, stability of the molecule, and the temperature coefficient. The last is in many chemical reactions near 2–3 for a 10° difference in temperature. From this it follows that mutability, if based upon such a process, must have a temperature coefficient. This is the case, as Muller first noticed (1928). The coefficient was found to be in the neighborhood of 5; in a more recent report by Timoféeff and Zimmer (1947) it was 6.5. From the actual data, the energy of activation (needed to overcome the stabilizing forces in the molecule) can be calculated for the normal mutation rate as well as for the rate increased according to the temperature coefficient. The two values were found to be the same (under the assumption of 500 genes with 20 alleles in the X-chromosome), approximately 1.4 ev. Delbrück now calculated the expected temperature coefficient of the mutation rate as a measure of the rate of such molecular changes, to be accomplished when the amount of energy of activation was eventually reached. A temperature coefficient of 5 was expected, approximately the value that was actually found.

From these facts the conclusion was drawn that mutation consists in a change of equilibrium between the atoms, produced by temperature oscillations or an outside energy source. The primary process of absorption of a quantum might lead to very different secondary processes, such as simple steric rearrangements or dissociation of definite bonds setting free a reactive radical. A new residue may be attached from the surroundings and thus the whole molecule may be changed. From this it follows that the gene itself must be represented by such an invisible atomic combination or molecule.

Do these facts and deliberations by Delbrück now prove that there is a definite, corpuscular gene (and the chromosome a gene string) and that this gene is a single molecule? There are many reasons why such a conclusion cannot be considered as established. Delbrück realized that the same reasoning could also apply to any other compound which, if stable, consists in the end also of atomic assemblies to which, on whatever level of complication, the same reasoning applies. Delbrück's analysis would also fit a concept of the nature of the genic material of the type we are going to develop. Timoféeff and Zimmer (1947), realizing this, are more cautious in their latest discussion, though basically they seem still in agreement with the former conclusions. They state that the gene or at least its important part must represent a physicochemical unit, a large molecule, a micelle, an autonomous part of a micelle, or a unified, delimited crystalline structure. But they add that it cannot yet be decided whether the gene is an essentially autonomous, large molecule, for example, a link in a chain of such strung-together molecules; or a delimited and largely autonomous part of a micelle; or even a more or less complicated micelle as a part of a compound structure made up of many concentrated micelles (which would be identical with a whole chromosome). The decisive point for our present discussion is that the most recently reported group of facts and analyses do not prove or even make probable that the gene is a solitary, single molecule, even in the opinion of those who developed the concept.

It should be added that the facts upon which the foregoing analysis was based are in no way uncontested. The Treffer theory, which plays such a great role here and which is accepted also by Lea (1947) and Lea and Catcheside (1945), has been under fire for a long time. Numerous reasons have been given why the biological action of radiations cannot be so simple, and it looks as if the ingenious theory were being abandoned by the specialists. This applies to the Treffer theory as such, as originally conceived by Dessauer (see 1954), as well as to its application to genetic change. A considerable part of the criticism is based upon the facts of chemical mutagenesis, which are difficult to understand in terms of this theory. A major criticism is derived from the discoveries of Stone and his school (see 1947, 1948, and Wagner *et al.,* 1950), indicating that the liberation of oxygen plays a major role in mutagenic action by affecting a peroxide. The decisive experiment is that an irradiated medium also produces mutation in bacteria. Whatever the role of the peroxide intermediary turns out to be, it is hardly possible to reconcile the facts with the Treffer theory.

Another major group of facts has to do with agents or conditions which change the radiation effect upon mutation rate. The most important of these is the role of oxygen concentration in altering the radiation effect (see Hollaender, Baker, and Anderson, 1951; and Hollaender *et al.,* 1951). Such a result may mean that the agent, actually oxygen concentration, affects the "gene" itself so as to change its X-ray sensitivity. In this case the Treffer theory would not be affected. Or there are mutagenic substances produced by X-raying in the chromosomal neighborhood. If so, the results would go in the same direction as those of Stone, against the Treffer theory. Experimental evidence (by Giles, Riley, and others; see Giles, 1952) indicates that chromosome breaks are produced in larger quantity when irradiation is done under oxygen tension, but not if oxygen treatment precedes or follows the irradiation. This is in favor of the mutagen explanation as opposed to the Treffer theory. The conclusion is greatly supported by the fact that the same curve for frequency of effect after irradiation with different oxygen concentrations is obtained for different effects as mutation, chromosomal breakage, and mitotic delay. This would be expected only when the production of a mutagenic substance is decisive, since a direct change of the "gene" could hardly be identical in all these circumstances (Hollaender *et al.,* 1951). Obviously, the mutagenic effect of the intermediary substance must occur near the chromosomes, for irradiation of sperm (closely packed chromosomes) produces the effect, while irradiation of egg cytoplasm before fertilization is ineffective. Extensive work on bacterial mutation leads to the same conclusions, using different media which affect the sensitivity to radiation. Again there is at least a strong suspicion (see Stone *et al.*) that a peroxide is involved which acts in *statu nascendi.* There is much more work available in this same line of antimutagenic agents and agents influencing the mutagenic actions. (See the large amount of work of the Hollaender group and the Soc. Exp. Biol. symposium on chromosome breakage, 1953.)

However, criticism of the theory of peroxides as intermediates and of the conclusions of Giles is not lacking. The details are not important for our present discussion, which is not concerned with mutagenicity as such but only with the Treffer theory as proof of the particulate gene.

Another group of facts and interpretations belongs to this discussion. Auerbach (1949, 1951) found that mustard gas induces mosaicism in *Drosophila*, which must mean that the mutagenic effect has been delayed for some time and several cell generations. She assumes, within the theory of the gene, that the treatment can produce labile genic states which may persist in "a shallow trough of energy" for a variable time until they either return to the old condition or turn to the new one, the mutant. This mosaicism was found to have a temperature coefficient which suggests that a stabilization of some intermediate product is involved. (We might call it a temperature-dependent threshold condition for the ultimate jump to the mutated or non-mutated condition.) Here belong McElroy and Swanson's (see 1951) experiments on effects of pressure upon chemical mutagenic action, which also require the presence of an intermediate of metastable nature. McElroy and Swanson propose a theory of mutation which embodies these facts and explanations and is based upon a theory of absolute reaction rates by Eyring. For a discussion of mutation in terms of this theory (which does not concern us here as such) it is assumed that alleles differ from one another in molecular configuration, and that the change of this through mutation takes place by means of an activated complex, with which the molecule passes over the peak of the energy barrier. In the formation of this intermediate complex some free energy of activation is required to surmount the barrier and therefore the passage of one gene state to the other is governed by the height of the barrier.

At this point McElroy and Swanson emphasize that it makes little difference for their theory whether we consider each gene to be a molecular individual or whether we consider that particulate genes do not exist as such. In either event some molecular change is involved; whatever the change, it will conform to the laws of chemical kinetics. (The authors are not yet prepared to include rearrangements, but our subsequent discussion will show that these are in no way different, except that a chemistry of supermolecular patterns is involved.) The decisive point (for our discussion) is the establishment of an intermediate condition of different length of time which can be influenced by temperature or pressure, a condition which precedes the actual mutation effect. Whatever the theoretical explanation, the facts do not agree with the Treffer theory and cannot be used as a proof for the corpuscular gene or, specifically, the one-molecule gene.

It will be well to heed the warning of Muller (1950*a,b*), given in a discussion of all these and many more facts, pointing in the same direction. He says that the diversity of possibilities would show what a high degree of caution is necessary when the attempt is made to interpret biological events on the basis of simple physical principles, without regard to the chemical complexities that might be involved. Haldane (1954) also states his conviction that the action of radiations is fundamentally biochemical. (The Treffer theory will be further discussed in a subsequent chapter on the number and size of genes.)

b. Return mutation

Another point suggests caution. In the calculations of the schools interested in the Treffer theory, a considerable role is assigned to the quantity of return mutation and its temperature coefficient. Actually, the occurrence of return mutation, for example, white eyes to normal or white to the intermediate allele eosin in *Drosophila*, is of the greatest importance for many problems of genetics. We might expect this phenomenon to be safely established, but it is not. The cases always quoted, Timoféeff's for the white locus (see Timoféeff and Zimmer, 1947) and those of Johnston and Winchester (1934), have turned out not to be reproducible in recent experiments made by L. Kellen Piternick (1949) in our laboratory, and also by others (e.g., Hinton and Dipple, 1947), though rather high rates of return mutants had been claimed. More recently Timoféeff (for details see Timoféeff and Zimmer, 1947) claimed more return mutations than mutations for the forked or purple loci, and Johnston and Winchester (1934) found return mutants for eight sex-linked loci and a great many for forked. Since the old experiments were performed, it has been found that return mutation can be imitated easily by the appearance of specific suppressors, and the forked and purple effects are specially liable to genetic suppression, as are color effects like vermilion and sable. In addition, we know that a break near a mutant locus may produce the wild type as position effect. The studies of return mutation in *Drosophila* and other organisms were made with X-radiation, which produces predominantly chromosomal breaks, but return mutation can be proved only if suppressors and position effects are excluded. Whenever this was checked in *Drosophila* (e.g., Oliver, 1937, 1938), the case turned out to be doubtful and is probably attributable to a breakage with position effect.

All the older claims for reverse mutation, even those which seemed to be best established, must be looked on with suspicion, because position effect was not known then, and no detailed cytological check was made. An ordinary genetic or cytological check would usually overlook small rearrangements which are not apparent genetically. I might mention the following case: for a long time we carried a mutant of yellow as a stock, in which later the mutant white appeared, and a yw stock was carried and used as any ordinary marker stock. When, for some reason, a cytological check was made (see Goldschmidt, 1945*a*), it turned out that both mutants were position effects of small, homozygous viable inversions. If a similar situation had appeared with a reversion to true breeding wild type, probably nobody would have checked the possibility of small rearrangements involving a few bands.

Though reverse mutations in *Drosophila* have become very doubtful, they play a considerable role in the genetics of *Neurospora* and in bacteria, where reverse mutation for biochemical requirements seems to be almost as frequent and is even inducible at will. Giles (1951; Giles and Partridge, 1953) has made a special study of such reversals of biochemical (nutritional) mutants, both spontaneous ones and those induced by irradiation with ultraviolet or treatment with nitrogen mustard. In some he could establish, by genetic tests, that the apparent reversal was due to a suppressor locus, which could be transferred to other strains with the same effect. In a number of others (inositol-dependent strains returning to inositol independence), Giles thinks that he has proved genuine reversal, because the reversals behave in every respect like the it-strain, segregate normally in crosses, do not show ascospore abortion or segregate the mutant after crossing. Furthermore, no changes in crossover values were found. These results seem to exclude gross rearrangements as an explanation.

However, there are other facts which to Giles favor the explanation by reverse mutation but make me still more skeptical. In a group of eight inositol-less mutants, marked differences were found in regard to the frequency of return mutation, varying between the extremes of frequent spontaneous reversal and complete stability. These frequency differences segregate in the asci and are therefore inherited; they seem to be bound to the locus or its neighborhood, as experiments with closely linked markers show. It is furthermore important that X rays are more effective in producing reverse mutants. Giles thinks that he has demonstrated a series of multiple alleles of inositol-less distinguished only by their ability for reverse mutation (see, however, McClintock's "reverse mutation" in maize). He also claims different susceptibility to reverse mutations for different loci and for inductions by different chemicals (Kolmark and Giles, 1954). Thus diepoxybutane immensely increases reversal at the adenine locus as compared with the inositol locus. It is obvious that a test for small rearrangements (see the powerful action of X rays) cannot be made in *Neurospora.* However, in view of the fact that temperature-dependent biochemical mutants are frequent in *Neurospora* (see Horowitz and Leupold, 1951) and that in the flour moth a biochemical mutant may still have the necessary enzyme for normal action (Caspari, 1946), we might ask whether the biochemical reversals will not find a completely different explanation. I should certainly hesitate to use them for conclusions upon the nature of the gene.

Thus it looks today as though return mutation were at best very rare and probably non-existent. This would mean that mutation is an irreversible (or almost irreversible) event, a result which must be taken into account when theories about mutation and the nature of the gene are developed. We did not mention in this connection, except in a short parenthesis above, the so-called mutable loci, which are frequently referred to as return mutations. We shall see later that this phenomenon has found a completely different explanation. It is actually based upon a typical position effect, and thus constitutes a strong endorsement for our skepticism.

c. Counting the genes

In discussions of my views on the non-existence of the corpuscular gene (to be presented below), the following argument is frequently heard. Many people have counted the number of genes and measured their size with nearly identical results. How can something not existing be counted and measured? The answer is that we can get any answer to questions if the proper elements are fed into the question. We can calculate the number of people on Mars if we assume that the canals are dug by people and that they accomplish as many man hours as we do in digging, that slave labor prevails on Mars, and so on. Does the result of such a calculation prove that men are living on Mars? Indeed, this simile applies literally to the counting and measuring of the genes.

We do not intend to review these calculations, which are still being made (e.g., Herskowitz, 1950), and are based upon the Treffer theory. If actually one hit producing ionization suffices to produce a mutation, it follows that the mutation of a gene is based upon the absorption of the energy of one ionization within a small volume (the gene), which has been called the target area (see Timoféeff, Zimmer, and Delbrück). If the number of atoms within a cubic centimeter of organic substance is known, and also the number of ionizations produced by one r dose of X rays in organic material, and, further, the probability of producing mutation by one dosage unit in the radiation experiments, then the radius of a target area can be calculated in which one ionization must take place to produce a mutation with the probability of 1. The result calculated from experiments with many radiations was a radius of 1.39×10^{-7} in one set and 1.77×10^{-7} in another set (see Timoféeff and Zimmer, 1947). These are supposed to be minimum numbers and, in addition, it is assumed that the gene itself is larger than the target area. The conclusion is that the target area and also the gene has the size of known large organic molecules. Another calculation by Lea (1947), using the same principles, comes to the conclusion that the molecular weight of the gene is 10,000–100,000, with a diameter, if spherical, of 2–6 mμ. A similar value was obtained by a calculation for lethal mutations.

These are the data from which the number of genes (capable of lethal mutation, which is assumed to mean all genes) can be calculated. Following Lea (1947), the gene diameter applied is 4 mμ; the dose of X rays required for an average of one mutation per gene is 2.9×10^{-7}r. The dose required for an average of one lethal mutation per X-chromosome is 3.46×10^4r. Therefore the number of genes in one X is $2.9 \times 10^7 / 3.46 \times 10^4 = 838$ and, within the possible different values of target area size found, varies from 280 to 1,000. This result can be compared with calculations made from the structure of the salivary gland chromosomes. The number of bands in an X-chromosome is near 650, and one-band deficiencies are known to act as if a single locus were involved. If 1,000 genes are assumed to be present in a salivary X-chromosome of 200 μ length, about 200 mμ would be available for one gene, or according to Muller's measurements, for two genes. Taking the estimated thickness of the chromosome into account, the upper limit for the size of a gene would be 100×20 mμ with a molecular weight of about 25 million, which compares well with some virus weights of 11–42 million (see Lea), which are known to be nucleoproteins. The conclusion from these deliberations is that genes are autonomous nucleoprotein molecules "regimented in chromosomes to facilitate synchronization in division" (quoted from Lea).

To return now to the counting and measuring of genes, it is clear that the entire argument is based upon the correctness of the target theory, with the premise that the gene is a definable unit. Without this premise, conclusions on the basis of the target theory would be worthless. In other words, the proof of the existence of the gene molecule by calculating its size is based upon the premise that there is a gene molecule the size of which can be calculated and that the target size is its size. Here is a good example of this type of reasoning. Kurnick and Herskowitz (1952) measured the DNA content of salivary nuclei in *Drosophila* and came to the conclusion, by comparison with other somatic cells, that the salivary chromosomes have about 1,000 polytene strands. (The proportionality of the nuclear volume to the number of chromonemata also agrees with this; see fig. 3*b*.) They argue that the molecular weight of DNA polymerized is about a million, and thus the mass of a single molecule is 1.6×10^{-15} mg. In the 1,000-tene nucleus, 710×10^{-10} mg. were found. A haploid chromosome set would contain 0.71×10^{-10} mg. of DNA, that is, 44,000 such molecules. The largest estimate of gene number in *Drosophila*—arrived at by the Treffer theory by Timoféeff—is 10,000. Therefore, either the gene must consist of a number of molecules, or the DNA in the gene has a much greater weight. A number of 44,000 genes would be improbable, because a mean distance from one to the other of 17 $m\mu$ would result. "It is difficult to conceive of how resolvable bands could be derived from the unbanded state with units so closely spaced." I may be excused if I say that this and many former calculations are exactly of the type of the somewhat facetious example of counting the inhabitants of Mars.

The Treffer theory is the major unproved premise of all these calculations. Muller (1950*a*) has assembled powerful arguments against the theory based upon genetic facts as well as upon better knowledge of ionization effects. (See our discussion of the Treffer theory in I 3 B *a*.) He insists that there are abundant data which demonstrate the importance of intermediate chemical reactions in mutagenesis. It is difficult to estimate, in terms of atomic distances, the spatial range of the reactions from which mutations result. We do not even know whether they originate within or outside the chromosome, especially the genetic material, and it is by no means certain that the mutagenic effect resides within the particle that is hit. Some other arguments of Muller, shared by many workers in the field, are as follows:

In radiation experiments, made under different conditions, results are obtained which, if calculated, lead to different volumes of the target. Stadler has found eight times more mutations in sprouting seedlings than in dry ones with the same dose, in spite of strict proportionality effect to dose in either case. A similar group of facts shows that the number of mutations differs widely according to whether spermatozoa or ordinary sex cells are irradiated. Another group of facts shows that the number of mutations varies according to different physical, chemical, or thermal conditions to which cells are subjected before irradiation. This shows that an activation or ionization within a sensitive volume may or may not produce a mutation, and that facts are not so simple as the Treffer theory assumes. Another group of facts relates to production of mutants by a hit outside the genetic material as evidenced by two break deficiencies produced by a single hit. Muller, who certainly knows more than anybody else about all aspects of the problem and has himself ventured calculations of the size and number of genes, is very cautious in regard to such calculations as those reported and actually discounts them. Thus the argument as to a molecular gene derived from calculations based upon uncertain premises, even upon reasoning a posteriori, may be considered highly biased and improbable, and it does not seem worth while to enter further into this topic. It is true that we read frequently in texts, general books, and even in genetic or evolutionary papers that the number of genes in *Drosophila* is around 3,000 (or any other number) and in man from 20,000 to 30,000. In my opinion such statements are gratuitous and should be regarded with the greatest caution. All the subsequent discussions will bear out this statement.

C. THE THEORY OF CHROMOSOMAL HIERARCHY

We have come to the conclusion that the classic concept of the chromosome as a gene string, after the model of the string of pearls, and its development into the theory of the gene molecule cannot be considered as incontrovertible facts, as some geneticists would like to make us believe by strongly worded dicta, or by emphasizing the (unknown) size of the majority who remain faithful to the classical gene, or by acknowledging that the ideas of the gene are undergoing a change which, however, must not be a real change. The foregoing discussion of this situation was meant as a starting point for the analysis of other possibilities which have presented themselves during the past decades (Goldschmidt, 1938*a*, 1938*d*, 1944, 1946*b*, 1952*a*; see also Mather, 1946, 1948; Whiting, in Lewis, 1951). It might be of interest to report, as a kind of historical introduction, some of the groping attempts to get away from the inflexible and unsatisfactory classic theory of the gene.

a. Precursor ideas

Perhaps the first step in this direction away from the classic gene was made by the author (Goldschmidt, 1920*a*, 1927), still within the theory of the corpuscular gene, when he tried to make this theory more flexible and amenable to physiological interpretation by the assumption that the gene consists of a definite number of molecules and that mutation changes this number. Thus a series of multiple alleles became a quantitative series of gene molecules. The idea was derived from facts which showed a relation between mutants and multiple alleles, on the one hand, and rates of developmental processes, on the other hand, which could be reduced to simple terms of chemical kinetics by the assumption of a simple relation between genic mass and genic action. The hypothesis allowed the elaboration of a detailed physiological theory of heredity which accounted for many facts of genetics and physiological genetics. If it could be proved that the classic corpuscular gene exists, this theory still accounts for more genetic facts than any other theory of mutation. In addition, it gives a chance of interpreting many genic actions for which other theories of the gene have no explanation. (We shall return to the subject when we study genic action, dosage effects, exaggeration phenomenon.)

Within the Treffer theory it might also be assumed that the gene is a group of molecules and that one hit knocks out one of them (say by denaturalization). Adherents of the target theory have discussed this possibility and have come to the conclusion that this interpretation is impossible because of the alleged facts of return mutation. Actually, I had anticipated this argument when I still believed in the theory of the gene quantity, and had concluded that return mutation must be non-existent or extremely rare. It seems that later developments (reported above) agree with this conclusion.

I consider these deliberations to be of only historical interest; they are relevant only when the classic theory of the autonomous gene is valid, which I now deny. But the part of the theory which has to do with genic actions of a dosage type will have to be discussed later in its meaning for newer ideas on the nature of the genic material.

Some other theories that attempted to go beyond the simple gene molecule deserve to be mentioned as precursors of present-day ideas. The first of these, proposed by Eyster and Anderson (1924 ff.; see Goldschmidt, 1938), tried to account for variegation produced by what formerly were called unstable genes. The general idea was that a gene consists of subgenes (genomeres) which might be separated in mitosis, thus leading to different genomere arrangements, which look like somatic mutation visible as variegation. Clearly this is the same conception as my old one, but applied to the specific case of "unstable genes." The reason for mentioning this is that the authors realized the existence of a group of facts which raise difficulties for the classic concept of the gene, the same group that has recently induced McClintock (1951) to come to conclusions very much akin to my own regarding the non-existence of the corpuscular gene.

The most elaborate of such theories involving subgenes in a specific case was the theory of step-allelomorphism by Serebrovsky, Dubinin, *et al.* (1929 ff.; see Serebrovsky, 1930), again based upon a group of facts which seemed to defy the classic concept of the gene. The main point is that different alleles of scute (1st chromosome of *Drosophila*) could be arranged in a definite series according to the pattern of bristles which were removed by each allele, that is, the scute effect. In any compound of two alleles only those bristles were removed which were affected in common by each allele. Let ABCD be four different bristles and abcd their suppression. The allele sc^n may produce the pattern AbcD and the allele sc^0 the pattern abCD. The compound sc^n/sc^0 is AbcD/abCD and, therefore, only the bristle b is missing. If we write only the changed bristles in the compound we have $\frac{\quad}{a}\Big|\frac{b}{b}\Big|\frac{c}{\quad}$. The affected areas are steplike, and only the common part (b) is affected. Therefore, it is assumed that such a steplike pattern is present in the gene itself, and a consistent pattern for many alleles was elaborated. The gene, then, would be a body of definite length, made up of a series of smaller elements arranged like a bundle of sticks the ends of which do not coincide stepladder fashion. It is obvious that the authors had vaguely in mind a condition which we shall later discuss as pseudoallelism, though with the addition of the stepladder system. The general point was that behind special genetic phenomena a pattern problem of the genic material is hidden, which clearly goes in the direction of present-day ideas.

This theory lost its usefulness when it turned out that many of these scute alleles are chromosome rearrangements, and also that the phenotypic facts are not exactly as described (see Raffel and Muller, 1940). Nevertheless, the fact remains that the authors of the brilliant idea realized that they were dealing with a body of facts which did not fit into the classic theory of the gene. Actually, the data on scute alleles will be used below to support the newer theories.

The theories mentioned looked for subunits within the gene, which still remained intact as a unit, though composite. But theories of the opposite type also cropped up which, though still accepting the corpuscular gene, did not consider it autonomous but tried to integrate it into a larger functional whole. It was repeatedly assumed in a rather vague way that the chromosome itself is one large molecule; and the genes, side chains of it (e.g., Castle, Renner, Correns). The most detailed elaboration is that of Koltzoff (1928, 1939). He considers the genic part of the chromosome to be a long protein molecule or a bundle of such (the genonema). To these are attached radicals in a definite position, and these are the genes, in which atomic change represents a mutation. Complicated molecules like agglutinins are also supposed to represent such genic radicals and these radicals reproduce their like directly for use in the cell. Somewhat comparable ideas were proposed by the chemist Wrinch (1936). She calls the chromosome a molecular aggregate composed of chain molecules placed end to end and held together by the links with nucleic acid molecules. The gene then becomes a group of molecules between the natural breakage points, that is, the bonds between the different molecules in the chain. These and similar ideas (including some of my own, 1930, 1932*a*) have this in common: they try to consider the gene (which is still acknowledged as a unit) as a non-autonomous integral part of a whole, thus leaving room for genic actions on a higher level of integration.

These precursor ideas indicated a desire to break with the classic concept of the corpuscular and autonomous gene. Further progress was, however, not possible until the analysis of the salivary gland chromosomes in *Drosophila* brought to our attention the importance of chromosomal rearrangements after breaks, together with the phenomenon of position effect. Though an increasing number of prominent geneticists face this situation in one way or another, and have expressed themselves in concurrence with my conclusions more or less cautiously, there are many who still cannot decide whether to discard the classic theory of the autonomous gene. They prefer to look for interpretations of the critical and unfavorable facts in terms of a somewhat liberalized theory of the classic gene, which is acknowledged to be in a critical condition, but with some vague hope of ultimate salvage.

We hear the argument that the classic theory has done so much for genetics and explained so many facts that there is no reason to abandon it. I have repeatedly answered this argument with the use of a comparison. Just as most of the facts of genetics and especially the elementary ones can be described in terms of the autonomous gene, also the general facts of molecular constitution can be described in terms of a dash for valencies. Just as the average geneticist dealing with statistical consequences of Mendelism can do excellent work without ever thinking of the nature of the gene, simply using the primitive gene concept, it might never occur to the average chemist to inquire into the nature of valency bonds. But if he really wants to know what are the valencies with which he works all the time, he must turn to the work on valency electrons and quantum mechanics, which tell him that a valency is not a dash (to put it crudely). In the same way, the geneticist who meets with position effects and other advanced subjects will be constrained to look into the old notion of the gene and to find out whether its usefulness does not end at this level, though he will not hesitate to teach elementary genetics in the convenient terms of the classic gene, which are so useful for the beginner, and, in addition, are all he needs for statistical genetics, which, even to some geneticists, is the only genetics.

b. Chromosome breakage

We have discussed the basic fact of radiation-induced mutation, the law of proportionality of mutation to dosage, without inquiring into the nature of these mutants, though it was realized that sex-linked lethals which Muller's technique made the basis of all such quantitative work may frequently be deficiencies. Only after the introduction of the salivary chromosome technique and cytological techniques for discovery of chromosomal rearrangements in plant cells was it realized that the ionizing radiations and X rays actually preponderantly produce chromosome rearrangements, based upon breaks and their abnormal union. Since that time, much work has been done to check, separately, upon recognizable rearrangements in radiation experiments (Muller, 1947, 1950*a*; Kaufmann, 1941, 1948*a*; Sax, 1938, 1941; Catsch, 1948; Lea and Catcheside, 1942; Bauer, 1939, 1942; see also symposium on chromosome breakage, 1953).

It was found that rearrangements involving two breaks did not follow the simple proportionality rule but approximately a quadratic proportion, nearer to the exponent 1.5–1.7. The exponent 2 was of course expected if two different hits were required. (The small deviation was explained in different ways.) As a check, single breaks after radiation could be tested in some plant cells where they are visible, and in ring chromosomes of *Drosophila* (Sax, Bauer). These gave a simple proportionality curve. On the other hand, it could be shown that small rearrangements might be caused by single hits. There has been much discussion, some of it highly mathematical (see Lea, 1947; Muller, 1947, 1950*a*, 1952), as to why radiation experiments with high doses should nevertheless exhibit the proportionality rule, though more gross rearrangements with two breaks are expected. Lea maintains that this is expected, on the basis of the Treffer theory; while Muller shows that it is the consequence of different processes working in opposite directions. For our present purposes it suffices to say that the facts are so controversial that they cannot be used as yet to prove or disprove any theory.

For our inquiry into the nature of the genic material the next important point is whether, in view of the proportionality rule, the breakage of a chromosome and the production of a mutation are based upon the same physical event. Needless to say, the adherents of the classic theory of the gene would welcome the establishment of a difference between the two effects, and so do the adherents of the Treffer theory. A detailed review would include a huge body of facts of radiation biology. We shall discuss here only what seems directly relevant to the question.

The most important fact is that powerful mutagenic agents like X rays and mustards produce with equal frequency so-called gene mutations and chromosome rearrangements based upon two breaks (or one break for minute ones). Both types follow the proportionality rule with its variant for two breaks. A gene mutation or point mutant in such experiments means, of course, a mutant which with the best available methods does not show a cytological rearrangement. But not all mutants can be checked cytologically. In the salivary chromosomes some regions are more favorable than others. In favorable regions a deficiency, down to a single band, can be checked easily; in others it is more difficult. Small inversions are even more difficult. Inversions of a few bands may or may not be detected without a very detailed study, which usually cannot be made in connection with large-scale quantitative work. If an inversion of a single band should occur, which Goldschmidt and Hannah (1944) claim to have demonstrated, it will hardly ever be noticed. The so-called gene mutations will include many small rearrangements in the best material, *Drosophila*, and many more in other material where radiation effects are studied quantitatively. In the next best material, maize, the best preparation of pachytene chromosomes, where the most reliable check is made, does not permit more than one-tenth the chance of discovering small rearrangements than the salivary chromosomes allow. Thus any conclusion on mutation drawn from the number of gene mutations versus rearrangements rests upon a very slender base and is, in the best of cases, weighed in favor of point mutants. Even in the salivary chromosomes the cytological evidence may be deceiving. Kodani (1947) has shown that chromosome tips may contract and a single thicker band be formed out of a series of distinctive bands. This shows that some bands may be compound, and a break within them almost impossible to detect. If we look dispassionately at the cytological facts, we realize that rearrangements might be of any size from almost the whole length of a chromosome to a single band, and even smaller than this in the salivary chromosome containing up to 1,000 bands. Hence the separation of gene mutation from rearrangement by cytological criteria is completely gratuitous and is only an indication of the limitations of our methods. The problem of whether there is a difference between a radiation-induced mutant and a chromosome break cannot be solved by the direct cytological method. It has to be solved indirectly, from evidence derived from radiation effects.

The most important group of facts tending to show, in my opinion, that there is no difference between point mutants and chromosomal breaks concerns the action of oxygen upon both phenomena. Stone *et al.* (1947, 1948) have shown in their important experiments that mutants are produced after the irradiation of the medium in which bacteria grow, and it was considered most probable that the production of peroxides by irradiation, especially the H_2O_2, is responsible (see also Wagner *et al.*, 1950). Since that time, Thoday and Read (1947) found that the amount of breakage also is increased with irradiation in the presence of oxygen. It may be added that there is at least a strong suspicion that chemical mutagenesis also acts via the production of a peroxide (Auerbach, 1951). Such facts lead to the question whether the dualism inherent in the Treffer theory in interpreting point mutants and chromosome breaks is still tenable. According to Timoféeff *et al.* (1947), Lea and Catcheside (1945), and Lea (see Lea, 1947), a point mutation is the result of a single hit, as discussed in Delbrück's theory, producing within the target, that is, the gene molecule, a pair of ions. A break, however, is induced by the production of a series of ion pairs during the passage through the chromosome of primary or secondary charged particles. Chemical changes resulting from this cluster of ionizations within the molecules of the chromosome result in the chromosome breaks. Different radiations may effect a different distribution of ionization along the tracks and thus affect breakage in different ways.

The work on oxygen with identical results in root tip chromosomes of beans (Thoday and Read, 1947), barley seeds (Hayden and Smith, 1949), and *Tradescantia* cells (Giles and Riley, 1949) leaves no doubt that peroxides are again the intermediary between radiation effect and breaks. We do not intend to discuss the special question of how this result reflects upon the Treffer theory. Giles, as well as Thoday, thinks that there is no contradiction here. To quote Giles: "The essential requirement is that the action of ionizing particles, whether direct or indirect, be relatively localized. If the effect is principally indirect, it appears that a substance such as H_2O_2 must be produced along the track of an ionizing particle and must have a relatively limited effective diffusibility (or short half-life). In fact it seems necessary that its effective distribution within the nucleus must correspond in pattern rather closely to that of ionization distribution along particle tracks."

For our discussion of the nature of the gene the decisive result is that there is still less reason to assume that there is a difference between gene mutation and chromosome rearrangement as a result of irradiation experiments. To this conclusion we may add that an increasing number of facts have come to light which show that different physical and chemical conditions influencing radiation effects act alike for general radiation damage, point mutation, and chromosome breakage.

Muller, while realizing the conclusions just drawn and emphasizing that the two effects (gene mutation and rearrangement) must have much in common, still warns against assuming their identity. In his opinion, some facts do not support the identity. To quote Muller (1950*a*): "One of these [facts] is the very great difference in the mode of response to X- and gamma rays of the higher plant [cereal] material studied by Stadler and of the *Drosophila* material. In the plants the gene mutations are induced with a frequency so low (supposing them to be induced at all) relative to the frequency of breaks and rearrangements, as to have been practically impossible to demonstrate; while in the *Drosophila* material the two phenomena occur with comparable frequency." I cannot see why these facts must bear upon the mode of production of the two effects by, for example, different types of ionization. I should prefer to conclude that the difference relates to chromosomal structure. In the cereal there may be a clustering of potential breaking points away from loci which are easily caused to mutate. Such an assumption or one involving similar chromosomal conditions appears to be a more plausible explanation.

To continue with Muller's quotation: "If now, instead of comparing the two different kinds of material, we compare the two different agents, ultraviolet and X- or gamma rays, we find an analogous situation. For, with both materials, ultraviolet produces far more gene-mutations, in comparison with gross rearrangements, then do X- or gamma radiation. In the plant material [Stadler, 1933, 1941] it is also clear that ultraviolet produces far more gene mutations in comparison with minute rearrangements (small deficiencies) and in comparison with single breaks, than do X- or gamma radiation." Again the argument does not seem convincing to me. Ultraviolet specifically acts, as proved by Stadler as well as Knapp, by absorption at 2537 Å in the purine and pyramidine groups (see fig. 4) of the DNA molecule. How this absorption produces a mutation we do not know. If these rings are not themselves the genic material, which is most improbable, the action must be indirect. This means the same type of action through formation of a peroxide, which we know is liable to produce breaks. Why these breaks tend to be more frequently on the submicroscopic level, that is, two very nearby breaks as opposed to more distant breaks which may reunite into visible rearrangements, is difficult to say. It seems to have something to do with the specific absorption in the DNA moiety, while X rays seem to strike all molecules alike. However this may be, I cannot see a cogent reason for separating point mutation and breakage.

Another argument was recently proposed by Lefevre, Jr., Ratty, and Hanks (1953). They found that X rays used to produce Notch deficiencies in *Drosophila* never produced point mutations at the split locus, which is one of the deficient loci in the Notch chromosome. They think that this shows that X rays can produce breaks only, and not point mutation, which therefore are two different things. I should conclude that the X ray is such a powerful agent that there is an overwhelming probability that the two distant breaks are produced simultaneously, which leads to visible rearrangements of all kinds; while two nearby (submicroscopic) breaks, in the absence of a distant one with which to form a visible arrangement, are rather rare.

Muller finishes his discussion by saying: "All this clearly shows a difference in the processes whereby these changes originate. It thereby becomes legitimate to draw a distinction between gene mutation, on the one hand, and structural changes, even of minute size, on the other hand." To me it seems that the facts favor the assumption that there is no difference in principle between the processes resulting in so-called gene mutations and those resulting in rearrangements; the differences observed are only in the size of the effect, that is, invisible versus visible rearrangement.

This conclusion must not be confounded with the ideas of Lea (1947) and Herskowitz (1946) that gene mutations are accompanied by a chromosome breakage nearby. If this is repaired, or healed, we find only the gene mutation; if it unites with another break we have, in their opinion, a rearrangement with the simulation of a position effect, which actually does not exist. We shall see that the facts of position effect completely rule out this hypothesis, which of course is the opposite of the thesis we shall develop: both are position effects of visible and invisible rearrangements.

c. Position effect

We come now to the second major group of facts which is decisive for the understanding of the genic material within the chromosomes. It is rather unfortunate that the historically justified term "position effect" cannot be changed. It connotes a description of the phenomenon exclusively in terms of a definite interpretation based upon the classic gene. The term implies that the action of a gene differs according to its position. The actual facts lend themselves to a different and much more justified interpretation. The unprejudiced description of the effect is the following. Chromosome breaks, resulting not only in rearrangements like translocations and inversions, but also in deficiencies and duplications, very frequently have a phenotypic effect, which commonly is identical with that of the mutant phenotype of a nearby locus. Cases in which no nearby locus is known, the mutant effect of which is imitated by the rearrangement break, suggest that such a locus is not known, because by chance it never mutated, though it cannot be denied that an independent, autonomous breakage effect may exist. The facts show only rearrangement breaks and phenotypic effects similar or identical with a mutant allele at a nearby locus, though this locus was not affected directly. An unprejudiced description of the actually observed facts does not require a consideration of genes and their position. I think it is important that the logic of this situation should be recognized and that the problem be attacked without the theoretical prejudice contained in the word "position."

aa. The Bar case

The name "position effect" was originally given by Sturtevant (1925) in his classic paper on unequal crossing over of the Bar "gene," a dominant mutant reducing the eye facets of *Drosophila*. By unequal crossing over this could double in one chromosome and thus quadruple in the homozygous condition (BB/BB) the phenotypically extreme, double, or ultra Bar. Another allele, infra Bar, could do the same. The effect of these combinations followed in a general way the dosage of 1, 2, 3, 4 Bar genes. (The details will be discussed in a later chapter on genic dosage.) Moreover, it made a considerable difference whether, in the case of two doses, these were heterozygous double Bar (BB/+) or homozygous Bar (B/B), since the former has more of an inhibitory effect on the formation of facets, which is the Bar effect. Sturtevant expressed this not as we did just now, but by saying that two Bar genes in one chromosome have a greater action than the same two located in two chromosomes. Thus the position of the Bar genes made a difference which might mean in a general way the location in the chromosomes (one or two) or, more specifically, a different neighborhood, namely, a "foreign" gene on both sides of B in the case of B/B, but on only one side of each B in the case of BB/+. This was the original meaning of the term "position effect," location of a gene in different neighborhoods.

It is important to see clearly that this interpretation, which was justified in its time, does not cover our present knowledge of so-called position effect. This is necessary at the outset because the old interpretation has come up again in important recent work which we shall have to analyze below. We now know many cases of "position effect" in which the phenotype of a locus at some distance from a break appears. Here the locus has remained in its normal chromosomal neighborhood, but is nevertheless changed in its action by a break at some distance. This shows clearly that it is not the direct position of a locus that is involved but its relation to a disturbed order within the chromosome nearby. We shall soon see that the classic Bar case also is included in this statement. We should forget, in analyzing the phenomenon, the position of an assumed gene, and think only in terms of chromosomal breaks and changes of order within the chromosome. Only thus will a unified understanding of the entire group of facts be possible.

The subsequent history of the Bar case bears out this statement, and so does the welter of other facts concerning position effect. In 1932 Dobzhansky found a translocation with one break near the genetic locus of Bar. This rearrangement had a phenotypic effect resembling Bar, and acted like an allele of the latter. Muller and Altenburg (1930) had already noticed that most translocations in *Drosophila* had some phenotypic effect like lethality, sterility, or changed phenotype. But Dobzhansky's baroid translocation was the first discovery of what we now consider a genuine "position effect," which should be called "rearrangement effect" if a change of terminology were still possible. This was clearly different from Sturtevant's position of two Bar genes in one or two chromosomes, since no mutant "Bar genes" were involved. The solution of the discrepancy in the causation of the two phenomena, both of which were called position effects, became possible when Bridges (1936) and Muller (1936) found that the "mutant" Bar is the phenotypic effect of a duplication of a number of bands (visible in the salivary gland chromosomes) in the region where the Bar effect is localized genetically (illustrations can be found in all textbooks). Bar had these bands twice in tandem, and double Bar had them three times. At first sight this could mean that the duplicated section contained a Bar gene which in one dose (or two homozygous) had no effect; but in two doses, namely, four homozygous, had the Bar effect; and in six doses, the double Bar effect. Expressed in Mendelian formulation this would mean, symbolizing the old Bar gene by B and the group of bands which are present in triplicate, B^b:

OLD FORMULATION	
1. B/B	= Bar homozygous
2. B/+	= Bar heterozygous
3. BB/BB	= double Bar homozygous
4. BB/+	= double Bar heterozygous, with position effect (see 1)

CYTOLOGICAL FORMULATION	
1. $B^b \mid B^b$	= normal
2. $B^b\,B^b \mid B^b\,B^b$	= Bar homozygous
3. $B^b\,B^b \mid B^b$	= Bar heterozygous
4. $B^b\,B^b\,B^b \mid B^b\,B^b\,B^b$	= double Bar homozygous
5. $B^b\,B^b\,B^b \mid B^b$	= double Bar heterozygous, with position effect (see 3)

An alternative would be to assume that no Bar gene is involved, but only a disturbance of the genic balance by the duplications and triplications which throws the eye facet development out of gear.

However, both of these explanations were ruled out by the work of Dobzhansky quoted previously, and much subsequent work in which the salivary chromosome technique could be used. Elaborate work by Offerman (1935) and Dubinin and Volotov (1936) proved that, in the presence of a very large number of rearrangement breaks in the neighborhood of the Bar locus, in each case the Bar effect was produced without any change at the Bar locus or region itself. The conclusion is inevitable that the Bar effect itself is a position effect of the duplication break. As no individual Bar locus is known, that is, no simple dominant or recessive point mutant (without visible rearrangement) in the Bar region, it must be assumed that such a locus exists, nevertheless, and shows all these "baroid" position effects. (According to Sutton, 1943*a*, the position effects are due mainly to breaks next to two of the six bands which make up the duplication.) Another possibility would be that a breakage effect of a definite type, in this case Bar eyes, could be produced independently of an assumed mutable locus, in the same region; this was mentioned above as a general possibility. (We shall return to this problem.) Thus we cannot avoid the conclusion that the Bar effect is in itself not due to a double dose of a Bar locus but to a position effect caused by the duplication break, the same cause as all other baroid position effects of the Bar phenotype. There are a few complications to this simple picture. According to Griffen (1941), the Stone translocation, a baroid, acts at one end of the section which is duplicated in Bar, but other breaks involving the left end of the section also have baroid effects. This must mean that there is either no (unknown) mutant locus producing a Bar effect, or that the baroid position effect works over the entire section and not only for certain breaks. This, of course, has nothing to do with the Sturtevant position effect.

Now the question arises as to what Sturtevant's position effect is. It is clearly not the same thing as the Bar effect, which turned out to be a position effect of a duplication break. This is of course an unending cause of error, owing to the use of the same terminology for two completely different things. The Bar effect is, as we showed, a position effect of a duplication break (in the general meaning of the term, breakage effect) and otherwise has nothing to do with the duplication as such. The same breakage effect is produced by inversions and translocations in the absence of any duplication. But the Sturtevant effect is superimposed upon the Bar effect and is due to the duplication and triplication. This effect is found when the following arrangements are compared, assuming only three bands abc instead of six, duplication breaks being marked by crosslines, each containing four Bar sections in different arrangement:

a	a
b	b
c	c
a	
b	
c	
a	
b	
c	

(1) heterozygous double Bar (BB/+) or $B^bB^bB^b/B^b$

a	a
b	b
c	c
a	a
b	b
c	c

(2) homozygous Bar (B/B) or B^bB^b/B^bB^b (See scheme, p. 121.)

The difference is between a homozygous rearrangement with two breaks in each chromosome (2) and a heterozygous rearrangement with three breaks in one chromosome and none in the other (1). In one rearrangement (2) we have only two breakage effects (though homozygous); in the other (1), three different breakage effects (though heterozygous) which seem to be additive. (The difference is retained under special conditions also: the presence of an enhancer for Bar described by Bonnier *et al.,* 1947, leaves the Sturtevant effect as it was.) This means that we compare the effect of a heterozygous three-break, triple position effect (breakage effect) with a homozygous double one. Now there is no way of predicting, even for ordinary Mendelizing pairs of alleles, the quantity of a heterozygous effect as compared to the homozygous dominant one. If DD has an effect measured as 100, Dd may show the phenotype of 100 (complete dominance) or any other value (incomplete dominance). An exact dosage effect for dominant heterozygotes, that is, 50 per cent action, is possible but not necessary. If we think for a moment of Bar in the old terms of a dominant gene, the knowledge of the action (in terms of facet inhibition) of B/B and B/+ does not permit us to draw conclusions concerning the action of BB/+, except when we know that the dominance of B is strictly proportional to dosage. Now breakage or position effect acts like a mutant in the region, and therefore the same argument is good for the baroid position effects and for the duplication effect Bar. This means that we cannot predict from the knowledge of the quantity of the effect of two homozygous breaks (Bar) versus two heterozygous breaks (heterozygous Bar) and three homozygous breaks (double Bar) whether the quantity of action of two homozygous breaks will be the same or different in the three heterozygous breaks, the double Bar heterozygote. It is possible that the four breaks in two chromatids have a greater action than three breaks in one chromatid, or it may be the other way around. In both we would have Sturtevant's position effect (in favor of one or the other combination). This, the original position effect, has nothing to do with position but is a phenomenon of dominance, proportional or not proportional to the number of breaks.

Actually, if we calculate as a measure of dominance the percentage of facet number decrease from normal (i.e., as loss of inhibiting action upon facet formation) in the heterozygote (i.e., in this case the improvement toward normalcy), the value for B/+ = $\begin{array}{c|l} B^b & B^b \\ B^b & \end{array}$ is 20 per cent; but for BB/+ = $\begin{array}{c|l} B^b & B^b \\ B^b & \\ B^b & \end{array}$ it is 50 per cent. Therefore it is impossible to predict that the latter value should be the same as that of BB = $\begin{array}{c|c} B^b & B^b \\ B^b & B^b \end{array}$ and to attribute the actually found discrepancy to the different positions. The Sturtevant position effect has ceased to exist, meaning, of course, the explanation in terms of location of two "genes" in one or two chromosomes. The Bar effect itself remains a standard position effect in the sense of breakage effect (i.e., change of pattern) and as such acts like any mutant. This includes also dosage effects, visible in the Bar–double Bar relation and demonstrated further by Rapoport (1939, 1941), who inserted a number of Bar duplications into a chromosome with increasing effect. (The problem of dosage effect will be discussed later with genic action.) It is interesting to see how defenders of the old concept of position effect in terms of gene neighborhood account for this situation, which as such cannot be denied. Lewis in his review (1950) concludes a discussion of the facts with the sentence: "These results then point to the conclusion that there are at least two separate components of the Bar phenotype to be considered (*a*)* a stable change in the action of a gene or genes lying next to the point of rearrangement, possibly within the 16A1–2 doublet at that point, and (*b*) an influence somehow exerted by the close juxtaposition of two sets of identical loci." After mentioning the Bar reversals without cytological change described by Dubinin and Volotov (1940) and Sutton (1943), and probably due to a suppressor mutant, Lewis continues: "In all of the above studies in which reversals of the dominant Bar phenotypes appeared, it was found as expected on the basis of a known Bar deficiency that loss of the 16A region does not give a Bar effect nor does it enhance or suppress Bar, that is B/Df-B resembled B/+ [Bridges, 1917]. Again the problem as to the nature of a gene change which can produce such results arises . . . if the bands 16A1–2 are considered as representing two closely linked genes with similar effects . . . the problem becomes a very complex one, indeed, in the Bar case." I add to this: how simple and logical it becomes when our viewpoint, discarding genes and their position, is adopted.

We finally return to a problem mentioned above, that no mutant locus is known in the Bar region which accounts for the position effects of Bar and the baroid rearrangements. We mentioned the possibility that a position effect, especially a dominant one, might sometimes have nothing to do with a locus near the break acting as if it had mutated, but might be a direct effect of the breakage, a change in chromosomal pattern. As opposed to Bar, a number of duplications with dominant position effect are known, usually small ones, in which a recessive mutant locus near or within the duplication is known (e.g., eyeless dominant and brown dominant). Others behave like Bar (e.g., Hairy-wing). Thus far only one recessive position effect of a duplication has been described in the known presence of a similar dominant mutant locus within the duplication, namely, Green's Beadex-recessive (1953*b*). The behavior of the Bar deficiency previously described seems to indicate for Bar the absence of an unknown locus for Bar mutation, that is, the alternative of a breakage effect per se.

It is strange that among the relatively rare dominant mutants in *Drosophila* many are described as "inseparable from translocation or inversion . . ."; that is, are position effects for which no mutant locus of similar action is known in the section involved. Bar, Dichaete, Curly, Upturned, Abrupt, Blond, Glazed, Xasta belong to this group. It is possible that in some the missing mutant locus may be found.

* From here on italicized in the original.

Thus I could show (1945*a*) that Blond may be a position effect for the nearby silver locus, as is also the dominant pointed (svr^P). Unfortunately, it is hardly possible to produce a direct proof that this type of position effect per se exists.

bb. Frequency and types

In order to derive conclusions about the nature of the genic material from the phenomenon of position effect, we must first convince ourselves that position effect is a general and typical feature and that in principle it is not different from the phenomenon of point mutation, which we wish to consider as an ultramicroscopic position effect. Fifteen or so years ago it was still possible for some geneticists to declare that position effect was such a rare and special phenomenon that it would be faulty to generalize from its occurrence, and I was severely reprimanded for doing so (by Babcock, Jenkins, and Stebbins, and by Plough). Today nobody can doubt that the effect is a general and widespread phenomenon, and has just the significance for the theory of the gene which I have attributed to it for two decades.

Most of our knowledge is still derived from *Drosophila* work. This will probably remain so, because the salivary chromosome technique permits exact location of rearrangement breaks within approximately one one-thousandth of the chromosome length and because the genetical localization of hundreds of loci makes a huge material available. However, McClintock's work (1951) has opened maize genetics to a large-scale study of position effect, which clearly is as frequent in maize as in *Drosophila* if the proper setup permits recognition of it. We still hear that, especially in plants, innumerable gross rearrangements are known without a position effect being noticed. According to an early observation by Muller and Altenburg (quoted above), some effect upon viability, fertility, and phenotype is found in all gross rearrangements of *Drosophila.* It is expected, but rarely checked (see, however, Jones' work, 1944), that physiological effects exist also in plant materials, including all the translocations studied by Anderson (1935–1941) in maize and supposed to have no position effect, a plant which is now a prototype of position effect. A scrutiny of the literature will bring to light many more such cases. Lamprecht (1949) described a "mutant" in *Pisum,* always "accompanied" by a translocation, which, of course, means a position effect. Hagberg and Tjio (1950) found that the mutant erectoides of barley is based upon a homozygous translocation. Now that position effect has come into its own, other examples will be found.

The two prerequisites for position effect and its discovery are as follows: (1) a rearrangement can be diagnosed genetically and (or) cytologically; (2) in the neighborhood of a break a locus is found which, if mutated, produces a recognizable phenotypic effect. (The cases discussed above stand excepted; namely, those in which a dominant position effect is possibly produced by the arrangement itself, without a nearby locus which acts similarly when mutated. A proof for the existence of this type is hardly possible.) The recognizable effect may be a distinct phenotype or it may be a physiological condition recognized only as different vitality, lethality, sterility, and so on. The first prerequisite makes it almost impossible to prove position effect directly in such materials as mammals and many plants. The second prerequisite makes negative statements on position effect of doubtful value. In addition, it must be recognized that it is possible that chromosomal structure can be such that breaks and mutable loci are never or rarely adjacent or neighboring. If, for example, easily breakable sections of chromosomes (known to exist) are relatively free of mutable loci which may be crowded in a poorly breakable section, position effects (i.e., visible ones) will be rare or absent. In Stadler's X-ray experiments with cereals, many rearrangements and hardly any "point mutations" were produced. A chromosomal structure as just postulated would account not only for such facts (under my interpretation of point mutants as position effects of ultramicroscopic arrangements) but also for an absence of position effect. If it is found that numerous gross rearrangements in plants do not show any visible position effect (forgetting for the moment the physiological effects that have not been checked), the reason may be a chromosome structure as described. McClintock's work shows that if the experimental production of breaks adjacent to known loci succeeds, position effect is always found. Thus the positive results alone have decisive value and we may say with certainty that rearrangement breaks always produce position effects, though they cannot always be seen. Therefore, position effect can be called a ubiquitous standard phenomenon of genetics with which any theory of the genic material must reckon, or, as I believe, from which it must be derived primarily.

The other important statement is that position effect shows all the characteristics of point mutation. It is well known that many mutants which were thought of as point mutants turned out on closer inquiry to be actually position effects of inversions, translocations, duplications, deficiencies; and new examples are found all the time (see my example in I 3 B *b*). This correction, linked with the available improvement of technique or its absence, shows that there can be no important difference between point mutation and rearrangement except the means of recognition. In a former paper (1944) I showed that approximately half of the mutants described for *D. melanogaster* (which included multiple alleles) were already known to be position effects. Thus we shall have to show first that any type of mutant action known can be duplicated by proved position effects.

Before presenting this material we must return briefly to some facts that have been mentioned repeatedly before. We defined the position effect as the action of an intact locus in the more or less distant neighborhood of a rearrangement break, as if it had mutated to one or another of its known (or not yet known) alleles. A break near the white locus produces a white phenotype, though it can be proved that the white locus has not changed (is still the wild-type allele of classic genetics). This position effect may be of two types. It produces the likeness of a standard mutant if on the yonder side of the break euchromatin is adjacent. (The reports on intercalary heterochromatin are not yet decisive.) If, however, chromocentral heterochromatin is adjacent, the mottled phenotype appears, which has been already discussed. We mentioned also the different eu-heterochromatin sequences which can result in mottling (see I 2 C *d bb*). In the present example it is a mottled eye of red and white (and also other colors) in different relative quantities and patterns. Some geneticists have considered the latter type as something different, and have tried to interpret it as the production of somatic mutations. We have explained (see the quotation from E. Sutton Gersh) that the difference is not one of principle but one of grade of function involving a narrow but not strict threshold for an all-or-none effect. There is no reason to separate the complete or incomplete effect except when discussing heterochromatin.

For these reasons we cannot accept Lewis' (1950) statement (in his review, which carefully avoids a discussion or even mention of our point of view, as well as of any of the facts we found; as was also pointed out implicitly by B. Glass in a critical review) that we are dealing here with two completely different phenomena and that the typical position effect (his S effect) is rare, while the mottling effect (his V effect) is frequent and alone important. The variegation effect might be more easily found because heterochromatin breaks more easily; it has been much studied because the mottling appeared more intriguing than the simple effect. Furthermore, simple position effects will, as a rule, be overlooked and discarded as ordinary mutants, if for some reason a cytological check is not made. (See my yellow-white case, I 3 B *b*). There can be no doubt, on the basis of our former discussion (I 2 C *d bb*), that the difference is purely quantitative. In the simple position effect, Lewis' S effect, the action of the rearrangement (i.e., pattern change) is so strong that it is completely above the threshold for the process in question. In the white-eye case, this means that in all ommatidial pigment-forming cells, the synthesis of pigment precursors is inhibited (not going into the well-known chemical details) just as in the white mutant. In the presence of the heterochromatic break the same inhibition occurs, but it acts so near the threshold that random variation among the different pigment cells pushes it in some cells below the threshold and pigment is formed; that is, mottled eyes appear. This statistical condition can be pushed in either direction by appropriate modifier action (e.g., extra heterochromatin), even to the point of disappearance of mottling (I 2 C *d bb*). This shows clearly that the two types are one and the same thing with varying degrees of action around a threshold condition. I realize, of course, how difficult it is for Lewis to accept this solution, as he adheres strictly to the one gene—one action concept, which, if applied also to position effect, requires a unitary result. But we shall see later that the concept does not work for ordinary mutants either.

There are, of course, loci like white, yellow, scute, for which both types of position effect are known, as expected. Different facts and deliberations have led E. Sutton Gersh (1952) and Baker (1953) to deny a basic difference between mottled and non-mottled position effect. Though Lewis' S and V position effects are clearly variants of the same phenomenon, there is a possibility that a type of position exists which does not fit the definition of a break acting as if a nearby intact locus had mutated. I refer to the repeatedly mentioned possibility that a dominant "inseparable from a rearrangement" is actually a position effect per se; this would constitute a direct effect of breakage and change of pattern without relation to a special locus. In the present section I have already emphasized the fact that the existence of this type of position effect is very difficult, if not impossible, to prove.

Still another point must be mentioned: the relation of return mutation to position effect. We saw that apparent return mutations are suspected of being the result of a rearrangement with dominant position effect and that there is a general suspicion regarding the occurrence of genuine return mutation (I 3 B *a*). In position effect the equivalent of a return mutation would be the complete restoration of a rearrangement to normal. There is clearly very little chance that the same two or four breaks would reoccur unless easily breakable points are involved. It is not surprising that only two such events have been described, by Grüneberg (1937) and Hinton (1950). However, there is also the chance that an apparent reversal of a position effect is due to the occurrence of a new break near the one causing the first position effect and acting in the opposite direction. Actually, a number of counteracting position effects have been described, meaning that one position effect disappears if another is superimposed. Such cases have been found for Curly, Glazed, Bar (all of them belonging to the dominant effects just discussed) by Griffen (1941), Griffen and Stone (1938), and others. It should be realized that this is just the opposite of the action that simulates return mutation of a recessive point mutant. There the rearrangement causes a normal dominant effect which covers the recessive mutant effect. In the present case, a dominant mutant effect is returned to normal by a superimposed position effect. This shows that reversal of the effect is a problem which offers the same difficulties and pitfalls for position effect that it does for so-called point mutants.

Furthermore, if a break near a given locus produces the position effect, we should expect to find frequently two position effects, one for each euchromatic break. Such cases seem to be very rare. One reason might be the small probability that two breaks are each located near loci with discernible phenotypic effect. Another reason is that, in view of the greater breakability of heterochromatin, there is a smaller chance of two euchromatic breaks. Sometimes an indirect demonstration may be possible. Thus I could show the following relation (Goldschmidt, 1945*a*): the recessive mutant bran at or near the arc locus in *Drosophila* produces broad wings. The mutant pointed (svr^{poi}) near the tip of the first chromosome makes for pointed wings. The combination bran/bran svr^{poi} has short, soft, and blistered wings. A small inversion in the first chromosome In(1)y^{pxbl} has one break near the yellow locus and therefore a yellow phenotype by position effect. The other break is in the silver region, but no second position effect is visible, perhaps because yellow and the paleness of silver, if both present, cannot be seen. However, in the homozygous combination of the yellow inversion with bran the wings are soft blistered, which means that one of the effects of the silver locus now becomes visible in the combination as a position effect of the second break.

We can now proceed to show that position effects closely parallel the actions of point mutants and, therefore, are indistinguishable from them if no special effort is made. Actually, the fact that about half of the mutants described for *Drosophila* (including multiple alleles) have turned out to be position effects illustrates the point.

In the present discussion we mean, by mutants, bona fide point mutants, that is, in *Drosophila,* mutants with normal salivary chromosomes in the proper section. For other organisms, only gross rearrangements may be distinguished with certainty from point mutants, since small ones, in terms of salivary chromosome size, cannot be checked. The following are some of the parallel actions between mutants and position effects that have been registered:

1. Mutants may act as dominants or recessives or anything in between. At the same locus in a series of multiple alleles, dominants and recessives may occur, although such dominants are rather suspected of being position effects of visible rearrangements (as also actually proved in some, e.g., eyeless dominant). Dominant mutants are frequently homozygous lethal. Some of these, like Beaded and Sternopleural in *Drosophila,* have normal salivary chromosomes as far as is known, but we must be cautious in assessing this fact. A great many homozygous lethal dominants in *Drosophila* have turned out to be position effects of visible rearrangements. Many of the Minutes have been shown to be deficiencies, while others have normal salivaries. Since, as we shall see, genetically proved deficiencies with normal salivaries exist, we must be cautious. However, one fact is certain: just as dominant and recessive mutants exist, both types of position effect are known, and wherever a phenotype is known, both as mutant and as position effect, the two may be (but are not always) phenotypically identical ("may be" meaning that the position effect may also act like a multiple allele of the locus).

2. Mutants frequently show combination effects. *Drosophila* eyes, in the presence of the mutants brown and vermilion simultaneously, are white, a fact for which the biochemical work has given the explanation. Kikkawa (1938) found that the combination of the position effect Plum (next to the brown locus and a variegated effect) together with vermilion also produced white. This fact has the

additional meaning that the biochemical action of the position effect is identical with that of the mutant it imitates, and further that variegation or lack of it is not an essential difference for position effect. If we accept here for argument's sake the one gene—one biochemical action hypothesis (to be discussed below), it shows that the position effect works the same way though the "gene" has not changed, or (if the word "gene" is used, as it frequently is, to mean a mutant locus) though no "gene" or mutant locus is present.

3. Mutants which affect general features like growth, fertility, sterility, and viability frequently cannot be isolated and localized like the standard mutants of elementary Mendelism. Many rearrangements produce such generalized effects (Muller and Altenburg, 1930) in *Drosophila*. The same has been shown by Roberts (1942) for a large number of maize translocations, which in a statistical study were found to produce deviations in growth, considered as position effects. Jones (1944) found chromosome rearrangements in maize connected with growth defects.

4. Mutants appear in all well-studied loci as more or less large series of multiple alleles. Position effects may be found also as series of multiple alleles, sometimes large numbers of them, as in the scute and brown loci of *Drosophila*. In this case mutants and position effects form together, indiscriminately, the series of multiple alleles; that is, a compound may consist of a pair of mutants, or a pair of position effects (where homozygous rearrangements are viable, as in the above-mentioned yellow and white inversion), or one mutant and one position effect.

5. Many mutants—rarely localized but sometimes so, as in the so-called vestigial dominigenes of Goldschmidt (1937)—are known to have no visible effects of their own, but to act as enhancers or suppressors of other mutant actions, which in a general way must mean a quantitative effect in shifting developmental conditions upon which the expression of a mutant depends. The same is true for some modifier effects. We (Goldschmidt, Gardner, and Kodani, 1939; Goldschmidt and Gardner, 1942; Gardner, 1942; Goldschmidt, 1952*a*) found specific actions of inversions, (themselves without known, i.e., visible effect) upon dominance and expressivity of other loci (Beaded, Beadex, and plexus), that is, a specific modifier action. We noticed also that this position effect modifying dominance or penetrance of a heterozygous (Bd) or homozygous (Bx) dominant can be used for discovering unexpected rearrangements, as was shown for an inversion in a wild-type stock. Recently this effect was rediscovered by Lewis

(1954), who described it as a "new transvection-effect" acting upon dominant Bithorax in a specific pseudoallelic setup (the latter is the only difference from our old findings); it was used on a larger scale for discovering rearrangements. It should be stated also that Green and Oliver (1940) found similar effects of translocations and inversions upon the vestigial phenotype. We might mention, in this connection, the crossover-enhancing effect of inversions in a different chromosome, assuming that mutants affecting crossover exist, though it is by no means certain that in this case an interpretation in terms of position effect is admissible.

6. Many mutants act as dominant or recessive lethals. Frequently these turn out to be deficiencies, but many cases are known in which lethals are not associated with visible rearrangements and therefore may be called point mutants (see, however, the Notch case). Visible rearrangements apart from deficiencies are frequently lethal, a fact which has been much discussed for other reasons and has already been touched upon in our discussion of the proportionality of rearrangement breaks to the dosage of irradiation. Lea had calculated that the data on lethals near rearrangement breaks allow only a small percentage of position effects, and that the majority must be considered as real lethals or lethal deficiencies. Muller's opposition to these conclusions, based upon a critical attitude toward the target theory upon which Lea's calculations are based, has already been registered. For the present discussion it does not matter how many of these lethals are position effects so long as we acknowledge that a position effect may also act as a lethal.

7. Mutants have more or less pleiotropic effects, meaning that frequently other phenotypic effects beside the most conspicuous one can be seen. This is true also of position effects: Dichaete, for example, acts upon wing posture and bristles. The white position effect acts upon eyes and Malpighian tubules just as the mutant does.

Altogether we may say that so far no difference in principle between mutation and position effect has been found, a fact which will be borne out in other observations to be mentioned. The most obvious conclusion from this, as well as from the foregoing discussions, is that so-called point mutations are really position effects of rearrangement breaks below the level of visibility with present techniques (to be discussed in detail later). But the cytological basis for such a conclusion is not completely missing: Palay and Claude (1949) found with the electron microscope a substructure of parallel bandings *within* salivary chromosome bands.

cc. Some special features

In the discussion of position effect some additional facts are relevant which go beyond the scope of those already mentioned. A rather strange fact relates to the covering effect of a duplication containing the normal locus over the otherwise present two recessives. A female *Drosophila* carrying two X-chromosomes with the mutants yellow and, in addition, a fragment of the tip of the chromosome in which the yellow locus is contained will be normal. But Sivertzev-Dobzhansky and Dobzhansky (1933) found that if the duplicated fragment has its break near the locus (yellow in the example), the recessive character appears (more or less). This means that the "covering" segment acts now, by a position effect, as if it were mutated (to yellow in the example). Of course this is expected, according to the foregoing discussion, but it is rather disconcerting if considered independently.

Another rather difficult problem has to do with deficiencies. A frequently found fact is that a deficiency for a normal locus in the presence of the normal locus in the homologous chromosome results in a phenotype which is more or less identical with that of a known mutant located in the affected region. A number of deficiencies, including the vestigial locus and heterozygous with a normal chromosome, have the phenotype of a vestigial allele. Different interpretations are possible; for example, the normal locus is not strong enough to keep the wing normal if present only in one dose. If the deficiency is rather large with breakage points far away, this explanation or one of a similar type suffices. If, however, the deficiency is small and one or both breaks are located near the vestigial locus, one could ask whether a break could produce a position effect (in this case a dominant one) even in the absence of the nearby locus. This would imply the question whether position effect is produced by the normal locus in the presence of a break nearby, or whether it is produced, more generally, by the change in the order of the constituents of the chromosome in a definite region (a problem which will be taken up later). Thus, then, the problem arises whether a deficiency might produce a mutant phenotype by a position effect of the break (i.e., a pattern change) even in the absence of the known locus. A recessive position effect, that is, a/Df(a), does not enter this picture, because a recessive mutant opposite the deficiency gives a haploid effect. The question must appear preposterous to anybody who considers position effect in terms of the position of a gene, and it is therefore not unexpected that an unbending adherent of the strictest classical theory of the gene has expressed his abhorrence of such an idea. How can there be a position effect in the absence of a gene? As we shall see below, the gene and its position are not involved at all in the problem. Here only the decisive fact must be stated: yellow deficiency can be obtained homozygous in a semilethal condition, in which the color can still be checked. It is yellow (Ephrussi, 1934; Stern, 1935). This is in no way a unique example. Here are a few others: scute (Sturtevant and Beadle, 1936), white (Panshin, 1941), roughest (Emmens, 1937), probably facet (Oliver, 1937), and a large number of loci in maize (McClintock, 1944). (In a discussion of this point I heard the objection that the + yellow ($+^y$) locus may not produce wild type but may prevent the appearance of yellow, which appears in its absence. If this were so, the mutant yellow should not be yellow but either normal or something between yellow and normal. But the whole argument, if applied to all the other cases, appears to be rather facetious.)

An interesting variant of these facts has been explored by Sutton (1940). She found a small terminal deficiency at the tip of the X-chromosome, not containing the yellow locus. If the other chromosome contained yellow, that is, not opposite the deficiency, the effect was yellow. This means that the deficiency break left of yellow acted like another rearrangement break, producing a recessive yellow position effect. Though this belongs to the general group of position effects, it is reported here because a terminal deficiency is involved, meaning that no other "gene" has been brought in contact with the yellow locus. Thus it must be the change in pattern itself which accounts for the effect.

It is worth while to consider thoroughly this group of facts when discussing the nature of the genetic material. Taking the yellow locus as an example, the phenotype yellow is produced by the following:

1. y/y = homozygous point mutant
2. $y/-$ = yellow deficiency opposite yellow
3. $-/-$ = homozygous deficiency for yellow
4. $\frac{+\,+\,y}{-\,-\,+}$ = Sutton's case
5. $\frac{R\,+}{+\,y}$ = yellow opposite a rearrangement near the locus
6. $\frac{R\,+}{R\,+}$ = homozygous recessive position effect of rearrangement

This group of facts shows us that the definition of position effect with which we worked does not cover all cases. We spoke of position effect as a term which actually means that a rearrangement break near a known locus makes this locus behave as if it had mutated. Later we saw that many dominant position effects were known in which a neighboring locus was not available. This might have meant that by chance such a locus had not yet been found. It might also have meant that a specific locus is not essential, that the rearrangement alone acts, the type of action depending upon the type of rearrangement or the general region of the breaks. Now we see position effects in the total absence of the locus which is supposed to act, only the general region in which the break occurs being of importance. These facts and their interpretation outside the theory of the gene will play a decisive role when we try to draw conclusions about the nature of the genic material.

A special, much discussed example of position effect is the so-called Dubinin effect (Dubinin and Sidorov, 1934; Dubinin, 1936). The basic facts are not different from the usual position effect, though the way of describing them may make the effect appear different. (Note here, as in so many instances of scientific interpretation, the power of semantics.) The usual description is that translocations involving a break near the cubitus interruptus locus in the fourth chromosome (ci) reduce the dominance of this normal locus over the ci mutant in the homologous chromosome. If we express the same facts by saying that the rearrangement break near the ci locus produces a position effect making the normal locus act as if it were mutated, we have, thus far, the same type of position effect as studied before. Nevertheless, one big difference makes the Dubinin effect rather distinctive. While R(+)/ci [where R(+) means the rearrangement break near the normal $+^{ci}$ locus] acts as if R(+) were ci, homozygous R(+)/R(+) and hemizygous R(+)/— are normal. In the cases studied above (e.g., yellow inversion), these combinations showed the mutant effect.

Before we continue with the specific facts we should remember certain details. Theoretically, a position effect might be indistinguishable from the parallel point mutant effect and often it is. However, it might also be a little different after the manner of a multiple allele, and this seems to be the more frequent situation. If position effect results in one or another allelic action, and if many "point mutants" and breaks affecting the same locus are known, the effects look like those of a series of multiple alleles. We can expect for a group of position effects any type of different actions known for sets of multiple alleles. One of the known causes of a recognizable difference between mutant and position effect phenotype is the location of the second break. Raffel and Muller (1940) showed this, and found also that the position effects of different rearrangements were more alike if the second breaks had occurred all in the same region of a chromosome. A special type of allelic effect (already discussed) is the variegation in the presence of a break in the chromocentric heterochromatin as cause of position effect. This, in our former analysis, proved to be a less intensive action of the break varying around a narrow threshold. We saw that this effect could be modified; for example, in the position effect for light (Schultz, 1947) the eye would be more normal—more red spots—in the absence of a Y-chromosome, more mutant—many light spots—in the presence of an extra Y.

Another group of facts to be remembered in the present discussion deals with so-called isoalleles (Stern): alleles which produce a change which cannot be detected phenotypically, because it is within the zone above the threshold for full normal action, a notion which had been widely used in my analysis of genic actions (1920 ff.). If a normal allele controls, for example, a full-length bristle, many isoalleles may be present acting above the threshold for full length, and therefore not changing the actual length, which for embryological reasons cannot go beyond "full length." The apparent absence of a position effect may in fact be due to an action of the isoallelic type, which could be proved only in favorable cases, as by comparing different heterozygotes. A probable example is a case found repeatedly: only the locus c shows a position effect, where the order break a-b-c-d occurs, the intervening loci a and b showing no phenotypic change. An isoallelic position effect would be the most plausible explanation. Altogether, a position effect may produce a series of different phenotypes: at one end of the spectrum, an effect beyond the extremest known effect of a point mutation at a locus; at the other end, no apparent phenotypic action due to isoallelic action. Moreover, all these effects are modifiable by extraneous action upon developmental processes, as the plus-minus shifting of extra heterochromatin clearly demonstrates. With all this in mind we return to the Dubinin effect.

The mutant ci causes a gap in the fourth wing vein, the length of which can be used for a quantitative measurement of the effect. Though the ci position effect is in general identical with other position effects, there is one difference that could be responsible for its specific features. The ordinary position effect involves a break near a given locus, and so does the Dubinin effect. The variegated variant of the ordinary position effect depends upon a break in heterochromatin near which a euchromatic locus comes to life. In the ci case the ci locus is adjacent to chromocentral heterochromatin. The break occurs in the heterochromatin between the locus and the spindle fiber so that after translocation to another chromosome the order is now: some euchromatic section—segment of fourth chromosome heterochromatin—ci locus (the latter two in their normal order). In contrast to the other position effects, the locus of ci remains flanked by its normal chromosomal structure on both sides, but on the spindle attachment side the heterochromatin is broken and attached to euchromatin of another chromosome. Expressing the situation in terms of action of the break (solely for clarity's sake and using terminology which we consider to be wrong), we should state that in the ordinary position effect the break acts directly upon the locus, in the variegated effect also, but with heterochromatin at its back, and in the Dubinin effect through a layer of heterochromatin. Therefore, we might expect phenotypic results of a peculiar type for the ci effect.

This is indeed the case, which follows from the elaborate work of Stern and collaborators (Stern, 1943, 1948; Stern *et al.*, 1943–1946). In this work the primary interest is in genic action, a problem which is attacked by dosage experiments (1, 2, 3 doses of ci, +, and R(ci) [rearrangement near ci] in different combinations). We are not concerned here with the theory explaining the different dosage results, but only with the comparison of the actions of the mutant locus versus position effect by rearrangement. Before comparing these, some other points must be realized first. The ci mutant is very easily affected by temperature. At low temperatures it is slightly dominant, so that only actions at stated temperatures can be compared. This fact indicates to the physiological geneticist special threshold conditions for the ci action. In agreement with this a number of isoalleles were found, multiple alleles which act at normal temperatures above the threshold in heterozygous condition, but show their different actions—some always above the threshold, some nearer to the threshold value—in temperature experiments and different compounds. One more fact should be mentioned (to be discussed and explained in the chapter on dosage). A mutant opposite a deficiency usually has a more extreme phenotype than the homozygous mutant, the so-called exaggeration phenomenon discovered by Mohr (1923*a*).

With these facts in mind we may study the following enumeration of the phenotypes of different compounds, in which − stands for deficiency, R(+) for a rearrangement near the normal ci locus, and R(ci) for a rearrangement near the mutant ci locus. Only haploid and diploid combinations are registered, and our interest is centered upon the position effect (Dubinin effect), not the problem of genic action as such.

A. Without R

1. $ci/+^{ci}$	normal at 25° slightly ci at 18° at 14° more abnormal than $+^{ci}/-$
2. $ci^1/+^{ci}$	slightly ci
3. $+^{ci}/-$	normal at 25°, slightly ci at 14°
4. ci/ci	ci effect
5. ci/−	more extreme ci effect

B. With R

6. $R(+)/+^{ci}$	normal (at 25°)
7. R(+)/−	normal
8. R(+)/R(+)	normal, but R(2)+/R(2)+ is like ci/ci
9. R(+)/ci	ci effect, sometimes intermediate between ci/ci and +, sometimes more extreme than ci/ci in different rearrangements
10. R(ci)/+	little ci effect, varies for different R, but more deficient sometimes than ci/+
11. R(ci)/ci	more extreme ci than ci/ci and R(ci)/− and ci/−
12. R(ci)/−	normal or almost normal
13. R(+)	extreme type from 9/−, less effect than ci/ci
14. R(ci)	with least ci effect in no. 10/R(+), extreme ci type
15. R(ci)/R(ci)	some similar to ci/ci, some more normal

A comparison of no. 1 with no. 6, and no. 4 with no. 9 shows what we may call the typical position effect, not different from other position effects. No. 10 or nos. 1 and 2 show that the variability of the ci effect around a threshold, both in different temperatures and with different alleles, applies also to the position effect. However, there is a great difference when a deficiency is involved. No. 5 shows the typical exaggeration, whereas the corresponding no. 7 is normal, meaning that here the position effect has failed to act. But when the position effect is put with homozygous ci (no. 11), it adds its action and a more extreme action results. The normality of the homozygous rearrangement no. 8 is the greatest difference from a standard position effect. The combination no. 13 is working in the same direction and does not show the exaggeration effect; actually it is more normal, in agreement with nos. 7 and 8. Nevertheless, in no. 14 the increase of the ci effect goes again in the opposite direction.

Our question is whether in view of these (at first sight) rather strange facts (which Stern explains by general ideas concerning the action of the gene, to which we shall return), the Dubinin effect is a special kind of position effect. We saw that this assumption is partly caused by semantics: instead of saying that a break near the normal ci locus makes it act like the recessive mutant, it is described as the break making the opposite ci act as a dominant. On the other hand, there is a real difference from ordinary position effects, which is clearly visible in the details of action just tabulated.

The confusing results are, however, understandable if we realize the special feature of the case and forget about misleading terminology like "the position effect stretches to the gene." The decisive fact, as already emphasized above, is that in the Dubinin effect we have the following arrangement in the translocation of the right arm of the fourth chromosome, say to the X-chromosome: X euchrom.—break—4 heterochrom.—ci locus.

We discussed the fact previously that a position effect based upon a break in chromocentric heterochromatin is weaker and therefore, under proper threshold conditions, results in the mottling effect, which is rather sensitive to temperature, extra heterochromatin, and so on. We therefore expect a weak position effect for the break R(+) in the rearrangement above. In the present case, the absence of a piece of vein, variegation or lack of it cannot be distinguished. Hence we expect for R(+)/+ a plus-minus normal condition and, with sufficient weakening of the effect, the same for R(+)/R(+). This is actually found (nos. 6 and 8) in the foregoing enumeration. However, one rearrangement, R(2)+ acts, when homozygous, like a standard position effect (deficient venation), showing an expected range of seriation for the weakening of the position effect from a complete one to almost nil. The next test is the break opposite a deficiency, R(+)/−. According to no. 6 and the fact of the exaggeration effect in ci/−, we expect a little less normality. No. 7 does not show this. Obviously, the shift is still below the threshold for the ci phenotype. But no. 13 shows it in action, when a little weaker allele is involved. Now we come to the most interesting combinations: ci/+ is normal, but with some isoalleles and in low temperature may be slightly abnormal. What is expected for R(ci)/+? If we use the definition of the position effect that a locus near the break is made to act as if mutated, the already mutated locus should not be influenced much by the break of weak action, and therefore ci/+ and R(ci)/+ should be essentially alike, though a little higher effect of the latter might be observable. Nos. 1, 2, and 10 show this to be true. Therefore, R(+)/– and R(ci)/– should also be alike, which is true, as nos. 7 and 12 show. In R(ci)/ci the small shifting effect of the break might have a better chance of becoming visible, and a phenotype more extreme than ci/ci could result, which actually occurs (no. 11). R(ci)/R(+) should be ci; if R(+) acts as much below ci as R(ci) does above, the effect should resemble ci/ci, and if R(+) is above that level the effect should be beyond that of ci/ci. The latter is the case (no. 14). Only one combination remains, which at first sight does not fit at all, no. 12, R(ci)/–. If the break near the mutated ci adds to the ci action (like producing a more extreme allele) R(ci)/– should be still more extreme than ci/– with the exaggeration effect, but it is almost normal. It would be almost hopeless to explain this result by the same theory as the others were it not for the fact that Stern (1948) found that R(ci) may have a break to the right of the ci locus; that is, the piece of heterochromatin with the break is not involved. Here it is not the Dubinin effect that is expected but a standard position effect. This may lead to a still more extreme ci effect, or may not influence the already present ci effect of one mutant locus, or may exercise a dominant position effect, that is, ci with R acting like +. The situation would be similar to that studied by Oliver and Green (see I 3 C *c bb*). This apparently aberrant result would have to be separated clearly from the real Dubinin effect, which involves the heterochromatic section left of ci. This is the weakest point in our entire analysis. (We shall return to these problems in the chapter on dosage.)

dd. Position effect and point mutation

As the foregoing chapters on position effect have indicated, there is no difference between position effect and point mutation except that in point mutation no chromosomal rearrangement can be made visible with the means available at present. The obvious conclusion is that point mutations are rearrangements at the submicroscopic level. What this means for the theory of the gene will be discussed later. In this chapter a number of specific facts will be assembled which point in the same direction.

aaa. Deficiencies and Minutes.—For a long time geneticists (e.g., Muller, Stadler) were impressed by the fact that in radiation-induced mutation no clear line of demarcation could be drawn between point mutants and rearrangements. With Muller's method of measuring mutation rate by sex-linked lethals (in *Drosophila*), these lethals were treated as one class, just mutations, though it was clear that they included gross rearrangements, more or less small deficiencies, and point mutation. This suggested that point mutations may, after all, be invisible rearrangements and deficiencies. The deficiencies were considered as actual absences of a gene (Stadler), while other rearrangements must have been position effects (Muller, Goldschmidt). Meanwhile it turned out, as we saw, that deficiency breaks also may produce position effects so that all rearrangements can be treated alike. The conclusions from such facts differed: either they were considered within the theory of the gene (e.g., Stadler's deficiencies in maize); or they gave rise to speculation on whether the gene is not a more complex structure with subunits (Muller); or whether the concept of the gene should not be replaced by that of a definite order of parts, the change of which produces the mutation and position effect (Goldschmidt).

The facts underlying such conclusions are very diversified and are derived from different types of experimentation. As a first type, comparable to the analysis of sex-linked lethals, we may mention the Minutes (see I 2 C *d dd*), that group of possibly heterochromatic dominant mutants scattered over all chromosomes and having similar effects (see Brehme, 1939, 1941). Many of these have been found cytologically to be deficiencies of different size, but many show normal salivary structure. It is hard to believe that this could be a genuine difference. Either we must assume that the deficiencies have nothing to do with the M effect and accompany it only by chance, which is very improbable, or we must assume that the Minutes with normal chromosomes actually are based upon deficiencies below the level of a salivary band. The latter assumption seems to be the logical conclusion.

In the same category belongs another remarkable fact. The dominant Notch is considered a deficiency for the facet and split loci in the X-chromosome, and frequently a number of nearby loci are included in the deficiency. For many of the numerous N alleles, deficiencies of different length have been demonstrated in the salivary chromosomes. Gottschewski (1937) first found a Notch genetically deficient for a number of loci but with a completely normal chromosome cytologically. Demerec (1941*a*) and Barigozzi (1942) have since added a number of similar cases. All these authors agree that in these cases the normal genes had not been deleted but inactivated.

This is hardly an explanation but rather a circumscription of the facts arising from the embarrassing realization that the theory of the gene does not seem to work here.

Another explanation, which is used by Lefevre, Jr., Ratty, and Hanks (1953) in a very important study of the N phenomenon, is the assumption of invisible submicroscopic deletions. If the deficiency effect, in spite of normal salivaries, were found for only one locus, we could agree. But if a number of loci over a considerable stretch of the chromosome show the haploid effect, a whole string of simultaneous submicroscopic deletions would be required, which is rather improbable. We know only the following situations in which a recessive mutant locus produces its effect in a single dose: (1) when it is hemizygous, that is, opposite a deficiency or in the X-chromosome of the hemizygous sex (a/−); (2) when powerful dominance enhancers have been selected or introduced by crossing (A/a + D.E.); (3) when the mutant locus is opposite a rearrangement with position effect (a/R(+)). The first two are excluded in the present case. The only explanation based upon known facts is that the Notch chromosome contains a rearrangement with a position effect of varying power, affecting one or more loci near the break: since no rearrangement is visible (though N position effects via visible rearrangements are known), we must conclude that here the Notch effect is produced by an invisible rearrangement of a type which affects a considerable stretch of the chromosome.

bbb. Stickiness and mutators.—A very different group of facts is also very suggestive. Beadle (1932) found mutants in maize which affect details of synapsis and chromosome behavior. One of them makes the chromosome sticky and results in special configurations in meiosis. In such a sticky line a great increase in both rearrangements and point mutations was found. It is easy to understand the increase in rearrangements, as stickiness should produce breaks during the synaptic movements and otherwise. However, the increase in point mutations makes sense only when these are unrecognizable rearrangements, since it could hardly be assumed that stickiness pulls out some side chain from a gene molecule. I have stressed this point repeatedly in former discussions of the subject. It seems that Resende (1945) has independently come to a similar conclusion. He calls it chromosomic agglutination, which he studied in many materials (see Pinto-Lopes and Resende, 1949). His opinion is that rearrangements occur only when two chromosomes happen to be near each other and when the kalymma is depolymerized, thus removing the protection from the chromonema. I cannot find any explanation of how this would lead to point mutation, or a statement that point mutations are submicroscopic rearrangements.

I consider as an example of the same or similar type a finding of Sturtevant (1939), who, after crossing two *Drosophila* species, found a large increase of both rearrangements and point mutations. These species have rather different intimate structures of the salivary chromosomes, and in the hybrid synapsis is correspondingly upset. It is not difficult to visualize that these tensions produce chromosome breaks and rearrangements mechanically, just as stickiness does. If the rate of point mutation also increases simultaneously, the same conclusion is in order: they are invisible rearrangements.

I am inclined to look in the same way at another group of facts, the so-called mutator effects, which are very difficult to explain otherwise. It is known that different strains of *Drosophila* have different tendencies to mutate. Sometimes an unusually high mutation rate is found, based upon a genetic condition in a chromosome which has been described as a mutator gene (Demerec, 1937; Neel, 1942*b;* Ives, 1949). We may distinguish three types. The first is the typical mutator effect. The second is a rather rare occurrence which thus far cannot be further analyzed and is, therefore, simply discounted by many geneticists, but there is no doubt of its authenticity. In all the observed cases (Goldschmidt, 1929*b*, 1939; Plough and Holthausen, 1937; for details see Goldschmidt, 1939) a kind of mass mutation occurred, producing suddenly in an otherwise normal line large numbers of highly diversified mutants. If such an event could once be analyzed properly, after early recognition, important results might be expected. The third type is also of the mass mutation type, with the addition that it seems that a mutator locus can be located (Mampell, 1945, 1946). Furthermore, in one of these latter events most of the mutants were Minutes, known to be, as a rule, deficiencies (see I 2 C *d dd*).

I think that these three groups of facts are all based upon the same thing. The mutator is a "sticky" section in a chromosome, which adheres variously to other chromosomes with the result that pieces are pulled out or breaks produced which result in any known type of mutation. Mampell's specific mutator action producing Minutes strongly points in this direction. It is to be hoped that an analyzable case may crop up or a method be found to produce it experimentally. I once believed (Goldschmidt, 1929*b*) that temperature shocks were such a method, but this turned out to be unproved (Goldschmidt,

1939). I still think it possible that it was not a real error but a rare effect working only when some previous condition was present in some chromosome.

At this point attention should be drawn to a little explored field. A number of records at hand, none of them studied very thoroughly, indicate that a causal relation between simultaneous or consecutive different steps of mutation may exist. Skovstedt (1943) has described such a situation in *Nadsonia,* and I have found very suggestive evidence in *Drosophila* (Goldschmidt, 1947). In both it appeared that the occurring of one mutation increased the probability of another occurring. In *Drosophila* cases have been described in which two mutations in different chromosomes appeared repeatedly together. Though a completely convincing analysis is lacking, the observations should be kept in mind as possible examples of the mutator type, better proof of which may be found one day.

However, there is available in maize very good cytological information (McClintock, 1941–1951; see 1951), which shows how a chromosome breakage without rearrangement of the usual type can produce other chromosomal changes; we might call this a mutator action. McClintock found what she calls the breakage-fusion-bridge cycle. There are two types of it. One is called the chromatid type of the cycle. It is found when a chromosome with a newly broken end enters the telophase of meiosis. Fusion occurs between two sister chromatids at the position of previous anaphase breakage, resulting in bridge formation in the next anaphase. This may continue over many mitotic cycles. If, however, a chromosome with a newly broken end is introduced into the zygote by each gametic nucleus, the broken ends of the two chromosomes—not chromatids—may fuse. This establishes a dicentric chromosome and a different type of breakage-fusion-bridge cycle is initiated. In the telophase nuclei the fusions now occur between the broken ends of chromosomes. The important point for the present discussion is that this cycle may initiate breakage events in other chromosomes and also the origin of mutable loci. In the terminology used before, this breakage cycle acts as a mutator. (We shall discuss these facts in more detail in the next section.)

ccc. Mutable loci in maize.—The most complete and interesting contribution to the present discussion comes from McClintock's work on mutable loci in maize (see 1951). It shows that maize, the most favorable genetic material in plants, second only to *Drosophila,* supplies the same type of information on position effect; hence we can no longer doubt that it is a general phenomenon. Simultaneously, it concurs with the material presented up to now in proving the identity of position effect and point mutation, the topic of the present discussion.

Mutable or unstable genes have been known for a long time, and there is an extensive literature on the subject for plants (Emerson, Stadler, Rhoades, Ernst, Demerec, Imai), but rarely have cases been reported in animals. The one example in *Drosophila*, studied by Demerec (1941*b*), cannot be interpreted with certainty. I have shown (Goldschmidt, 1943) that facts very closely paralleling those described by Demerec may be based upon special genetic situations combined with special morphological conditions. For the time being, the existence of the phenomenon in animals cannot be regarded as demonstrated beyond a doubt, and it will be very difficult to prove it finally. The prototype of the phenomenon is found in pericarp color in maize, which frequently shows variegation. Emerson showed (1914 ff.) that this variegation is based upon "mutation" from a colorless allele to a dominant colored one, taking place in somatic cells at definite places and times of development, and leading to colored spots. Their number and size give information about frequency, place, and time of these "mutations." If a colored spot engulfs sex cells (or their precursors) it can be proved that mutation is involved, or seems to be involved. (The latter fact puts *Drosophila* at a disadvantage. The assertion cannot be made that a mosaic spot on a wing engulfs the sex cells, for they are completely removed from the soma from the beginning of development. This is one reason why Demerec's interpretation had to be regarded with caution.) It is strange that "color mutations" always occur in the direction from recessive to dominant, also with intermediate alleles. Very few occurrences in the opposite direction have been described. This unexpected behavior, that is, not expected on the basis of our knowledge of mutation in maize, indicates some special feature.

Older authors like Correns assumed that these ever-sporting or mutable loci were "sick genes" and could not throw light upon genuine mutation, a notion which I accepted for some time but which can no longer be held, since a much better solution is available now. The link with our present discussion was forged by Rhoades' (1938) discovery that in a special line of Mexican maize a dominant locus Dt in the ninth chromosome exists in the presence of which the color locus aa in the third chromosome—no anthocyanin pigment—"mutates" after the fashion of unstable loci to its higher alleles; and only this one locus does it. Again it could be shown that the effect is inherited. Dt then acts exactly like a mutator, confined to a single locus. No rearrangements could be detected, but the Dt locus is near or within the end knob, which possibly is heterochromatic. Of course, rearrangements in maize must be, as we emphasized earlier, minimally of ten times the order of magnitude as in *Drosophila* salivary chromosomes in order to be detectable. In this and all other comparable cases the facts did not lead beyond these statements, based upon Rhoades' work.

It stands to reason that, in spite of the special features mentioned, these somatic mutations are genetically not different from standard mutations. Demerec expressed this by saying that we have all ranges of mutation frequency, rare mutations, frequent ones, very frequent ones in the cases of mutators studied above, and finally these extreme frequencies. His statement is certainly formally correct, but only when we give it a completely different meaning from the one intended. For Demerec the statement meant that only ordinary gene mutations are involved, but at different rates. To us it means that mutations are position effects, since the proof has been provided by McClintock that "mutable genes" are a special type of position effect caused by frequent rearrangements.

At this point, therefore, McClintock's work (see 1951) on similar phenomena is applicable to the present problem. It is very difficult to understand in its original terminology, which was chosen before the real meaning came to light. We shall present it so that the relation to the work on position effect in *Drosophila* is made clear by the use of the *Drosophila* terminology also for McClintock's work. We remember that the chromosomal breakage-fusion-bridge cycle in maize induced the rearrangements in other chromosomes. It also accounts for the origin of new mutable loci of the type discussed for the earlier maize work. This means that in plants which were the self-pollinated progeny of those which, in early development, had undergone that breakage cycle, a "burst" of new mutable loci appeared. It may help us to understand the complicated facts if we say that this breakage cycle (i.e., basically, the breakage) acts as a primary mutator.

The next fact is that, in the unstable line derived from the parents with "mutator," a break at a definite point of the chromosome appears with definite frequencies and at definite times, a break which we may call a secondary mutator. This break, obviously one of the direct actions of the primary mutator (as defined above, i.e., a consequence of the chromosomal abnormalities of the fusion-bridge cycle), is unfortunately described as a dominant locus, which then behaves like the power behind a mutable locus. This terminology is rather confusing, and could have been avoided if the facts from *Drosophila* genetics had been used for orientation. Ds (dissociation), the so-called dominant, actually means nothing but the presence of a break at one definite point during the mitotic cycle, caused originally by the fusion-bridge cycle. However, it is important that the way in which the Ds break appeared, permitting its ultimate effects to be described in terms of a mutable locus, led to the conclusion that all "mutable loci" (in the usual sense) may be somehow associated with structural alterations.

The break Ds was shown to be connected with an array of rearrangements all of which had the Ds break in common and could be treated as a series of different alleles. This means that the occurrence of the Ds break gives rise to translocations, deficiencies, inversions, ring chromosomes, dicentric and acentric fragments always with one breakage point at Ds. The primary break (the fusion-bridge cycle, here called the primary mutator) causes, in the course of the mitotic cycles of the next generation, the different multiple allelic Ds breaks at different times and places during development, which we termed the secondary mutator in order to clarify the description, since it is the cause of what appears as somatic mutation. So far, these are purely cytological facts.

In further studies a kernel was occasionally found in which the Ds break was located not at the standard locus but in a new position in the short arm of the ninth chromosome, between any of a half-dozen known loci, as determined both cytologically and genetically. Sometimes a break in another chromosome was found which also was called a Ds break. These new locations of the Ds break are clearly the consequence of further rearrangements. In McClintock's original terminology, Ds is a dominant mutant which changes place in the chromosome, jumps around, and causes somatic mutation wherever it goes. With the knowledge of the details now available, it is better to forget the older terminology and to express the facts, as done here, in terms of different rearrangement breaks at the first locus found or any other locus. Thus it is shown that the primary cause (f-b cycle, primary mutator) leads to secondary rearrangements with breaks at different loci; those in the left end of the second chromosome (the secondary mutator) have been studied most because of the available visible markers. If a Ds break is present in one chromosome together with dominant markers and only recessive loci without a break in the homologue, the break will often result in the loss of an acentric fragment containing the dominants. Therefore, a spot with the recessive characters will become visible as a variegation; the size, type, and extent will depend upon the time of the event and the location of the break. This explains the otherwise rare, recessive "mutable gene" effect.

An additional feature necessary for the production of the Ds breaks is the presence of a dominant Ac, controlling the time of incidence of the breaks in proportion to the doses of Ac present. Ac cannot be localized, for it seems to occupy many different points of different chromosomes. It also shows different alleles and in a general way acts like Ds; but the Ds break and its variants and effects usually do not occur in the absence of Ac. This is so far the least clear feature in the whole situation. (What Ac may mean will be indicated at the end of the next paragraph and in the following interpretation.)

The next important fact is that of a transposition of the Ds break next to the locus for color C (one of the "Ds jumps"). This locus behaves now (in the presence of Ac) as if C were mutated to c, and this, of course, is the typical position effect of a rearrangement break near a normal + locus as in *Drosophila.* The additional proof, possible in *Drosophila* only in a few rare instances, namely, in restoration to normal when the adjacent break is removed, was supplied in this case. The new fact is that this position effect, that is, no pigment in the presence of the break, assumes the character of a mutable locus. (Therefore, we compared the Ds break with a secondary mutator.) This means that it frequently reverts in some cells to normal or stages in between, which leads to variegation, the external sign of "mutable genes." It is at once clear that this phenomenon is similar in phenotypic effect to the mottled position effect in *Drosophila* (see I 2 C *d bb*). But whereas the latter had to be explained as a variable threshold effect of the position effect, McClintock considers the variegation in maize to be dependent on a reversal, a removal of the Ds break. The type of resulting variegation serves to supply further information. I wonder whether a reversal is really involved, or whether this is only a hypothesis. If the latter, the alternative would be a threshold effect as in *Drosophila.* If this is true, the role of Ac would become clear: it would control the threshold conditions.

Subsequently, exactly the same features were shown for other loci, giving position effect of the variegated type if next to the Ds break in presence of Ac. One is Bronze (Bz), another Sh (normal versus shrunken endosperm). However, some "mutable loci" arose in other experiments which did not require Ac for their action (meaning unknown). Again a locus began acting as its recessive and afterward produced variegation toward the normal type with irregular changes in both directions. This was found for luteus (chlorophyll color) and the A locus (color of aleurone and anthocyanin pigments), the latter originating in a line which already contained the former.

In different position effects at the same locus a considerable variation of the variegation effect was found, for example, in the Waxy effect. Some needed Ac and others did not; some produced definite grades of the effect ("alleles") or varying grades. Compared with *Drosophila* variegation, this means that the details of variegation (i.e., the conditioning of the effect by external or genetic conditions acting upon the thresholds) are, in this case, affected by the different kinds of rearrangement which produce the position effect (perhaps the second break; see Raffel and Muller). This presupposes that our assumption is true that no reversal of the Ds break occurs but that threshold conditions underlie the results.

These are some of the most important facts found by McClintock, omitting innumerable confusing details and describing the facts not in McClintock's language but in terms that make it possible to compare the results with the *Drosophila* work on position effect. Certainly not everything is perfectly clear and understandable. Much is obscured by the use of the original terminology (which we have tried to avoid as far as possible), which designates the appearance of variegation as mutation and its grades as alleles. Our present analysis is concerned with the question whether any information on the nature of mutation may be deduced from the study of so-called mutable loci. This question presupposes that the "mutable loci" actually produce mutants. McClintock's work, analyzed from the point of view derived from the work on position effect in *Drosophila,* seems to me to reveal the following situation (my interpretation only partly coincides with that of McClintock). The fusion-breakage-bridge cycle corresponds to a spontaneous or induced rearrangement within a chromosome (primary mutator). The presence of this produces further rearrangements (secondary mutator). One of them takes place in the heterochromatin (called the Ac condition), but it is not known what kind of rearrangement this is. The other is a visible break (called the Ds condition). If this break is located near a known locus, the latter acts as if mutated to its recessive, which is the standard position effect as found in *Drosophila* and is clearly typical also for all studied loci in maize. This part of the work permits us to say that position effect is a typical and general phenomenon and that all the conclusions we drew from it can be generalized.

The next group of facts shows that the different cases involve different rearrangement breaks (which was expressed by McClintock by describing Ds as a jumping locus). It further demonstrates that with the position effect break constant, the other break may be anywhere, which may lead to special phenotypic differences, just as in the above-quoted work of Raffel and Muller in *Drosophila.* (These different rearrangements and their effects are called by McClintock the different states of Ds, which again is a very confusing terminology.)

The activator, Ac, usually is needed for the variegated position effect to take place, but sometimes it is not required; also, it has different states in different cases. The Ac effect may be localized at different points. This suggests that Ac is the other break of the rearrangements, located in heterochromatin. It would act upon the threshold of the Ds position effect, sometimes more, sometimes less, or not at all, in different rearrangements. We could describe this, in terms of *Drosophila,* as a position effect of a heterochromatic break (not adjacent to the primary position effect break Ds), resembling the action of extra heterochromatin upon mottling in *Drosophila.* If a strict comparison is made with *Drosophila,* the Ds effect would require a moving of heterochromatin near the position effect locus, the primary cause of the variable threshold for expression of the position effect. On the other hand, it is also possible that this is merely a case in which variegation occurs without Ac. When Ac is needed, it could be that the Ds break is purely euchromatic and therefore produces only the recessive, complete position effect, while the Ac-heterochromatic condition shifts the Ds effect near or below the threshold. As far as I know, such a situation has not been found in *Drosophila.* It would mean, for example, that a typical white position effect became mottled when something happened to the heterochromatin somewhere else. Perhaps some of the cubitus interruptus effects recorded previously could be a comparable situation. If maize had salivary chromosomes, the secret of the Ac action could be unraveled. All this is so important that we must discuss it in more detail; the present brief discussion was intended only to make McClintock's work more understandable and to fit in with the known features of position effect.

ddd. Mottling in maize and Drosophila.—The end of the last section contains the gist of the present chapter. We must elaborate it further because a proper understanding of the similarities and differences between the variegation effects in *Drosophila* and maize is essential for a derivation of general conclusions upon the theory of the gene. We shall deal with some of the former statements in different language, and enlarge upon them. In *Drosophila*—assume eye color as a model for all other cases—variegation is the result of a rearrangement break which brings block heterochromatin near an unchanged normal locus. The mutant type (e.g., white eyes) is the product of a position effect, while the mottled type results from a weakening of the effect in the presence of heterochromatin together with a threshold condition for the position effect (white), which is not passed in all primary pigment cells, because of simple statistical variation of the action among many similar cells.

It is instructive to see how this effect in *Drosophila* would have to be described in the terminology of the work on maize. White eye would then be a simple mutant w, which became mutable toward normal W in some cells in the presence of a mutator like Ds in maize, known to be connected with rearrangements. However, this mutator, the rearrangement, would not act except in the presence of another dominant condition (the Ac in maize), which in *Drosophila* is, of course, the condition that heterochromatin has been transposed near the position effect locus. It is obvious that the maize variegation with all its peculiarities should be understandable in terms of the *Drosophila* effect, as the position effect of a break upon a known locus and the weakening of it, in a statistical way, around a threshold by some property of the rearrangement, which does not necessarily have to do with heterochromatin. To this is added the variation of the effect under the influence of other conditions, the type of rearrangement, and all the things described as states in McClintock's terminology. If this conclusion applies to all so-called mutable loci, we could answer our former question of whether or not these are "sick genes," or some such specific conditions of a "gene," by saying (1) there are no mutable loci; (2) the loci responsible for the variegation effect are unchanged normal loci; (3) these loci are located in the neighborhood of a rearrangement break causing a position effect; (4) this effect is variable because of some weakening effect of the heterochromatin or other unknown features. The effect in maize is not necessarily the same as in *Drosophila:* it does not require the presence of heterochromatin adjacent to the break. This variability includes change in both directions: more variegation up to normality, or less down to the ordinary mutant type.

Thus the great lines of the work on *Drosophila* and that on maize are completely parallel, and the theoretical conclusions about the gene are the same in both, as realized also by McClintock. However, there is still one very important difficulty. In maize the variegation may affect the cells of the germinal line which produce normal offspring as if a mutation of the recessive to the dominant (i.e., a reverse mutation) had occurred, though this is not always so (Stadler). It always appeared strange (Emerson, Rhoades, and others) that reverse mutation, which is usually so rare, if it exists at all, would be so frequent a phenomenon in this case and in the numerous parallel ones in plants, upon which an extensive literature is available. This indicated to me in the past that a different interpretation of the maize variegation would be found one day, an opinion frequently expressed in the course of years. I think that the new interpretation can be presented now. Take as example an aleuron color. In the kernels studied by McClintock, all cells containing the normal C or A locus were made to act as a recessive by the adjacent rearrangement break. This effect varied from almost colorless to normally colored under the influence of internal (genetic) and external conditions. How can these, if found in the germ line, remain true breeding?

We must first state that the "variation" in the mottling effect and its counterpart in maize variegation, both caused by weakening of the position effect, may be one of different grades, demonstrated in *Drosophila* by different eye colors between white and red (see Stone and Griffen), and in maize by different color conditions in the spots, described by McClintock as allelic effects (what a source of error in this terminology, in itself correct!). In addition, we may have an all-or-none effect (either white or red), probably, if not certainly, depending upon the genetically controlled threshold conditions (see I 3 C *c bb*; and Goldschmidt, 1950*b*). In discussing the relations between heterochromatin and sex determination, we have drawn attention to the close parallel between the variegated position effect and the variegated effect in some organs of intersexual moths (Goldschmidt, 1950*b*; Seiler, 1949). We pointed out that here a phenotypic effect (female or male structure, color, etc.) is based upon a developmental alternative within the intersex with its disturbed genic balance. The exact parallel is the position effect, an alternative of action at a locus, producing either the normal condition or, in the presence of a break, the mutant type. In those intersexes, two possibilities are given: either an all-or-none effect occurs, that is, the organ (e.g., wing) of an intersex is all female or all male; or the all-or-none effect is bound to a narrow threshold condition which, with little variation of the effect, will make for a mosaic of female and male spots, as explained above. In the same way the position effect in *Drosophila* and maize may be all or none throughout (e.g., normal or mutant type throughout), or it may be weakened and fluctuate around a threshold of action, resulting in mosaic *Drosophila* eyes or maize kernels. We cannot breed from mosaic spots in insects. But we can in maize, where the all-or-none type of weakening the position effect (the apparent return mutation) leaves the unchanged locus to act normally. This requires that the control of the threshold action in the cell is also of the all-or-none type. What this means in genetic terms is difficult to state.

It seems that such an all-or-none setup is present in many of the maize variegations, and especially those in which entrance into the germ line was described. If we can explain the constancy in the germ line, this does not necessarily mean that the same explanation applies to the somatic spots. It is quite possible that these are based solely upon the variability of the position effect and that only some cells may have changed so that they would reproduce their kind in the germ line. A first type of interpretation would not require this difference; a second type, the more probable one, would have to assume it. The first possible explanation is this: the genetic conditions which weaken the position effect to zero—we may call them modifiers, whatever they are—may be homozygous and thus counter the position effect for good. The second one is that in some of the completely colored cells a new rearrangement may have occurred—after the manner experimentally produced in *Drosophila* (see I 3 C *c cc*)—which counteracts the position effect completely by removing the break to another position. We have already mentioned that this is probably the explanation for so-called return mutations in *Drosophila,* and now we must draw the same conclusion for maize. This conclusion requires that sometimes germ-line cells from a colored sector reproduce this condition, but sometimes they breed true to the recessive mutant type.

At this point the danger of being trapped by semantics appears, which in the interest of clear thinking should be emphasized. If we call the new rearrangement a mutation (though not a return mutation, which it simulates), we may call the locus a mutating one (though the locus remains unchanged) as far as this one event is concerned, but it is not a mutating locus so far as threshold conditions alone produce the effect, as in the standard variegation effect. If the interpretation of the entire group of phenomena is correct, it is better to forget about semantics and to drop the notion of the mutable loci after it has been reduced to nothing but a *façon à parler.*

We must return to the work of Rhoades on a mutable locus in maize in which the decisive fact was the presence of a "factor" Dt located in or near the heterochromatic knob of the ninth chromosome, in the presence of which the recessive anthocyanin locus in a different chromosome "mutated" after the type of a mutable locus to the dominant color expression. McClintock compares Rhoades' Dt to Ac in her work, which seems unavoidable, but Rhoades did not find any rearrangement near the a locus or the Dt locus. For the evaluation of these facts in the light of the foregoing discussion, the following details must be considered. Dt acts specifically only upon the a_1 mutant, not on other mutants affecting anthocyanin formation like a_2, c, or r. We must conclude that just a_1 must have some peculiarity which allows this interaction. Now a_1, according to Rhoades (1938), originated once in a line studied by Emerson, and all a_1 lines are derived from this mutant. Another occurrence was in the same Mexican stock in which the Dt condition was found by Rhoades, and the two a_1's cannot be distinguished. I can draw only one conclusion from these facts: a_1 is a position effect due to an unseen (thus far) break near the a locus, and this effect is then comparable to a standard position effect, as it is for McClintock's Ds effects without Ac. Dt becomes the heterochromatic condition which changes a standard position effect of the recessive type like y, sc, and so on, in *Drosophila,* into a mottled one.

True, this is not the same heterochromatic effect as in *Drosophila,* where a break within adjacent heterochromatin is involved; it is rather comparable to the effect of extra Y heterochromatin. However, we have seen, in the necessity of Ac or the lack of it for production of the effect in maize, that there is a slight difference between the two materials, which, after all, is to be expected. If these deductions are correct, and in view of McClintock's results this can hardly be denied, all the facts fall into line, and the Rhoades' effect also ceases to be mutation of an unstable locus.

In favor of this conclusion may be cited the extensive experiments of Stadler (reviewed 1951). In appraising them we face again the semantic difficulty of terminology. Stadler speaks of mutation from A to a when the standard mutational effect is involved; further, of mutation from a to A when in the presence of Dt the mosaic spots appear; and again of mutation if extracted colored individuals from the germ-line mosaics produce colorless individuals. In the light of our former discussions, these are very different events, as Stadler's experiments also show. He states that A is a very stable locus in which he could produce no mutation to a in "fairly extensive trials." (See I 3 C *c bb.*) (The split locus in *Drosophila* behaved similarly, though rearrangements involving it were produced easily.) We have noted that a_1 appeared only twice spontaneously. The A alleles produced by Dt—"Dt-induced mutation"—behave differently. To avoid misunderstandings, I repeat that these are extracted different A types from variegation affecting the germ line, which, as explained above, are very different from ordinary mutation. Now these alleles "are not strikingly mutable, but they yield mutations to a at rates comparable to the mutation rates found in the various R stocks studied. These mutations have been found in 4 different A_1 alleles, each tracing to a separate Dt induced mutation of a."

Stadler proposes some interpretations of the fact, one in terms of subunits in the A gene, another assuming that Dt present in the derived line may cause mutation from A to a. I am convinced that the correct explanation must be derived from the assumption that a is a position effect, which works phenotypically in the direction of $A \rightarrow a$; further, that the colored patches which may enter a next generation are at least in part based upon subsequent rearrangements, working phenotypically in the opposite direction, as shown above. Therefore, the offspring of these derived colored plants will show different kinds of segregation for these additional position effects, some of which remove the secondary effect, leaving the primary a_1 position effect. Thus all the facts fall in line and, as said before, the mutable locus disappears completely, while position effect establishes its rule over this interesting group of facts.

ee. Theory of position effect and genic structure of the chromosome

aaa. Breakage and mutant effects.—The facts on position effect recorded thus far cannot leave any doubt that no distinction can be made between point mutation and position effect except visibility or non-visibility in the salivary chromosomes of *Drosophila*. The conclusion seems inevitable that so-called point mutants are rearrangements below the level of microscopic visibility. These invisible rearrangements may be deficiencies, inversions, duplications. We have mentioned one-band inversions in the salivaries, which may be recognized only in rare instances. A similar inversion in maize, that is, on a scale at least ten times cruder than in a salivary chromosome, could never be seen. We mentioned also the substructure of salivary bands as seen in the electron microscope (I 2 A).

It is quite possible, even probable, that the older view of Stadler (see 1933) that mutants are deficiencies will turn out to be correct as far as point mutations are concerned, or at least for many point mutations. As long as we thought in terms of genes, this view encountered great difficulties because of the series of multiple alleles at one locus, dosage effects, and so on. These difficulties have completely disappeared, since we know that deficiencies can produce a position effect and that known position effects act as multiple alleles to each other as well as to point mutations. This identity includes dosage effects. The meaning of multiple allelism has become completely independent of the assumption of a corpuscular gene. Furthermore, the dosage effects do not pose any more difficulties since Stern showed that R(+) ci ci acts as if it were ci ci ci; that is, a position effect substitutes for a mutant in dosage experiments. The most powerful argument is derived from the homozygous deficiencies. It has been mentioned that in *Drosophila* a homozygous deficiency for yellow has the phenotype yellow, and many other examples were registered. Recently McClintock (1951) mentioned again the same behavior for a large series of loci in maize. Hence it is clear that we are dealing with a fact which is not isolated. Whereas in these cases no locus or gene is present, we can only conclude that the change of order of structure within the chromosome from abcdefg to abcefg is responsible, which can be called a position effect if a position effect is not an action of a locus near a break but rather the action of a change in order within the chromosome. If we remember, further, all that was said on X-ray and ultraviolet-induced deficiencies and point mutants, it becomes clear that point mutants are not only position effects of tiny rearrangements but that, specifically, many or possibly most of them are tiny deficiencies of chromosome material. However, this cannot be true where the exaggeration phenomenon is found, which requires a point mutant different from a deficiency.

Lüning (1952*a*,*b*), like others before him, has tried to establish a difference between radiation-induced "gene mutations" and rearrangements (see also Bonnier and Lüning, 1951). He showed that irradiation during spermatogenesis in *Drosophila* results in different effects according to whether sperm is used 1–6 days after treatment or 7–10 days after. In the latter, many more breaks were produced leading to hyperploids and gynandromorphs. When a chromosome

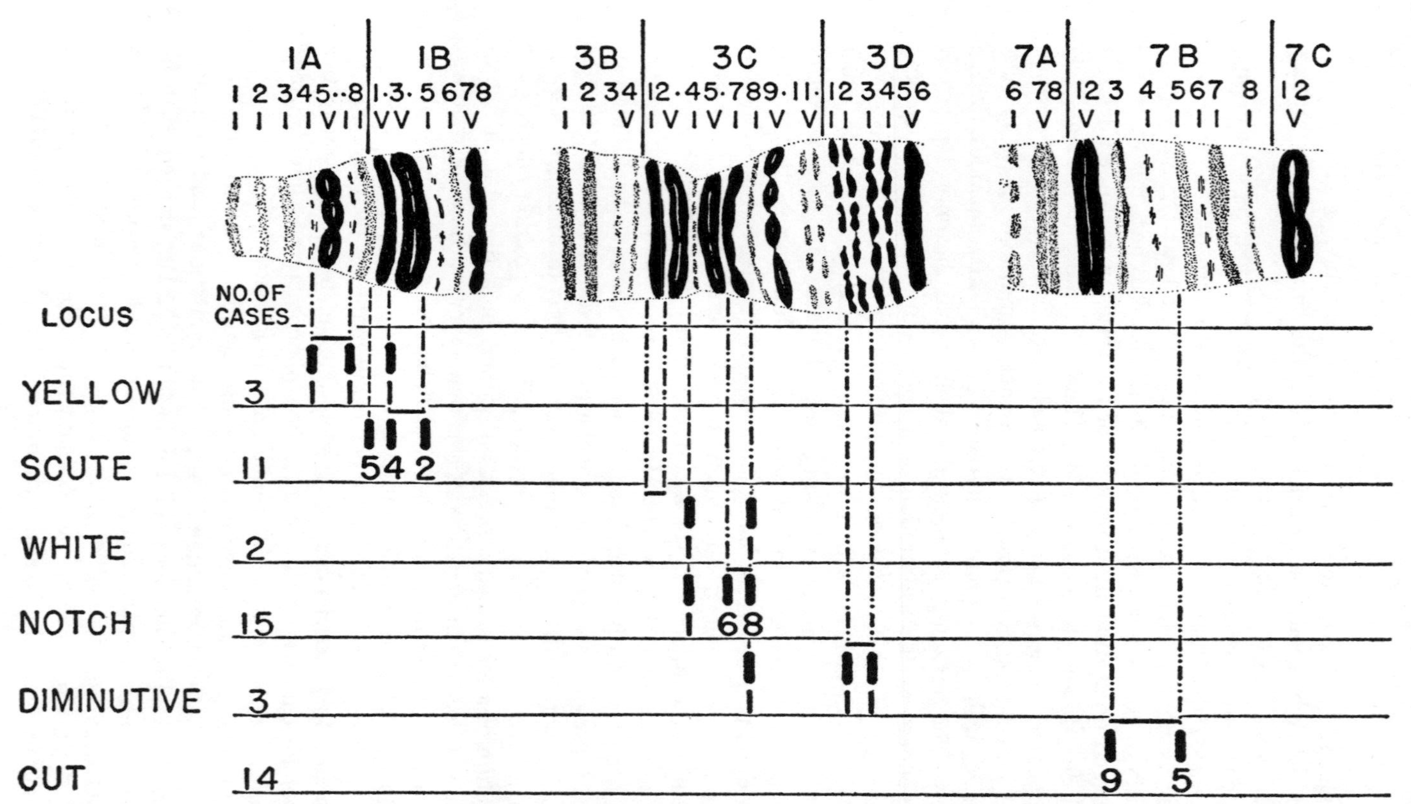

Fig. 11. Three sections of salivary first chromosome of *D. melanogaster* indicating locations of position effect producing breaks within euchromatic sections. Left, phenotype; vertical bars indicate breaks, beneath number of observed cases. (From Demerec, 1941*a*; reproduced by permission of the author.)

containing a scute inversion was irradiated, yellow mutants were produced in the same varying proportions. According to Belgovsky (1938), these mutants are position effects of small rearrangements. Nevertheless, other supposed point mutants and lethals did not show the same proportionality, though they were still more frequent in the second period, but not as frequent as the breaks. From this evidence it is concluded that the point mutations must be intragenic and not intergenic. (Similar results of D'Amata and Gustafsson, 1948, and Kaplan, 1951, for cereals are quoted, but it would be difficult to distinguish cytologically in cereals small rearrangements from point mutants.) I cannot see that the experiments prove the conclusion. The yellow "rearrangements" were not checked in salivary chromosomes and neither were the lethals and putative point mutants, many of which would probably have turned out to be rearrangements. Even if the facts should be found, after a check, to be what they are supposed to be, they do not prove the point. If it were certain that invisible changes were less frequent at a definite chromosomal stage of irradiation than gross breaks, this might have many reasons, for example, the smaller size of the breakable material within a band than between the bands. Many other interpretations of such a type could be thought out, and there is no reason to assume that the difference of effect in regard to aging, even if it were more reliably established, has any bearing at all upon the problem of gene mutation versus invisible pattern change by breaks (e.g., deficiencies).

bbb. The chromosomal sections of action.—This leads us to inquire in more detail into the relation between point mutants and allelic position effects. The results are of the greatest importance for the theory of the genic material. Demerec (1943) and I, with the collaboration of Kodani (Goldschmidt, 1944), independently made such a study with similar results. Since those of Demerec were based upon a much larger material, we illustrate them with his diagram (fig. 11). The salient points are these. The position of the assumed locus or gene within a given band or group of bands is derived mainly from the location of deficiencies giving the recessive effects. The map shows that the position effect (e.g., for yellow and scute) can be produced by rearrangement breaks at very different locations to the right and left of the assumed locus. For the yellow effect, breaks within a section of about six bands are responsible; for the scute effect the section is composed of five bands; about seven for the white effect; about five for Notch; and four for Cut. But, as figure 11 shows, these regions were considerably extended when the rearrangement brought heterochromatin to the neighborhood of the section of position effect. Here the position effects were produced by breaks even more than twenty-five bands distant. (Still more extreme actions were found for the Notch effect.) In the euchromatic case, sections of the chromosome are delineated containing about half a dozen bands within which the assumed locus of the "gene" is located and within which any rearrangement break produces the position effect (though in some cases certain points of breakage seem to be preferred as agents of position effect). Another very remarkable feature is that these sections may overlap, as can be seen in yellow-scute, white-Notch, Notch-diminutive. Hence a break at the same point may produce either effect. We do not know what this means, but we may think of an influence of the location of the second break.

What do these facts mean in terms of the theory of the genetic material? Let us first consider the normal locus, the location of which is established by the deficiency test. Can this test still be regarded as valid? I do not believe so. Since we know that many homozygous deficiencies produce the mutant effect, without any locus existing, since we know further that deficiencies located at different points (Sutton) can give the same deficiency effects, the localizing of a point mutant by the deficiency test has become obsolete. If, as it has happened, three distinguished researchers (Demerec, Muller, and Prokofyeva; see Muller and Prokofyeva, 1935) find the same locus in completely different bands, using the deficiency method, this is no longer a cause for quarreling, because we know that both may be right. This does not mean that there are two loci; it means that the concept of the locus in its strict form is wrong and with it that of the gene. What has actually been proved by all these facts is that chromosomal segments exist, probably of different lengths, which may vary from two to many salivary bands, within which any change of order of the elements by removal of parts (deficiency) or rearrangement (duplication, inversion, translocation) produces approximately the same phenotypical effect; and that all these rearrangement effects behave as multiple alleles. There is no normal locus within a segment and no point mutation of such a locus; an invisible rearrangement is prone to be localized in or next to any band of a segment. This conclusion, which tallies with all the facts analyzed in former chapters, is, in my opinion, unavoidable, though I realize how difficult it is for classic genetics to free itself of ingrained notions which have served so well. It is easily realized that this new point of view may be forgotten when dealing with elementary genetics, which can be described in terms of genes and their mutations, as long as we do not inquire into what a gene is and what a mutation is. The important point is that there is no individual locus and no gene which mutates, but a segment of a chromosome which is rather large in molecular terms, which has an orderly, internal structure of a definite sequence (i.e., polarized), and which may even overlap the next one; and that any happening within such a segment which changes this sequence visibly or invisibly appears as a mutant, all of which are allelic. If anybody would now call these segments the genes, in order to save the gene concept, the device would be pure semantics, for nothing is left of the classic gene and its mutation.

Sturtevant once said that anybody who holds such views does not know what a gene is. What he probably meant was that a gene is a chromosome section between two crossover breaks, and by that definition he assumes he is in possession of the secret of what a gene is. Such *dicta ex cathedra* touch only the semantics of the case and leave the problems where they were.

The definition of position effect which we had to use thus far in a descriptive way, in terms of action of a locus near a break, now becomes obsolete. The position effect is, like mutation, the effect of a change in the serial order of the structural elements of a section of a chromosome. The diagram illustrates some of the possibilities.

	Chromosomal segment and its structural order								
Normal	a	b	c	d	e	f			
Deficiency visible	a	b		d	e	f			
Deficiency invisible	a	b	$\frac{c}{2}$	d	e	f			
Deficiency invisible	a	b	c	$\frac{d}{2}$	e	f			
Large inversion or translocation	a	b	c				x	y	z
or	a	b	c	d	e		x	y	z
Microinversion (visible or not)	a	b	c	d	ə	f			
or	a	q	c	d	e	f			

c/2 means that instead of submicroscopic $c^1c^2c^3c^4$ only c^1c^2 is present; q or ə means that instead of submicroscopic $b^1b^2b^3b^4$ the orders $b^1b^3b^2b^4$ and so on are found.

This diagram and the preceding discussion make it appear as if the segments in which a disturbance of order produces the position effects or apparent point mutants were well-defined morphological structures. This can be true only to a certain extent, namely, as far as the limits of the segments can be made visible. However, there are two phenomena which require a less morphological definition of the segments. The first is the overlapping of neighboring segments, as described above. If a break between bands a and b and between b and c may produce the phenotypes of the segments to the right of c as well as to the left of b (see fig. 11 for yellow and scute), it cannot be the morphological segment which counts, but a field-like function of the segment which under certain conditions—probably the residual heredity and (or) features of the heterochromatin—reaches from its center in the segment to different distances. The understanding of the meaning of this requires the realization that there is no gene or locus within the segment, but only a definite polarized order on a molecular level which functions or is disturbed in its function (mutation and position effect) by a change in the structural sequence. If this function has the character of a field, it may change in range under proper conditions. A similar interpretation is hardly avoidable in the case of the position effect of heterochromatic breaks which act upon a series of sections to a considerable distance. The description of these facts in terms of genes, namely, an action of adjacent heterochromatin upon genes far away, provides no insight and is devoid of meaning. Obviously, the phenomenon belongs in the same category as the overlapping effect. Described in the same terms, it would mean that the change in order, substituting heterochromatin for a more or less distant euchromatic sector, stretches the fields of many adjacent sections way down to the break. We could call this an extreme type of overlapping. Such an effect is not so unexpected if we remember that heterochromatic changes (e.g., extra Y-chromosomes) can have a considerable influence upon many genetic actions (see I 2 C *d ee*). Distance actions within and between chromosomes are becoming better known and will in time contribute to a more definite theory of all these effects, especially when studied without reference to the classic gene. We mention only one: the rather mysterious effect of inversions in one chromosome upon crossing over in another (see Schultz and Redfield, 1951), an effect which is already being used as a standard experimental method (Lewis, 1952).

The time has not yet come to endow these discussions of the chromosomal sections and the field-like type of their action with a more definite biochemical meaning. But it should at least be mentioned that ideas have been proposed by others, quite apart from the facts and interpretations taken from my former work (reviewed 1951) and just presented, which might be considered as putting out feelers in the same direction, so far as they replace the concept of mutation and (or) position effect as a chemical change by one involving patterns and features of a field. Let me quote from a general paper by a plant physiologist, who probably never had a chance to hear of the facts and ideas just presented (Mothes, 1952). After discussing the proteins as possible hereditary material, he continues (in translation):

"One may safely say that the often mentioned, to all purposes infinite number of chemical combinations of about 20 amino acids possible in the formation of giant protein molecules receives its importance only from this: namely, the chance that by diverse folding, packing, spiralizing certain active groups may come to the outside of the molecule and become active while others remain hidden inside, as a kind of reserve which tomorrow in a new step of nature may suddenly become exposed and thus endow the whole with new properties. What we call a gene mutation does not necessarily consist in a great change of chemical nature. It may just as well be a change in pattern, which brings into action already present but thus far hidden parts and thus produces new combinations and neighborhoods of active groups and new electric fields."

A second quotation of a similar character may be inserted here, a statement by a cell physiologist and biochemist. In discussing the problem of whether DNA may be considered as the genic material, Mazia (1952) writes: "The 'physical basis of heredity' is something in the chromosome which may or may not be DNA, but which follows DNA for all the practical purposes of cytogenetics. We cannot be sure that the question 'what is the genetic constituent of the chromosome?' is a meaningful one. The structure of the chromosome as a whole is so astonishingly reproducible that the skillful cytologist can always recognize a given one and, indeed, likes to give it a name or number. It is well known that rearrangements even at the microscopic level have hereditary consequences, and some have gone so far as to contend that the genetic unit should be the whole chromosome. The regularities of chromosome structure may reflect regularities of intermolecular relationships so decisive that it may prove to be misleading in terms of molecules at all. We have seen in a previous section how little is known of the intermolecular associations in the nucleus. The fractions that we isolate may be extremely artificial entities, telling us a little about the weak points in the fabric but nothing about the associations as they actually function." I expressed the latter point in genetical terms by saying that the mutant locus is a reality, but not the normal gene. It may be added that the recent experiments of Mazia (I 2 B *a*), which may lead to a better understanding of the supermolecular associations in the chromosome, will hardly change the situation described in the quotation.

Some of the ideas presented, or rather hinted at, by Watson and Crick in discussing their new model of nucleic acid structure are relevant at this point in our discussion. We quoted their statement (I 2 B *b bb*) that the different possibilities for attachment of the purine-pyrimidine rings to the molecular axis spell out the code for different genic action. The idea, if I understand their hint correctly, is that the innumerable possibilities of permutation within a polymerized molecule in regard to the many different monomeres possible, as well as to the presence of different sets of the flat rings, may have different genetic effects (assuming DNA to be the genetic material; but it would not be difficult to transfer the same idea to the protein if DNA is the template or scaffolding). It seems that Watson and Crick took the step from the molecular to the chromosomal level rather lightly. If we think in terms of a gene molecule, and assume it to be one polymerized DNA, we do not gain much. We should expect innumerable possible permutations of the single gene, with very different actions (the spelled-out code). These do not agree with the genetic facts, which show only a few (20 or 30 are a few in this connection) different actions with only small quantitative differences, the multiple alleles. If, however, we could regard the genic part of the chromosome as a single giant hypermolecule in which the individual subpolymeres (perhaps identical with Mazia's particles?), the parts of the whole, behave as assumed in regard to molecular permutations, we could parallel such a structure with the ideas on segments, patterns, fields, and hierarchy which we have developed. We hope that the biochemists, who, as a rule, hear only of the classic concept of the gene, will get acquainted with these newer ideas and see whether they do not agree more closely with their fact findings.

We have not, thus far, assembled all the theories of position effect which have been proposed, though some of them were mentioned. (My former discussions of this subject are found in Goldschmidt, 1938, 1944, and 1946.) A brief enumeration may suffice:

1. A gene near a chromosomal break mutates. Very few geneti-

cists would accept this today, though the idea crops up again from time to time.

2. A gene produces primary products at its locus in the chromosome, which react with those of other loci. The first reaction will be with the neighboring products; if these are changed by the rearrangement which brings different genes into the neighborhood, a different reaction is produced. More specific is the modification of these theories used by Stern, partly in explanation of the dosage effects (Last, 1948; see below). He assumes that the gene has two independent attributes: combining power for a substrate, and the efficiency with which the substrate is converted into gene product. The position effect then is the disadvantage of the gene in the new position in regard to access to the substrate with consequent decrease in gene product. In the Dubinin effect, the advantage of the allele in the normal chromosome comes also into play.

Even if we assume that genic action takes place in this way (we shall return to this point in the next chapter, when discussing Pontecorvo's and Lewis' ideas), we do not understand why the effect is never anything but the typical mutant effect of the assumed gene and not at times something quite different, though in Stern's formulation a plus-minus effect is assumed. I cannot help feeling that this is nothing but a pseudochemical circumscription of the phrase "position of the gene," and we shall see later in the chapter on dosage that Stern himself has moved away from these notions.

3. Our own interpretation is presented in this chapter and is based upon replacing the gene by a chromosomal pattern.

4. A completely different theory has been proposed by Ephrussi and Sutton (1944). After showing that a theory involving chemical interactions at the surface of the chromosome does not work, they conclude that one must look for a structural hypothesis. This means that some change in the physical state of the chromosome must be involved. Muller (1935*b*) had already discussed such a possibility pointing to the forces of attraction between different chromosomes. If a similar force should act between different loci, a kind of stress could be produced by abnormal neighborhoods which would result in distortions and therefore change of chemical action of the gene. (We might think of such "distortions" as mentioned in the quotation from Mothes, I 3 C *c ee bbb*.) Following these ideas of Muller, Ephrussi and Sutton argue: Recent work on the myosine molecule has shown that a fibrous protein exercises an enzymatic property

when stretched. It is now assumed that the synaptic association of chromosomes in Diptera leads to a stretching of chromosomal molecular structure. The presence of a rearrangement may lead, through changes in the pairing condition, to modifications in the state of stress in the immediate vicinity of breakage points.

I do not think that a more detailed discussion of this hypothesis is needed. The paired condition does not exist outside the group of the Diptera, but position effect does. The group of facts presented in the foregoing pages lends no support to the hypothesis and does not derive any explanation from it. The former discussion shows that it is not possible to take position effect as a kind of freakish and specialized feature which has to be explained away rather than understood. It shows that position effect, mutation, chromosomal structure, and the theory of the gene are closely intertwined aspects of the nature of genic material and therefore must be explained as a whole. Thus I do not think that this theory helps us to understand the facts as they are known now. However, this type of theory, if separated from the no longer tenable classic theory of the gene, is of the same general structure required for our discussion here: it stresses what may be called field actions within the chromosome, in preference to chemical changes within a supposed gene molecule.

5. A kind of compromise between the genic and non-genic theories of position effect has been proposed by Serra (1949). We have mentioned previously that he considers "heterochromatization" of euchromatin a fact, meaning that heterochromatin is matrix nucleoprotein which may envelop euchromatin and impede its functions, thus leading to the mottling effect. The general idea has been criticized before (I 2 C *c*). It was pointed out that such views do not take care of the non-mottled position effect. We have noted also that Lewis (1950) considers the two types of effects (his S and V effects) as completely different, a point of view which we refuted. Now Serra introduces a completely different explanation for the standard (S) position effect: it is due to the genes being composite and becoming separated into two parts, which can no longer work together as a + allele. This means that a gene which is a composite of subunits breaks up and its parts are relocated at different points, causing inactivation. Rearrangements cause a sequence of genetic materials capable of forming a new gene. This has no equivalent + allele and now can mutate; that is, a position effect results, which is no more than another name for an incipient new gene.

Following up these ideas to encompass mutation also, it is

assumed that the gene is a composite of several blocks, the nemomeres. The functioning of the gene takes place in definite steps, a certain number of levels of functioning, the quantum levels Q (a kind of offspring of my former ideas on gene quantity). There are Q + 1 levels of activity for each gene, Q being in the order of magnitude of 3–10, and level 0 being total inactivation. Now the number of nemomeres is equal to Q (again my old theory of gene quantities—valencies, and their relation to genic action). The nemomeres are joined to each other by relatively weak links, and intergenic links are like intragenic ones. The nemomeres can be activated and reactivated after inhibition by an all-or-none process. Each gene has a haptogene specificity to matrix nucleoproteins and so has the nemogene, and the haptogene (haptene group synthesized by the gene) takes part in the formation of catalysts as primary gene action. Special theories are presented describing how the molecules are parallel and unfolded in the active gene parts (the haptogene sections) and arranged without order otherwise. Without going into further details of the theory of the gene developed here, we realize that the phenomenon of position effect is no better explained than by the other discarded theories. We shall return to this again.

ccc. Pseudoallelism and position effect.—We return now to one of the important features of the position effect segments: all changes at any point of the segments, including rearrangement breaks, deficiencies, invisible point "mutations," produce effects which are allelic to each other. (This, by the way, is what has now become of Serebovsky and Dubinin's intuitive precursor idea of step-allelomorphism; see I 3 C *a.*) Already there is available a considerable group of facts that touch upon the problem and the explanation, as derived above, from a different angle—the facts concerning so-called pseudoallelism. Some of the finest analytical work of recent genetics has gone into the study of the facts in the hands of Lewis, Stadler, Green and Green, Pontecorvo, Roper, Stormont, Laughnan, Irwin, and others. Simultaneously, interpretations have been proposed within the classic theory of the gene, which presently we shall contrast with our own (Goldschmidt, 1946*b*, 1952*a*).

In a general way, the decisive facts are as follows. What had been known as two or more multiple alleles of one locus turned out to be separable by very rare crossover breaks (Lewis, 1941, 1945, 1952). A number of similar cases have since been discovered by Laughnan (1949, 1952*a,b*), Stephens (1948, 1951*a,b*), and others. What had been assumed to be multiple alleles turned out to be separate "genes" with similar but clearly distinguishable effects. In some cases, each has its own series of multiple alleles. The important and unexpected fact is that these mutants behave, nevertheless, like alleles; that is, if one chromosome contains one mutant and the homologous chromosome the other (the same for three mutants), an effect like a homozygous mutant is produced. Since it is assumed that two different "genes" in different position are involved, which, therefore, should not be allelic, the phenomenon has been called "position pseudoallelism" (Lewis). In terms of genes, these facts could be written $\frac{a\,+}{+\,b}$ = mutant type by pseudoallelic action, $\frac{a\ b}{+\,+}$ = normal. Thus strictly adhering to the classic notion, we could also say (Lewis) that the two genes in the one chromosome have no effect, but, if located in two chromosomes, they act like alleles. This was likened to Sturtevant's original description of the position effect of two Bar alleles in such arrangements, a position effect which since has found a different explanation, as we have seen. Therefore, the term position alleles was proposed by Lewis.

It is desirable at this point to realize the logic behind these conclusions. The fact is that there are two different but adjacent mutants, different because they can be separated by crossover, and, in some cases, show slightly different effects and different series of multiple alleles. Both are recessive and therefore normal if heterozygous; but their distinction as two loci breaks down when they are present in a compound and act as alleles. Therefore some special condition must be present which changes the classic relationship of allelism. This special condition may mean that the classic concept of allelism does not suffice. This conclusion is not drawn, but in order to preserve the classic concept it is assumed that it makes a difference, here, whether the two genes are located in the same or in different chromosomes, that is, the old Sturtevant effect for Bar which turned out to be something quite different.

This leads to a further step in the explanation within the classic theory: the two genes (or more of them) have originated by tandem duplication of one. After the duplication, one of the duplicates has assumed a new function (mutated to a new allele), but the old allelism has been retained, thus becoming pseudoallelism. If this effect should disappear, we would face the origin of a new gene, though by definition the new gene would act just like a multiple allele of the old gene, but without allelism. This would require the change of the gene, released from the fetters of allelism, into one with completely new activity. To me both of these happenings after duplication (first postulated by Bridges) appear to be rather mystic. But I realize that some other geneticists have asserted that they have no difficulty in envisaging this.

We may at once oppose to this our own interpretation of the facts (Goldschmidt, 1950*c*). It appears to be a necessary consequence of the idea, which I regard as proved, of the position effect segments, which we discussed at length. If a crossover break could occur within such a segment—and there is no reason why it should not—the described facts of pseudoallelism would be expected. Any two "point mutants," deficiencies, or rearrangement breaks within a segment are allelic, and if two of them, called mutants (which, we know, behave like multiple alleles), are separated by crossing over we get exactly the situation described for pseudoallelism. No position alleles are involved, no position effect in the old sense of Sturtevant, and no pseudoallelism, just ordinary allelism within the new concept of the genic material.

After this general statement of fundamentals, let us consider some of the detailed facts. A number of cases have been described by Lewis (see 1951) which fit exactly into the general description given for two "pseudoalleles." Such are the mutants Star and asteroid, Stubble and stubbloid, white and apricot. More remarkable still are those involving three mutants. There is first the work of Green and Green (1949) on the lozenge locus. Among many lozenge alleles, all of which affect the quantity of eye pigment, the eye structure, and the absence of spermathecae in the female, and all of which behave as a typical series of multiple alleles, three groups could be shown to exhibit a small amount of crossing over (resulting in one normal chromosome and one chromosome with more than one lozenge locus). Thus they behave like individual loci in close proximity, but permit crossover breaks between the pairs of alleles. Nevertheless, they act as alleles. This is best realized if combinations with at least one allele in both chromosomes are compared with those in which one, two, or three alleles are present in only one chromosome. In a standard case of Mendelian inheritance, individuals should all be normal in these constitutions: $\frac{a + c}{+ b +}$, $\frac{a\ b +}{+ + c}$, or $\frac{a\ b\ c}{+ + +}$. Only the last is normal, however; the others show the compound lozenge effect: a, b, and c behave as pseudoalleles. This disagreement with the elementary rule of genetics is explained by the assumption that a, b, and c, if located in different chromosomes ("trans," according to Pontecorvo), give a position effect, but not if they are in the same chromosomes ("cis"). That is, they are position alleles, in Lewis' terminology. We have stated that this unusual behavior is considered to be the consequence of a, b, and c being repeats of the same original gene which acquired somewhat different actions of the order of multiple alleles but retained their function as alleles, though now separable by crossover breaks. Therefore, according to one definition of the gene, a, b, and c constitute different genes. The logic behind describing this as an effect of position is not quite clear, since alleles should be located in different chromosomes. It is based, I assume, on the original explanation of the Bar case as due to unequal crossing over of a pair of genes, which has since been explained as the position effect of a duplication break (see above). My own explanation, which does not need any of these unusual assumptions, has already been presented. The three (or more yet undiscovered) separable lozenge loci are part of a chromosomal section in which every visible or non-visible change produces an allelic effect, as shown in many instances. Recently, Chovnick and Fox (1953) tried to obtain more information by studying the antigenic properties of these lozenge alleles. They found differences but not pseudoallelism of the different properties. Whatever the reason for this, it is clearly not a problem of genic structure, as the authors seem to believe, but of the chemistry of action involved, which we know is somewhat different for antigenic properties in allelic condition (see blood groups) from those found in other pairs of alleles, for example, independent action of both partners. I think, therefore, that it is an error to draw conclusions upon the underlying theory from such facts. At this point in our analysis we shall not discuss possible chemical explanations, but shall do so later.

Another well-analyzed set of three "pseudoalleles" is Lewis' (1951) work on the "bithorax" group of mutants, which affect the metathoracic segment of *Drosophila,* in the extreme case making the metathorax resemble a mesothorax. Each of the separated loci has its specific, multiple allelic type effect, and in addition may itself have a number of multiple alleles. Further, the pseudoallelic effects of the compounds—the so-called position allelism—parallel those described for the lozenge alleles. At the first locus (separable by crossing over at 58.8 of the third chromosome) three recessive alleles are found; at the second locus (0.02 unit to the right) a dominant Bx is found; and at the third locus (0.01 unit to the right), another recessive.

A third case with three members has been found by Roper

(1950) and Pontecorvo (1952*a,b*; 1953) for biochemical mutants of *Aspergillus,* namely, three adjacent loci affecting biotin synthesis (bi). Again the "position allelism" (to use Lewis' term in a purely descriptive way) was ascertained. A comparable case in *Neurospora,* affecting synthesis of nicotinic acid, has been reported by Bonner (1950).

It would be of great interest to know whether cases of pseudoallelism involving more than three units exist. With the rigid methods available in *Drosophila,* no such cases have yet been found. Only one group of facts is known the explanation of which I expect to find through a larger series, meaning, in my way of looking at it, a larger chromosomal segment of allelic action. These are the facts described for blood groups in cattle (see Stormont *et al.,* 1951; Irwin, 1951; Stormont, 1950). There are more than thirty distinct antigenic factors, each behaving as a Mendelian factor toward its absence. They are arranged in subgroups, some of which are known in different combinations while others exist only in definite combinations. For example, the antigenic property called K appears only with B and G as the complex BGK, while B, G, or BG can exist separately. The details may be described in different ways: as a group of closely linked genes, as a set of multiple alleles, or as a set of "subgenes" of a single locus. Finally, a non-genetic explanation by multiple reactions of the same antigen is possible. There is a strong suspicion I think—Irwin has not overlooked this—that pseudoallelism in Lewis' terminology, with a considerable number of separable effects, is involved. A proof of the type of the *Drosophila* cases is hardly possible; the main obstacles are the numbers needed to demonstrate crossing over, and the peculiarity of loci producing antigens, which exhibit not compound effects but separate effects for each allele.

We turn now in more detail to the interpretation of the group of facts under discussion. The hypothesis that pseudoallelism—if we use this now generally accepted term as a brief characterization of the entire group of facts without accepting the implied meaning—is the consequence of duplication of a gene without loss of allelic action, provided the partners are located in different chromosomes, is considered to be strengthened by cytological facts. Lewis has pointed out that in three cases of two "position alleles" the salivary gland chromosomes show doublets, capsules of two bands of typical configuration. This is true for white-apricot (see also McKendrick and Pontecorvo, 1952), Stubble-stubbloid, and Star-asteroid, which seems to agree with Bridges' notion of repeats. Another case is vermilion, according to Green (1954). The details (Lewis, 1952), however, are not as clear as such a general statement may suggest. In Stubble-stubbloid there are two bands not forming a capsule and not completely equal. Still less convincing is the bithorax situation (fig. 12). Here the section in question shows a doublet (89E1–2) and the bithorax locus is assumed to be "in the immediate vicinity of, if not within" this doublet. "The locus of bithoraxoid is most probably in the adjoining 89E3–4 doublet, although the possibility that it lies one or two bands to the right of this structure is not

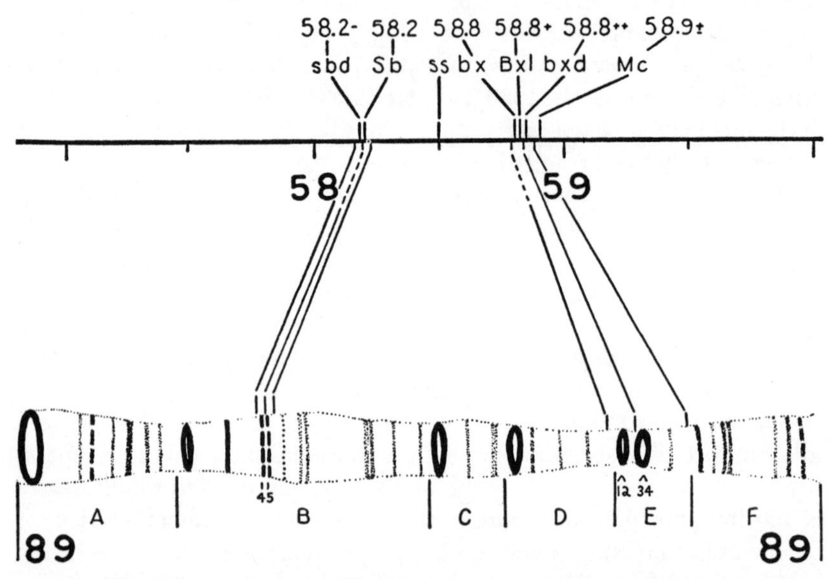

Fig. 12. Section from middle of right arm of third chromosome of *D. melanogaster* showing location of pseudoallelic series of bithorax (bx), bithoraxoid (bxd), and Bithorax dominant (Bxl). (From Lewis, 1951; reproduced by permission of the author.)

excluded. The two doubles of subdivision 89E are possibly partially homologous to one another, in the sense that they frequently appear as one coalesced structure" (Lewis, 1951). The theory of repeats, it seems to me, should lead us to expect a clear-cut triplet here as the proper location for the "genes." The foregoing description by Lewis seems to fit much better the idea of a chromosomal segment in which whatever happens on a microscopic or submicroscopic level produces an allelic effect. In the present case, Lewis excluded the presence of visible rearrangements. He produced, however, by X-raying, a number of rearrangements with a break left of the region just described which showed an extreme bx phenotype as position effect, as expected within our interpretation.

The question arises now whether some further argument for one or the other genetic interpretation can be derived from a study of the different phenotypic effects of the "pseudoalleles." This problem was first put by Pontecorvo (1952*a,b*); see also Roper (1950; and in Pontecorvo, 1952, 1953). We have mentioned that they found cases resembling those of pseudoallelism in *Drosophila* in the mold *Aspergillus* involving synthesis of biotin and para-aminobenzoic acid. The experiments were performed upon the hypothesis that "the action of genes is in some way mediated by corresponding enzymes, either each gene playing a part in the synthesis of each enzyme, or on the conditions for the enzyme to act, including structural organization." Should these enzymes, by acting on a series of reactions of millimicromolar order, be arranged in proximity to one another, vestiges of this spatial organization might be reflected in the corresponding genes. Thus the positive result for two cases of mutants affecting different steps of synthesis of one substance made Pontecorvo think (with emphasized caution) that "one of the ways in which genes are clustered along the chromosomes is that of small assembly lines of those genes which are involved in successive steps of the metabolism of a scarce, ephemeral or non-movable intermediate."

Pontecorvo realizes that the facts may be interpreted in two different ways (which are those of Lewis and myself), and in his latest review (1953) draws the following conclusions from his extensive work with the biotin alleles: "Two explanations at present seem possible. The first, and less likely, is that the results are convalidating the working hypothesis which prompted the investigation. The wild type alleles at the three bi loci would then control different biochemical reactions, the differences not being detected by the tests used. The wild type alleles would function normally only when they were all three on one and the same chromosome. This would be the case if the intermediates in the reactions, controlled by the wild type alleles were labile, or nondiffusible, or present in very low concentration. Thus the unexpected phenotypes would be explained." The essentials of the second and more plausible hypothesis are that "the gene as a working unit in physiological action is based on a chromosome segment larger than either the unit of mutation or recombination. Mutation at different sites in the biotin gene gives at least three, and possibly many, mutant alleles, any one of which inactivates the gene. In some cases recombination between alleles will be possible. The phenotype of the double heterozygote in repulsion is then as expected, since, in this diploid, both biotin genes are inactivated by mutations at different sites. Assembly of all the normal parts of the gene on a single chromosome is necessary for the normal functioning of the gene." Needless to say, Pontecorvo does not use the term "gene" in the classic sense, and thus agrees with my conclusions at many points.

Recently Green (1954) has studied a new case of pseudoallelism at the vermilion locus. He finds that the two "genes" respond differently to the action of specific suppressors; this indicates to him that the pseudoalleles are really two different genes. This conclusion presupposes that multiple alleles cannot show such different relations to suppressor action. But I have shown in another case (the svr^{pol} alleles; Goldschmidt, 1945*a*) that within an allelic series different alleles may have different qualities as suppressors. If this is possible, there is no reason why the reaction *to* suppressors (as opposed to reaction *of* suppressors) should not differ among alleles.

It seems that in microörganisms much additional evidence of the same type is available. Kaplan (1952) has reviewed a considerable series. Besides the mutants in *Aspergillus* and *Neurospora* already cited, he emphasizes the streptomycin-resistant mutants of *Escherischia coli* (Demerec *et al.*, 1949*b*, 1950*a*). It seems that there is a rather large series of closely associated loci for different degrees of resistance, concentrated in a small region of the chromosome map. Kaplan accepts for these facts my interpretation in terms of a chromosomal segment, which he calls "isophenic segments" as opposed to "genes," a term which might be adopted.

In the present discussion we have emphasized cases in which a chromosomal segment was involved in different steps of chemical synthesis, though formerly we discussed pseudoalleles which showed definite morphological effects. It may be added at this point that cases exist in which it must be supposed that the causes for different but closely related morphological effects are located within such a segment. (The facts will be discussed also in a later reference to chromosome sections.) We have called attention to the work of Dunn, Gluecksohn-Schoenheimer, and others on tail mutations in the mouse. A series has been discovered in which the members are all closely linked, though a crossover analysis is rather difficult. A lucid discussion of the implications has been presented by Gluecksohn-Schoenheimer (1949*a*) and Gluecksohn-Waelsch (1951). Generally speaking, these mutants T, t^0, and Ki affect the notochord-mesoderm material in development, but at different times and in different ways. Thus one chromosomal section is concerned in the determination of one basic feature of development. Actually, many more such loci are known in the same region of the chromosome and no other kinds of mutants. Obviously, these facts are of the same order as the others discussed before, and must be explained in the same way.

In this chapter I have refrained from going into the detailed hypotheses of pseudoallelic action which attempt to explain it in terms of genic actions and the primary and secondary substances produced by such actions. The gist of these ideas, which derive more or less from Stern's explanation of position effect, is that nearby loci, originated by duplication, may have assumed consecutive functions in a series of synthetic steps. Since these theories do not have so much to do with the nature of the gene, under discussion here, as with the genic action at the chromosomal site, they will be discussed in a later chapter. But it might be asserted that the mere possibility of construing such theories is in itself a proof for Lewis' phylogenetic theory of pseudoallelism. The quotation from Pontecorvo demonstrates that such a conclusion would be unwarranted. I realize that some workers may think that those action hypotheses, couched in biochemical terms, are a necessary part of the phenomenon. Chovnick and Fox (1953) express this by saying that it is wrong "to use phenotypic and physiological observations as a basis for conclusions regarding transmission phenomena. The practice of operationalism as defined by Bridgman and used by Wright reconciles the apparent contradictions between the physiological and transmission aspects of pseudoallelism."

Whatever this may mean (see also Stadler, 1954; and discussion in I 3 C), I prefer to look at the problem in general terms of the theory of the gene and position effect, in order to unify the genetic and cytogenetic facts without being bound to particular ideas on genic action. Thus I shall discuss genic action apart from the present topic. The discussion confirms my opinion that the explanations for the entire group of facts in terms of the classic gene require special assumptions for every part of the phenomenon—for the similarity but also the diversity of the individual alleles, for their different actions whether in the same or different chromosomes. My interpretation takes care of all aspects of the problem without special hypotheses *ad hoc* and, in addition, links this problem closely with the understanding of position effect, thus integrating the facts in a general system of the pattern and function of the genic material of the chromosomes. In both interpretations, the problem of action of the genic material enters. (We shall return to this in the proper chapter.) In my opinion, the interpretation based upon the classic gene and pseudoallelism requires quite a series of assumptions in regard to the fate, location, sequence, and interaction of the reaction products and, in addition, phylogenetic considerations as exemplified in Lewis' elaborate discussion. In my way of looking at the facts, any interpretation of genic action also covers the facts of the present discussion.

A final word about terminology. The term "pseudoallelism" has had such wide acceptance that it can hardly be replaced, though it implies a definite interpretation, just as the term "position effect" does. Other terms proposed are "semi-allelic" (Muller, 1949; Komai, 1950), "twin genes" (Komai, 1950), and "isophene segment" (Kaplan, 1952). Laughnan (1952*b*) has proposed "pair-alleles," which he thinks contains the notions both of close linkage and similar phenotypic effects. Of course he is considering the "anomalous" situation of side-by-side arrangement of genes instead of the usual opposite orientation. This would mean that a rare, not typical phenomenon is involved, based upon duplication of a locus. He thinks that this view does not necessarily require the particulate gene, but would also work with our segments of mutant action. I have already expressed my disagreement with such views. We shall see whether the term "pseudoallelism" can still be replaced or will remain in spite of mistaken inferences, just as "position effect" and "cell" have remained.

ff. On allelism

In the present discussion the term "allelism" and its meaning have played a considerable role. We may consider this phenomenon basic for genetics and try to endow it with a definite meaning. As a rule, we take allelism for granted. Genes appear in pairs of alleles. Mendelian segregation as well as crossing over work with pairs of alleles. So does the elementary cytological aspect of genetics in which the synapsing points of the homologous chromosomes are in some way identified with a pair of alleles. Also, the secondary phenomena of Mendelism like dominance, dosage relations, deficiencies, multiple alleles, and multiple factors deal invariably with pairs of alleles, and so does any theory of mutation. Therefore it is of fundamental importance to know what allelism means; this knowledge, if acquired, would necessarily include the theory of mutation.

We are not interested here in a definition of allelism, which could be derived from the elementary facts of cytogenetics, but in the difference between the partners in a pair of alleles, and the problem of why the relation between a pair of alleles is so different from that between different loci.

In classic genetics—apart from the presence-absence theory or its later modifications—a pair of alleles is the result of one gene mutating to its allele, and allelism is thus a matter of descent. Rather different meanings have been assigned to this relation. First, it was the absence of the gene which was allelic to its presence (Bateson). When multiple alleles were discovered, a partial absence was assumed. This is not different from the idea (Goldschmidt, 1917*a*, 1920*a*) that a gene is a group of molecules and that mutation consists in changing the quantity of the gene, thus making alleles different quantities of the same substance. We have discussed the recent revival of this idea by Serra in the form of gene quanta, subsections of the gene with specific structure which individually can produce haptene groups; mutation, then, denotes this production by only a part of the substructures. In the course of our discussion we shall meet, or have already met with, facts which favor the quantitative idea of allelic relationship: the dosage experiments; the behavior of loci opposite a deficiency; the deficiencies caused by irradiation; some, though not all, facts relating to multiple alleles; and many facts of phenogenetics, as discussed in detail in Goldschmidt (1927, 1938*a*).

Opposed to this quantitative view of allelism is the qualitative one, which has been expressed in different ways by various authors, too many to be all recounted. One position is that the chromosome is a giant protein molecule; the genes, side chains or prosthetic groups; and mutants, replacement of the prosthetic group by a similar but different group. Another view is that the gene is a single molecule, and a mutant either a stereoisomere or the replacement of one radical by a different one. A variant is that doubling of the gene requires a template and that a mutant is the result of a small failure in the exact duplication of the molecule by a little mishap in the template mechanism. The result might be the absence of a radical or prosthetic group or a stereoisomeric pattern change within the molecule. An interesting variant has been mentioned by Haldane (1954), that between two copying actions the genic material has changed so that it cannot be copied exactly with the available materials. Somewhat related, though different in detail, is the concept based on the idea that DNA is the genic substance and the recent views of the constitution of this molecule (Watson and Crick, 1953). According to such views, a mutation would mean a change in the relative number and order of purine and pyramidine rings (but the difficulty is that the same type of process would have to account for mutation of the gene and for differences between different genes).

We have considered in an earlier section (I 3 B *a*) the mutation theory of McElroy and Swanson (1951), derived from the existence of intermediate states and delayed mutation subject to a temperature coefficient, and requiring the application of chemical kinetics to explain the change of state by activation. This led also to a theory of allelism which is essentially of the stereoisomeric type. The assumption is that a gene, being a complex protein molecule, can exist in many states differing in geometrical relationships and stability. Only some of these can be recognized as different alleles, namely, if the state is combined with a visible effect. The possibilities of such stereoisomeric changes, directly or through an intermediate condition, are almost unlimited. But they may be influenced or governed by preferred intermediate states, the height of energy barriers, and the interdependence or independence of different sites in a large molecule. The hypothesis deals with an intramolecular pattern which is easily changed without material change, and no difficulty will be found in applying this hypothesis also to a supermolecular pattern.

All these hypotheses, except possibly the last, require a gene pair at a definite locus in the chromosome, and allelism is the consequence not only of this identical location but also of the basic chemical identity of a pair of alleles (except in the presence-absence theory and its derivatives). Therefore, it should be a corollary of this view that different genes cannot be allelic because they are chemically different. However, if by chance or by origin through translocation two genes at different loci were alike chemically and thus could have mutants for which the same is true, they should be allelic. Moreover, they should act as a series of multiple factors, actually polygenes in the sense of Mather, and in combination show additive and dosage effects. Furthermore, such polygenes would fall by their origin under the definition of position alleles (Lewis) and would have to exhibit all their features, though located in different chromosomes. Actually, the so-called position alleles, assumed to be the result of duplication (triplication, etc.) of one gene, fulfill only one of these conditions: namely, behaving as alleles with no trace of dosage action. Thus none of these theories offer a very promising explanation of the nature of allelism.

Our modern theory of the gene considers a mutant to be a change of order or pattern on a supermolecular level within a section of the chromosome of different, overlapping, and not strictly delimited size. Since a position effect is, under this theory, the same as a mutant and thus also as an allele, allelism means any deviation from a normal sequence of parts within these overlapping sections; that is, no chemical or quantitative change on the molecular level, but rather a change in the arrangement of parts within an otherwise identical field, the normal condition being that most frequent in the species.

Thus far we have considered allelism only from the point of view of substance and location, not of action. Actually, alleles have a similar action which differs only quantitatively in the two alleles. (The only apparent exception is the difference between the alleles spineless-aristopedia in *Drosophila,* which requires an explanation in terms of thresholds in order to fit it into the general scheme.) As a rule, alleles in the heterozygote of a diploid organism work together. This means that these alleles in the two different chromosomes must produce something which reacts with the same substrate in such a way that the two primary actions are additive or summative (this includes also one positive plus one negative action) *ceteris paribus* (no special modifiers). The result may vary (see below under dosage and dominance) according to the threshold conditions of the entire system. The resultant will be either half of the normal action, that is, a pure dosage effect, or any condition between full effect (dominance) and pure dosage effect. (This may be observed in the presence of isoalleles; see below.) Within the classic theory we might think that the action of alleles is a function of the gene and its nature. We shall see, in the chapter on dosage effects, that a system of classification of genes has actually been built upon this assumption. We think that this is an erroneous conclusion. The genes (or, better, mutant loci) are not different in regard to their general type of structure and action. What is different is the developmental system which their action primarily and secondarily affects, with all its special conditions of substrate, thresholds, and velocities.

But the possibility remains that the two alleles have a primary action which is not at once submerged in the additive effect upon the substrate. Moreover, it might remain independent for some time for each allele, which might mean a reaction first near, later away from, the chromosomal site. In the extreme case of individual allelic action, a condition would be reached as known for the blood-group alleles or, possibly, for the sickle-cell anemia loci, where each allele controls a different globin in the hemoglobin molecule (Pauling *et al.*, 1949). For the blood-group loci the heterozygote shows the products (the agglutinogens) of both alleles. (But this is not the entire story, as the quantity of agglutinogen, e.g., of A, is different in A/B from that in A/O.)

It is probable that a comparable type of effect works in such cases as the Sturtevant effect in Bar, where the presence of three rearrangement breaks in one chromosome and the absence of breaks in the other chromosome produce a quantitatively different position effect from that with two breaks in each chromosome. The critical problem of allelism is still far from a satisfying solution. But I believe that the recent ideas on the nature of the gene will help future work on the problem.

d. Further members of the hierarchy

aa. Larger segments

In the introduction to the present chapter I showed that the theory of the organization of the genic material within the chromosome, independent of corpuscular genes, requires a complete hierarchical order of active chromosomal fields up to and including the entire chromosome. This means that the action of genic material in the chromosome may be based at different moments upon any segment of a chromosome acting as an individual field, from a submicroscopic section below the size of a salivary chromosome band to the sections just discussed, to larger sections of unified field action which may be delineated or overlapping, to still larger field units which finally may embrace the whole chromosome. If the molecular structure of the chromosome, starting from the centromere, is marked as 1 → n, the functional units in the course of genic action in development may be any possible fields, as indicated by the braces in the diagram.

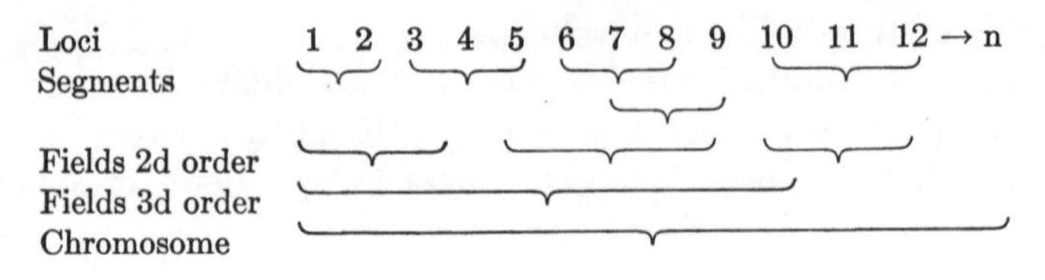

I realize how difficult it is for the geneticist thinking in terms of individual genes to visualize this. Mather (1946, 1948), who joined me in these deliberations, overcame the mental difficulty by calling the chromosomal sections of genetic action of varying size "fields of coöperation," and used as an illustration the diagram reproduced in figure 13, which is essentially the same as the one above. Of course the word "coöperation," though conveying a rather plastic view of the idea, involves the danger of being understood as additive actions of individual genes. This is not what is meant; rather, it is a

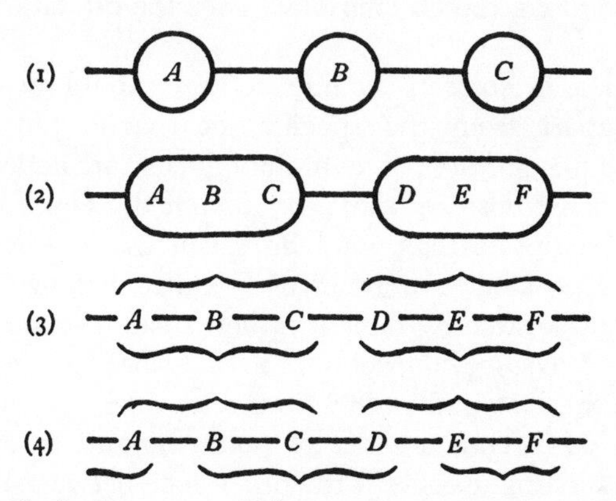

Fig. 13. Mather's discussion of chromosomes and genes: "In 1 and 2 the genes are units of physical structure of the chromosome as well as physiological units of action. They may be likened to either simple (1) or composite (2) beads on a string. In 3 and 4 the genes are not delimited in any special physical way. The parts of one gene are related physically in the same way as adjacent parts of neighbouring genes. The gene is then delimited only as a physiological unit, by the special co-operation or integration of its parts in action, as indicated by brackets. In 3 the fields of co-operation, and hence the division of the chromosome into genes, are constant throughout the life cycle. In 4 the fields of co-operation, and hence the division of the chromosome into genes, vary during the life cycle."

field action which in an electromagnetic field, for example, may also be described in terms of coöperation of the innumerable points of the field. I have occasionally used another simile which may help the visualization if not taken too literally. If we study the effect of light waves upon an organism, we may find definite actions of ultraviolet light of one single wave length which we compare to the workings of a single genetic locus. We might then find actions which are essentially the same over a number of wave lengths, say within the ultraviolet. Other actions may be typical for the entire ultraviolet or other part of the spectrum; still other light effects may be based upon still larger spectral sections, for example, the yellow-green and, finally, some upon white light, that is, the entire spectrum. In this simile we compare the single wave length to the mutant locus; a few wave lengths, to our chromosomal sections of allelism; the other light effects, to still larger sections of the chromosome; and, finally, white light represents the whole chromosome. The simile would be still more impressive if it were worked out further for chemical effects, in this case, photochemical ones. But, together with the diagrams, it may help to illustrate the concept of a hierarchy of fields of action along the chromosome. (See the quotation from Mazia, I 2 B *a.*)

If the idea is correct, genetic actions should be found which imply that, apart from the specific local action involved in the definition and recognition of a mutant locus, an action of a larger section of a chromosome must be assumed. The following facts (which can be duplicated) may be given as an example of what I mean. We know that a number of so-called homoeotic mutants in *Drosophila* are located within a rather small section of the third chromosome of *Drosophila:* polycomb ca. 45.0, proboscipedia 47.7, tetraptera 51.3, aristopedia 48.5, bithorax 58.8, ss-suppressor 63.7, pointed wing 94.1. Thus a series of point mutants is accumulated in a section of a chromosome (with other loci between) all of which affect the determination of segmental appendages (and, in part, segmental determination itself). This may mean that the segment of the third chromosome as a whole (a field) is vitally concerned with the processes of segmental determination. These processes can be interfered with by changes at different points within the field (the mutants just mentioned) or outside the field (the 2d chromosome mutants tetraltera 42.5 and ophthalmopedia 45.0, obviously members of another field). The loci within the section, the field, if not mutated, do not individually control the development of the respective imaginal discs so as to prevent them from sidestepping, while the mutant locus produces the sidestep. Rather, the whole intact section controls certain parts of the processes of normal development of the discs; but a disturbance of this action at individual points inside this field or inside another similar field (in the 2d chromosome) leads to upsets of development of the discs, all of the homoeotic type but individually different, actually much more different than is the case in the "pseudoallelic" disturbances within a segment described previously.

We should expect to find more such facts in support of the general idea of the hierarchy of fields. A considerable number of cases have been reported which point in this direction. Some of them certainly belong to the group of pseudoallelic sections (see review by Komai, 1950), while others will probably fall under the head of the present discussion. Unfortunately, decisive tests are difficult in most organisms, and therefore it is only pointed out that Dunn and Caspari's (1945) T factors affecting the mousetail (see also Dunn and Gluecksohn-Waelsch, 1952), and Nabours' (see 1950) finding that all the many mutants affecting the color pattern of the grouse locust are located in a definite section of one chromosome, probably belong to the phenomenon under discussion. (See later chapter on pleiotropy.)

At this point what looks like a serious objection should be registered. It is known that a normal or a mutant locus when transposed into a new position in a different sector of the same or a different chromosome still acts as before. For the normal locus this has been discussed as the covering effect. Of course we are excluding here the presence of a position effect break near the locus in question, which would result in a reversal of its action. If the normal or mutational functioning of a locus in a different setup of chromosomal pattern is a general fact, as it seems, how does this fit into the scheme of the hierarchy of fields? It must be realized at once that such transpositions involve a rather large segment of a chromosome (measured with a salivary chromosome yardstick). The majority of the mutants studied in such cases are those involved within the segments of mutant action, segments which are relatively so small that they remain intact in such transpositions. Thus, as far as the segment and its pattern, or changed pattern in the mutant, are concerned, nothing has changed. Only the chromosomal actions which are bound to the larger fields should be different in such transpositions and translocations. It may be safely assumed that the larger fields act upon more basic (i.e., earlier) developmental processes, while the smaller segments are concerned with the control of late, more or less superficial features of development. Hence we would expect that, in most transpositions, and so on, of larger segments, the usual effects would not be found, as with small segments, but we should rather expect abnormalities or lethality. It is true that the ill effects of heterozygous or homozygous translocations may often be due to position effects. However, when major damage like lethality is found, we may attribute it to the causes just stated: change of pattern of larger sectors, that is, fields of action. It has never been explained why homozygous translocations are so frequently lethal.

Here a simple explanation becomes visible. Systematic experiments with the above-mentioned sections of homoeotic mutation might give surprising results. This assumes that most of these mutants are euchromatic, while we had concluded that podoptera is a heterochromatic effect. I wonder whether the detailed data of McClintock's work on variegation in maize, when available, will supply such information.

bb. The chromosome as a whole

The last point of the argument should be, whether the hierarchical order of the possible sections or fields of genetic action would lead to its logical conclusion, eventual unified field action of an entire chromosome. We have mentioned the work of Lima-de-Faria, who demonstrated a visible chromosome structure involving a gradient-like arrangement of the chromomeres which requires the presence of some organizing field covering an entire chromosome. It is very difficult to imagine genetic facts that could prove the existence of such a chromosomal field. Loss or addition of entire chromosomes involves a change in genic balance, and observed effects may or may not be entirely due to this upset. Cases in which actions of entire chromosomes are suspected, as in sex determination, might be due to such special features as heterochromatic action (see discussion in I 2 C *d ee*) or simply to complete linkage of different loci. The so-called *Drosophila artificialis,* with its reshuffling of entire chromosome arms (Dubinin, 1936), would not be expected to be different, in view of the well-known independence of arms in this genus. The same might be true of plants like *Datura* in which exchanges of complete, unitary arms seem to occur. The best hope lies with pericentric inversions in chromosomes in which two arms right and left of a centromere can be considered as independent chromosomes, as in the *Drosophila* species. But it is not certain that a visible effect of such rebuilt chromosomal arms, if found, must be attributed to a chromosomal effect rather than to an ordinary position effect, as already discussed for other translocations. Only if it were found that all such inversions lead to one and the same type of large effect (e.g., lethality in the egg stage or gross malformations) could a decision in favor of chromosomal action be reached.

A group of facts of indirect importance for this problem is found in the comparative cytology of the species of *Drosophila* (excellent review in White, 1945). Sturtevant and Novitski (1941) and their followers (see details in Patterson and Stone's book, 1952) have shown that the configuration of the chromosome sets in *Drosophila* species can be understood largely on the basis of a definite primary set of rods and dots which can unite in different ways to form V's. Certainly in the course of phylogeny the intimate structure of these chromosomal units must have changed considerably, and it may be conceived (as it is by classic geneticists) that this intrachromosomal genic change, perhaps along with duplications, deletions, and transpositions, suffices as an explanation of the evolution of these species in spite of the morphological constancy of the chromosomal units. The different rearrangements of the same basic arms would, then, be without any genetic meaning. This might mean that the reshuffling of the arms is due to chance or to some exigencies of the mitotic mechanism, whatever the special mechanism may be in the individual instances. It is rather difficult, at least to my way of thinking, to dispense with such a typical and clear-cut process of cytological evolution by considering it without meaning, a chance product, or, at best, a means of keeping a group of genes together because of some selective advantage. To work out the latter idea in detail would, I think, lead to a hopeless welter of hypotheses *ad hoc.* I realize, of course, that the classic theory of the gene requires either some such explanation as that just hinted, or an assumption of chance happenings without meaning. If, however, our way of looking at the genic structure of the chromosome is accepted, this chromosomal phylogeny may have a deep meaning in the sense of producing new patterns of action of the entire chromosomes, involved in basic processes of development, needed for evolution on the superspecific level. It should be added that in these changes of the chromosome sets some pericentric inversions and translocations also have been involved (see Patterson and Stone, 1952). This does not affect the general argument.

There are a number of facts already available which one day may turn out to be connected with chromosomal actions. Why are so many homozygous translocations lethal which do not change anything in genic content according to the classical theory of the gene? A position effect, as an explanation, is difficult. It works well in mutant effects of translocations (e.g., Blond, Xasta in *Drosophila*). The same is true of vitality changes and small generalized effects, as emphasized in a previous chapter. But complete lethality as a typical effect seems to be on a different level. Although the possibility of a homozygous position effect for a lethal locus cannot be denied, it sounds rather odd. A systematic quest for physiological differences between organisms with normal chromosome sets and derived ones with translocations changing the chromosomal unit (e.g., stocks with a part of the X attached to the 4th chromosome, if homozygous viable or with pericentral inversions) might lead to unexpected results. The work thus far done in *Drosophila* (reviewed in Patterson and Stone's book) did not consider possibilities of the kind presented here and was concerned only in the effects upon crossing over in pericentric inversions, and in phylogenetic possibilities in the case of chromosomal fusions and translocations. The only argument at present available is that such fusions would hardly have persisted in phylogeny if they did not produce some new genetic effect.

D. CONCLUSIONS: THE MODERN THEORY OF THE GENE

The foregoing discussion contains all the conclusions which, in my opinion, should be drawn from recent developments in genetics regarding the nature of the genetic material. Since the presentation of numerous details obscures the simple sequence of ideas, the argument will be worked out once more, together with a few additional facts and deliberations. The oldest idea concerning the gene and its mutation is Bateson's presence-absence theory, meaning that a mutant is the absence of a gene. After much discussion the theory was abandoned, mainly because of the discovery of the ubiquity of the existence of multiple alleles (also because of the alleged frequency of reverse mutations). Whatever these were, the existence of different grades of absence could not at that time be defended. This is a valid argument for the classical theory of the gene if one accepts the idea, for example, that the gene is a single molecule.

But there is also the possibility of making different assumptions about the nature of the gene which would still allow the working of the presence-absence theory. If the gene should consist (as I formerly supposed) of a definite number of molecules, the loss of one or more could be the mutation process. It might then still be claimed that a mutant is a deficiency—either a total or a partial one, the latter assuming a divisible gene or a gene with some substructure—and this has actually been done by Stadler (see 1933). The facts which have been discussed above put the old Batesonian idea in a different light. There is no longer a gene molecule but a definite molecular pattern in a definite section of a chromosome, and any change of pattern (position effect in the widest sense) changes the action of the chromosomal part and thus appears as a mutant. Multiple alleles are no longer different conditions of a single gene but changes in pattern within small sections of a chromosome which are not necessarily of the same extent but may overlap. These changes may be repatterning by rearrangement breaks within or near the overlapping sections; they may be repatterning by loss of parts (deficiency) of a section of different size; they may be submicroscopic rearrangements like inversions and, even more probably, submicroscopic deletions. The latter might be called absences in the sense of Bateson and also Stadler; but it is not the absence which counts, but the disturbance of a definite pattern, a position effect in our description of this phenomenon. The deficiency, microscopic or submicroscopic, does not act by an absence of something but as one of the different ways in which a definite pattern, necessary for normal function, can be changed. It is thus not different in action and causation from any other rearrangement. Anybody who wishes to see these things clearly should look closely at the fact, now proved in a number of instances reported before, that homozygous deficiencies for a locus or "gene" produce the same effect as the mutant locus, and, also, of any other position effect of a break nearby. Since the facts cannot be doubted any longer, and since it is a logical procedure to explain them by a single concept embracing the entire field of manifestations and structure of the genic material, I cannot see how we can make progress without adopting ideas based upon patterns and their changes as underlying the behavior of the genic material.

I must criticize severely the statements, found in the literature, which maintain that only a few geneticists follow me (which is becoming less true every day), though at the same time it is acknowledged that the theory of the gene is in a state of crisis. If a way out of the "crisis" has been shown, why not try it instead of glancing backward longingly at the good old gene? I think that this attitude is just as bad as the formerly quoted pronunciamento that geneticists who have different ideas from the classic ones do not know what they are talking about.

At this point mention should be made of a recent very fine discussion of the opposing points of view by Stadler (1954), in a posthumous paper. He believes that the difference can be solved by introducing Bridgman's idea of operational procedure as opposed to hypothetical. (See also Chovnick and Fox, 1953.) This means that a phenomenon cannot be defined in terms of assumed properties beyond experimental determination, but must be defined in terms of the actual operations applied. Thus, operationally, a gene cannot be defined otherwise than as the smallest segment of the "gene string" that is associated with a typical effect. The difference between what I represented as the classic and the modern views would, then, be that the former deals only with the operational, the latter with the hypothetical, gene and, in this sense, both can be right. In view of the facts discussed, I have my doubts whether this philosophical solution of the differences is possible. It seems to me that both views are of the operational type, but the classic one is simply more primitive. This is what I meant when I repeatedly emphasized that all of classic genetics can be described in terms of the corpuscular gene; but, when it comes to the question what this gene is materially, the facts force us to give up this simple notion. Actually, Stadler's own important work is witness to this. But, after all, the question of definitions may be left aside and the problem treated pragmatically.

I mentioned that there are still adherents of the idea that a position effect break makes a nearby gene mutate. It has long since been shown by Dobzhansky, Panshin, and Catcheside that a locus showing position effect may be removed from the break and then ceases to act like a mutant (using the old way of expressing the facts). It might be answered that this involves a return mutation, but such an answer could hardly be taken seriously. The whole idea explodes if the position effect of a deficiency is contemplated, especially the homozygous deficiencies with typical mutant action. The gene which is supposed to mutate to and fro is not there at all. It is the same set of facts, completely ruling out the interpretation of ordinary position effect, which is most popular with authors who try to save the classic concept of the corpuscular gene. They assume that the break, or the new neighborhood in case of translocation or inversion breaks, inhibits the action of the nearby gene so that it does not produce or produces less of its typical reaction product. But if there is no "gene" there? The only way out of this dilemma would be to declare that the deficiency effects are something completely different. Taking the yellow locus as an example, we might say that all residual heredity makes for yellow color but that the gene $+^y$ prevents this. If this gene is taken away, yellow must appear. We must consider all the mutant loci known to act like yellow in order to realize that such an "explanation" amounts to no more than sophistry.

An important role in the detailed discussions was played by the series of more or less small chromosomal sections within which any visible or invisible change of pattern produces a mutant effect. All these effects behave like multiple alleles; but some pattern changes (breaks) at a distance from the section in question (the overlap effect) can still produce the allelic effect. We should have more information on this overlap effect to be certain that it is not different from the effect within the segments. However this may be, the problem remains why pattern changes within the segments are always allelic to each other and those in different segments are not; though the facts of overlap show that the latter is not completely true, but that there is a tapering off of the allelic features beyond the end of the segment. Some authors are content with the answer that the segments are the genes and therefore allelic. Those who are not satisfied with this answer may try to find a solution in terms of genic action. The chemical constitution of each section may be such that its direct products control a master set of reactions leading to an end product which is necessary for a certain developmental step. Pattern changes within the segment do not affect the master reaction as such (just as many stereoisomeres of an active substance might not change its activity). Some other repatterning might impair the master reaction and therefore be more or less lethal (just as some stereoisomeres of an active substance prevent the activity; good examples are found in Ruzicka's work on testosteron isomeres). But most repatterning will produce secondary effects in speed of reaction, quantity of the products, and the like, which become visible in the slight departures in the end product, the visible mutant effect. As allelism relates to this end product, it is the expression of the one untouched master reaction.

Thus far this interpretation would also fit a new definition of the gene as a chromosomal segment within which any change at any point produces an allelic mutant effect and within which, also, crossover breaks may occur. Such a definition would make the gene a more or less large, visible element with a visible substructure. The classic beadlike gene would remain and not only change in size, complication, and divisibility, but also in lack of definite limits (the overlap effect). However, the facts have forced us to turn from an independent, homogeneous corpuscle to an indefinitely limited part of a whole having a typical serial pattern which alone allows for normal function. The logical consequence is that the section, acting as a small field, is itself only a part of a larger field or different fields, also overlapping ones. In terms of the model of function just presented, this would mean that the "master reaction" controlled by the small field, the segment, is related to the still more primary effects of the larger field, as the pattern change within the segment is related to the whole segmental action. This means that a pattern change—mutation—within any segment would not much disturb the action of the next higher member of the hierarchy of fields, but an accumulation of such pattern changes would impair the higher field functions. If the higher members of the hierarchy are concerned with more basic, less specialized developmental processes, the result would be more or less lethality, which agrees with well-known facts.

One of the corollaries of such deliberations would be that the pair, normal allele—mutant allele, would not exist unless the small section in question is considered separately. If the entire chromosome with all possible genic actions is taken into account, the normal allele, the gene of general usage, ceases to be an individual unit. The logical situation can best be grasped by using the one gene—one enzyme theory of genic action only as a good model for our discussion. Because a certain step in the synthesis of a genetically controlled product is prevented from occurring by a mutant—presumably by the absence of the specific enzyme for that step—it is concluded that there is a normal gene that controls the production of this enzyme. We are concerned here only with the extrapolation from a changed action upon the normal action, that is, the conclusion that the absence of the enzyme in the mutant proves that a normal gene produces the enzyme. Now the existence of position effect precludes this conclusion, since the mutant effect is produced without any change of the so-called normal gene. These facts force us to conclude that the presence of the normal order in the entire small field within the chromosome ensures the formation of the proper enzyme. This does not necessitate our calling this field, overlapping with the next one, a normal allele. One or more mutant patterns in the field prevent the formation of an enzyme or its proper function. However, the unchanged pattern is not the property of a delineated body but of a field of action which can shrink or expand according to circumstances (e.g., heterochromatic association). In this sense there is no normal gene. The following simile may help to clarify this position—a simile which, by the way, may contain some element of truth. We compare, in the simile, the chromosome or its parts, described as a hierarchical order of fields, to a single molecule. An ordinary molecule is known to react in a definite way, which we can call its normal action. If, at one point of the molecule, a different radical is substituted, say by methylation or amination, or if only the order of some side chains is changed to a different position, the resulting substituted molecule or stereoisomere may produce completely different reactions. Can we conclude that the point in the molecule at which the substitution was made or at which the order was shifted is in control of the standard reaction of the molecule? In either case, does not the whole molecule react and not its loci? (I repeat that this is meant as a simile. I certainly do not intend to enter upon a chemical discussion on the relation of visible or active properties of a substance to its molecular constitution.)

At this point another argument may be added. It is a necessary corollary of the theory of the gene that there must be an evolution of genes. (See also the chapter on evolution.) A man should certainly have more genes than an amoeba, and therefore a chromosomal phylogeny paralleling an increase in the number of genes should be apparent. Actually, the pattern, size, and number of chromosomes have not changed from protozoa to man. The chromosome complement of some gregarines and relatives, or flagellates, looks exactly like that of higher animals. The size and length of the chromosomes, their intimate structure, behavior in synapsis, and so on are exactly the same as in higher forms. Thus they should contain a similar number of genes. A popular way out of this dilemma would be to say that these protozoan chromosomes contain much inert material. We have already discounted the idea of inert material. Here the only explanation for the preponderance of inert material would be that its function is to keep room in the chromosome for future evolution of new genes! Another way out would be to say that it is not the number of genes which is different but their ability to produce more and more complicated products. This would not agree with the fact that typical products of genic action like vitamins, enzymes, and sterols are more or less alike in all living organisms. I cannot see any way out of this difficulty except the assumption that the evolutionary process within the chromosome means an increase of the diversification within the hierarchical pattern adding more and more chances for permutation within the whole. (We shall return to this subject in the short chapter on evolution.)

It might seem to some diehards that all these discussions are exercises in semantics without any relation to the facts. This is not so, however. The discovery of position effect, of genic actions in the absence of assumed genes (position effect of deficiencies), of visible, relatively large segments of allelism and their overlapping (i.e., variable delineation) force us to re-examine the fundamentals of classic genetics, and we find that they do not suffice for an explanation of these discoveries. Therefore, we must try to develop broader ideas which describe the facts not only in a different terminology but with a basically different mental attitude. In this new way of looking at fundamentals, the atomistic view of collaborating independent units is replaced by a concept of unified action of a field type which results in a hierarchical order of not strictly delimited fields. The formulation of such ideas is necessarily not specific enough to be entirely satisfying. A completely satisfactory theory can be developed only in the future, when biochemists have explored the molecular structure and physical properties of supermolecules, far beyond the size and complication of structure of the largest known units. If the chromosome is not a mechanical assembly of many different molecules, kept together for the sake of equal distribution, but a hypermolecular unit, we must look for a structure in which entire, chemically different nucleoprotein molecules are assembled into a supermolecule after the model of amino acids being assembled into an ordinary protein molecule. The resulting units may have completely unexpected physical and chemical properties which might give specific and detailed meaning to what we can conceive today only in the general terms (e.g., fields) that were used in the discussion. (See, above, the discussion of Mazia's 1954 findings.)

PART II THE CYTOPLASM AS SEAT OF GENETIC PROPERTIES

1

PROLEGOMENA

The nucleus with its chromosomes and genetic material is an integral part of the cell which can function only with the rest of the cell, the cytoplasm and its inclusions and structural parts. The cytoplasm, in contrast, differentiates in development, performs the physiological functions of life, is involved in the processes of growth, movements and shifts, interrelations with neighboring cells, and all the morphological and physiological features which constitute development and differentiation. The facts of genetics prove that all these features of the cytoplasm (i.e., of the cell as a whole) are under the control of the genic material in the nucleus. In such extreme cases as somatic mosaics involving single cells, in which the chromosomal constitution has been changed by elimination of whole chromosomes or parts thereof or by somatic crossing over, the genic control of chemical (pigment) or morphological (e.g., bristles) traits can be seen within a single cell. Thus we are confronted with the problem of the interrelations between genic material in the chromosomes and the effective parts of the cell, the cytoplasm in the broadest sense.

Among these interrelations, the first place is occupied by the removal of the primary products of the genic material from the nucleus into the cytoplasm, the place of their action; and, vice versa, by the entry of the raw materials for nuclear growth and duplication from the cytoplasm. The study of these relations is basic in developmental or physiological genetics dealing with the actions of the genic material in controlling development.

In the present chapter, the cytoplasm enters only as substrate in a broad sense, which includes the specificity of its matter and structure, some parts of which may be just the expression of actual continuity with the ancestral plasms, while other features may be the product of genic action in the original egg cell. We might call the cytoplasmic specificity its hereditary constitution, meaning no more than the fact that the cytoplasm of a fly or lily cell is continuous with the cytoplasm of the ancestral cells and, in this general way, speak of cytoplasmic heredity. (We shall see, below, that this phenomenon exists.) It will then be necessary to separate such ancestral, direct specificity of the cytoplasm from a specificity which already is established in the unfertilized egg under genic control, as can be verified by proper embryological and genetic experimentation. We may reserve the term "cytoplasmic specificity" for the genuine specificity by cytoplasmic continuity with the ancestors, and designate the specificities produced in the egg under genic control as "predetermination," a term in use in experimental embryology, or, as I proposed (Goldschmidt, 1951*a*), as "conditioning of the cytoplasm." The latter phenomenon must show what Toyama (1913) called, rather unfortunately, "maternal inheritance," while the former will show real matroclinous heredity.

There is a condition intermediate between these two types of cytoplasmic specificity, a cytoplasmic condition of specific nature which is not continuous with the ancestral cytoplasm but is induced at a definite moment by external means, experimentally. Such a condition has been called *Dauermodifikation* (Jollos, 1913, 1921). Theoretically, it might result in a lasting change into a new specificity; or it might be diluted in subsequent cell divisions and fade out completely.

Of the three groups of cytoplasmic specificity thus far delineated—specificity through ancestral continuity, through genic conditioning in the egg stage, and through experimental change—only the first may properly be called a type of cytoplasmic heredity. It is characterized as a generalized biochemical and antigenic condition of the cytoplasm as a substrate. This would, therefore, become recognized in genetic experiments, when a shift of genically controlled reactions takes place according to the type of cytoplasm present (usually in reciprocal crosses or in nuclear transplantation). It cannot be expected that such a cytoplasmic effect of a specific substrate could be distinguished in all or even in many of the developmental effects under nuclear control (i.e., Mendelizing traits). Whatever that specificity means biochemically (e.g., serological specificity), it may be assumed that such effects of different cytoplasmic specificity would be shown only in Mendelizing traits that are capable of small but recognizable quantitative variations. The reason for this expectation is that in genetic experimentation only nearly related forms may be successfully crossed and bred to further generations. Cytoplasmic differences of such an order that developmental processes would be changed qualitatively according to the cytoplasm present would be expected only in crosses between species and still higher categories. But they might be recognizable in experiments with merogony and nuclear transplantation.

At this level of what in its entirety is called cytoplasmic inheritance, another problem enters. As a rule we think only of inheritance within the cytoplasm of the egg; and, therefore, all tests for cytoplasmic inheritance are based upon reciprocal crosses. The difference in quantity of egg and sperm cytoplasm is obvious, and it is safe to assume that the sperm usually does not bring any undifferentiated cytoplasm into the egg, or at least not much of it. But this is not true either for non-filiform sperm or for the plant "sperm." We shall see that facts in favor of an action of sperm cytoplasm have actually been found.

Cytoplasmic inheritance could, however, be expected to occur on a higher level than the one just discussed. This would mean that the cytoplasm is not simply diversified as a substrate for genic action, but by itself has a type of hereditary function which is comparable to that of the genic material. This means that the cytoplasm as a whole, the "plasmon" as von Wettstein called it, may determine, without any nuclear interference, specific characters which then exhibit purely matroclinous inheritance independent of whatever nucleus is present. It is imaginable that all transitions exist, from a specific and independent plasmon through many gradations of collaboration with nuclear genic effects to the simple substratum action. The technique for the study of such possibilities is of course the continued backcross among the descendants of reciprocal crosses, thus replacing step by step the proper nucleus by a foreign one in the respective opposite cytoplasm. A large part of the work on so-called cytoplasmic heredity deals with this problem.

A specific type of plasmon action, meaning control of hereditary traits independent of the nucleus, would be established if we could locate visible or invisible self-duplicating structures which are responsible for definite, specific hereditary features. A number of geneticists have used the term "plasmagenes" for these visible or invisible parts, and some of them speak of plasmagenes as an indisputable counterpart of the nuclear genes. I do not think that such an attitude is justified as yet. I have considerable misgivings in regard to the terminology. Though this is a minor point, terminology has a tendency to be suggestive of ideas which may be completely wrong. I do not want to point out that the idea of the gene itself is becoming rather shaky, though we might use the classic term simply for the sake of convenience without going into the details of its meaning. But the gene, or genic material as I prefer to say, is historically so completely linked with the chromosome and Mendelian inheritance that it can only produce confusion if any self-duplicating body or substance is called a gene. Certainly, self-duplication is a prominent feature of the genic material in the chromosomes, but it is not the totality of its properties. If we call all self-duplicating particles genes, we give up an important, well-established, and basic insight into the hereditary process by calling completely different things, with only one feature in common, by the same term, the meaning of which is diluted and made vague. Self-duplicating cell organelles, parasites and symbionts, intermediates between cell structures and symbionts, as which we could describe plastids and probably mitochondria, all become genes. Why not simply speak of self-duplicating cytoplasmic elements of different types, and avoid the danger of advancing unproved theories of the gene as the basic element of the living world by a suggestive terminology? (We shall return to this at the end of the chapter.)

2

THE CYTOPLASM AS SPECIFIC SUBSTRATE

A. MATERNAL INHERITANCE AND CONDITIONING OF THE CYTOPLASM

At first sight Toyama's "maternal inheritance" does not seem to have anything to do with cytoplasmic heredity, for maternal inheritance is simply Mendelian heredity of a character determined in the egg before fertilization. As a result, an apparent F_1 is actually the P generation with the maternal character, while F_2 in the experiment is actually F_1 for the egg character, and so on. This fact, by the way, is sometimes much confused by saying that in this case there is a lag of a whole generation in the action of a gene (e.g., in Darlington and Mather's textbook, 1949). A "gene" can of course not act upon a character of a grown egg cell before this cell is there. To return to the facts: for a trait like the pigmentation of the serosa of the egg (in the silkworm) as studied originally by Toyama and Tanaka and recently by Kikkawa (see 1953), the foregoing characterization covers the entire story, though interesting complications may arise which are due to the chemistry of the product involved. Such is the case in the work of Caspari (1933) on a pigment-reducing mutant in *Ephestia,* which acts during the whole larval period, though it starts in the unfertilized egg; the reason is that the mutant affects the production of kynurenine needed for pigment synthesis. Some such variants which have to do with transformation of kynurenine into 3-hydroxykynurenine in *Bombyx* have been found by Kikkawa (1953); the mutant, which shows maternal inheritance, prevents the precursor substance from diffusing into the egg. But in a number of cases of maternal inheritance based upon a mutant locus within a chromosome acting upon the egg before fertilization, the action affects a generalized plasmatic feature of the egg (e.g., handedness of spindle), expressed not simply as a Mendelizing trait of the egg but as a general predetermination or conditioning of the cytoplasm, which may show its effects throughout the development of the organism (e.g., the asymmetry in a mollusk). Though controlled by a mutant locus primarily, and thus being in the nature of an ordinary Mendelian trait, the consequent conditioning of the cytoplasm of the egg is of general consequence for development and therefore may be described as a kind of intermediate condition between nuclear and cytoplasmic heredity, or more correctly as a model for the way in which the simplest, most generalized type of cytoplasmic heredity works. In view of this, a few of the different types of maternal heredity may be discussed.

The least generalized of these and also the best analyzed, because both genetics and cytology are known, is the maternal effect in the production of mosaics in the silkworm (Goldschmidt and Katsuki, 1927, 1928*a,b*). A recessive mutant conditions the cytoplasm at the time of the maturation divisions so that it prevents the normal linear arrangement of the four resulting nuclei, of which only the proximal nucleus is fertilized normally. Instead, the second polar nucleus moves to a position parallel with that of the first, the egg nucleus, so that now two egg nuclei are in correct position for fertilization and are both fertilized, giving rise to somatic as well as sex mosaics in the proper genetic and chromosomal combinations.

Here the plasmatic conditioning is visible only in the movements of the reduced nuclei. In the well-known cases of sinistrality in snails (Boycott *et al.,* 1930), previously mentioned, the mutant locus affects the molecular orientation of the cytoplasm, resulting visibly in counterclockwise torsion of the spindles and subsequent sinistral spiral cleavage. Thus the conditioning of the cytoplasm on a molecular level controls a major feature of subsequent development. Here we see what I meant by calling these, in a sense, models of cytoplasmic heredity: it might be supposed that in other cases counterclockwise cytoplasmic orientation was a hereditary cytoplasmic property independent of nuclear control. (Actually no such case is known.)

It is rather probable, but not proved, that the determination of the germ track in animals belongs to this group, but the facts are not accessible to genetic experimentation. In a number of animals (Diptera, Copepoda, *Sagitta, Ascaris*) the part of the egg cytoplasm which will later supply the cytoplasm of the germ-track cells is already visibly different in the unfertilized egg (predetermined). It may be safely assumed, though it cannot be proved, that this differentiation, which takes place during oögenesis, and all other predeterminations found by experimental embryology are under genic control, just as in maternal inheritance. Actually, here the cytoplasmic conditioning becomes visible in the production of stainable substances, the "germ-track determiners" which stay strictly within the future germ-track cells in subsequent development. From Boveri's classic work on chromatin diminution in *Ascaris* we know that the conditioned cytoplasm in this organism even affects the behavior of the chromosomes (controls the occurrence or absence of chromatin diminution; see I 2 C *b*). Thus we have a lasting cytoplasmic function of a determinative nature, once the cytoplasmic difference is established. Again we see why we may consider this a model of real cytoplasmic inheritance of the plasmon type.

The most extreme cases of conditioning of the cytoplasm of the egg prior to fertilization by genic (nuclear) action are found in the realm of sex determination. We call these the most extreme cases, because here the conditioned cytoplasm is important for sex determination; an all-pervading feature of the organism, it affects practically all development and every single cell. A typical case is that of *Lymantria dispar*, the gypsy moth. The female determiners are located in the Y-chromosome and, since the female is heterogametic, all eggs contain a Y-chromosome up to meiosis. The male thus has no Y-chromosome and no female determiners after fertilization of the egg from which it develops. Males, however, may become intersexual (including complete sex reversal), and it can be shown that the too strong female determiners responsible are located in the Y-chromosome (Goldschmidt, 1920*c* ff.; last discussion, 1953*a*). In the silkworm the female determiners in the Y are so strong that the presence of a Y-chromosome produces a female even when many male determiners (X-chromosomes) are present (Tazima, 1943, 1944). Therefore, the actions controlling female determination must have taken place in the unfertilized egg by way of cytoplasmic predetermination or conditioning, which remains active in the once determined way throughout all the development, since it controls (in balance with the X-chromosomal male factors) all the processes of sexual differentiation. We may safely assume, on the basis of our knowledge of sex hormones in higher forms, that this control exercised by the conditioned cytoplasm is a relatively simple chemical control, and we may derive from this a model for a comparable purely cytoplasmic action. This situation in *Lymantria* is, by the way, *mutatis mutandis,* not unique. In *Drosophila repleta* crosses, Sturtevant (1946) described a dominant locus which makes hybrid females intersexual; that is, it has a masculinizing influence which acts only in the unfertilized egg by conditioning of the cytoplasm. In a comparable way, a partially feminizing influence is acting in *Drosophila melanogaster* in the presence of Beaded and Minute mutants with a considerable effect through protoplasmic conditioning (Goldschmidt, 1951*b*).

Some authors (e.g., Ephrussi, 1953) define predetermination as an action of a dominant locus before meiosis, a locus which may be absent after meiosis though the "predetermined" phenotype appears. Such a narrowed definition does not include the really decisive characteristic, the genic action upon the cytoplasm before meiosis. Therefore, any such action is predetermination, as in all the examples just mentioned, regardless of what happens to the respective locus in meiosis. Recessive predetermination is actually the case best analyzed genetically, though a dominant one—for example, the action of the Y-chromosome in the moth egg producing a male, which does not possess a Y after fertilization—is more spectacular.

The inferences we wish to draw from such cases of typical maternal inheritance, with conditioning of the cytoplasm by genic nuclear factors acting before meiosis, are fortified by the existence of closely comparable facts involving the cytoplasm alone. Oehlkers (1938–1952) has described some very interesting phenomena of intersexuality in *Streptocarpus* crosses which we shall analyze below and arrive at a somewhat different explanation in detail. I could show (Goldschmidt, 1938*b*) that they closely parallel the *Lymantria* situation so far as the sexual balance and its disturbance in the crosses are based upon a system involving female determiners in the X-chromosomes (male heterogamety) and a purely maternally inherited condition, which can be inherited only in the cytoplasm of the egg. The complications involved because of monoecism do not concern us here.

preserved for some time just as if by inheritance. But they remain reversible in the same way, as the cellular constitution has not changed. In classic genetic language this would mean, I think, a genic alternative reaction norm with stability over some cell divisions, that is, one of the general features of genic action and nothing of cytoplasmic nature. (The physical term "steady states," which has been used to describe this situation, seems to be unnecessary as far as the genetic facts are considered. The term "alternative norm of reaction" covers the facts; I have used this concept repeatedly in these discussions.) Thus no genuine cytoplasmic heredity is involved, and the recourse to "plasmagenes," originally favored by Sonneborn, is ruled out. Sonneborn (1955) formulates the result as follows: "The important point is that alternative steady states based on mutual inhibitions can give cytoplasmic inheritance without resort to self-duplicating cytoplasmic particles." I should prefer to say "can be erroneously taken for cytoplasmic inheritance."

Sonneborn thinks that the facts of antigenic inheritance generally parallel those of *Dauermodifikation.* This would mean that the traits showing *Dauermodifikation* are also gene-controlled traits (though there are no facts available to prove this) with an alternative norm of reaction which remains more or less self-perpetuating until internal or external conditions switch it over. I wonder whether Jollos' original data, especially the arsenic experiments, could be explained this way; I doubt it.

Some apparently unrelated facts may help this discussion. I am thinking of the remarkable features of vernalization in cereals. The traits involved, winter or summer wheat, are undoubtedly genically controlled. But by appropriate treatment (e.g., with cold) at the proper time the physiological alternative can be induced; for example, winter wheat can be made to behave like summer wheat. This may be described as an induced self-perpetuating cytoplasmic change. Self-perpetuating may mean, as in the former cases, the presence of changed self-perpetuating bodies like mitochondria, but it may also mean a strictly alternative chemical property of the cytoplasm (a "steady state"), which remains until forced again into its original condition. The details (see Melchers' excellent discussion, 1952) are as interesting for our present discussion as for plant genetics and physiology generally, and may be described in the same terms as the antigenic properties in *Paramecium,* involving an alternative norm of reaction of the cytoplasm but not cytoplasmic inheritance.

The materials presented in the last chapter and our analysis of the sexual conditioning of the egg cytoplasm before fertilization by nuclear determiners are relevant to the present discussion also. There we have, as in the antigens in *Paramecium,* an alternative norm of reaction of the entire cell which we can call a cytoplasmic condition induced by genic control, remaining through the subsequent cell generations. However, it may be shifted to the alternative by genic as well as external action, as in genetic or induced intersexuality.

Coördinating such facts and deliberations, it seems to me that we must be very cautious when lining them up for a discussion of cytoplasmic heredity. It is clear (assuming the correctness of Sonneborn's interpretation of *Dauermodifikation*) that the facts demonstrate one of the ways in which the genic material can control processes within the cytoplasm. In a broader sense we are dealing with the classic conception of genic action as a "norm of reaction" which might be one-tracked or alternative or still more complicated, depending upon internal (threshold) conditions or external ones controlling such thresholds. The cytoplasm enters here primarily as the substrate of genic action. If the facts demonstrate, as they seem to do, that environmentally induced modifications of the genically controlled products of reaction may be more or less self-perpetuating, a very important insight has been gained into the ways in which the genic material exercises its control of cellular (i.e., cytoplasmic) conditions; and, further, how the cytoplasm is fitted to perform its genically controlled duties. As a matter of fact, the possibility that cytoplasmic conditions induced by the nuclear genome may become self-perpetuating is one of great importance for the problem of genic action. Waddington (1953*a*) has discussed it under the name of "epigenetic momentum," and we shall meet with many facts which lend themselves to such an explanation, when discussing genic action. Actually it is difficult to understand genetic control of development without such a process. Nevertheless, calling this a form of cytoplasmic heredity is wholly mistaken, and I consider it completely misleading (though it is advocated by some prominent geneticists) to use the term "plasmagenes" for self-perpetuating, nucleus-induced cytoplasmic conditions.

There is a large group of facts known in bacteria and yeast which, if understood completely, would shed light on the problems of *Dauermodifikation.* These are the facts of so-called adaptation (reviews in Catcheside, 1951; Monod and Cohn, 1952). A microörganism, unable to metabolize an unusual substrate, learns to do so by producing the necessary adaptive enzyme, if kept for a more or less long time in the new substrate. The details are variable and somewhat conflicting. But some or all of the following possibilities may be involved: (1) a selection of already present rare mutants controlling the specific enzyme; (2) a "steady state" condition, as discussed before, allowing the genic material to produce one or another product according to the environment; (3) this condition may be self-perpetuating even in the absence of the genic material (after segregation) or may not; (4) the condition may be reversible by exhaustion of particles or by inverse environmental action; (5) mutation may play a role in different ways; (6) induced mutation of plasmagenes may take place (my own opposition to such a view has been registered). *Dauermodifikation* and enzymatic adaptation will probably be found to have the same background; but, since neither is yet understood completely, it is impossible to explain one in terms of the other. This is a frontier which must be watched.

C. PLASMON ACTION OF THE SPECIFIC SUBSTRATE TYPE

If we call (see II 2 D) a specific action of the cytoplasm as a whole a plasmon-type action, we may distinguish two major categories: (1) a specific physicochemical structure or biochemical nature of the cytoplasm affecting genically controlled processes in the nature of a specific substratum which remains constant within a genetic line; (2) a specific constitution of the entire cytoplasm which alone controls specific features of structure or function, and might therefore be considered a genuine cytoplasmic inheritance.

a. Mendelian segregation in different cytoplasm

The first type of plasmon action would be recognized when an ordinary Mendelian character changes its phenotype in the presence of cytoplasm of different origin. Experimentally this would involve phenotypical difference of reciprocal crosses and constancy of these differences in the maternal lines of following generations. A large number of experiments demonstrating this situation was performed with the gypsy moth *Lymantria dispar* (Goldschmidt, 1924). A series of geographic races exist with, among others, differences in the markings of the caterpillars. Some races show a bright pattern of light spots of epidermal origin which remains through all instars. In other races this pattern is present but less extended, and these quantitatively different patterns are based upon multiple alleles with additional control of multiple modifiers. In addition to this basic pattern, a simple Mendelian factor in some races produces a cuticular dark pigment which overlays the bright pattern and covers it more or less completely, a process which increases during the different molts. Two extreme genetic types are a Japanese race with a bright pattern and no overlying cuticular pigment, and a European race with so much overlying pigment that even the young caterpillars do not show the bright pattern. The factor for cuticular pigment may be called AA, and its allele without production of this pigment aa. AA individuals are grayish black; aa is bright-patterned. The largest bright spot may be classified according to its size, and the variations produced by the amount of covering with dark pigment can be expressed in a curve of variation. If we consider only the crosses with the brightest and darkest race—those with intermediate degrees gave the same results, though less clearly demonstrable—F_1 AA × aa is much darker than the reciprocal aa × AA; that is, F_1 is matroclinous. In F_2 (correspondingly RF_2) the segregation AA:2Aa:aa occurs; this, in view of the fluctuation, results in a curve of pigmentation with one mode in the dark classes comprising about 25 per cent of the individuals and another mode covering the 75 per cent in the medium and light classes, which overlap. In reciprocal F_2 crosses, however, these curves are not identical but they are still matroclinous: with the dark maternal grandmother the lighter part of the curve is shifted toward the dark end; but with the light maternal grandmother it is shifted toward the light end. The accompanying diagram illustrates this (numerous exact curves and tables in the paper of 1924).

CLASSES

	Dark				Intermediate				Light		
1	2	3	4	5	6	7	8	9	10	11	12
P	AA									aa	
F_1				A × a							
							a × A				
F_2		$(A \times a)^2$									
		25%					75%				
			$(a \times A)^2$								
			25%							75%	

Since the same results were found (more or less clearly, according to the differences between the parental races) in a number of different racial crosses, they may be regarded as typical for this material. Moreover, Kühn (1927) described a close parallel in *Habro-*

bracon, also involving a pigmentation process, and carried it to one more generation.

The question arises whether a more detailed characterization of the cytoplasmic effect in these experiments is possible. It is clear that no effect of a qualitative type takes place. The affected phenogenetic process is the quantity of melanin deposited at certain points of the cuticula, and this again is due to the speed with which melanin is formed, as a statistical check upon the progress of pigment formation in all the instars of the larvae demonstrated. Thus some kind of generalized substrate action is involved in the cytoplasmic effect. This does not necessarily mean a biochemical quality or a condition of viscosity or colloidal behavior of the cytoplasm as an entity. Another possibility might be a difference in formed constituents of the cytoplasm of a type which we have already met in the visible germ track determining substances discussed previously. The most obvious corpuscular elements are the mitochondria, which sometimes contain a complete set of respiratory enzymes. These may be involved in the speed and quantity of melanin formation. A few remarkable results point in this direction. According to Winge and Laustsen (1940), a haploid ascospore in yeast may be fertilized and form a diploid clone; or it may do so by autogamy (called direct diploidization). The latter clones have a low viability, which is inherited. For this the mitochondria are believed to be responsible. Winge and Laustsen think that in autogamy the mitochondria have no time to duplicate and, therefore, are present only in a quantity which suffices for a haploid but not for a diploid cell.

A very remarkable case, which probably is of the same type as the *Lymantria* experiments, has been described by Oehlkers (1952*a*), though it is a little more complicated. The hybrid *Streptocarpus Rexii* × *Wendlandii* is fertile, and the F_2 and all backcrosses can be obtained. The two parental forms have the same kind of sympetal flowers, and therefore no segregation for flower form can occur. The reciprocal hybrid *Wendlandii* × *Rexii* has no anthers (see about intersexuality in these crosses later) but can be crossed as a female with *Rexii* × *Wendlandii,* which, as far as the genome is concerned, amounts to the same F_2 as before. In this F_2 (also similar RF_2) a new recessive form of laciniated flower segregates (choripetaly). Obviously, the recessive mutant for this form of flower is present in *Rexii,* but can become visible only in the presence of the *Wendlandii* plasma, not in its own. The situation is similar to that in *Lymantria,* though here a recessive action is not modified but is completely suppressed in one cytoplasm, strangely enough, its own.

Another set of facts may point in the same direction. It is generally assumed that the sperm does not carry cytoplasm into the egg. But both sperm head and middle piece contain mitochondrial products in the form of spiral fibrils and derivatives of the mitochondrial body. In a little-known paper, Held (1916), a very good histologist, showed that in *Ascaris* (where the sperm contains a considerable amount of cytoplasm) egg and sperm mitochondria may be stained differentially. He could trace the sperm mitochondria into the egg and their dispersal among the mitochondria of the egg. (Held was a follower of Meves, who thought that the mitochondria are the real genic material, not the chromosomes.) We might conclude that similar behavior of the mitochondria occurs in fertilization with filiform sperm. An additional fact is known for Lepidoptera. Here normal polyspermy occurs and each sperm head transforms into a nucleus surrounded by a bit of specifically staining cytoplasm (see photos in Goldschmidt and Katsuki, 1928*b*). It is not proved that this cytoplasm is derived from the sperm. But if it is, the 6–10 sperm heads in an egg might contribute a rather large amount of paternal mitochondria.

If this is true and if the cytoplasmic effect of shifting genically controlled reactions is actually based upon mitochondria, we should expect to find paternal cytoplasmic effects also (excluding here such processes as transfer of chloroplasts by the pollen, to be mentioned below). Actually such effects were recorded for the same material as before, the pigment in *Lymantria* caterpillars. I had noticed early (but had not dared to report on it for years in view of the general attitude at that time*) an effect which could be explained only in terms of an action of the sperm cytoplasm. Only after it was found repeatedly did I present the data (Goldschmidt, 1924). Double reciprocal F_2 crosses, for example (A × a) × (A × a) versus (A × a) × (a × A), are identical in regard to Mendelizing genes and egg cytoplasm (always A in the example). But the presumed sperm cytoplasm is different (derived from the paternal grandmother), namely, a in the second cross. Many such double reciprocal crosses in both directions were checked for the pigmentation character reported above, and in many instances differences in the curves of pigmentation were found between the two double reciprocal crosses, which

* I had reported on it in an unpublished talk at Bateson's invitation in the John Innes Institute.

went in exactly the direction expected if the sperm plasm influenced the egg cytoplasm (many curves and tables in 1924). This result strongly favors the mitochondria as the suspected cytoplasmic agent. Since mitochondria are the seat of cytochrome oxidases, a racial difference affecting the kinetics of melanin production sounds reasonable. We shall see later that in plants, also, comparable though not identical differences between races were found by the Michaelis group.

b. Genomes in different cytoplasm

In the cases discussed thus far the substrate action of the cytoplasm in influencing quantitative features of genically controlled developmental processes was clear, because the effect could be analyzed in simple Mendelian segregations. This applies to the cases reported just now as well as to the material involving alternative norm of reaction. However, in many cases analyzed in plants, the cytoplasmic effect is a generalized one: it cannot be attributed to interference with individual known genic actions, but rather interferes with the whole genome, or major parts of it, if the genome is located in the wrong cytoplasm. The diverse cytoplasmic actions may be characterized, in a general way, as a weakening or inhibition of general processes of growth, as a consequence of nuclei working in the wrong cytoplasm. The technique, introduced by Correns (1908), is as follows. Reciprocal crosses giving matroclinous phenotypes are the starting point. These are backcrossed over generations to the paternal form, with the result that the maternal cytoplasm remains but the chromosomes are finally replaced more or less completely by those of the paternal form, which are supposed not to fit into the foreign cytoplasm. In a general way, the results are always the same: continuation of the maternal effects over all generations without visible influence of the replaced genome or, as we shall see, with very little influence of it.

It is remarkable that practically all the manifold effects found are simple inhibitions. Many are in the sexual sphere, like suppression of the male phase in monoecious plants (gynodioecism), as in Correns' work on *Cirsium;* or degeneration of male gametes at different stages (pollen sterility) in Rhoades' work on maize (1933); or the work of Lehmann and Michaelis and their students on crosses of species and geographic varieties with backcrosses up to twenty-five generations, which followed the pioneer work of Renner and Kupper (1921). (See review by Michaelis, 1954.) It is characteristic that the disturbances produced by the genome-plasmon incompatibility are lethality, sterility, abnormalities of stem, leaves, and flowers, cripples, dwarfs, loss of anthocyanin, and also heterosis. In addition, degrees of cytoplasmic viscosity and permeability, sensitivity to poisons and fungi, different enzymatic activity, and different general physiological reactions were found. Michaelis reports that nearly all properties of the plant are altered by cytoplasmic differences. This variability is not much lower than that which would be produced by a series of gene mutations. Michaelis concludes that this is definite proof that the cytoplasm contains autonomous genetic constituents.

I cannot concur in this conclusion. The type of effects studied suggests rather a completely unspecific cytoplasmic action, which we described in terms of substrate action. A good model for it is a different constitution in regard to the oxidation-reduction system, localized within the mitochondria, which works successfully only with the proper products of the genic material; in the wrong combination, therefore, it probably upsets basic reactions in development only in regard to their kinetics, with the result of widespread defects. In more descriptive than correct language we might say that the wrong cytoplasm "poisons" developmental reactions.

The problem is so important that we may repeat our conclusion in other words. It is safe tc say that in this whole group of facts cytoplasmic heredity in a strict sense is *not* involved. The cytoplasm or plasmon does not control the development of definite hereditary traits. It is rather a substrate for the action of the genic material, and it functions properly only when it has the proper chemical composition needed to react correctly with the products of genic action. The chemical composition may differ in somewhat different species or geographic varieties; it may be extreme; or it may be completely absent. The difference may affect only the quantitative features of certain gene-controlled processes as in *Lymantria.* Or it may affect only the all-or-none reactions involved in the decision of the sexual alternative. (See above the parallel facts in the chapter on maternal inheritance.) Or it may "poison" many of the gene-controlled reactions involved in the general processes of growth and differentiation. The part of the cytoplasm that has to do with the control of oxidase action, as in mitochondria, would fulfill most if not all the requirements on which the cytoplasmic action under discussion is based.

This conclusion is considerably strengthened by experiments of the Michaelis school themselves. They found, when crossing a Jena race of *Epilobium hirsutum* with 390 other races of widely different origin, and introducing (by continued backcrossing) the nucleus of 22 of these into Jena plasm, that all hybrids, if reciprocally different, show deviations of the same kind. The activity of peroxidase and respiratory enzymes is increased, but to a different degree in different combinations, with the result that positive or negative heterosis is found in some, cripples and dwarfs in others, and lethality in still others. "It is possible to transform the lethals into dwarfs and the dwarfs into vigorous plants by inactivation of the oxidizing enzymes at low temperatures or by augmenting the carbohydrates" (Michaelis). This should show conclusively that the interpretation proposed above in terms of generalized substrates is correct, and perhaps also in terms of mitochondria.

It is hardly necessary to go into the details of other cases studied in the plant kingdom, which have been ably reviewed by Caspari (1948). At one extreme are found the facts relating to male sterility in flax, studied by the Bateson school (see Gairdner, 1929), where a Mendelian locus in homozygous condition produces pollen sterility only if it is transferred to the cytoplasm of another species. In other examples the results resemble those in *Epilobium,* so far as modification of many morphological traits, in the direction of the type present in the form which supplies the cytoplasm of the hybrid, remains constant over generations; or remains so though being changed somewhat in the course of generations. In a general way this is the situation both in Wettstein's (1924, 1928*a*) moss crosses and in crosses of *Oenothera* studied by Schwemmle *et al.* (1938). Apart from specific features concerning the plastids (which will be treated separately), the foregoing discussion covers the essentials. The main point in each instance is that the action of known Mendelian loci or of a considerable part of the genome, though not severally referable to single Mendelian units, differs in different cytoplasm. In some this means an impaired function leading to generalized abnormalities, including certain kinds of sterility and extending to complete lethality. In others, where growth and similar quantitatively varying processes are involved, it means a shift of gene-controlled reactions and processes toward the type of form which supplied the cytoplasm, that is, more or less of an influence upon developmental kinetics.

Renner and Kupper (1921) introduced, for this type of action, the term "plasmon-sensitive genes," meaning that the action of some genes requires a definite cytoplasm in order to succeed fully or at all. Though the idea behind the term is derived from unequivocal facts, I think that this theory might lead to confusion if it were misunderstood to mean that there are different kinds of "genes," some dependent or partly dependent and others not dependent upon the specific features of the cytoplasm.

We shall meet again with the same logical situation and the danger that genic actions, varying under different conditions, or in different systems, or as a consequence of a qualitatively different kind of action, will be mistaken for differences in the nature of the "gene" which suggest characterizing types of genes. (See chapter on dosage.) In the interest of clear notions on "cytoplasmic heredity," I prefer to look at the facts in terms of genically controlled processes, all of which take place in the cytoplasm as substratum and are therefore dependent upon its biophysical and biochemical nature. If it is a fact that these substrate conditions are different in taxonomically different forms (in the widest sense of the term), the full and normal performance of these genically controlled processes (reaction chains) is possible, within a foreign cytoplasm, only when its substrate activity lies within the threshold limits of the gene-substrate interaction in question. Thus the cytoplasmic maternal effect is the combined result of the threshold conditions of the individual or combined genically controlled processes, and the amount of biochemical difference of the foreign cytoplasm which shifts those reactions within or beyond the thresholds. The biochemical cytoplasmic difference, being probably in the nature of a basic, quantitative property like the various levels of the oxidation-reduction system, affects the actions of the entire genome, and it is only the quantity (visibility and localization) of the effect that changes with threshold conditions for individual traits. Oehlkers (1952*a*), in his review of cytoplasmic heredity, draws basically similar conclusions when he says that the alleged plasmon-sensitivity of some genes is relative. "As a matter of fact there is no special 'sensitivity' of the genes but only a special reaction among other possibilities of reaction, which alone is conspicuous because it falls outside the normal . . . in principle all genes are plasmasensitive because we may connect all with some specific collaboration with the plasmon."

A few experimental or theoretical attacks have been made on the problem of what these cytoplasmic conditions are. We considered them to be of a rather simple generalized type affecting threshold conditions for genically controlled reactions with a substrate. Schlösser (1935), who found plasmon actions on growth in crosses of wild tomatoes, thinks that the decisive features are osmotic conditions. The genically controlled growth requires an optimum osmotic pressure, while definite osmotic values are controlled in the cytoplasm and may be inadequate when the wrong cytoplasm is present. This may be expressed also in terms of thresholds. Von Dellingshausen (1935, 1936) tried to find the physiological conditions responsible for plasmon effects in Michaelis' *Epilobium* crosses. He found differences in permeability and viscosity, that is, physical differences. Lehmann and his students (Ross, 1940) found deficiencies in heteroauxins in the plasmons which inhibited growth, and could overcome the effect by treatment with auxins. More important still is Ross's (1941) finding that peroxidase activity in the foreign plasmon is higher than in the proper one. All the different effects of growth inhibition in the hybrids with foreign plasmon may be traced to this primary difference. These results tend to point in the same direction as our foregoing analysis, and to show that in a general way the interpretations adopted above are correct and preferable to the ideas on genic cytoplasm or cytoplasmic genes.

I prefer a statement of the facts in terms of generalized biochemical features of the cytoplasm, like respiratory enzyme levels, which either allow genically controlled reactions with the substrate to occur within the normal threshold limits or prevent them. Explanations in terms of plasmon-sensitive genes certainly account for the same facts, but, I think, only in a formalistic way. To mention only one such theory, Caspari has elaborated the idea, based upon Stern's hypothesis of genic action (to be discussed later), that each allele has a characteristic combining power with the substrate, the genic product being the result of this combination with the substrate for which different genes compete. As the amount of substrate is limited, the final result will depend upon the outcome of the competition among different alleles. It is assumed that the substrate produced in the cytoplasm of different strains is somewhat different; further, that the foreign gene has a higher combining power but a lower efficiency toward this particular substrate, and transforms it into a physiologically inactive product. In the hybrid the foreign allele takes the substrate away from the rightful one, which thus cannot produce enough product. This would be the essential feature of a "plasmon-sensitive gene."

I have the feeling that this and similar ways of looking at the facts from the point of view of different types of genes are rather formalistic, because of the desire to endow genes with definite specific properties which explain whatever is found. Furthermore, such theories are completely unnecessary. A physiological point of view relating genic actions, which in themselves are the same in all the crosses, to differences in general physiological features present in different cytoplasm seems more appealing and is definitely simpler. We shall see below that Stern himself has become skeptical about his theory of genic action. Thus I conclude that there are no plasmon-sensitive genes. Any genic material may act differently if the cytoplasm does not provide the proper substrate tuned to the thresholds, velocities, and so on, of the reactions involved. It is gratifying to see that Oehlkers (1952*a*), in a clear discussion of all these problems, has come, at least in principle, to very similar conclusions, opposing the idea of plasmon-sensitive genes, as the quotations above show.

It is rather interesting that in *Epilobium* (just as in *Lymantria*) indications of paternal effects have been found. (The same is true of the *Oenothera* crosses.) Michaelis found that in the course of his matroclinous backcrosses some paternal effects appeared, shifting the cytoplasmic action somewhat toward the normal side. We think at once of cytoplasm introduced by the pollen and adding up in the course of generations to a kind of dilution of the maternal cytoplasm, though Michaelis is not friendly to this idea.

c. Evidence from merogony

Since the classic work of Boveri and Godlevski, experiments on merogony have played an important role in experimental embryology. Merogony—the development of an enucleated egg fragment fertilized by foreign sperm—should yield information on the relative roles of nuclear and cytoplasmic heredity (recent review by von Ubisch, 1954). In repeating Boveri's experiments, Hoerstadius (1936) found that reciprocal merogons of sea urchin species show differences in regard to the skeleton. The details do not indicate any cytoplasmic inheritance, but can be referred to oöplasmic predetermination and the well-known fact that the nucleus plays only an inferior role during the first stages of development, up to gastrulation. This may be regarded as certain in view of the fact that these haploid merogons do not develop very far, and die when normal genic action sets in. Using a clever method of producing merogonic mosaics from amphibian eggs, Baltzer (1933) and Hadorn (1936) again found some cytoplasmic effect, which, however, does not prove cytoplasmic inheritance proper, and parallels the sea urchin case in fact and interpretation. In this connection also the little-known work of Haberlandt (1935) on plant chimeras (*Crataegomespilus*) should be mentioned. In periclinal chimeras containing the epidermis of only one of the species, he found epidermal structures that were intermediate between the species. In this case cytoplasm can hardly be involved; instead, diffusible cytoplasmic products like auxins would seem to account for the effect. Though not strictly concerned with cytoplasmic inheritance, the facts suggest caution.

The most important experiments in merogony, as far as our present discussion is concerned, are those of Harder (1927) on basidiomycetes. By a very intricate technique, made possible by unique features of the apical cells of mycelia, hybrids between two strains of *Pholiota mutabilis* could be produced containing a mixture of the cytoplasms of the two strains with the haploid nucleus of one. The mycelia obtained from these cells showed intermediate growth habits similar to those of a real (nuclear) hybrid. Again the same interpretation should be given as in the other cases: quantitative shifts in genically controlled reactions owing to a foreign substrate, combined with threshold actions.

It is rather surprising that the cytoplasmic substrate differences studied are in a number of cases typical for the lowest taxonomic categories. In the pigmentation of *Lymantria* caterpillars, the cytoplasmic differences were found in crosses of all geographic races which were sufficiently different for detection of the feature. In Michaelis' *Epilobium* work this goes still farther. Here the cytoplasmic difference goes down even to otherwise indistinguishable local communities. This means that a cytoplasmic evolutionary divergence exists, which is even more sensitive than genic differences. If it should turn out eventually that the well-founded suspicion that the mitochondria are involved in all this is an actual fact, interesting new problems of evolutionary divergence would arise. Formerly I doubted (Goldschmidt, 1940, p. 250) that the cytoplasm is a major factor in evolution. The facts alluded to suggest caution for the time being.

D. GENUINE PLASMON

In the introduction to the last chapter it was pointed out that a distinction should be made between a cytoplasmic influence upon genically controlled processes which shifts the latter in a quantitative way, and an actual cytoplasmic heredity, a genuine plasmon, which by itself determines definite hereditary traits in the same sense as genes are supposed to control characters. Such a distinction is a priori necessary and, in addition, useful in view of the fact that a considerable number of geneticists speak rather loosely of cytoplasmic genes when nothing has been established but a cytoplasmic substrate action in all the cases discussed thus far. If a real plasmon in the sense just defined could be proved to exist, the term "cytoplasmic genic material" could be used by analogy, but "cytoplasmic genes" would still be an indefensible term, in my opinion. An objection might be made to the distinction of a genuine plasmon from a cytoplasmic substrate on the ground that, just as genic material cannot be imagined without the collaborating cytoplasmic substratum, in the same way no plasmon could exist without collaborating genes. Furthermore, it could be said that it is impossible to prove the existence of a genuine plasmon action because an interaction with genically controlled actions can never be excluded. Both criticisms are to the point in themselves. However, just as we deal in classic genetics with genic control of hereditary traits, evidenced by the criterion of Mendelian inheritance, forgetting about the cytoplasm, we might be able to describe cytoplasmic heredity proper as the result of traits which are inherited purely maternally and do not exhibit any effects of different genic constitution. If, for example, the form of a leaf were inherited in this way, the form should be essentially, if not completely, the same in all descendants in the maternal line, in F_1, F_2, F_n, and in all replacements of chromosomes by those of another form.

The question then is whether indubitable cases of this type exist. I once believed I had found an example in the sex determination of *Lymantria*, where the female determiners are inherited strictly maternally, as shown for the degree of intersexuality obtained even in the most complicated multiple crosses, introducing all kinds of chromosomes of different genetic constitution. If A, B, C, D are different races known to have different X-chromosomes in regard to the relative potency of the sex factors, the crosses (female first) A × B, (A × C) × B, (A × B) × (C × D) × (E × F) × B, and so on, all give the same result, depending exclusively upon the female factorial potency of the maternal, grandmaternal (etc.) race A and the male (X-chromosomal one) of the race B. A special experiment seemed to confirm the conclusion (Goldschmidt, 1934*a*). But finally I had to realize (Goldschmidt, 1942*b*) that my original interpretation, location of the female determiners within the Y-chromosome, was the correct one. (I have mentioned the latter fact in relation to the predetermining effect of Y in the future male-determined egg, and shall return to the subject later.)

Oehlkers (1938 ff.) analyzed species crosses of the plant *Streptocarpus* in which pure plasmatic inheritance of sex-determining actions seems to be established. He crossed six different species of *Streptocarpus* (Gramineae) and found that they fell into two groups. Crosses within the groups do not show the plasmatic effect, but those between the groups do. In reciprocal crosses (*Rexii* = A; *Wendlandii* = B) the hybrids show the following differences. Flowers of A × B are hermaphroditic like the parents, but B × A have no anthers, only staminodia. In RF_2 (B × A) × A half the offspring are like B × A; in the other half, all anthers are replaced by female organs in a series of transitions from staminodia to five complete female organs. In RF_2 (A × B) × A, however, a segregation occurs into normal hermaphrodites, which, though externally normal, are sterile and may have rudimentary ovaries. Thus B cytoplasm makes for an intersexual shift toward femaleness, and A cytoplasm moderately toward maleness.

Different interpretations have been proposed by Oehlkers (1938, 1940, 1941), by Hartmann (1943), and by Goldschmidt (1938*b*), but all require that in the cytoplasm of the pure species a condition exists, a plasmon, which acts in the opposite direction from the nuclear genome. The distribution of this plasmon among the species indicates an old evolutionary diversification. (See the remark on cytoplasm and evolution in II 2 C *c*. The details of the present analysis will be taken up later in the chapter on the theory of sex determination. They will turn out to be more complicated than is assumed here.)

In Wettstein's early work there was a tendency to assume the existence of genuine plasmon heredity. However, it seems that only one trait in his mosses, the length of the midvein of the moss leaf, remained purely maternal. All other traits influenced by the cytoplasm were matroclinous and therefore fell into the category of cytoplasm-influenced genic action. Later Wettstein (1946) thought he had found a case of genuine plasmon action in *Linum*, in which plasma-dependent pollen sterility had already been described by the Bateson school (see II 2 C *b*). Wettstein made long-continued backcrosses which resulted in completely homozygous genomes of the race "tall" in the cytoplasm of "procumbents." After the eighth generation the homozygosity was made still more certain by using a little trick of making the haplont diploid. The pollen sterility in this combination remained constant. Wettstein considers this to be real proof of an independent plasmon, though, I think, an interpretation of different genic interaction with different cytoplasmic substrate is not excluded.

In the vast collection of data found in the work of the schools of Renner, Lehmann, Schwemmle, and Michaelis, innumerable variations in the quantitative behavior of the traits affected by the cytoplasm were found, but not a single convincing case of genuine plasmonic, maternal control of a definite hereditary trait. It is very doubtful whether such a type of heredity exists, at least outside the sphere of sex determination.

All this is very important for the problem of so-called cytoplasmic genes, which had become a kind of genetic fashion but are in eclipse again at present. If the mitochondria play the role we discussed previously, they cannot be called genes, since their action can be only a generalized one, with possible differences in regard to their quantity. There is no reason to suppose that different types of mitochondria exist which can be sorted out, each kind controlling a definite character. In the same way, the assumption of a plasmon, which could be conceived of as an assembly of cytoplasmic genes, would require different kinds of cytoplasm, separable and endowed with definite hereditary actions. No such case has been analyzed thus far, and it is extremely improbable that one will turn up. Of course, differentiated cytoplasm which controls the fate of nuclei within it (or of Lwoff's kineties) is completely different (see I 1). It is true that Darlington (1944) once tried to interpret some of the features of Michaelis' *Epilobium* crosses as indicative of cytoplasmic segregation and Michaelis (1954) insists upon it. The zoölogist will be extremely skeptical if he thinks of cytoplasmic differentiation in development, which is certainly different from genetic segregation. Thus I consider it a fact that so far *genuine* cytoplasmic heredity (i.e., not of the substrate-for-genic-action type), or the existence of what could be called cytoplasmic genes, has not been proved, with the probable exception of stuffs related to special features of sex determination in *Streptocarpus*. This conclusion applies thus far only to the facts which have just been analyzed; none of them deal with visible or invisible but analyzable cytoplasmic substances of a particulate type, though we came near this subject when discussing mitochondria.

E. CYTOPLASMIC HEREDITY OF THE PARTICULATE TYPE (PLASMAGENES)

The adherents of the theory of plasmagenes frequently go so far as to speak of plasmagenes whenever cytoplasmic functions are involved. Thus, as we shall see below, all plasmatic actions and differentiations are made the work of plasmagenes, though there is not a single fact which requires this assumption. The basis for such generalizations is the idea that self-reproducing substances have to be assumed in the cytoplasm. If a large protein molecule can be synthesized only through a template mechanism, as is probable, every protein molecule might be called a plasmagene. In the interest of clear notions and in order to avoid the danger of taking a suggestive terminology for an explanation, we should speak of plasmagenes only when a proved particulate, self-duplicating structure in the cytoplasm can be shown to produce definite genic actions of the type known for the genic material in the chromosomes. (Personally I should go still farther and reserve the term "genic" and "genes" for chromosomal material which can be analyzed by means of Mendelian behavior.) But apart from what I consider rather wild and not helpful notions about plasmagenes being involved in whatever the cytoplasm does, there is a large body of facts, dealing with more or less certain particulates, as well as visible ones, in the cytoplasm, that have remarkable genetic implications. It is this group of facts which is mainly responsible for the past popularity of the idea of plasmagenes.

a. Genoids

L'Héritier and Teissier (1937, and many further papers; see L'Héritier, 1951) discovered a remarkable set of facts relating to CO_2-susceptibility in *Drosophila.* The main observations are these (following L'Héritier, 1951). Ordinary flies can resist the gas for a long time and recover at once from narcosis. Sensitive ones do not recover; or, if they do, they are paralyzed. The seat of the latter effect is the thoracic ganglion. The sensitivity is inherited by what appears to be a cytoplasmic self-reproducing unit, which was called a "genoid." A normal fly can be made sensitive by transplantation of organs taken from sensitives or by injection of an extract of sensitives. This looks like the action of a virus. But the specific feature is that, once in the organism, the particle enters the germ track and is transmitted to the offspring in a definite way. (This is known also for certain parasites like the microsporidium of pebrine in the silkworm and the yeast-like symbionts of many insects, as detailed in Buchner, 1953.)

For the evaluation of these basic facts a number of details are important. In many respects the active factor behaves like a virus. Inactivation and filtration experiments reveal a size on the order of that of a virus. By continuous dilution of an extract a concentration can be reached which is no longer infective. In this case the individual particles behave independently, since the logarithm of the percentage of resistant flies varies linearly with the inverse of dilution. This permits an exact assay of infection results and work with arbitrary units of infection. A study of the incubation time revealed a curve which indicated an exponential multiplication of the particles, until death occurs. This incubation time is dependent upon external and internal factors. A further study of the progress of infection in the fly yielded results closely paralleling those for virus infections.

The next important point is that flies sensitive by birth yield a constant amount of virus during their whole imaginal life, but this amount varies according to the parent from whom the sensitivity comes. If sensitivity comes from the father, the yield is about 100,000 units, which is the same as after a one-unit injection. This shows that the spermatozoön contains a small number of particles. If the sensitivity comes from the mother, the virus content is much smaller, a few thousand to 30,000 units. This could be due to waste of some indispensable material in the egg, whatever this means. The facts thus far reported fit the idea of an infective virus.

We come now to the genetic features of the case. A female made sensitive by injection always produces some sensitive offspring from which a pure sensitive line can be derived. A male made sensitive does not transmit this, but the sons of sensitive females transmit sensitivity to a part of their offspring. This means, then, that in females, but not in males, acquired sensitivity always enters the germ track. Further, a fly which has inherited sensitivity from the father alone (who had a sensitive mother) behaves like an injected one: if it is a male it is resistant; if a female, some of its offspring are sensitive.

There are indications that mutation of the virus particle can take place. A line was isolated in which sons of sensitive females hardly transmitted the sensitivity, and this property remained constant. If a mixture of both types was administered to a fly, only one or the other type entered, or was found in, the germ line. Such preferences are, however, known for genuine viruses. Another rather complex case of behavior is attributed to mutation of the infective particles, but on the whole the facts recorded bear a striking similarity to the behavior of lysogenic bacteria toward phage.

The problem for our present discussion is whether the undoubtedly existing particles responsible for CO_2-sensitivity are viruses with a definite behavior or are plasmagenes behaving like viruses. A number of geneticists deny, a priori, a difference between genes and viruses: such a problem does not exist for them. It must be realized that for a long time the possibility has been discussed (see Buchner, 1953) that typical cellular inclusions like mitochondria are really symbionts or were such originally. Such a view has been considerably strengthened by the amazing facts on intracellular symbionts in insects with specialized nutrition which Buchner and his school (see 1953) have revealed in a series of remarkable papers and books, showing that these organisms of a yeast type supply the host organism with basic biochemical substances which it cannot synthesize. These symbionts are also transmitted in a specific way through the eggs. Of course nobody would speak here of plasmagenes, but we might make the point that such symbionts show one step in a process whereby external organisms may become part of the cellular structure. A brilliant discussion of this point in terms of biochemistry and virology has been presented by Lederberg (1952). We shall mention his conclusions later.

At present such phylogenetic speculations are not very fruitful. We may restrict ourselves therefore to the question whether the facts which L'Héritier analyzed so beautifully can be interpreted as proving a particulate cytoplasmic heredity. L'Héritier himself is very cautious, though his term "genoid" indicates the interpretation he would prefer. The facts seem to indicate to me the following. Different kinds of viruses are known: for example, the crystallizable ones and the bacteriophages with a complicated organization. Also, different kinds of substrates for virus reproduction are known: for example, ordinary bacteria and lysogenic bacteria. The facts discovered by L'Héritier show that the particles in question have all the important properties of viruses. Certain puzzling details, like the different behavior of sperm of different origin and the differences in propagation of the virus in infected and hereditary carriers, seem to indicate specific features of the cytoplasmic substrates. The apparent mutations may be described also in terms of virulence and substrate changes. Therefore, it seems that we are dealing with an infectious virus of special properties and substrate relations, which are extremely interesting, especially because the entrance of the virus into the germ cells leads to situations which simulate heredity in some respects. Still, I am unable to see that cytoplasmic heredity in any sense is involved, unless the facts might be advocated as demonstrating an evolutionary step that leads from an infectious virus to the establishment of a plasmagene. The legitimacy of the latter speculation may be accepted or doubted.

It was Muller who, after d'Hérelle's discovery of the bacteriophage, first suggested the idea that viruses are a kind of free living genes. But only after Stanley's work, proving one virus to be a nucleoprotein molecule (RNA!) visible and measurable in the electron microscope, did the comparison between virus and gene become popular. The reasons for the comparison are, of course, self-duplication, nucleoproteinic nature, and dependence upon a substrate. There can be no doubt that a comparison of bacteriophage with genes is wrong, since we know that the phage is an organism with a genetic structure which permits linkage and crossing over. Thus only the virus proper remains as a basis for the speculations maintaining that there is no difference between a virus and so-called plasmagenes, since all transitions are supposed to exist. The genoids of L'Héritier and the kappa particles are supposed to be such particulates, which we might call viruses or plasmagenes equally well. The main reason for such assumptions is that these cytoplasmic parasites or symbionts are controlled in their existence, number, and properties by genetic conditions of the host nucleus. It is overlooked, when such a conclusion is drawn, that all chemical, physical, and antigenic properties of the cytoplasm are under nuclear control. Since the cytoplasm is the environment for these parasites, anything that influences the environment, including normal or mutant loci in the nuclear genic material, may also affect the behavior of the parasites. The behavior of the tubercle bacillus is in some ways controlled also by the constitution, that is, the genetic makeup, of the host.

b. So-called cytoplasmic mutation in yeast

Ephrussi *et al.* (reviews and literature, 1950, 1951, 1953) have analyzed a "mutation" in yeast which results in the appearance of small colonies due to a respiratory deficiency: namely, the inability of the mutant cells to synthesize cytochrome oxidase (and other respiratory enzymes). Yeast may thrive on respiration in the presence of oxygen or on glycolytic fermentation in its absence. In the small mutant, cyanide-sensitive respiration is suppressed. The enzymatic details have been worked out by Slonimski (1952). An important point is that the study of fractions of homogenates shows that the mutant action is confined to a particulate structure of the cell. (See discussion below.) These "mutants" are vegetative mutants because they arise at a vegetative division (bud formation). The "mutation rate" may be small or rather high. In the presence of some acridines, like euflavine, it increases immensely, up to almost 100 per cent, meaning that each bud is a "mutant." This was checked for individual buds of single cells; an explanation by selection is thus excluded. These changes remain irreversible in the vegetative cycle. The high spontaneous "mutation rate," the occurrence of the "mutation" in several yeast species, the occurrence at a cell division, and the fact that the "mutation" can be induced in haploid and diploid cells lead to the conclusion that the mutant character is due to the loss or inactivation of an extranuclear, particulate, and self-reproducing factor required for the normal synthesis of the respiratory enzymes (see, above, Slonimski's fractionation). As a result the "mutants" are dependent upon accidental non-inclusion of the hypothetical particles in a forming bud, and the mutagenic action of the acridines is due to an elective toxic effect on these particles, which may then be excluded from the bud. (Ordinary genic mutations resembling these "vegetative mutants" also have occurred.)

It is rather interesting that the effect of euflavine in producing the "mutated" buds lasts over a number of generations even if the cells are returned to normal medium, which is not unexpected for a cytoplasmic effect.

The check for possible gene mutation is rather difficult because the enzyme-defective cells do not undergo meiosis. However, a normal yeast and a vegetative "mutant" of opposite mating type can be crossed with simultaneous introduction of markers. A normal 2:2 segregation follows for the markers, but no segregation for the respiratory effect, thus proving that the latter is of a cytoplasmic nature. Ephrussi therefore speaks (with an unfortunate terminology) of a cytoplasmic mutation based upon a cytoplasmic factor that is self-reproducing and particulate. If these particles are few in number, the possibility exists that a bud does not receive any of them, and is therefore a "loss mutant." (See the terminology below.) Euflavine would simply favor such an unequal division.

In a series of interesting experiments, Ephrussi further analyzed the way in which the acridines act in inducing the "mutation," whether an unequal distribution of particles is involved, or rather a poisoning of some of them; finally, whether the experiments could be explained by gene mutations (some with similar effects had been found) of the type of the so-called unstable genes which we discussed as position effects. These, as we have seen, can lead to variegations on the basis of threshold conditions (see I 2 C *d bb*). But the results of these special experiments agree best with Ephrussi's explanations given above, and we do not need to present them in detail.

In evaluating these important and beautifully analyzed facts for the problem of plasmon action of the substrate or particulate type, I should like to state that the description of the facts in terms of mutation, mutagenic agents, and even loss mutations—though perfectly justified in a purely descriptive sense, if we define mutation as any hereditary change—is apt to prejudicate a definite type of interpretation. In his last book (1953), Ephrussi himself mentions (fn., p. 34) this objection, but prefers to hold to what I consider an objectionable terminology, namely, in terms of plasmagenes. To make my point clear, I mention a well-known cytological fact which closely parallels the features of this case. It shows that a description of such processes without using misguiding genetic terms may clarify the problem and simultaneously prevent the suggestive implications based more on terminology than on the naked facts. It is known that in the spermatogenesis of the aphids a maturation division occurs in which one spermatocyte receives the X-chromosome, and is female-determining; the other is without X and should be male-determining. But this division is an unequal one for the cytoplasm so far as the major part of it goes into the female-determining daughter cell together with all the mitochondria. The small cell without mitochondria degenerates, obviously because of the absence of the respiratory enzymes. Theoretically, it is possible that the small budlike spermatid could survive and end its cycle as a somewhat pathological cell. If this were so we would have a complete parallel to the behavior of the yeast. We might call the unequal division a mutation, and even a loss mutation as far as the mitochondria are concerned, though this would only obscure the understanding.

This example is much more than a chance similarity. It is a clear hint that an unequal division involving the unequal distribution of a cytoplasmic component, the mitochondria, is a cellular possibility which may be caused by different external or internal agencies. The work of Winge and Laustsen (see II 2 C *a*) clearly suggests the hypothesis that in the present case the mitochondria, the carriers of respiratory enzymes, are the unequally distributed cytoplasmic particulates.

However, I want to emphasize that, in continuing the use of the term "loss mutation," and so on, the danger increases that superficial readers of this beautiful work are swept off their feet by the terminology and believe that here "plasmagenes" and their mutation have been demonstrated. I think that a careful consideration of the aphid example just discussed will show that the facts are rather simple and that there is no need to complicate the explanation by introducing the wobbly concept of plasmagenes, as some have done in referring to these facts. We should think twice before describing as mutation special features of cytoplasmic division involving unequal distribution of cytoplasmic components, and thus intimating that we are dealing with a process comparable to mutation of genic material. Actually, the fact of a 100 per cent mutation rate should suggest caution. This conclusion is independent of the details of the action of the active material (in this case the euflavine) upon the cytoplasmic constituents, whether it affects only their quantitative distribution, or sorts out different kinds of them, or dissolves, poisons, and agglutinates them. (See Ephrussi's detailed discussions.) It should again be emphasized that here, just as in the former cases, the cytoplasmic elements under suspicion are the mitochondria, and "cytoplasmic action on heredity" amounts to a generalized interference with the respiratory enzyme system (by removing the enzyme carriers) with consequences for all genetically controlled processes which are sensitive to such changes of what we may call, in a general way, the substratum. (See discussion of Michaelis' work, II 2 C *b*.)

An illustration of the good reasons for my warning against wrongly suggestive terminology occurs in further work of Ephrussi (see 1953). He found in a different strain what turned out to be a Mendelizing mutant for respiratory deficiency. This could be crossed to a clone, with that deficiency based upon the absence of the cytoplasmic carriers of the enzymes. The result was as expected: normal F_1 and 2:2 segregation in F_2, since this was an ordinary Mendelian cross and the zygote had the cytoplasmic particles from the parent normal in this respect. But Ephrussi calls both strains mutants, and therefore needs long explanations and many illustrations to explain the simple fact, which is made complicated by the terminology he uses. Of course the existence of these genuine recessive mutants shows that the cytoplasmic particulates (mitochondria?) are not completely autonomous, since a recessive mutant locus can prevent their function. In principle this is not different from the fact that a recessive mutant in *Drosophila* prevents the formation of kynurenine from tryptophane. The only difference, I think, is that in the first example the site of an enzymatic action can be located as some particulate constituents of the cytoplasm which can be centrifuged and fractionated; in the latter example we do not know the place in the cytoplasm where kynurenine is formed, though in *Ephestia* (Kühn, 1948) we know the sites where it takes place. In other words, we face a general relation between a mutant locus and a biochemical function, which is found in all appropriate studies. With due respect for the brilliant analysis, I conclude that serious misunderstandings and misuse of the facts as support of the plasmagene hypothesis would have been avoided if the experiments had been described in the following terminology. Absence of a group of respiratory enzymes in yeast can be caused by a recessive mutant locus (I have explained elsewhere why I consider unjustified the extrapolation upon a dominant locus responsible for the normal function). The same phenotypic effect as a phenocopy can be produced by the action of euflavine, which removes the carriers of the enzymes. So far this is the only case in which we know how a phenocopy is produced: by removal of a formed cytoplasmic particle from the cell via an unequal division in regard to this particle, while in the mutant the synthesis of the enzyme or a needed coenzyme or any other irreplaceable stuff for synthesis or for the function of the enzyme is probably prevented. In addition, the phenocopy is reproduced by vegetative propagation because of the special feature of loss of something. The fact reported by Ephrussi that recessive mutant loci exist which influence the frequency of these abnormal divisions is interesting, but it does not change the general feature. After all, the occurrence of the abnormal divisions, like any other organismic variation, may be due to chance variation (i.e., environment) or to genetic change.

c. The killer effect

One of the most brilliant pieces of genetic analysis has been performed by Sonneborn and his school (see 1947, 1951*a*) for the killer effect in *Paramecium.* This work is mainly responsible for the reawakening of interest in cytoplasmic heredity in the United States, while in Europe it has been ever present since the early work of Correns, Bateson, Goldschmidt, and von Wettstein, quoted previously. It seemed that here a clear case of particulate cytoplasmic effect had been established, until Sonneborn himself found decisive facts which do not favor such an explanation. Sonneborn's own position will be discussed in the conclusions, at the end of this chapter, on cytoplasmic heredity.

The main facts are these. Certain lines of *Paramecium aurelia* were found (rather rarely) which secreted a substance called paramecin, later proved to be a nucleoprotein. This substance kills other paramecia called sensitives. It is formed only in the presence of an allele K (homo- or heterozygous), but not in the presence of kk. Since, in normal conjugation, only nuclear material is exchanged, the exconjugants are genetically alike but different in regard to cytoplasm. All sensitives remained sensitives and killers remained killers, showing the killing capacity to be a purely cytoplasmic property, though working only in the presence of K. The cytoplasmic property is called kappa. If, under proper conditions, cytoplasm is exchanged between the conjugants, the former sensitive becomes a killer, and so do his descendants. Sensitives can further be transformed into killers by exposing them to broken up bodies of killers; and killers can lose this capacity after treatment with X rays or nitrogen mustard. All this suggests the presence of kappa particles in the killer cytoplasm. The first proof of this conclusion was found when it was shown that kappa could be diluted by quick growth of the well-nourished cytoplasm with which kappa could not keep pace. Or kappa could be accumulated by the opposite process. Such experiments permitted a very ingenious way of calculating the number of kappa particles present in the cytoplasm (Preer). Finally it turned out that these particles are visible, can be stained, consist of nucleoprotein (DNA), and look and behave like viruses of the *Rickettsia* type. Also mutants have been found which change the killing effect in a number of visible details in the victims. The number of kappa particles in the heterozygote is half of what it is in the homozygote.

If we look at these general facts, in what I should like to call the naïve way, it is difficult to see why the kappa viruses should be called cytoplasmic genes, or why cytoplasmic inheritance would be involved at all. All facts point to viruses, which produce a poisonous product, deadly for non-carriers of the virus. The viruses are self-propagating within the cytoplasm, and their propagation can be influenced by environmental conditions such as temperature and food, and also by genetically controlled chemical properties of the cytoplasm. They may mutate, may be transferred artificially, in short, may show any known property of viruses, including the chemical composition. It seems to me that this "naïve" view is the one we should apply in the interest of clarity. Such a view, which does not detract in any way from the importance and brilliancy of the work, is the only safe one. It is something different if we say, with Ephrussi (53), that, whatever the ultimate origin of kappa, it provides us with a *model* of a cytoplasmic particle responsible for a specific hereditary trait. But I think it dangerous to say with Ephrussi (1953) in another place—actually italicized—that "the killer phenotype offers us another example of a character, the development of which depends both on the cytoplasm and on the nucleus." Kappa is no character; it does not depend upon the cytoplasm in a genetic sense, but lives and propagates in the cytoplasm if it is not prevented by a definite genetic (i.e., nuclear) constitution. The non-immune cytoplasm is the natural environment of the "parasite" and therefore may influence it. This is clearly no genetic relationship, but one between two organisms. The kappa particles have been hailed many times as the real plasmagenes. Their story should make us wary of these imaginary entities. We shall return to this below in a more general discussion, where Lederberg's interpretation will be taken up.

At this point I might add that, according to Hämmerling (1946), the symbiontic chlorellae of *Stentor* and *Paramecium* (real cells with nucleus in this case) show most of the features of kappa particles. They can be removed by differential cell division and reinfected; they have a constant number, and also are genetically specific, meaning specifically reacting to genetically different cytoplasm. One more important point in favor of the naïve interpretation is that the kappa particles contain DNA, which is otherwise not present or very rarely present in the cytoplasm (except in developing eggs) and thus suggests a virus.

It should be emphasized that the kappa particles are completely different from the assumed genetic particles in yeast (mitochondria) carrying the respiratory enzymes, though both types have been claimed in favor of the theory of plasmagenes. The two types of bodies could be homologized only through phylogenetic speculations on the origin of mitochondria, which actually have been tried, but should at present be treated with caution. (See further discussion below.)

d. The plastids

aa. Nature of plastids

Clearly the most difficult topic in the discussion of particulate cytoplasmic effects is the problem of the plastids in the plant cells. The relation of these cell organelles to heredity was first studied by Correns in classic experiments (see his review, 1937), and interest in the topic never abated (see Renner, 1922–1936; Rhoades' review, 1946;

Weier and Stocking, 1952). A discussion from the point of view of particulate cytoplasmic inheritance must start with an appraisal of the nature of the plastids. Plastids as the seat of chlorophyll, xanthophyll, and so on are the seat of the autotrophic metabolism of plants synthesizing starch by photosynthesis. The localization of this property in definite bodies, included in the cytoplasm, is certainly a very specific feature and not a general protoplasmic one. Thus it is understandable that some students distinguished the totality of plastids as a plastidome from genome and plasmon to which nowadays could be added also the chondriome (Dangeard, Renner). If this distinction is correct, the genetic behavior of the plastids would be a problem outside that of cytoplasmic inheritance. This is not a purely academic or semantic question. It is well known that a number of animal species in Protozoa, Hydrozoa, Platyhelminthes, and Mollusca have returned to purely or partial autotrophic metabolism by incorporating in their cells symbiontic unicellular algae. This suggests the possibility, greatly enhanced by the recent work on symbiosis by the Buchner school, that the plastids may be considered as symbionts of the plant cells, that is, dependent organisms like parasites and viruses. Many biologists are favorable to such a view which, however, can neither be proved nor disproved at present. But the possibility that it may be true makes us very cautious when it comes to treating plastid behavior as a phenomenon of cytoplasmic inheritance or even as an example of plasmagenes.

There is still no consensus regarding the cycle of the plastids. There is no doubt that plastids, once seen, multiply by division, as do centromeres and kinetosomes (see I 1). We may call this a property of self-duplication, though it seems rather formalistic to identify it with the self-duplication of genic material. Unfortunately, there is no final information in regard to the autonomy of the plastids. Some cytologists believe that plastids can be formed *de novo,* but more frequently it is assumed that they are products of transformation of mitochondria (Guillermond). There is a primary probability that this is true in view of the fact that both structures have to do with the respiratory function (in the widest sense) of the cell. Mitochondria, like plastids, are self-duplicating. Some authors (see DuBuy, Woods, and Lackey, 1950) are very outspoken in asserting that "the chloroplasts of higher plants derive from the mitochondrial elements of the cell and possess extranuclear hereditary entities." They base this definite statement on their work, showing that plant mitochondria like those of animals contain all the enzymes of the oxidation system and that also the chloroplasts contain oxidizing enzymes. They claim further that so-called plastid mutation (cases of variegation) produces a derangement of the enzyme systems which becomes visible in the mitochondria as well as in the plastids. Assuming the correctness of the findings, they might, however, be explained in more than one way.

Another opinion is that developing plastids go back to granules which look exactly like mitochondria but are different from the beginning. Others maintain that they have demonstrated such a difference by staining reactions. Further claims are that the primordia of plastids go down in size to the limits of visibility and beyond that into the molecular level. If the latter is true, the plastids may be actually autonomous but changing from a molecular unit to a visible granule to a large disc of complicated chemical constitution (permitting all the steps of photosynthesis). If this is so, we might compare the plastid, for description's sake only, to an organism and its development from primordia to the development of an organism from an egg, the egg in this simile being the equivalent of the invisible molecular plastid primordium. In favor of this view is the fact that plastids may be affected by antibiotics and then cease multiplying! (see Ephrussi, 1953). A parallel to the vegetative phase of phage could be established, especially since it has been maintained that chloroplasts contain DNA as well as RNA (Metzner, 1952).

This brief survey already shows that the morphological facts do not permit us to decide upon the nature of the plastids, though it looks as if they were autonomous, self-reproducing, organism-like structures with a kind of life cycle, but certainly not cytoplasmic differentiations. The electron microscope reveals a disc-shaped structure with different layers, which at present does not help the understanding, though it may have a special meaning for the process of photosynthesis. We mentioned already that it has been maintained that plastids contain DNA. But the experts on staining reactions are not convinced that these claims are valid, and it is therefore indicated that no conclusions should be based upon the statements. Conclusions concerning the nature of the plastids and their possible relation to cytoplasmic inheritance will have to be reached mainly from a study of the genetical facts, as there is clearly an interrelation between plastid behavior and genetic constitution.

Correns (1937) states that the decisive difference between plastids and symbionts is that the behavior of the plastids is controlled in the majority of cases by the genic material in the chromosomes. The simplest case is, of course, given when differences in the quantity of chlorophyll per plastid, or differences in shape and chemistry of the starch formed, show simple Mendelian behavior. For the present discussion, the most important examples are found in the group of variegations based upon chlorophyll-bearing plastids. Variegation may often be the result of ordinary Mendelizing mutation, but the chief interest is centered upon less simple facts.

For the interpretation it is also of importance to know whether the pollen transfers plastids (or leucoplasts) into the egg at the time of fertilization. The overwhelming majority of cytological and genetic evidence is not in favor of this. But we mentioned before some facts (II 2 C *a*) which lend themselves to the interpretation that a little sperm cytoplasm enters the egg. If leucoplasts may vary down to submicroscopic dimensions, as is generally accepted, the possibility cannot be denied that the pollen nucleus carries with a cytoplasmic sheath some leucoplasts into the egg. We shall report below that genetic facts exist which require this.

bb. Plastids and surrounding cytoplasm

The first group of facts which led to very different interpretations in the discussion carried on over almost fifty years since Correns' (1903, 1909; see 1937) basic work, relates to what Correns called the "status albomaculatus." Plants in this condition show a mosaic of more or less large green and white spots. In the cells of the white sectors the plastids are colorless and also degenerated. Flowers of pure green branches produce only green offspring with whatever pollen; those from pure white branches, only white offspring. The inheritance is purely maternal. Mixed branches produce white, green, and mixed offspring.

Baur (1909) had proposed the explanation that the white (or "sick") plastids were derived from normal ones by mutation, that the egg cells contained both types, and that during development they were sorted out by chance. The mixed condition might be the result of fertilization involving transmission of plastids by the pollen. Correns proved experimentally that this does not happen. Thus the egg cells must already have contained both types. If this is so, Correns argued correctly, mixed vegetative cells should be frequent, especially at the borders of white and green sectors. Actually, they are absent or rare, and may require a different explanation. Correns showed then that an arithmetical study of the consequences of the chance sorting out of two types at cell division leads to results which do not agree with the actual structure of albomaculatus. Correns therefore proposed a different hypothesis, by which the problem entered the field of cytoplasmic inheritance while doing away with plastid mutation and sorting out. He assumed that in the cases of status albomaculatus the cytoplasm is in a labile condition between normal and "sick," the latter not permitting the plastids to become green. Unknown conditions (i.e., chance) decide which condition prevails and remains constant (we might speak of an alternative norm of reaction decided by unknown causes). From the point of view of cytoplasmic inheritance, this explanation puts the case in the same category as all the other previously discussed ones of the type of cytoplasm as substrate, with additional alternative norm of reaction.

Rhoades (1947), who generally agrees with Correns' position, likes to go a step farther. He bases his views on the work of Anderson (1923) and Demerec (1927), who found that in maize the maternally inherited variegation results in green, yellow, and striped seedlings not distributed at random on the ear. To Rhoades this indicates that segregation of some discrete cytoplasmic component controlling plastid development occurs, which might be called a plasmagene. He thinks that there are two possibilities: either a plasmagene affecting plastid development exists in a normal or abnormal form; or only one type of plasmagene exists which is not present in sufficient numbers to be handed equally to both daughter cells, one of which does not receive enough. "On the basis of the first alternative, the ratio of abnormal to normal plasmagenes would determine the type of plastid development. Those cells with a critical percentage of abnormal plasmagenes would contain poorly developed plastids, while those cells with higher proportions of normal plasmagenes would have more normally developed plastids. The occurrence in Anderson's strain of a transition zone—with graded intermediate plastid colors—between green and yellow stripes that have different cell lineages, suggests that these plasmagenes are able to pass through cell membranes. It also argues in favor of the first alternative . . ."

I do not think that this argument is very convincing, apart from the objection which Correns already made on the basis of showing that such a sorting out does not work when considered in detail, and apart from the rather offensive idea of genes passing through the cell membrane. The hypothesis tries to explain the facts in terms of different particulate determiners and their shuffling. As long as it is possible to understand the facts on a physiological basis (i.e., actions), such an explanation seems to be simpler. If, in green-white variegation, an all-or-none effect of a specific ("sick") cytoplasm is involved, there is no reason why in green-yellow variegation, involving different chemical processes of chlorophyll synthesis, transitions between the green and yellow product should not be possible, dependent upon any type of environmental effect which may include the position of the first cells in the whole. Correns possibly thought of such an interpretation when he said that the features in maize are caused by the structure of grasses and therefore are not of genetic importance. I realize that the difference between the explanation of some special features in terms of plasmagenes and that in terms of physiological processes involves a difference in basic thinking, as I have tried to show for a number of examples in different fields of genetics (Goldschmidt, 1954).

Thus I like to conclude that the facts relating to status albomaculatus in plants demonstrate another example of cytoplasmic, hereditary differences of the substrate type, which, however, are not collaborating with or modifying genically controlled reactions but are affecting chemical processes within an autonomous inclusion of the cytoplasm, the plastids. In an inquiry into the genetic properties of the plastids, the facts show only that the function of the plastids is dependent on the surrounding cytoplasm, which after all is not surprising, even if they are autonomous in regard to duplication.

It should be added that Renner (1922 ff.), who analyzed cases in *Oenothera* with undoubted genetic differences of plastids which can be sorted out, thinks that Correns' experiments might be explained on the basis of plastid differences as opposed to cytoplasmic ones. Renner's analysis will be discussed in the following sections. Here it may be stated that Correns, Wettstein, Noack, and Rhoades agree that some facts may be explained best in Correns' way by a labile cytoplasm affecting plastid function. Renner, however, thinks that in all cases genetically different plastids and their sorting out may be involved, and Wettstein (in Correns, 1937) accepts this, at least for a majority of cases. But there are also claims by Noack that within the same material both types occur simultaneously. In the remarkable material of Andersson-Kottö (1930) in ferns, the experimental facts are so complicated that it is hardly possible to explain them in one or the other way. The present discussion does not intend to analyze the problem of plant variegation. We are interested only in knowing whether the genetic behavior of the plastids may be taken as a proof for the existence of plasmagenes and, generally, what their behavior means for the problems of cytoplasmic inheritance.

cc. Primary plastid differences

While in Correns' and his successors' material of hereditary variegation the facts were in favor of the absence of genetic differences between the plastids, a considerable group of experiments show in other cases that actually the plastids themselves can be genetically different. The classic work is that of Renner on *Oenothera* crosses (see Renner, 1936) in which a most penetrating theoretical discussion is found. The type of experimentation is made possible by the complex-heterozygotic composition of *Oenothera* which easily permits the combining of entire genomes of one type with different cytoplasms, just as if only a single Mendelian difference were involved. The procedure is to produce, by crossing, combinations of the homozygous and heterozygous genomes with the reciprocal cytoplasms containing the respective plastids, including also possible transfer of plastids by the pollen. In some cases, the plastids from one species cannot form chlorophyll in the presence of a hybrid or foreign genome. If plastids are transferred with the pollen, a plastid mixture can be obtained which later segregates and produces variegation. Thus it is shown that plastids may be physiologically different. We may say that this difference is a different norm of reaction with their environment (e.g., success or failure in chlorophyll synthesis). Not only a substrate type difference between the two plasmons is demonstrated, but also a genetic difference between the plastids from different species. Proof of this may be derived from the fact that plastids which have gone through many hybrid generations in the wrong cytoplasm act normally at once when inserted into the proper cytoplasm. Furthermore, in such crosses, cases are found in which both types of plastids may function in the cytoplasm of a heterozygote. If such hybrids are crossed to a third species, the genome of which permits only one of the plastid types to function, the result is variegation, demonstrating again the plastid difference. From an immense body of such facts Renner concluded that plastids may be genetically different as autonomous, self-duplicating bodies and that therefore one might speak of a separate "plastidome."

Though there can be no doubt that these conclusions are correct per se, it does not mean that all comparable cases of variegation are necessarily based upon the same principle. Thus it may be imagined that both types, plastid difference and segregation and a labile cytoplasm influencing plastid function, may occur together, which leads to complicated results and may account for basic differences in interpretation such as those of Noack and Renner (see Renner, 1936). However, such and other imaginable complications would not change the fact that genetically different and constant plastids exist. Rhoades (1946) pointed out that in view of the lack of visible differences between the plastid types and the exclusive presence of differences of reaction with a definite cytoplasm, we cannot exclude the possibility that different plasmagenes are present which may be sorted out—a dangerous terminology, I think, because it suggests a segregation of plasmagenes, comparable to segregation of nuclear genes (whether this is intended or not). Therefore I prefer to speak of genetically different plasmons which may be mixed and separated; this amounts to an explanation in terms of Correns' view, though with a different terminology.

A further step in the analysis of genetic properties of plastids has been made in Schwemmle's work with crosses of *Oenothera Berteriana* and *odorata* (see Schwemmle, Hanstein, Sturm, and Binder, 1938), in which plastid behavior and plasmon inherited characters were studied simultaneously. According to Renner's experiments a hybrid plant may contain the plastids of the two parental species in the maternal cytoplasm (plastids introduced by egg and pollen). This results in a variegated plant; and, in proper plastid distribution (i.e., sorting out), pure pale or green branches may be formed, which can be propagated. Thus from the cross A × B a line can be obtained with A cytoplasm and B plastids plus different genomes. Accordingly, many lines of *O. Berteriana* × *odorata* were established in diverse combinations. This allows distinguishing the maternal effects due to cytoplasm (of the substrate type) from those which must be due to plastids. It was found that leaf shape is influenced by the plastids present, which must interact in some way with the genome in the control of a morphological character, certainly a remarkable fact. This may sound less astonishing if we realize that a difference in physiological function of plastids will necessarily result in some biochemical difference of the surroundng cytoplasm, which then acts as a different substrate for genic function, just as in the cases studied above. It would be wrong to consider these plastids as part genetic determinants for leaf shape. Their role is better compared with a temperature or chemical action upon cytoplasm, which, as we saw, shifts genic effects in a quantitative way.

The next consequence of such facts is to look for plastid mutations. This is not an easy task. It is well known that plastid characters may be controlled by genic changes. In such well-analyzed plants as maize, dozens of chromosomal loci are known the mutation of which affects the color or distribution of the plastids. This can hardly be said to be a mutation of the plastids, since the genic material obviously controls cytoplasmic conditions, which provide a different environment for the plastids to grow in. An actual mutation of plastids alone would result in a cell containing two types of plastids, normal and mutant ones, with the consequence of hereditary behavior identical with that found in Renner's and Schwemmle's work. In a number of cases such a result has been claimed (see review by Rhoades, 1946), not as a spontaneous occurrence in the plastids but as a result of genic action. It is of course known that genic mutation may be caused by the presence of "mutator" loci, as discussed above. Thus it might be concluded that genic action could as well produce plastid mutation (though the logic of such a conclusion might be regarded as doubtful).

The general trend of such experiments, as exemplified by Rhoades' (1943) work on the iojap locus in maize, is that differently colored sectors appear in the presence of the mutant locus, which, if isolated, turn out to be henceforth independent of the genic constitution and remain constant in breeding. Rhoades found many details in the behavior of these plastids which would suggest that the ij locus affects the cytoplasm rather than the plastids, the fate of the plastids being controlled by the cytoplasmic change, meaning that the plastids had not mutated, but only failed to develop normally when the cytoplasm was little modified. They were changed irreversibly with a large change in the cytoplasm. The latter would then be called mutation of the plastids, but it cannot be distinguished from an irreversible change in the cytoplasm alone. Only experiments of the type performed by Schwemmle, hardly possible in maize, could distinguish this alternative. Thus for the time being a genuine or induced mutability of plastids may be considered as not yet proved. Recently Rhoades (1950) reported that the same mutant iojap also induces a cytoplasmic condition, male sterility, similar to that which we studied before (see II 2 C *b*). We considered it there as one of many cases of plasmon effect of a generalized nature, all being of the type of inhibitions. In this discussion we showed that the facts do not prove the presence of autonomous genetic units in the cytoplasm, but rather indicate an inhibitory effect upon the respiratory enzyme system located in the mitochondria. Rhoades (1950) tends to localize his sterility effect in the mitochondria, so that our previous discussions apply to this case also. Its special feature is, however, that the same mutant affects both chloroplast and, if the assumption is correct, mitochondrial behavior. This might be used as an argument for the mitochondrial origin of plastids (see Sonneborn, 1955), but it might just as well mean a direct (mitochondria) and an indirect (plastids) inhibitory effect upon respiratory activity of the cytoplasm, conditioned by the respective mutants.

We have spoken many times of cytoplasmic features under the control of the nucleus. Since the genome is supposed to exercise its controlling function upon the cytoplasm, which is the seat of all morphogenetic and physiological processes in the cell, it is not surprising to find specific differentiations of the cytoplasm like plastids and mitochondria (whatever their nature and origin) under genic control. We have also mentioned that features of the nucleus and its chromosomes may, vice versa, be influenced by the cytoplasm. This may look like primary cytoplasmic conditioning (i.e., cytoplasmic heredity) which controls even the nucleus, but such a conclusion would be wrong. If we take examples like *Ascaris* diminution or the germ-track cells of insects, discussed earlier, there can be no doubt that the differentiation of the oöplasm, which controls nuclear features, has been brought about by processes taking place during oögenesis under the influence of the nucleus. All the facts of predetermination discussed previously prove this to be true. This does not exclude the existence of cytoplasmic features which are not autonomous but rather dependent upon the environment. If, as Schleip (1929) reports, the polarity of the egg cell is sometimes determined by its primary location in the ovarial epithelium, we have an example of a non-autonomous determination, namely, conditioned by the environmental one; a similar example is the relation of the symmetry plane in the frog egg to the path of the sperm. These facts clearly have nothing to do with cytoplasmic heredity via autonomous differentiations.

A good example of this nucleo-cytoplasmic interrelation in both directions is found in Sonneborn's work on mating types of *Paramecium* (1955). He showed in very ingenious experiments that mating type is controlled by the macronucleus. But under the influence of specific cytoplasm the mating type can be changed (the active cytoplasm is introduced by bridge formation in conjugation). However, the cytoplasmic action takes place only when newly formed macronuclei are present (by division of the syncaryon). If, under specific circumstances, a macronucleus in the exconjugant is formed from rests of the old macronucleus, the cytoplasmic action in changing the mating type fails. Further experiments by Nanney, Sonneborn, and others (see Sonneborn, 1955) now show that, after all, this strange cytoplasmic property which acts upon the macronuclei is not autonomous but is itself under nuclear control, just as in *Ascaris* and other cases we have mentioned.

In view of these facts Sonneborn draws general conclusions which are much more cautious than those usually presented by the believers in plasmagenes. To quote: "These considerations, like others set forth in recent years by other investigators, render less sharp and simple our concepts of mutation, self-duplication, genetic materials, and the genetic system. The undisputed two-way interaction between nucleus and cytoplasm does no violence to the simple, monistic concept that genetic control resides ultimately in the nucleus alone, so long as the nucleus is the only genetic material in the system. However, if by genetic material we mean any material which controls the formation of more of its own kind and which, if changed, controls the formation of the new kind, then some of the results . . . speak for the inclusion of the cytoplasm as genetic material and as part of the genetic system." We have made it sufficiently clear where we stand after considering the entire body of facts.

One more point may be made in regard to cytoplasmic control of the nucleus. It is well known that in aphids, after many generations of diploid parthenogenesis producing only females, males appear—sometimes from special arrhenotoke mothers—by a strange process of eliminating one X-chromosome from the egg during the equational division of the parthenogenetic diploid egg. Since this process is influenced by the number of preceding parthenogenetic generations, by temperature, and sometimes by the maternal organism (the females producing only males), there can be hardly any doubt that the causative agent is a cytoplasmic condition. The fact that all imaginable variants are realized in different forms—for example, no males, males after few or many generations, males only from certain females, which produce the elimination of one X in all their eggs, and males and females from the same mothers—suggests the presence of threshold conditions in the cytoplasm and the accumulation of some substance in the course of generations which, when concentrated beyond the threshold, exercises the effect upon chromosomal behavior. The same interpretation must apply to the fact that the males as well as the simultaneous females suddenly undergo typical meiosis (meaning reductional divisions) while, thus far, the females had only equational ones. Furthermore, Seiler (1920) could control the movements of the X- and Y-chromosomes in the meiosis of the moth *Talaeporia* by temperature action upon the eggs. Here is a body of facts, hardly analyzed in respect of our problem, which show definite cytoplasmic control of nuclear behavior; but this control can hardly be called cytoplasmic heredity, much less one by plasmagenes.

3

CONCLUSIONS AND THEORETICAL

The views on cytoplasmic heredity have been in constant flux since Correns brought up the subject in early Mendelian days. For a long time biologists talked about the monopoly of the nucleus, which meant that the cytoplasm is only the place in which the genic material of the nucleus acts. When cases became known in which the specific cytoplasm affected the results of genically controlled actions, the cytoplasm was endowed with hereditary properties. Correns already had developed some general ideas on this subject in 1900. He assumed that the cytoplasm contains a mechanism (an unfortunate term because a chemical condition was meant) which is necessary for genic action. During development these mechanisms are sorted out and the different genes act only upon the proper ones. This mechanism (chemism) is specific for the species. This is a somewhat awkward statement of ideas on genic action in development (we shall later discuss them in detail), which are based upon the facts of experimental embryology.

When cases of specific cytoplasmic action were later found, the idea of a kind of substrate action of the cytoplasm as a whole gained ground; it found its expression especially in Wettstein's concept of the plasmon, and in Strasburger's idea of the idiocytoplasm. At about the same time, when Goldschmidt (1924) presented the first case of cytoplasmic effect upon gene-controlled characters in animals, Winkler

(1924) spoke of plasmagenes, and Harder (1927) followed him. Correns countered this idea with the statement that we should speak of plasmagenes only if many different ones could be found to be sorted out in the course of cell divisions. If, however, the entire cytoplasm is involved, as in all the early work, the logical assumption is that the cytoplasm is involved in all genic actions; that is, the cytoplasm is a specific substrate or plasmon. We saw how the successors of Wettstein changed this simple idea, to which Correns clung, into that of the plasmon-sensitive genes, which I criticized as a rather oblique view of the facts.

The great new upswing of the interest in cytoplasmic heredity came when viruses entered the field of genetic study and still more when Sonneborn's work on *Paramecium* introduced what looked like corpuscular plasmatic entities of heredity, plasmagenes. Cytoplasmic heredity via plasmagenes became so popular that in textbooks and symposia plasmagenes were presented as established facts, and geneticists who remained cautious were considered fossils. Some geneticists and even embryologists ceased speaking of cytoplasm in genetic discussions, but used the term "plasmagenes" for whatever property of the cytoplasm they discussed. Then Sonneborn in his indefatigable search for a full knowledge of the killer effect, the cornerstone of the theory of plasmagenes, found that the plasmagenes were visible virus-like bodies of the *Rickettsia* type. This discovery dampened the enthusiasm for plasmagenes, and we are now again in a phase which recognizes the plasmon in a certain sense but is skeptical about plasmagenes. I have always been among the skeptics, and the foregoing presentation amply illustrates the reasons for it.

Most informative and eloquent discussions of the subject in its present state have been made by Sonneborn (1949, 1950, 1951*a*,*b*, 1955). He realizes that in many cases the cytoplasm acts as a substrate, affecting quantitatively gene-controlled reactions. Self-duplicating elements in the cytoplasm exercise their own effects interacting with those of the genes. He expresses this interaction in terms of reaction norm. "What is transmitted during reproduction is genetic material with a particular reaction norm. The reaction norm denotes different responses under different conditions, without change in the responding genetic materials. The cytoplasmic genetic materials constitute or control part of the conditions to which the genes respond, and the nuclear genetic materials constitute or control part of the conditions to which the cytoplasmic genetic materials respond. The phenotype is the result of interaction between the two components of the genic system under the conditions in which they are operating." One such interaction is given when alternative genic actions in the same cell are decided by a specific cytoplasmic condition, as is the case frequently in sex determination. Regarding the self-duplicating parts of the cytoplasm, he feels sure that kinetosomes, plastids, and probably mitochondria are such, though I believe that we can consider these (except mitochondria) as specific features of certain cells which can hardly be put in the same category as the general hereditary properties of the cytoplasm. Sonneborn expects the main emphasis in the future to be on a particular self-perpetuating molecular pattern, which could include the surface of plastids and mitochondria as well as the fibrillar protoplasm. Up to this point these views of Sonneborn are borne out by the material reviewed, and in general are not different from the conclusions presented here with the individual facts. Recently he goes a step farther in regard to mitochondria (1955). I quote: "Taken altogether, the various lines of evidence discussed above raise the possibility—to put the matter cautiously—that the mitochondria will prove to be a physical basis of normal cytoplasmic inheritance—a view that has a long history . . . The theoretical importance of this possibility is far greater than the already well-established role of chloroplasts in cytoplasmic inheritance, for mitochondria, unlike chloroplasts, are common to all organisms, animals as well as plants." I have enlarged sufficiently upon this subject and shown that it is not advisable to call mitochondrial (and plastid) conditions and their change cytoplasmic heredity (see II 2 E *b*).

Unfortunately, as I look at it, Sonneborn is still in favor of speaking of plasmagenes, which includes all self-perpetuating and mutable plasma constituents, such as plastids and mitochondria but also kinetosomes, centrioles, and even kappa particles. "Meanwhile I shall employ the term plasmagene for those cytoplasmic structures known to manifest genic properties, however infelicitous this may seem when applied to bodies large enough to be microscopically visible" (Sonneborn, 1950). One might say that a discussion of this attitude amounts to semantics or is purely academic. Sonneborn himself holds this view on the question whether kappa particles and "genoids" are viruses or proviruses (Darlington), both being borderline cases. This view would have been correct twenty years ago. Today the situation is that the plasmagene terminology may induce those not acquainted with the facts and their interpretations, and also those whose enthusiasm gets the better of their cool thinking, to talk and write about plasmagenes as if they were a well-established counterpart of nuclear genic material. This is bound to lead to hypotheses in many fields which, then, will be based not on established facts but on a suggestive and misleading terminology. Therefore I should like the term "plasmagene" to disappear from the genetic vocabulary. Sonneborn himself says, only two pages after the quotation: ". . . a priori considerations render improbable the possibility that such plasmagenes could persist and multiply except in cytoplasm of a definite constitution, which could scarcely be free from decisive gene modification. I therefore doubt whether totally gene-independent cytoplasmic inheritance exists in any form, based on plasmagenes or otherwise."

One might discuss the problem of whether viruses, kappa particles, mitochondria, genoids, and cytoplasmic genetic material are a series of external aspects of the same basic thing, and thus lead to a comparison with the nuclear genetic material resulting in the conclusion that all of them are "genes." I am convinced that this is a speculation not based upon the facts, either those relating to the so-called gene, or those relating to viruses, or those concerning cytoplasmic inheritance including the plastids. For the time being it appears safer to be noncommittal and to look at the entities involved, genes in the classic or modern sense, a generalized plasmon, mitochondria, plastids, virus-like parasites, or symbionts and genuine virus as different organizations with different physiological activities. Ephrussi (1953) has proposed treating the kappa particles at least as a kind of model for cytoplasmic particulate inheritance. I do not agree with this compromise because it can serve only to put another prop under the tumbling plasmagene. Why not simply let it drop out?

My point of view, of course, does not exclude the formulation of ideas on the relative values, merits, and even phylogenetic origin of all these entities. A most penetrating analysis of the whole situation, drawing mainly upon facts of bacterial and yeast genetics, has been made by Lederberg (1952). He considers as one of the decisive points involved a clear notion of what genetic autonomy or self-reproduction is. Therefore he asks what criteria are applicable when deciding whether small units in the cell are self-reproducing or rather reproduced by the organism as a whole. "The problem is usually approached by abstracting the unit in question from the organism. If it is then no longer produced by the organism, it is concluded to be self-reproducing. This has unfortunately been taken to mean that the unit is autosynthetic, but the proof shows only self-dependence, not self-sufficiency. In this context, self-dependence describes a wide range of reactions from simple autocatalytic reactions which may direct the chemical evolution of intracellular metabolites, to self-contained autotrophic organisms. The position of the gene in this hierarchy is not established." He stresses that an experimental proof for self-dependence of a visible particle is very difficult, requiring (as with nuclear genic material) a complete parallelism in the distribution of the particle with the effects of the plasmids (a term he prefers to plasmagenes). Also the capacity for mutation is not necessarily a criterion; it may be only the expression of structural complexity, rearrangements of the pattern being interpreted as mutations of the complex. (See our discussion of mutation as pattern change given previously.)

In making the step from the assumed "plasmids" to viruses and symbionts, Lederberg cautions that the properties of plasmagenes may be imputed readily to viruses and vice versa. He thinks attention should be focused on plasmid functions which may change from adaptive to pathological . . . "Present evidence points to the nucleus as the predominant, if not quite exclusive, seat of hereditary factors in most organisms . . . However, we learn less, not more, if we exclude extranuclear agents as hereditary factors because they may also simulate symbionts or parasites; such behavior is important but incidental to their genetic functions. The cell or the organism is not readily delimited in the presence of plasmids whose coördination may grade from the plasmagenes to frank parasites . . . How then shall we choose the boundaries of the gene-complex that constitutes an individual organism? If hierarchical definitions are to serve the scientist, rather than the scientist serve an Aristotelian category, different uses should dictate different usages. The geneticist may well choose that entity whose reproduction is unified and, hence, functions as an individual in evolution by natural selection. The microbiologist will focus his interest on the smallest units he can separate and cultivate in controlled experiments, in test tubes, eggs, bacteria or experimental animals. Genetics, symbiontology and virology have a common meeting place within the cell. There is much to be gained by any communication between them which leads to the diffusion of their methodologies and the obliteration of semantic barriers." Our former discussion indicates how far I am able to follow this attitude and where our ways are parting at present.

I have refrained thus far from more than mentioning the idea that viruses are directly comparable to genes and that there is a complete series of transitions from virus to plasmagene to nuclear gene. This idea, though always highly speculative, has lost any sense, I think, since we know that viruses are highly complicated organisms. There are, of course, very different kinds of viruses. The crystallizable plant viruses, being RNA in nature, are a special group which at present it is rather difficult to compare with animal viruses and bacteriophages. At the other end are the microscopically visible *Rickettsia* (and kappa particles), which possibly have a still higher level of organization. The best information (I mean for the geneticist) comes thus far from bacteriophage and animal viruses like the influenza virus. There is no doubt that these have a complicated structure permitting mutation, genetic recombination, linkage, and even linkage groups (most recent reviews in Cold Spring Harbor Sympos. 18, 1953). Thus a comparison with a gene is ruled out. But it is true that in the life cycle of a virus a vegetative, non-infectious phase occurs in which the particle seems to be free of protein and consists mainly of DNA. In this provirus condition in which the recombinations occur the genic level may be represented. The amazing facts and theories recently discovered at this level will certainly sooner or later lead to information on the genic material as such, and also on unexpected variants of its behavior on the organizational level of a virus or phage. However, they exclude so completely the somewhat naïve theory of the identity of viruses, plasmagenes, and genes that a further discussion is hardly needed. Much of the confusion stems, I think, from the identification of self-reproducing particle with a gene, as we discussed earlier. While refusing to accept what I consider to be unwarranted identifications of viruses and genes and statements to the effect that genes, plasmagenes, and viruses cannot be kept apart any longer, I am certain that the special features of bacterial and virus genetics will eventually help us to formulate exact ideas on the nature of the genic material. But this is completely different from the more or less gratuitous comparisons of the unknown gene, the more than dubious plasmagene, and the collection of organizational levels called viruses.

PART III THE ACTION OF THE GENETIC MATERIAL

1

INTRODUCTION

In the preceding discussion of the nature of the genetic material we had to touch many times upon the action of this material, since many of the inferences concerning the nature of the genetic material are derived from an analysis of action. We have mentioned a number of facts and interpretations which, however, were not discussed in detail, such a discussion being reserved for the present chapter. When speaking of the action of the genetic material it is at once realized that in some way practically all of biology falls into this chapter. In the last analysis, all morphological, physiological, and psychological features of organisms are genetically controlled, directly or through a reaction norm. As a consequence, evolution may also be considered dependent on genetically controlled processes. In view of this, the impossibility of an exhaustive analysis of all genic action is apparent. It appears to be the task of genetical theory to unravel the generalized laws and concepts that cover all possible types of genic actions in such a way as to make them generally intelligible, whatever the additional details may be if a specific case is to be analyzed; further, to lay emphasis on genic actions which might throw light, in turn, upon the nature of the genetic material. Though all morphology and physiology, embryology, and especially experimental embryology should contribute to such an analysis, most insight will be expected from a study of the facts of organization as accomplished by the processes of development with different genetic basis. Such a study has been called "physiological genetics," meaning by the term "physiological" the functional aspect, that is, genic action or dynamic genetics as opposed to static or statistical genetics. (This term was brought to the fore, if not actually introduced, when I surveyed the field analytically in my *Physiological Theory of Heredity*, 1927.) When the emphasis is upon the developmental features of the genetically different phenotypes, the term "phenogenetics" (Haecker, 1918) is frequently used. In any case physiological genetics and phenogenetics have a broad line of contact with experimental embryology, since many of the facts brought to light by the latter are relevant for genetics.

Experimental embryology, however, keeps aloof (and rightly so) from such parts of the common field which are predominantly genetic (e.g., dosage problems). It is rather strange that some embryologists consider the physiological geneticist to be a kind of intruder. Spemann once attacked Haecker rather violently when the latter proposed the term "phenogenetics" for work on genic action in development, and insisted that this is embryology and nothing but embryology. Only recently De Beer (1951) has taken up this cudgel, when he wrote, "He [the geneticist] need not have worried about the production of the effects, for that lay in the province of the experimental embryologist, and not his." In spite of such isolationism or possessiveness, the geneticist will continue to worry about the problem of genetic action and take the risk of climbing over the fence erected by some jealous embryologists, who, while claiming the kingdom for themselves, do not set out to till its soil.

The special division of physiological genetics which deals with genically controlled, definite biochemical syntheses has been termed by Beadle "biochemical genetics." This term might raise false hopes if it is not realized that it is used for one selected aspect of genetics only, the genetic interference with the synthesis of nutritional requirements of the organism and definable end products of metabolism and other deposits, though it is acknowledged that a distant ideal is the resolution of all genetic actions into their biochemical components. At this time biochemical genetics would become identical with genetics.

Altogether, physiological genetics in the wider sense covers: (1) the biochemical nature of the genic material; (2) its primary action at the site of its location in the chromosome; (3) its action within the nucleus; (4) its action upon the cytoplasm of the individual cell; and (5) its supracellular action in controlling growth, differentiation, development, and biochemical specificity of the organism. It comprises also the special part of no. 4, which has been termed biochemical genetics.

Though complicated in detail, in a general way genic action should follow a relatively simple pattern. I have repeatedly emphasized (e.g., 1920*a*, 1927, 1938*a*) that one of the marvels of living nature is the exactness of timing and type of developmental processes. Anybody who has watched thousands of sea urchin eggs developing simultaneously one like the other must have been impressed with this fact. This means to me that the most complicated developmental processes must, in the end, be controlled, steered, by rather simple causative agents.

I have tried to work out what I just called a simple pattern (Goldschmidt, 1920*a*, 1927), which in its general form seems to have stood the test of time. The genic material must catalyze chains of reaction which in the end produce the active substances that control morphogenesis. Since the best-known active substances of this kind were the hormones, I extended the meaning of this term to include every substance which plays an active role in embryonic determination. The reason for such terminology is obvious. There is no type of morphogenetic (also physiogenetic) process known which cannot be controlled in some cases by genuine hormone action. The phenotypic differences which can be induced by sex hormones, pituitary and thyroid hormones, molting hormones, and auxins in plants include all known types of differentiation, which may be qualitatively as different as any known or imaginable genetic difference. This suggests that the interrelations of these known active substances with the cellular substrate, as developed under control of the rest of the genotype, are of the same basic type as all the more simple and specialized actions of the end products of genically controlled reactions, which thus, in a wider sense, may also be termed hormones (which, in this case, includes specific enzymes).

In Germany, later, the term *Genwirkstoffe* was introduced (by Kühn) to characterize chemically identifiable products of genic action endowed with the capability of controlling chemical or morphological developmental processes. The term has led to much confusion as well as to unjustified beliefs in certain desired but not accomplished insights. *Genwirkstoffe* could be interpreted in two ways. First, it might mean identifiable substances produced by the work (*wirken*) of genes. If this were meant, the term would be superfluous, since it would include all the long known Mendelizing differences of a chemical nature like plant pigments, chlorophylls, and oxidases. The other meaning of the term, the one which was given it generally, is that of active substances which are gene products and control developmental features. Clearly, hormones produced by genic action, also inductors and morphogenetic substances, would be included in the term. But when one of the substances needed for production of eye pigment and absent in certain mutants was isolated by Kühn and Caspari and found to be kynurenine by Butenandt, this was hailed as the chemical isolation of a *Genwirkstoff*. In the same way Beadle and Ephrussi, who independently made the same discoveries, called the substance a hormone. Long before the chemical nature was known (by Beadle and Tatum's work) I warned (on the basis of the known facts of genetic and chemical control of melanin) that probably these "*Genwirkstoffe*" and "hormones" would turn out to be amino acid precursors of melanin, just as it had been known for a long time for tyrosin and dopa. This is exactly what occurred.

The reason for insisting on this discussion is that, in my opinion, the wrong terminology is deceptive and dangerous. Thus the great chemist Butenandt glorifies the discovery of *Genwirkstoffe* in papers read by chemists and general readers (e.g., 1952), who are led to believe (as the author does himself, who as a chemist takes his biological terminology from the biologist) that definite active substances have been isolated by which the genes control development. Actually, only one step (or more) in the consecutive synthesis of a chemically complicated, depository product of the organism (melanin) has been elucidated by the analysis of an intermediate product, a precursor. The brilliant work by the aforementioned pioneers is in no way minimized by the demand for a terminology which does not raise the meaning of the facts to a plane where it does not belong.

While the genetic and biochemical analysis of pigment precursors cannot be used as an example for our theory (1917*a*, 1920*a*) of genic action through production of morphogenetic "hormones," the general idea seems unavoidable, whether these "hormones" are real hormones or enzymes or inductors or definable substances like DNA or RNA. Within the simple frame of the generalized system of action—to which the cytoplasmic substrate also belongs—the details of genetic control of development are to be understood by the interplay of timing, order, velocities, competitions, and threshold conditions of these reactions, what I called their attunement, together with the movements and distribution of the substrates and products and the threshold conditions present for each individual step, which means the same dynamically as the term "genic balance" expresses statically. It should, of course, be called "balance of genic actions." "Genic balance" involves the same type of error (discussed above) as does the term "plasmon-sensitive genes" (to be discussed again below). Within such a system a great many details of gene-controlled processes above the level of direct and simple biochemical synthesis can be described adequately. In the end, the question of the special biochemical meaning will always appear, and biochemical genetics will take over wherever there is a chance. Unfortunately, at present such a chance exists only for stuffs deposited somewhere in the body, like pigments in animals and plants or end products of metabolism, and for blocks, of whatever origin, to synthesis of amino acids and vitamins and similar processes. For all the rest of genic action, especially the most important actions, controlling development and morphogenesis, we have still only the generalized (i.e., in biochemical terms) vague ideas mentioned, my physiological theory of heredity of 1920 and 1927.

Here, at the start of our discussion of genic action, one point should be made clear. It is one of the general tenets of genetics that a mutant locus or the gene, assumed to be the normal allele, does not control a character but is only a differential; the visible character depends upon a large number of genes, if not on all of them. This idea is frequently illustrated by the fact that many loci are known to influence the same character if mutated. Thus the numerous eye-color mutants in *Drosophila,* scattered over all chromosomes, would indicate that there are at least that many genes for eye color. The work on biochemical genetics of eye colors as well as nutritional requirements in *Neurospora* shows that a number of mutant loci individually interfere with different steps of organic synthesis from the lowest raw material: for example, in eye-color synthesis, from tryptophane to kynurenine, then to 3-hydroxykynurenine and further steps not yet well known. A corollary is that for each of these steps a number of mutant loci are known, which interfere with it specifically. If we wish to express this factual situation by saying that a phenotypic trait is the product of action of many or all genes, we must realize that this *façon à parler* is nothing but a circumscription, in terms of the atomistic theory of the gene, of the fact of the unity and integration of the organism. We may assume, for argument's sake, that one of the mutant loci which prevents normal eye color by interfering with step A of synthesis affects the pH of the cell group where events take place, a definite pH being needed for step A. According to the standard description, this "gene" would be classed as one of the many eye-color genes, because its influence upon pH, among other actions, also affects the synthesis of eye pigment. Clearly we face here not the action of an eye-color gene but the fact that the normal integration within the organism requires a series of more or less generalized conditions which thus affect also whatever differential trait we happen to be studying (here, by the way, is the explanation of the usual lower vitality of mutants). Thus, if we study genic action in controlling development we must always keep in mind this basic situation, which, in general dynamic terms, may be expressed also as the attunement of simultaneous determinative reactions or as the balance of genically controlled actions.

2

A GENERALIZED EXAMPLE

Before entering the detailed discussion, the study of an example of the general problems involved will enable us to visualize the over-all problems of physiological genetics within the compass of a single cell. We refer to Hämmerling's experiments on *Acetabularia* (see 1947, 1953). This marine green alga (Siphonocladiales) is unicellular, though superficially it looks like a multicellular plant. It is attached by a whorl of threads, a rhizome, from which a long stalk rises at the top of which an umbrella-like structure (the cap) is located so that the whole looks like a toadstool. At the base of the stalk in the rhizome lies the single nucleus. The experiments analyze the formation of the umbrella or cap in relation to the nucleus. Figures 14–16 review diagrammatically the main results.

The first group of experiments is illustrated in figure 14. When the cell is separated into a piece of the rhizome containing the nucleus and the rest, the nucleated part, however small, grows into a whole. Also, the enucleated parts may live for a long time, up to seven months; the nucleated ones, for years. The stalk of a nucleated piece always regenerates an umbrella. An enucleated piece sometimes succeeds in doing so, but regeneration is more frequently successful when an upper sector of the stalk has been cut out than when a lower one has been cut. The details show that the nucleus must have produced formative substances controlling the formation of the umbrella; these substances are produced in quantity and accumulate in the stalk in a gradient from top to base (*d*). The ability of an enucleated stalk to form an umbrella depends upon the amount of these stuffs in the cut-out section, within which the migration of the substance toward the top continues to take place.

The next group of experiments (figs. 15, 16) deals with transplants between two species *A. mediterranea* and *A. Wettsteinii*, which have completely differently constructed umbrellae (fig. 16). It is possible to transplant a *W(ettsteinii)* umbrella on top of the stalk of a *med(iterranea)* nucleated base and vice versa (fig. 15). When afterward the umbrella is cut off, a new one regenerates; it is not of the type belonging to the stalk out of which it grew but of the type which supplied the nucleus. It must thus be concluded that the formative substances produced by the nucleus, controlling the character of the species in regard to the structure of the umbrella, are the result of genic action. Here, then, we have in the simplest form, within one cell, the general type of genic action which we have postulated: production by the genic material of an active, diffusible substance

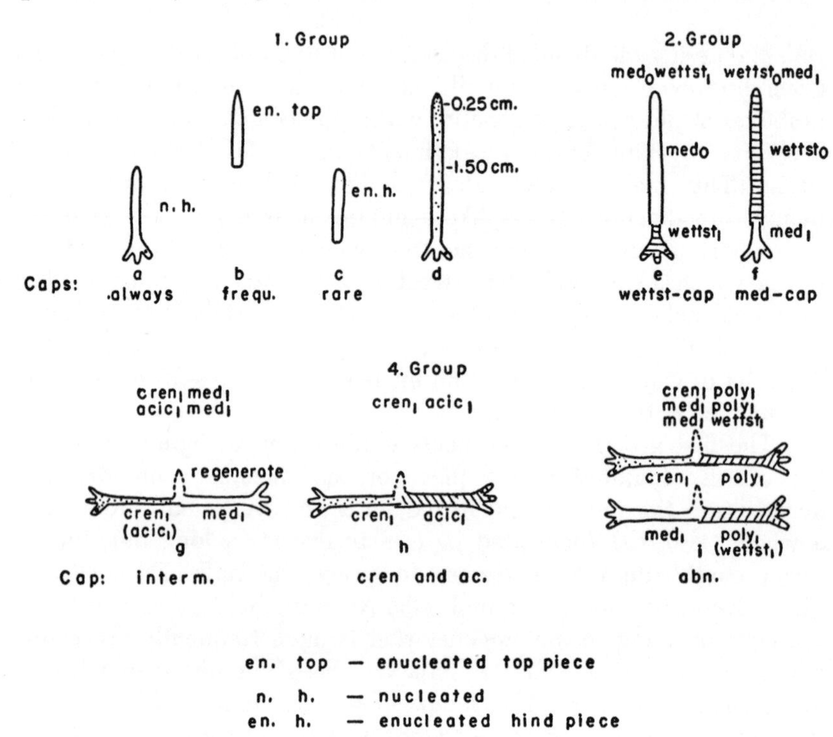

Figs. 14, 15. Diagrams of basic experiments with *Acetabularia.* (From Hämmerling, 1953.)

which controls the specificity of a morphogenetic feature. If this substance could be analyzed chemically, we should have the right to speak of the isolation of *Genwirkstoffe.* (See, below, Brachet's work on the nature of these substances and discussion of his theories; also new contributions by Hämmerling.) In this case, moreover, it is not the decision of an independently inherited alternative, as in the model of the sex hormones, but a direct and specific morphogenetic determination at a given point of a single though morphologically complicated cell. It will be well to keep this in mind for the subsequent discussion of genic action within a differentiated cell or cells. It should be added at this point that, unfortunately, no. individual Mendelian mutants for umbrella characters are known in this alga; hence the experiments deal only with the genome as a whole.

These facts are further confirmed by experiments in which nucleated pieces of two different species were combined and regenerated as a common branch, presumably under the influence of both nuclei.

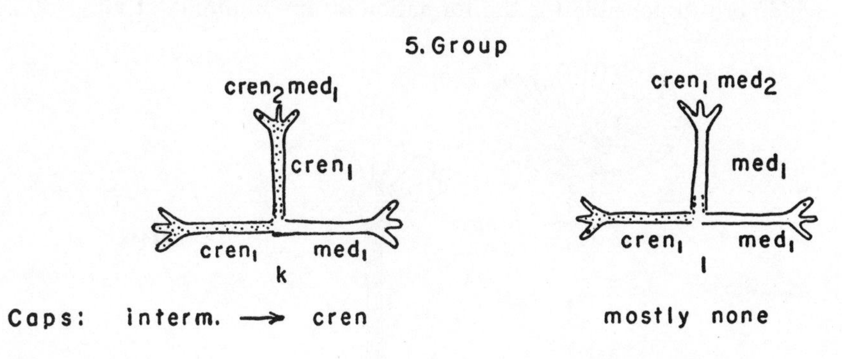

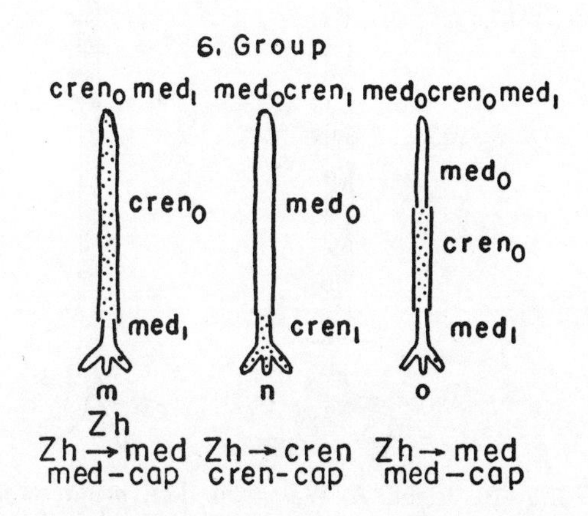

The regenerated umbrella was intermediate between the two species (figs. 14, 15). When the difference between the species was greater, the compromise regenerate was more or less abnormal, though showing the mixture. Combinations of three pieces of which two had the nucleus of one species, the third that of another species, point in the same direction. The regenerated umbrella had more resemblance to the species that had supplied two nuclei (fig. 15). Thus the quantity of the determining stuff is related to its action. Finally (fig. 16), the effects of those umbrella-forming stuffs were tested which had been present previously in the stalk and, therefore, should contribute to the result until exhausted. Afterward, a purely nuclear effect should prevail. This could be determined by producing uninuclear combinations of stalks from different species. Indeed, early umbrellas were intermediate; later ones followed the species which supplied the nucleus. In these experiments it turned out also that the stuffs which control the specific features of the umbrella are different from those which are responsible for the formation of any umbrella at all.

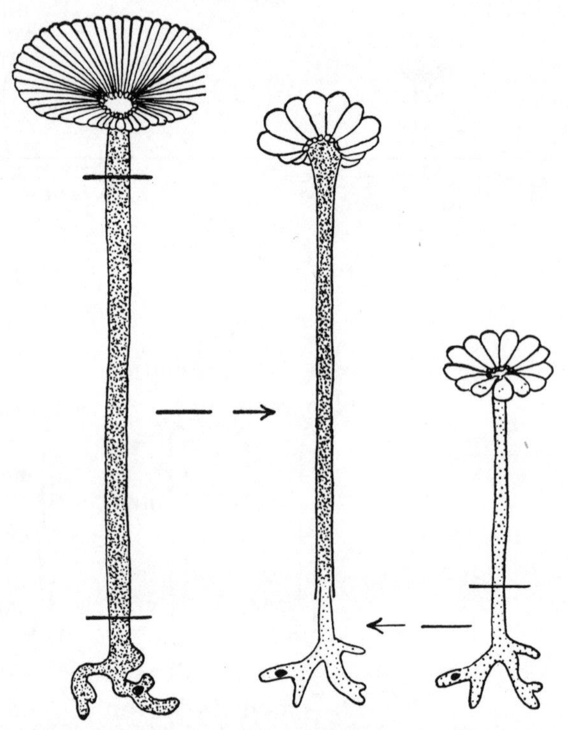

Fig. 16. Right, *A. Wettsteini;* left, *mediterranea;* center, transplantation of *mediterranea* stem on *Wettsteini* base and formation of *Wettsteini* cap on regenerate. Lines of cuts indicated. (From Hämmerling, 1953.)

At this point one might be inclined to bring in cytoplasmic heredity, because the nucleated section always contains some cytoplasm. (Experiments with nuclear transplantation have not been made.) Such cytoplasm may act independently and be self-propagating. The following fact is not in favor of such an assumption (Hämmerling, 1953). In the species *acicularia* no regeneration of a cap occurs in the absence of the nucleus, and in its presence only 15 per cent regenerate. But when the nucleated part of the species *med* is combined with the tip of *acic* a cap is regenerated. The cytoplasm of the regenerating piece has not been changed, but the *med* base supplies the necessary formative substances.

We mentioned, earlier, Boveri's famous proof that a chromosomal behavior, chromatin diminution, is controlled by cytoplasmic substances. This can be shown in *Acetabularia* also. Before reproduction the single nucleus divides into many, which migrate into the cap to form the gametes. This happens only when the cap has reached a definite size. If the cap is cut off in time, the nucleus does not divide, but first controls the production of a new cap; thus gamete formation could be held up for two years. Vice versa, if an immature base receives the transplant of a mature cap, the nucleus begins at once to divide. The substances involved in this induction can be shown to be species-specific.

These experiments provide an excellent model within a single cell, demonstrating, in a general way, how genic material in the nucleus is connected with specific determination in differentiation.

3

PHENOCOPY AND NORM OF REACTION

A. NORM OF REACTION

Another group of facts of a generalized nature should be kept in mind at the outset of a study of genic action. In the early years of Mendelism, Woltereck defined the genotype as a "norm of reaction." What he meant was that the genic action does not control a definite phenotypic effect but an effect which is the resultant of the genic action and that of external and internal environment. A certain mutant does not control the deposition of black pigment, but has this action, provided that all other external and internal conditions are the required ones. This definition is still good and has been used in some of our former discussions. It applies also to detailed biochemical actions, as the more recent development of biochemical genetics has shown. It includes the border cases in which the steps between genic action and end products are so few and of such a limited scope that for practical purposes the norm of reaction is invariable, for example in the production of the blood group antigens. At the other end of the line would be the border cases in which the final products of genic action perform their determinative activities under special threshold conditions for success or failure, an all-or-none effect discussed earlier in connection with the mottling position effect. The consequence is that these actions and reactions are so easily affected by features of the external and internal environment that the result looks as if it were completely under environmental control. Between these extremes all intermediate conditions exist (e.g., vernalization; see II 2 B). We might say that the analysis of cases at one extreme of this spectrum, with disregard of the definition of genic action as a "reaction norm," led to the now abandoned one gene—one enzyme hypothesis, abandoned when the results of different norms of reaction were studied. An example of error at the other end of the spectrum, committed for the same reasons, is Hartmann's mistaken notion of phenotypic sex determination, which is actually genic sex determination with a norm of reaction of the decisive process (the decision of the F/M balance), which makes it highly susceptible to shifts by environmental factors. (See discussion later.)

B. PHENOCOPY AND MUTATION

Of the greatest interest for the meaning of norm of reaction and simultaneously one of the basic features, if not the most basic, in physiological genetics is the phenomenon of phenocopy. Our information on genic action is derived almost completely from the study of aberrant genic action, that is, the changes in heredity caused by mutation. Looking over the manifold mutant actions we find many variants. We find mutants which produce a definite effect with very little variation in the presence of the same genetic background (the modifier systems), whatever the external conditions. At the other end are mutants which do not produce any visible effect except in a definite environment (e.g., at a certain temperature). In between are the mutants which always produce a certain type of effect, say wing scalloping in *Drosophila,* the expression of which is dependent upon temperature, with overlap into normal at the extreme end of the series. There are mutants of all these types, which, in addition, are rather insensitive in their action to genetic modification, and there are others which respond very easily to genetic modifiers. The actions of some mutants work with a threshold system that permits overlap of the effect with normal in different degrees. This condition is described as different degrees of penetrance. At one end are mutants which succeed only rarely in passing the threshold and thus have such a low penetrance that they may be overlooked as genically controlled actions. At the other end are the isoalleles which produce effects that are always above the threshold of normalcy, producing the same phenotype as the normal allele, and therefore can be found out only by roundabout means. In between are all imaginable penetrance grades. These types may be more or less subject to shifting by external or genic environment. All these variants tend to show that the mutant action has not only a qualitative but also a quantitative element.

From this conclusion it is only one step to the phenomenon of phenocopy. If the quantitative element of mutation is so sensitive to external and internal environment, it might follow that all or most mutational effects take place within a spectrum of possible developmental changes the range of which alone determines the possibility of appearance of both mutational or environmental effects. The old, long-forgotten, and erroneous, but nevertheless at that time justified discussion of so-called parallel induction was the outcome of this situation, which at that time was not analyzable. This old idea, derived from certain experiments with butterflies (see discussion in Goldschmidt, 1927, 1938*a*), was that the same agent which has a purely environmental effect upon the phenotype may sometimes simultaneously affect the genotype so as to produce a mutant with the same phenotypic effect.

Some of the classic experiments of Dorfmeister, Weismann, Standfuss, Merrifield, and Fischer in changing the pattern of the butterfly wing by appropriate temperature shocks seemed to require such an interpretation, the facts themselves being thoroughly established. The solution of this problem comes from the discovery of phenocopy (Goldschmidt, 1929*b*, 1935*a,b*), which was made when I was trying to check the possibility of parallel induction with a genetically well-known organism, *Drosophila*. Even in the first experiments it turned out that the phenotype of a large number of standard mutants of *Drosophila* could be exactly copied as a non-hereditary variation if temperature shocks were applied at a critical stage of development. Other investigators later found that many other shocks like cold, mustards, X rays and other radiations, and many chemicals could produce the effect. The decisive points were: (1) treatment with strong agents, powerful beyond the normal range of the environment; (2) treatment at definite critical periods of development; (3) the genotype of the material which influences the result. It may be said that in *Drosophila* (and therefore everywhere, if adequate experiments were made) every known type of mutant can thus be copied as a phenocopy. The only group about which there is uncertainty are the biochemical mutants (pigments, etc.), for which no unequivocal positive result exists as yet. Some which have been claimed were probably misinterpreted (e.g., straw as a chemical phenocopy). But this statement applies only to *Drosophila;* in microorganisms, also, biochemical mutants have been phenocopied. Positive results for production of phenocopies have been obtained from man to bacteria; so there can be no doubt of the ubiquity of the phenomenon. For *Drosophila* the most detailed data are found in Goldschmidt (1935), Henke *et al.* (1941), and Ma (1943). Henke *et al.* think they can distinguish between genuine and false phenocopies, the latter being those the critical period of which does not coincide with that of a similar mutant studied. I do not think that this distinction carries any weight. Most mutant phenotypes are known for a number of loci. Innumerable mutants are being discarded all the time; others have by chance not yet been observed. Thus it is impossible to say that a mutant (or a few of them) checked against a phenocopy is the right one. Another unchecked mutant may have the proper critical period.

In view of the fact that practically any kind of shock treatment produces phenocopies in well-worked material, it is very difficult to assume that the shock produces differentially a chemical product, enzyme, substrate, active substance, identical with one produced by a mutant locus. It is much more probable that the kinetics of a chain of reaction, elaborating such active substances, is influenced in such a way that velocities of processes, quantities of products, relative timing of collaborating reactions, and concentrations amounting to threshold settings will be the main factors that are being shifted in plus or minus directions. If this is so, it might mean also that the mutant action affects essentially such processes, though it cannot be denied that in individual cases a phenocopy might take a different path from that leading to the corresponding mutant phenotype. This does not mean that mutant actions do not exist which directly affect the quality of a substance needed for development, but it will be very difficult in many cases to decide. For example, an eye-color mutant in *Drosophila* which prevents the synthesis of kynurenine from tryptophane may be due to the non-synthesis of an enzyme controlling the synthetic step, that is, a qualitative feature. But it may also mean that the enzyme or a coenzyme or a pH condition needed is not available when and where needed because of pure timing changes in the set of interlocked reactions which have to be in tune in order to work. A quotation from Bonner (given below) shows that a prominent biochemical geneticist has also come to the conclusion that the kinetic side of genic action may be more important than the qualitative aspect embodied in the one gene—one enzyme theory.

To make the situation clearer, let us visualize the case of a mutant and its phenocopy based upon a qualitative chemical difference. Let us assume that we know chemically the substance needed to produce a normal leg in *Drosophila,* its absence being responsible for a dachs leg. This means that we take it for granted that the morphological difference is based upon the presence or absence of a single gene-controlled substance, enzyme or otherwise, and not upon quantitative changes in the velocities of growth and differentiation (though these may ultimately be caused by the presence, absence, or quantity of a "growth hormone"). The same morphological effect as a phenocopy could be produced by the different means mentioned. Should we conclude that the substance in question is also missing in the phenocopy?

We know now that many unspecific shocks at the proper time can produce the same phenocopy, but also that one and the same shock may produce different phenocopies. It is hardly conceivable how such facts could be understood in terms of a substance, while they strongly suggest interference with the kinetics of a system of reactions, as I emphasized above. Moreover, this argumentation shows another very important point. It is possible that the facts of phenocopy indicate that also the mutants which are copied are based upon an interference with the kinetics of determinative processes. However, this does not mean that the primary causes are the same in both cases. Thus it is quite conceivable that in the phenocopic experiment the shock interferes with the velocity of some reaction by affecting its kinetics directly (e.g., through the temperature increment), while in the mutation the same effect upon the velocities is produced by a more remote change (e.g., an insufficient quantity, or quality, of a growth substance). In this case both phenocopy and mutant are caused by the same thing, a change in growth rate, but the phenocopy, by direct action upon the rate; the mutant, by an indirect action through the change of a causative agent for the control of the rates. I think that this point is important for any discussion of the relation of mutant and phenocopy, though it has been largely overlooked. (Hadorn, 1948, emphasized somewhat similar ideas.)

This deduction becomes important when we think, for example, of Landauer's (1945–1953) recent work on phenocopies in the chick, about which we shall hear more below. He finds that he can induce certain phenocopies by treatment of embryos with insulin. In further experiments he found that the phenocopic action can be suppressed by nicotinamide and riboflavin, but that the same treatment does not inhibit the mutant effect. This makes him skeptical toward the assumption that the mutant produces its effect by the same processes as the phenocopy. The above-mentioned considerations show where the error of such conclusions lies: the treatment in the case of the phenocopy directly affects the process which has been changed by the insulin treatment, restoring it more or less to normal and thus preventing its effect upon the growth rate. The treatment of the mutant with riboflavin may be effective or not effective (the latter being the case) according to the nature of the primary process, which may or may not be the same as that after insulin treatment. If it is not the same, riboflavin remains ineffective, though mutant and phenocopy act by influencing growth rates, whatever the primary cause for this change. Thus the conclusion is correct that both mutant and phenocopy produce the same phenotype because both interfere with the same kinetic processes of development, though there is no reason to expect that this interference works by the same means. Theoretically, it would be possible to find many more types of interference than those found in the experiments, for example, direct interference with the kinetics of growth by temperature action. Thus Landauer's beautiful work does not at all change our concept of the relation between mutant and phenocopy. It is fair to state that Landauer (1952*a*) realizes this situation when he says, in regard to the experiments preventing the phenocopic insulin action by riboflavin, while riboflavin does not prevent the mutant action: "It is also possible, however, that such experiments cannot succeed, either because the mutant genes change the events of development too early to be repaired by supplementation or because they affect metabolic links different from those involved in the origin of our phenocopies, or because of still other reasons."

Let us return to the statement made above, that the primary

process through which the mutant works may or may not be the same as in the phenocopy. In Landauer's work the primary process in the phenocopy of rumplessness, and so on, after the treatment of the embryo with insulin, pilocarpin, and boric acid, was clearly an interference with carbohydrate metabolism. It would be wrong, however, to demand that the mutant works also by interference with this phase of metabolism, but this does not mean that in a given case both primary actions might not be the same. This problem would have to be decided from case to case, though it might be safe to say that phenocopies produced the same way by radiations, temperature shocks, and chemicals will not belong to this category, but rather work by means of the kinetics controlled by the primary action, whatever this is.

If we keep this in mind, the further exploration of the chemical situation in such cases as Landauer's will be very interesting. It is an important fact that substances like insulin, sulfanilamide, eserine, boric acid, and pilocarpin produce many similarities in their over-all effects, though there are dissimilarities in details of expression. In all these cases, nicotinamide serves as a protective supplement, thus pointing to a common biochemical basis for the activity of these compounds, though the grade of "protection" is different with different compounds. Now it turned out that the skeletal abnormalities produced by boric acid are very similar to those known for riboflavin deficiencies. Thus the hypothesis is made that the effects are mediated by means of riboflavin-containing enzymes. Chemical data (see Landauer, 1952*a*) on the action of boric acid on riboflavin-containing molecules agree with such conclusions. "It is well known that one of the fundamental purposes of the riboflavin enzymes is to serve as 'bridges' over which the hydrogen atoms accumulating on the nicotinic acid coenzymes can be passed to systems which will carry out the reduction of oxygen" (quoted from Williams by Landauer). According to Landauer, these neighboring functions of nicotinamide and riboflavin enzymes in carbohydrate utilization, and their disruption by insulin and boric acid, respectively, presumably explain that allied yet separate teratogenic results are produced in the two instances. Without going into further details, it is obvious that this type of analysis of phenocopies (which many of these teratogenic effects are) can lead to important insight into the biochemical control of growth processes. Applied to favorable material, it might one day also permit conclusions upon the primary effect of mutants, which are phenocopied.

Thus it is highly probable that the view is correct which considers phenocopies produced after shock treatment as the result of quantitative interference with rate processes in development and their interlocking actions, whatever the primary effects, identical or not identical, for mutants and phenocopies may have been. This idea, first worked out in explanation of the above-mentioned experiments with butterflies before the phenomenon of phenocopy was properly established (Goldschmidt, 1918, 1920*a*), and since presented repeatedly (e.g., 1935*a*,*b*, 1938*a*, 1940), covers the overwhelming majority of facts. An immense, partly experimental material is available, also, from the study of teratogenesis. Ancel (1950) has recently assembled a good deal of it in a book, and, though he has never heard of the extensive amount of work on phenocopy, is forced to draw conclusions almost identical with mine.

These discussions and my earlier ones (Goldschmidt, 1938*a*, 1940) should make it clear why I have considered and still consider the phenomenon of phenocopy the basic phenomenon for any study of genic action. Landauer (1952*b*), who recently contributed so much to our subject, expresses the same attitude by referring for comparison to the results of radiation work. He quotes Pontecorvo saying that we would not expect to get a deep insight into the nature of a ship by studying the efficiency of different types of gunfire in sinking it. "The same skepticism should be applied to the hope that studies on the developmental effects of major mutant genes will lead to an understanding of the role in growth and development of those genes which make up the normal genotype of fowl or any other higher organism . . . Studies on the production of phenocopies, together with the search for means by which the organism can be protected against such experimental modification, may offer a technique with which the holes made by our experimental gunfire may be repaired . . ."

C. CHEMICAL PHENOCOPIES

In the discussion of Landauer's work, we have anticipated one aspect of the work on chemical phenocopies, because we wanted to show that, in principle, chemically induced phenocopies will find the same explanation as all others, though the causation of that part of the effect which is identical in mutant and phenocopy may involve completely different primary actions. Even in Landauer's experiments the different agents employed had a certain specificity of action upon beak, extremities, and skeleton, though all of them acted in a similar way. The most interesting facts on such specificity of action have been found in *Drosophila*.

Rapoport (1947) found that among a large number of chemicals tested certain ones always produced the phenocopy of one definite mutant, and this occurred in 100 per cent of the treated cases. The experiments have been repeated in different places and found to be correct in a general way. But my own (unpublished) work shows that there are more details with which an interpretation must reckon. Thus, in some cases, it is clearly a single metal ion which is responsible, since all inorganic and organic compounds tested always produced the same phenocopy (e.g., arsenic). We might conclude that a single enzymatic process is inhibited by the arsenic ion, which is one of its known actions. But such known inhibitions work upon very basic enzymatic processes which occur all the time in all cells. For example, arsenate uncouples fermentation and phosphorylation (Meyerhof). Luciferin and luciferase in distilled water do not produce light, but they do when magnesium or manganese salts are added (Harvey). Numerous other examples are available to the biochemist. Thus it is not imaginable that arsenic could affect only a single, very specific synthesis which is the chemical basis for the morphogenetic effect. We would have to make some extra hypothesis, based upon the fact that all these phenocopies appear only when the treatment is almost lethal. We might assume that the change of development leading to the phenocopy is simultaneously such as to countermand the lethal effects of arsenic; this means in the end a selection of those individuals which produce, by starting on a side path of development, a condition of arsenic tolerance. This tentative explanation is not very satisfactory, but it shows at least that the chemical agents for the production of the specific phenocopy do not necessarily act by a direct biochemical change.

Other ions tested (unpublished work), for example, boron, have different effects in different compounds; hence a simple inhibition of an enzymatic process by the ion is improbable. Also, in this case, definite phenocopies appear, not a single one only, but different ones according to the intensity of treatment. Again it is very improbable that a specific enzymatic action is changed by the agent. As we have already seen, boron interferes with carbohydrate metabolism by means of a riboflavin-containing enzyme, which can hardly be concerned with a single developmental feature like the development of the antenna. I think that this situation is rather different from that in chicken. Here the phenocopy means that a growth process affecting major parts of the body is interfered with, which could be accounted for by a generalized biochemical effect (meaning one involved in all development). Thus we shall have to look for a different explanation of the *Drosophila* work, which probably does not involve the features of the chemical basis of morphogenetic change. For the time being, we may say frankly that the specific chemical phenocopies are not yet understood, though the fact of their existence is very provocative. But we may safely predict that a future explanation will shed light on some phase of the problem of mutant action of the genic material.

One fact which has been found in some of my unpublished experiments may be relevant here. It is known that many mutants produce a very variable phenotype (which might be made constant by selection of proper modifier systems, or in the presence of "strong" alleles). This is very conspicuous in mutants producing very large effects like the homoeotic mutants (see my papers on podoptera). One mutant may produce a whole gamut of effects from almost normal through all intermediates up to the complete, extreme type. We shall discuss these facts below in regard to their meaning for genic action. In one of our experiments on chemical phenocopies, one mutant was specifically copied (Scutenick), and always in a variable form involving a series of effects from hardly visible ones through all intermediates affecting more and more structural elements to the extreme pleiotropic expressivity. I shall later propose that such variations in expressivity can only be understood in terms of interplay of rates and thresholds. This identity of the phenomenon in mutants and phenocopies is in favor of the conclusions drawn for non-chemical phenocopies.

In future discussions of the interpretation of phenocopies, all the facts of chemically induced morphogenetic change in animals and plants, since the classic work of Herbst (1901), will be included, though it does not directly relate to phenocopy because in most cases no identical mutant effect is known. However, as we might say safely that all these effects are of the same general type as mutant effects, they also become relevant for the problems of specific biochemical phenocopy and, thus far, all of them seem to indicate general quantitative effects upon rates of growth and differentiation, just as we expect will be true of all phenocopies.

It might be objected that it is hardly probable that all the diverse manifestations of morphological mutants and phenocopies may be reduced in the end to relative rates of individual processes of growth and differentiation, but there are many examples which point in this direction. We shall consider later Vogt's work on homoeotic mutants which led to such conclusions. Here I mention only one example, the seasonal dimorphism of butterflies, the classic example of which is

Araschnia (*Vanessa*) *levana-prorsa.* The spring form and the fall form differ as much as if they were separate species. By treatment of pupae in a sensitive period with temperature shocks, one form can be transformed into the other with all intermediate conditions possible. The spring generation is the form *levana* with a yellowish brown and black pattern. The summer form *prorsa* is almost entirely black, with a white band across both wings. *Prorsa* produces offspring which develop up to the pupal stage when the diapause sets in for the hibernating pupa. In the spring the imago hatches and its offspring develop without diapause into *prorsa.* By action of cold upon the pupae of the summer generation, which were to metamorphose into *prorsa, levana* resulted; by action of different low temperatures a series of intermediates can be produced. The summer form could also be produced by action of heat upon the hibernating pupa.

We know now that diapause in the silkworm is controlled by hormones. Here it is not the pupa which hibernates, but embryonic development stops in the so-called univoltine races with diapause, while it goes on in the multivoltine races without diapause. Fukuda (see 1953) showed that the subesophageal ganglion secretes a diapause hormone, while the brain is able, in the multivoltine races, to suppress this action.

To return to *prorsa* and *levana,* Süffert (1924) found that the results reported are not simply temperature effects, as Weismann had believed in his pioneer work (1875). Actually, two different causative agents come into play: the alternative of diapause or no diapause, and the action of temperature. Pupae with diapause always metamorphose into *levana,* even if kept in warm temperature. Thus *levana* is linked with the presence, and *prorsa* with the absence, of a diapause. If diapause is prevented, invariably *prorsa* hatches. If after the first diapause, producing *levana,* a second diapause is induced experimentally, again *levana* is the result. The result can be obtained by the influence of cold upon the caterpillar in a temperature-effective (critical) period, an effect which we must now ascribe to an effect upon the hormonic function of the brain. Also, if partial diapause is induced in this period, intermediates result, their grade being roughly proportional to the time of diapause. Thus the existence or nonexistence of the resting period controls the wing pattern.

Now there is a second causative chain leading to the same phenotypic effects. Another critical period for pattern change occurs in the early pupa. Cold shocks applied in this period produce *levana* even without diapause, and also the graduated series can be obtained by a graduated action. In the latter case we know from the mass of temperature experiments in Lepidoptera that temperature directly influences developmental processes connected with pattern formation. Thus the problem arises of explaining the two different sets of facts which lead to the same phenotypic result by different means.

The explanation must start from the fact that it is possible to shift the wing pattern of all Lepidoptera by applying extreme temperatures at a definite time after pupation, the sensitive period, though the shift is not as extreme as in *levana* and *prorsa*. Since the same effect can be produced by other means (cold, narcotics), just as in the production of phenocopies, we concluded that this action involved changing the velocity of a process concerned with wing pattern, relative to other developmental processes, different processes having different temperature coefficients and critical periods (Goldschmidt, 1918, 1920*a*). This interpretation may be applied directly to that part of the experiments dealing with the effects after pupation. The unusually extreme effect is, of course, a function of a specific genetic condition in the form of a special norm of reaction or special threshold conditions. The other special feature is that another hereditary norm of reaction involving the production of specific hormones by the brain before pupation, thus determining diapause or non-diapause, simultaneously affects the wing pattern in the same way as post-pupal shocks. In view of the identity of the two effects we must conclude that diapause also affects the relative velocity of the patterning process. As diapause is known to almost completely stop the metabolic processes, it is quite possible that it works upon the pattern by inhibiting those temperature-sensitive processes which would occur soon after pupation. There is thus far no possibility of a detailed explanation; but it seems certain that it will be found on the side of quantitative, kinetic actions rather than in terms of qualitative biochemical features.

4

PRIMARY ACTIONS

A. THE CHROMOSOMAL SITE

Since it must be considered as certain that the chromosome remains intact in the resting nucleus, the first step in genic action must take place at the site of the genic material, whether we consider this to be in the form of individual genes or as patterns in a larger unit. Only two possibilities are apparent. First, the initial product of genic activity is a duplicate (eventually in reverse) of the genic material or any part of it. This might mean a duplicate of the genic nucleoprotein, or only of the nucleinic or proteinic parts thereof. If this is so, part of the genic material itself is also its first active product, in the beginning localized at the locus of the genic material, at a point on the surface of the chromosome. The other possibility is that the genic material acts as an enzyme which catalyzes the first reaction product using the surrounding materials as a substrate, different products occurring presumably along the length of the chromosome. Also, these primary products would first accumulate at the fixed sites of the genic material in the order of its pattern along the chromosome. Hence, in the end, both possibilities lead to the same result as far as the site is concerned.

According to the first assumption, the genic material behaves after the manner of an autocatalyst (first emphasized by Hagedoorn, 1911). It has been repeatedly pointed out (e.g., Pauling, Muller) that the term autocatalyst does not cover the duplication of the genic material, which is rather a re-creation at the surface of the chain molecules according to one or the other theories of template action discussed previously. Though realizing the difference, it might be useful to speak of autocatalysis and heterocatalysis in the sense of self-duplication versus catalyzing a different reaction. In this sense it would be autocatalysis also if duplicates of the genic material were the first product separated from the chromosome. In detail, these primary products would look different according to the theory of the genic material adopted. With the classic theory of the gene, we would think of replicas of the individual gene molecule. Within the recent theory as developed above, the duplicates may be those of any chromosomal segment, anything from a part of an individual chain molecule up to a hypermolecular body of any size, pattern, and delineation. If this is called autocatalysis it means only that the primary product of the genic material is a more or less large duplicate or replica of it. This view emphasizes that the genic material is primarily characterized by its self-duplication, and that its action in producing the primary genic products cannot be separated from the self-duplication, but is a part of it. In this sense the genic material would be only autocatalytic, with the heterocatalytic functions beginning only after the duplicate parts have been liberated, and may now serve as enzymes as well as substrates. It sounds reasonable (see discussion of the genic parts of the chromosome) that these primary duplicates are only the replicas of the proteinic part of the genic material, or, preferably, that at this moment DNA and protein are separated and severally duplicated with different subsequent fate of these substances. Autocatalysis of the genic material in this sense would then mean: (1) the duplication of the genic material within the chromosome as a structural unit; (2) its duplication in parts, including separation of DNA and protein; and thus (3) providing the first active genic products.

The other possibility, that the genic material, while in its normal location in the chromosome, itself directly catalyzes reactions with the surrounding substrate, has very little a priori probability, in view of the fact that chromosome duplication cannot be of the nature of genuine autocatalysis in the chemical sense (though we used the term for the sake of opposing it to heterocatalysis); that is, one of the products of the catalyzed reactions is the duplicate (this was originally assumed by Hagedoorn, 1911; Troland, 1917; Goldschmidt, 1916*a*, 1920*a*). If this were so, we could assume that, during the process of autocatalysis, heterocatalytic actions also would take place, producing the primary genic products. But it is generally accepted today that the duplication of the organized genic material cannot be of the type of genuine autocatalysis. This makes it almost mandatory that the primary genic product is formed by the same process as the duplicated genic material, namely, by a process of the template type. Only with this understanding and by enlarging the meaning of the term autocatalysis to include duplication by some template mechanism can we say that the genic material is both autocatalytic and heterocatalytic. Thus it is both right and wrong to say that the genic material acts like a catalyst: it is wrong when the genic material, as organized in the chromosome, is meant; it is right when the free duplicates of different size are meant. The rather vague idea that the genic material itself is also its first product set loose in the cell is an old one, though worked out in detail only by Koltzoff (1928 ff.). The idea of autoheterocatalytic action from Hagedoorn to Troland (1917) received a meaning for genetics only when I was able to link genic action with reaction velocities (Goldschmidt, 1916*c*) and to work this into a complete theory of genic action (Goldschmidt, 1920*a*, 1927).

It is obvious that in this discussion we assume the proteinic part of the nucleoprotein to be the genic material, as was discussed before in detail. If DNA were considered the genic material, the difficulty would arise as to how to bridge the gap from the nucleic acid molecule to enzymatic gene products, which should be proteins. Since it is hardly possible to base primary gene actions upon nucleic acids, this seems to be a major difficulty, though I mentioned previously (I 2 B *b bb*) that Watson and Crick speak of possible enzymatic actions of the nucleic acid molecule. Another point of view which is coming to the fore is that DNA produces RNA, which is decisive in protein synthesis. The biologist must wait, then, for the biochemist to solve these problems. Meanwhile, he must use some picture of what happens at the chromosomal site, realizing that he works with a picture which may have no resemblance to reality.

Assuming, then, the first genic products to be partial duplicates of the genic material, from free radicals and side chains up to polypeptides and proteins, released by the breaking, or the nonestablishment from the beginning, of hydrogen-phosphorus-peptide bonds, they are present first in molecular or submolecular quantities. If not at once moved away to the nuclear sap, the natural place of their next interactions, they would occupy the surface of the chromosome according to the fixed pattern of chromosomal architecture. Chemical interactions of whatever kind would require direct contact, which, on the surface of the chromosome, could be accomplished by different kinds of foldings. But it is very difficult to conceive of such a folding process which would bring together the necessary partners and in the necessary order. This would be still more difficult to accomplish if the classic theory of the gene were accepted and the units of interaction were entire genes. Thus it is rather improbable that the first reactions involving the primary gene products take place *in situ* in the chromosome. But such an assumption is frequently made, even taken for granted, by the adherents of the classic gene. Actually it plays a decisive role in many attempts at an explanation of position effect in terms of corpuscular genes, as well as of a number of phenomena of genic action. We have considered some of these problems (see I 3 C *c ee ccc*), and return to them now exclusively from the point of view of primary genic action.

Muller as well as Offerman (1935) at first suggested (since abandoned by Muller) that position effect is caused by a gene acting in a different neighborhood. This would mean that the primary gene products react directly at the chromosomal surface with those of other genes and especially with those of adjacent genes. Therefore a changed gene neighborhood would interfere with these reactions. This idea does not work, for many reasons. As we discussed in detail before, the position effect makes a "gene" act as if it had mutated, though we had to qualify this simple description (I 3 C *c cc*). If this is due to an abnormal neighborhood, it would mean that an intact gene cannot be affected except in one direction, namely, its typical mutant action. Whatever neighboring material has got away from it or whatever distant material has come near to it, whenever there is an effect it is always the same (with a little variation within essentially the same effect). This would mean an obligate all-or-none effect in the function of the gene, whatever change occurred in the neighborhood. Logically, this could not be distinguished from a gene mutation. This idea has not much to recommend it, and has been abandoned by all but the strictest believers in the classic gene.

A recent revival of the general idea in a more modern form goes back to some suggestions by Sewall Wright. Stern's explanation of genic action (see Stern *et al.*, 1943–1946) was formulated in order to solve the great difficulties of a consistent explanation of his dosage experiments. He assumed that the gene has two independent attributes, namely, its combining power with a substrate, and the efficiency with which the substrate is converted into gene product. Thus access to the substrate is linked with the proper elaboration of the gene products. More details will be given in the chapter on dosage effects. For our present discussion the theory involves a gene at its locus, a substrate which must be localized at the chromosomal surface and must be different from point to point, in order to be used for an explanation of position effect, and gene products which may or may not be localized.

From another point of view, involving the idea of position effect in a different sense, the problem of primary genic reactions *in situ* (chromosomal) has come up in the work on so-called pseudoallelism discussed previously (I 3 C *c ee ccc*). Pontecorvo (1952*a*) started from the claim (Horowitz; see below) that most genes are involved in only one metabolic reaction. This might make one expect that genes with similar actions could be distributed in an orderly fashion along the chromosome. Pontecorvo proposed a hypothesis which was prompted by McIlwain's evaluation of the rate at which certain reactions involving vitamins take place in bacteria: rates of the order of a few tens of molecules per cell per second. The idea was that chains of reactions, the rate of which is very low, or chains of reactions involving labile or non-diffusible intermediates, must be localized; the reactions must take place either on surfaces or in microvessels within the cell. (A long-forgotten idea of Hofmeister is that the alveolar structure provides such microvessels; salivary gland chromosomes may show alveolar structure; Metz.) "We know that some genes are specifically involved in individual steps of series of reactions. We assume that the action of the genes is in some way mediated by corresponding enzymes, either each gene playing a part in the synthesis of each enzyme, or on the conditions for the enzyme to act, including structural organization. The idea was that should the enzymes, acting on a series of reactions of millimicromolar order, be arranged in proximity to one another, we might find vestiges of this spatial organization reflected in the corresponding genes. The heuristic value of this working hypothesis lies in the fact that while the biochemical techniques for discovering grouping or other kinds of spatial organization of enzymes are still in their infancy, the genetical techniques for discovering fine details of grouping of genes are already available" (Pontecorvo, 1952*a*). This ingenious hypothesis, then, requires microchemical reactions of either the genes or the primary gene products *in situ* on the chromosome, as discussed above. Haldane (1954) considers this idea to be basic for all future research on the biochemistry of genic action.

We have already reported that a group of three loci, behaving like pseudoalleles, all affecting biotin synthesis, were found when looked for systematically by Roper. A similar case was reported for nicotinic acid in *Neurospora* by Bonner (see 1951). Now these three loci act like pseudoalleles. Pontecorvo expresses this in the following manner: a normal action is possible only when all three normal alleles are adjacent but not if they are in different chromosomes (i.e., separated). Pontecorvo is very careful to say that we are still very far from being entitled to say that one of the ways in which genes are clustered along the chromosomes is that of small assembly lines of genes which are involved in successive steps of the metabolism of a scarce, ephemeral, or non-movable intermediate. We discussed before our ideas on pseudoallelism, which are based upon pattern effects within a chromosomal section without recourse to individual genes. Pontecorvo realizes that his results may also be interpreted in this sense. We may expect, in this case, he writes, "all genes to show, to a greater or lesser degree, the behavior of those mentioned here. This means that there would not be, at the biological level, any further divisibility of the action of the gene, and that of the mutant alleles of a gene, taken two by two, some may recombine giving the normal allele—i.e., those in which the mutated or damaged elements are not in common—and some may not—i.e., those having in common part or all of the mutated elements."

My objections to this general idea stem mainly from the fact that the millimicromolar action of genic material or its first products remaining *in situ* would be a special feature of some chains of reactions requiring the assembly line because of the scarcity or immovability of the components. Since such reactive partners would at best be relatively rare, we would have an explanation which does not include all primary genic actions but only one class. All the regularities of genetics and cytogenetics make us expect that the primary genic actions are of the same type for all of them. Thus I am not certain that one should conclude from these experiments that reactions *in situ* between adjacent or nearby genic materials or primary products (in the sense of duplication products) are the typical beginning of genic action.

The most important genic products should be the specific enzymes, and a great deal of discussion in biochemical genetics touches upon this fact. We shall discuss this later from the point of view of general genic action. Here we are concerned only with primary genic action at the site of the genic material. The first product, either remaining and reacting *in situ* or immediately pushed off into the nucleus, may be an enzyme or a direct precursor of an enzyme, formed as a duplicate of a part of the genic material, as discussed in the introduction to this chapter. This would imply the possibility of a primary relationship between the genetic material and one of its final products without intervening steps. Monod (1947) and Spiegelman (1948) have developed ideas concerning the formation of enzymes and their specificity. They assume that the same enzyme precursors may be transformed into different specific enzymes in one unique biochemical step. If this were so at the primary level, a single primary genic product *in situ* might be such a precursor destined to be transformed later into many individual enzymes either from accumulated precursors or through autocatalysis. We shall return to this problem later. In the present context it is very difficult to see how the nature of a primary product *in situ* could be analyzed. At this point only indirect evidence from genetics, of the type just discussed, is available.

Lewis (1951) has used the case, discussed above, of three "pseudoallelic" loci with bithorax effect to draw some conclusions concerning primary gene products *in situ*. The situation is *mutatis mutandis* similar to Pontecorvo and Roper's case, the main difference being that a morphogenetic effect is involved and that the primary chemical events are purely hypothetical, based completely upon a literal interpretation of Beadle's one gene—one enzyme hypothesis. The derivations are further based upon an unfaltering belief in the classic corpuscular gene, and finally upon the premise that the three pseudoallelic loci are the result of duplication with subsequent change in function of one original gene (as already discussed in the chapter on pseudoallelism). Thus a powerful preoccupation with the problem of the origin of new genes by means of duplication is at the basis of the analysis. Like Pontecorvo, Lewis assumes that the genic product *in situ* is produced in such small amounts or is so limited in its ability to diffuse that the reactions take place independently in one of the homologous chromosomes. The direct products of the genes are assumed to be highly complex molecules. The actions of the pseudoalleles is then assumed to be a sequential one: if S is the available substrate, and A and B the products of the two duplicated genes $+^a$ and $+^b$, the reactions would follow in the order $S \rightarrow A \rightarrow B$. This seriation is the product of evolution, which Lewis conceives in the following way. The reaction controlled by the old gene is a reversible one: $K \leftrightarrows L$. The old gene would be expected to share a specificity for both the substrate K and the product L of the reaction. If a mutation to a new function occurs, the new gene could use both K and L as substrates. If the new gene also utilizes K, it is in competition with the old gene for the substrate. But if it uses L, a new product M may result, and the sequential reaction $K \rightarrow L \rightarrow M$ is established. These progressive steps involving complex molecules may be possible only when the genes in question had a common origin, since unrelated genes would not be similar enough in structure to share a specificity for the same complex molecule. The consequences of this argumentation for the explanation of pseudoallelism are the same as those developed above, following Pontecorvo.

Recently a new and remarkable example of pseudoallelism was found both by McKendrick and Pontecorvo (1952) and by Lewis

(1952). It turned out that the well-known multiple alleles apricot and white are pseudoalleles in Lewis' sense, each with its own series of other alleles, the order being apr-w. Again, the explanation of the so-called position effect (wild type in coupling, pinkish in repulsion) is that the mutant gene apr impairs the functioning of w^+ or that w impairs that for apr^+. Thus one of the genes controls a step $A \rightarrow B$ and the other a step $B \rightarrow C$ in a biochemical reaction chain $A \rightarrow B \rightarrow C$. The "position effect," then, results from the failure of substance B to diffuse from one chromosome to the other; the reaction chains in the two homologues are carried out independently of each other. For our present discussion these interpretations contribute the assumption of primary gene products acting *in situ,* further competition of the products for a substrate, and a sequential order of this reaction, which is the new addition. The details, it is clear, are worked out so as to fit the principle of the classic gene and the origin of pseudoalleles by duplication of genes with subsequent small changes in function. But the basic postulate is the same as that discussed in Pontecorvo's case, and so are the objections.

Lewis applies further the idea of the sequential reactions to an explanation of the phenotypic relations in different bithorax alleles. For our present discussion the details of the hypothesis are not relevant, except that they are an expression of the belief that the primary gene products *in situ* already take part in reactions which decide the trends of all subsequent phenotypic development. There is no reason to assume that the action of genic material in so-called pseudoallelic series differs basically from that of other genic material; hence it would follow that all genic actions are initiated by reactions *in situ* between the primary genic products. Since the whole idea works only with millimicromolecular, not diffusible, substances, it is difficult to believe that this is typical for all genic actions. The entire hypothesis is based upon the unproved premises mentioned above. Thus I cannot believe that it has yet been proved that primary genic products start their decisive reactions at the chromosomal site. We shall return to the problem of the primary products and the chromosomal site when discussing polyteny in relation to differentiation.

Altogether, we may say that in spite of a good deal of clever hypothesizing, we are still completely in the dark about what happens at the genic sites of the chromosomes when genic action produces the first reactive genic products. We do not know what the primary products are, how they are produced by the genic material, how and with what they react, where the reactions take place, and what the secondary products are and what they do. Certainly Pontecorvo is right, that the genetic methods for attacking these problems are further advanced than the biochemical methods (a point which I have made repeatedly in former works), but when the genetic analysis is being transposed into biochemical terms, which we all enjoy doing in a layman's way, or occasionally in a professional way, we may say that we are swimming far out in the ocean with no land visible. I can understand it when a biochemist, hearing about the present and similar speculations of the geneticists, once said, "This is certainly not biochemistry as we know it."

B. THE INTRANUCLEAR SITE

Whatever the origin of the primary genic products, and whether or not they start reacting with their near neighbors at the very chromosomal site, the primary or secondary products of genic action must be found sooner or later within the nuclear sap, unless these products stayed at the chromosomal site until a mitotic division allowed them to be shed into the cytoplasm.

This problem has been discussed many times (Stern, 1938; Huskins and Steinitz, 1948; N. G. Anderson, 1953). It has many aspects: the morphological one, which claims to show that formed substances are visibly eliminated from the nucleus in interphase; the genetical one, which tries to prove the point by showing that a genetic action upon the gametes (or the gametophyte in plants) must have taken place between two divisions (e.g., characters of starch in pollen grains); and the biochemical approach, proving experimentally the exchange of molecules through the nuclear membrane.

In favor of extrusion of genic products at the time of mitosis is an old observation of Conklin and Lillie that the determinative processes in the mollusk egg are suddenly changed when the germinal vesicle breaks down and its contents enter the cytoplasm. It is in agreement with this observation that the oöcyte nucleus contains all kinds of structures in addition to the chromosomes (see, later, the discussion of Brachet's work and of lampbrush chromosomes) and that all these substances are poured into the cytoplasm when the germinal vesicle disappears before the meiotic divisions. But it must be kept in mind that the oöcyte is a very special cell, in which not only all the processes of genetically controlled predetermination take place but also the accumulation of yolk, both of which are certainly based upon nuclear processes, the latter function at least partially so, since the cytoplasm also takes up DNA from outside sources. (See discussion of nurse cells, I 2 B *b dd.*) Thus it is quite possible that the immensely swollen germinal vesicle with its multifarious contents does dismiss substances into the cytoplasm as well as keep some of them until the nuclear membrane disappears.

Actually, it is the oöcyte nucleus (in addition to that of gland cells) for which most morphological descriptions of extrusion of materials have been described. Most of these are based upon the study of stained material. This is true for the many instances studied by my own school between 1904 and 1910 and in part for later work, especially that of Schreiner (1916). But there are also reports of observations of extrusion of "nucleoli" through the nuclear membrane in vivo. For the discussion of the genetical problem the decisive point is, of course, whether genic products, which must be assumed to be of macromolecular size, can pass through the nuclear membrane and do so. Today there can be no doubt that this is true. For the nuclear membrane of the germinal vesicle Callan (see 1952) and Mazia (see 1952) showed with the electron microscope that rather large pores are visible which permit the passage of particles of the size of nucleoprotein molecules. N. G. Anderson (1953) assumes a rather complicated structure, but with the same conclusions. Thus there can be no doubt that the oöcyte membrane is permeable in both directions to molecules of the size needed for primary genic products. This is in agreement with direct biochemical work on isolated tissue nuclei which proves by direct analysis (including work with tagged molecules) that an exchange in both directions through the nuclear membrane can take place for large molecules (for details see Anderson's review, 1953).

If we take it as proved that macromolecular genic products can pass through the nuclear membrane, our problem still remains. Do the primary genic products remain and interact with each other at the chromosomal site until mitosis, when the contracting chromosomes get rid of them and permit them to enter the cytoplasm? Or are these products, when formed at the chromosomal surface, immediately removed into the nuclear sap and do they enter the cytoplasm through the nuclear membrane, or only at mitosis, or in both ways? Is it possible that different types exist, that the genuine genic products, meaning those responsible for hereditary determinations, are released only at mitosis after interactions at the chromosomal site, while the materials of secretion, the trophic materials, also formed under chromosomal influence, are pushed immediately through the membrane?

There are some facts available to answer such questions. All the facts of predetermination in eggs require the release of genic material from the intact germinal vesicle, and some cases of maternal inheritance, especially those of sexual conditioning, require the same. Since it is probable (see Anderson, 1953) that the nuclear membrane can change its permeability and thus act selectively, a complicated and orderly removal of different genic materials through the membrane can be visualized (which might also include the retention of some molecules until mitosis).

Another point is, however, whether the primary genic materials, responsible for heredity, will behave in the same way as the purely trophic products of chromosomal action, a question which brings us back to the former discussion of the genic material in the chromosomes. A decisive answer to these problems can hardly be expected before we know what the genic material is and what its primary products are. But the facts already known may shed light upon the nature of the genic material. If we assume (see I 2 B *c*) that the DNA is the genic material, not only do we face the greatest difficulties with the genic products which directly or indirectly must be enzymes (i.e., proteins), but, in addition, nothing known about the intranuclear chemism makes sense any more. For this reason alone, we must consider the proteinic part of the nucleoprotein the genuine genic material, that is, the one which by replica formation produces the different kinds of primary active gene products. The known facts to which allusion was made relate only to the nucleinic part of the chromatin, actually only to a small part of it.

Caspersson's (see 1950) work on the localization, movements, and transformations of the nucleic acids within the nucleus has resulted in the following picture, major parts of which must be correct. In the region of the nucleolus organizer (McClintock, Heitz) in one or more chromosomes, RNA accumulates, produced in some way by the DNA. Together with proteins rich in diamino acids, this moves into the nucleolus. From the nucleolus the RNA (or its parts) moves to the nuclear membrane outside of which concentrated RNA accumulates and there plays a role in protein synthesis. Thus DNA is needed for the morphological organization of the genic material (which includes the mechanism of its duplication, and also, I think, of the release of primary gene products), while RNA takes care of diffuse protein synthesis. If these views of Caspersson are correct, it follows that the genic function and the trophic function of the nucleus are separated. It would hardly be possible to conclude that the RNA, from nucleolus to cytoplasm, was also genic, responsible for production of the specific proteins which comprise a major part of genic action. If this were so, nothing in the detailed genic organization of the chromosome would make sense. Obviously, the nucleolar apparatus responsible for the production and transport of RNA is a generalized metabolic function, which we called trophic, while the genic function, though dependent upon DNA structure, is a strictly patterned, specialized process. If we take together all the facts mentioned here and before, such conclusions seem unavoidable.

It is not surprising, then, that masses of RNA may be followed in the nucleus by Caspersson's subtle methods and, similarly, the quantity of DNA as a whole by these and more recent methods, as discussed before. Thus far, however, no way has been found to check biochemically upon the primary genic products with which genetic theory deals (though this may be possible one day for non-nucleated microörganisms). The analyses of nuclear sap made by Callan (see 1952) reveal only different colloidal proteins, no nucleinic acids. In view of the most recent work on the structure of the DNA molecule, the question may be posed whether RNA, which in the end must be derived from DNA, or, expressed more cautiously, may be made from DNA, is not produced primarily in the chromosome and transferred to the nucleolus, say for storage. An interesting finding by Stich and Hämmerling (1953) agrees better with Caspersson's view. They isolated the huge nucleolus of *Acetabularia* and found that it takes up avidly P^{32} and synthesizes RNA.

It is remarkable that all these recently elaborated facts tend to return *mutatis mutandis* to apparently long-discarded views which I developed half a century ago (Goldschmidt, 1904). Using R. Hertwig's term "chromidia" for what was originally described as extranuclear chromatin in Protozoa, I came to the conclusion that all intensively active nuclei extrude "chromatin" from the nucleus in the form of chromidia, which appear in many different forms in the cytoplasm and are basic for its activities. It was further concluded that within the nucleus two types of chromatin exist: idiochromatin and trophochromatin; the former is the hereditary chromatin in the chromosomes; the latter, the trophic chromatin expelled from the nucleus as chromidia. The two types were assumed to be a primary, always present condition of the nucleus. In spite of errors in detail, the theory is in a general way not much different from present-day ideas, if idiochromatin is identical with DNA plus protein and trophochromatin with RNA.

At this point Brachet's work on the biochemistry of differentiation enters the picture. However, as it deals primarily with differentiation, it will be discussed in a later chapter.

C. SPECIAL THEORIES OF GENIC ACTION

In an introductory discussion to the chapter on genic action I presented a very generalized concept of genic action, which probably fits all sides of the problem, including all the more special theories. We shall now discuss such special theories, which attribute specific effects to the genic material. In these theories it is of no great importance whether the primary gene products act at the chromosomal site or within the nucleus or in the cytoplasm as long as their effect can be described in biochemical terms characterizing one decisive result of genic action. The most elaborate theory of this type is Beadle's original one gene—one enzyme theory and its subsequent formulation as one gene—one function. The general theory was first conceived (but overlooked by all of us) by Garrod (1909) for the genetics of human metabolic disturbances, and was also briefly stated by Haldane (see 1954), but was independently derived later as a result of different attacks upon problems of biochemical genetics in more or less concrete form by Kühn and Caspari and by Beadle and Ephrussi for the determination of eye pigments, by Lawrence and Scott-Moncrieff for plant pigments, and by Moewus for sex-determining stuffs in *Chlamydomonas.* However, its strict formulation and experimental underpinning on a large scale are due to Beadle and Tatum (1941*a*) and their students and followers in their famous work on nutritional mutants in *Neurospora* and bacteria.

a. The one gene—one action theory

The general trend of the facts and conclusions is well known and has been reviewed many times, especially by Beadle (1945, 1949), Horowitz (1950), and Catcheside (1951). It will suffice here to mention the general setting for facts and conclusions. If it is known that a certain material, vitamin, or amino acid is needed for normal growth, a deficiency of the stuff or its absence prevents growth. Mutants are found which have such specific effects; for example, nicotinic acid cannot be synthetized, and growth occurs only where this is added to the medium. Of course, such additions provide the method of finding the specific deficiency. If it is known that nicotinic acid is normally synthetized in a series of consecutive steps—tryptophane, kynurenine, 3 hydroxykynurenine, 3 hydroxyanthralinic acid, nicotinic acid, or, in short, A-B-C-D-E—it can be tested by the aforementioned method how far this synthesis has gone or where it has been interrupted in the deficient mutant. In many cases the actual seriation was revealed only by these experiments. The general result in testing many mutants was that each interrupted synthesis at one point only, between C and D, or between A and B, and so on. Since all synthetic steps of such kind are controlled (catalyzed) by specific enzymes, it may be concluded that in the deficient strains the mutant gene was unable to produce the specific enzyme catalyzing the step A → B, and so on. From this the conclusion was drawn that the normal gene produces this enzyme in a one-one relation, a conclusion which we have discussed as a not cogent extrapolation.

This one-one relation was interpreted to mean the following. The genes (following the template idea; see above) are permanent models in the image of which enzyme proteins are constructed. (This is, in my opinion, an unavoidable theory of the production of the primary gene products as duplicates of genic material. Beadle's concept is more narrow than ours because his idea is linked with the classic concept of the gene. Our concept permits these primary gene products to be of many different molecular compositions according to the part of a pattern which is copied. However, for the general discussion this is irrelevant so long as we understand that one gene and its replica, the enzyme, is only one of the possibilities.) As each synthetic step requires a specific enzyme, and as each synthetic step is supposed to be controlled by one gene, each specific enzyme has its master pattern in one gene. In the absence of or deficient function of the gene (mutation), the specific enzyme cannot be formed.

For our subsequent discussion it might be useful to state here in advance the specific progress made by this theory as well as its general trend. We mentioned previously the early authors who had assumed that the gene acts as an autocatalyst (the school of J. Loeb, especially A. R. Moore, 1910, 1912; further, Hagedoorn, 1911; Troland, 1917; and Goldschmidt, 1916*a*, 1920*a*). Since, at that time, the chemistry of the enzymes was practically non-existent, a specific idea linking genes and products could not be proposed. Therefore, the kinetics rather than the material of the gene-controlled reactions were moved to the foreground in my theory of genic action through rates of reaction (Goldschmidt, 1916*a*, 1916*c*, 1920*a*). Beadle's work shifted the center of interest to the protein specificities, proposed an actual chemical nature of the primary gene products, thus studied a step prior to those with which our early work was concerned, and, of course, introduced specific biochemical notions for our very generalized ideas. If we refer to the preceding discussion of the processes at the chromosomal site, we are not quite sure whether Beadle assumes the primary enzymatic activity of the direct gene products (the duplicates) to take place *in situ* of the origin or in the nucleus or after removal into the cytoplasm, or perhaps in all these places. The question is not relevant for the one-one theory, but it is so for the problem whether the primary gene products are actually the final ones. This is a basic difficulty of the theory.

A number of us have not felt happy with this original formulation of Beadle's theory. The extrapolation from the mutant effect to the normal one is not convincing, at least to me. If a mutant prevents an enzyme from action, this does not mean necessarily that the normal locus produces the enzyme. If the normal locus controls any of the manifold physical and chemical conditions of an enzymatic synthesis, a mutant might prevent the latter by many indirect means (e.g., the control of pH). In time, Beadle's own group as well as others (e.g., Caspari, 1949*b*; Wagner, 1949) showed that in such biochemical mutants the specific enzyme may be present without acting for different reasons, for example, because of a temperature dependence or because of a block to diffusion (Garrod, 1909; Jucci, 1949, quoted from Haldane, 1954). Such cases accumulated so that Beadle changed the one gene—one enzyme idea into one gene—one function. This means that the gene is not connected by means of a one-one relation to an enzyme, which is a kind of replica of the gene, but to any function necessary for accomplishing one synthetic step. Thus the one-one relation remains, though it is no longer a unique biochemical effect producing one type of substance, an enzyme. It is rather the production of some direct or indirect or even remote condition which is necessary for a single synthetic step.

It is clear that this formulation now takes away the great appeal of the original theory, which made the primary gene product directly the specific active substance and simultaneously a copy of the gene structure. Furthermore, it no longer supports the classic theory of the gene, since the present formulation can be applied to any concept of the genic material. However, both formulations raise the question whether a general law of genic action has been found or only a feature of a limited type of genic action, relating to the biochemical ingredients of metabolism. Specific pigments like the melanins, ommins, anthocyanins, carotenes, and flavines may be described as metabolic end products; amino acids are ingredients of protein synthesis; and vitamins, those of coenzymes. Metabolism and the processes of growth as well as of production of specific intracellular and extracellular products are based upon the stepwise syntheses to which the theory refers.

Even at this end, difficulties arise when we come to such active substances as enzymes and hormones in the wider sense discussed above. Are they also synthesized step by step, each step being in some way controlled by one gene? Here again we meet the danger of loose terminology, already discussed in detail (III 1). It is very unfortunate that the Kühn school, upon their discovery of the gene-controlled synthesis of such pigment precursors as kynurenine, called these precursors *Genwirkstoffe,* while they are only steps in the synthesis of a completely inactive product to be deposited. Butenandt, the great chemist who did the chemical work, still uses this term (1952, 1953), thus deceiving himself (and his non-geneticist readers) into the belief that the pigment precursors are the active substances which are the organs by which the genes control hereditary traits. Simultaneously, Ephrussi and Beadle used (and sometimes still use) the term "hormones" for the same substances. Though I do not doubt that they realize the danger of such terminology, I am afraid that many biochemists and others not sufficiently trained in biology take the term at its face value and assume that the secret of *Genwirkstoffe* has been exposed and that here my old theory (1920*a*) that genes act by producing the hormones of differentiation has been demonstrated.

b. Relation to other ideas

Let us return to the generalization. Pigments and plant colors are good materials for Mendelian studies because they are easily classified. In molds and bacteria the production of metabolites may be grouped in the same category, thanks to the creation of ingenious techniques by Beadle and Tatum (1941). But the hereditary control of development in all its phases must entail much more complicated processes. Though it is understood that in the end they will go back somehow to a biochemical basis, it is difficult to believe that all genic action begins and ends with one step in a biosynthesis and that therefore all heredity can be compounded from such individual steps. Although I realize that it is difficult to define exactly what more is needed to understand genic action, still I am convinced that the one gene—one function idea (apart from the criticism of the gene theory) applies only to metabolites and their like (from the study of which Beadle and his precursors, like Garrod, Onslow, Scott-Moncrieff, and

Haldane, derived the idea). To this should be added such genically controlled specific substances, not of the metabolite type, which are found within the organism, for example, the specific antigens and hemoglobin. Both of these are gene-controlled, or, in more cautious language, are not produced or are produced with a wrong constitution (hemoglobin after Pauling *et al.*, since 1949) if a mutant locus is present.

Before mentioning other possibilities, it is fair to state that the one gene—one enzyme or one gene—one function hypothesis has been defined in a somewhat broader sense by Horowitz (see 1951). He argues thus: the concept is that of a gene whose sole activity (in addition to self-duplication) is that of functioning in the synthesis of a particular enzyme or enzyme precursor. Other loci may, however, also be concerned directly with the formation of the enzyme. The hypothesis does not imply that the final phenotypic expression of a mutation is necessarily restricted to a particular structure or function of the organism. The ultimate effect of a mutation is the result of an enormous magnification of the initial gene change, brought about through a system of reactions which, originating at the gene, rapidly branches out in various directions and coalesces with similar networks derived from other loci, to form a reticulum of as yet indeterminate extent and complexity. It is impossible to decide from the end effects alone whether the gene has one or many primary functions, since, on either assumption, a complex pattern of effects is expected in most cases. A mutation which induces a deficiency of an amino acid must secondarily affect the synthesis of virtually every protein of the cell, and an exhaustive enumeration of the end effects might well include every structure and function of the organism. In such a case, the secondary damage can be prevented by supplying the deficient amino acid. Therefore, the sole function of the gene in this case is to play some essential role in the synthesis of an amino acid. Actually, this role is restricted to a single step in the synthesis: a single reaction is abolished in the mutant, while all others proceed normally. The assumption follows that the gene plays a role in the synthesis of the enzyme which catalyzes the reaction.

It seems to me that this argumentation is essentially the same as our old physiological theory of heredity (1916*c*, 1920*a*, 1927) with the addition only that the product catalyzed by the gene is always first an enzyme for a single synthetic step. In my theory the accent was on the kinetics of the primary reactions, in order to explain their time interaction, the "network" of interaction; here the accent is upon the quality. We have mentioned previously that many biochemical geneticists, including Beadle, have moved away from this specific qualitative theory as a general description of all genic actions and speak more broadly of single functions controlled by the gene. Thus we have not moved very far away from the old concepts, to which essentially only one fact (a very important one, though) has been added: that at one point in the gene-controlled determinative reactions a single synthetic step for some substance is in some way, of many possible ones, interfered with by the mutant action in cases which are accessible to the deficiency-restoration type of experiment.

A rather interesting discussion of this subject by Atwood and Mukai (1953) emphasizes another aspect of the problem. They start with the idea of indispensable functions, which are the ones knocked out by the mutants in the deficiency experiments. They assume, however, that specific complex intermediates are shared by a fair number of different enzymes or other large molecules. A mutation that affects a single complex intermediate would affect the synthesis of a number of different enzymes, leading to the loss of an indispensable function. The detectable mutations would be confined to genes controlling the final assembly of the complex fragments into macromolecules; thus the total synthesis of an enzyme is not due to a single gene. Atwood and Mukai think that medium-sized polypeptides are these intermediate gene products. These ideas are still well in line with Beadle's one gene—one action concept, although, by emphasizing the intermediate products and the interplay of genic actions, a bridge is made toward the views to be discussed.

It is interesting to compare my general attitude in the present discussion with that of a biochemical geneticist who thinks that the one gene—one enzyme theory is "manifestly unimportant, at the present time" (D. M. Bonner, 1951). He points out that we have no criteria for a primary genic function, that we cannot distinguish between one or more gene-controlled primary effects, and that, therefore, the one gene—one function idea "does not serve a useful purpose at the present time."

It is true, he further argues, that the biochemical reactions within a cell are under nuclear control, since biochemical alteration has inevitably been traced to genic alteration, but this tells us little about the mechanism of genic control. Since the majority of cellular reactions require participation of a specific enzyme, and since these enzymes must be formed before the reaction takes place which they catalyze, it is logical that the genes control the formation of enzymes.

Enzymes, like other macromolecules, possess specificity; therefore we must examine the possibility that genes function only in specificity-conferring steps in enzyme formation. While there is no evidence that mutation results in a change of enzyme specificity, there is evidence to the contrary. These facts indicate that genic control may be exercised at some point of enzyme formation other than in specificity-conferring steps. I quote now from Bonner: "As mentioned earlier, substrate, both normal and heterologous, has a profound effect upon the rate of enzyme formation . . . Genetic alterations are known to affect this response to substrate, and thus to determine rate of formation and concentration of enzyme. The timing of appearance of enzyme is affected by substrate and is also subject to genetic alteration. Thus one might advance the view, that in formation of enzyme specificity there is no direct genetic control. . . . Genetic control may enter, however, in determining the time and rate of enzyme formation. How genes act in determining time and rate of enzyme formation is as much an enigma as how genes act in determining enzyme specificity.

"A concept of gene action involving time and rate factors fits the data of microbial genetics at the present time far better than does a concept involving specificity . . ."

These conclusions of a biochemical geneticist, who obviously overlooked the literature on physiological genetics prior to the time of so-called biochemical genetics, are the same which I drew (1920*a*, 1927) from purely genetical analysis. Of course at that time we did not yet deal with enzyme systems as known today, and I had included specific enzymes in the more general group of active substances, for which I used the more inclusive term "hormones," perhaps unwisely, for even at that time the term was criticized by J. Huxley. But in a general way I may call the quoted sentences a return to the essence of my old "physiological theory of heredity." This reminds me of a review of my later more comprehensive book (1938) by J. B. S. Haldane, who pointed out that all that work on rate genes and attuned reaction velocities is very interesting, but that the real thing is (what at that time had not been baptized thus) biochemical genetics, which relates the genes to actual substances. A long time has elapsed since, and biochemical genetics has had its triumphant run, and brilliant discoveries of a biochemical nature have been made. But when it comes to the understanding of genic action, an incisive analysis such as that of Bonner leads back to the long-forgotten theories of the 'twenties. I may be excused for deriving some satisfaction from this.

In all the present discussions we have taken it for granted, as the biochemical geneticists did, that the primary gene products are certainly duplicates of the whole or of parts of the proteinic moiety of the genic material. The possibility that the nucleinic acid part is actually the genic material was not taken into account. I have already mentioned the idea, actually the fact, that ribonucleic acid is removed from the nucleus in some way and enters the cytoplasm. As RNA is derived from DNA in the nucleus, we might think of RNA as the specific first product of genic action (assuming that DNA is the genic material). This would require that as many kinds of RNA are dismissed into the cytoplasm as there are genic types. The known facts are very difficult to reconcile with such a view (see, above, Caspersson). If all the RNA were accumulated in the nucleolus, one would think that all its different specific types were mixed within the nucleolus; when it is removed into the cytoplasm, the problem of sorting out the different RNA's arises, a process needed for orderly action in genetic determination. All the facts (some to be discussed in the next chapter) seem to speak against genic qualities of the RNA within and without the nucleus, and to justify the old designation as trophochromatin (see III 4 B). This conclusion puts the discussion of plasmatic RNA into the chapter on differentiation. The aforementioned discussion (I 2 B *a*) of the work of Seiler and Ris and Kleinfeld showed that masses of ribonucleic protein, almost as large in size as the remaining chromosomes, or actually larger, may be sloughed off from the chromosomes in meiosis of Lepidoptera with clear indications that they have no further function.

5

GENIC CONTROL OF DEVELOPMENT

Development consists of a series of steps of morphological, physiological, and biochemical diversification which are exactly timed, graded, attuned to each other, and properly placed within the whole. All this is certainly controlled by the action of the genic material, as follows from the fact that mutational changes may affect every stage of development, though the minor changes at or near the end of development are the favorite materials of genetic research. We hear frequently that orderly development is the result of an interplay between genic activity and environment. This, in my opinion, is a completely misleading statement in spite of its apparent truth. If a silkworm egg, immersed in sulfuric acid, does develop parthenogenetically, as it otherwise would not do, this is an environmental effect. If an egg reared in calcium-free water changes its type of cleavage, this is an environmental effect. An axolotl injected with thyroxin metamorphoses as a result of the internal environment. But in all these cases and a thousand others, the new environment is an unnatural condition to which the normally developing organism is not exposed. It is just like changing the environment of a motor by pouring acid into the gasoline. But if we consider the organism within the environment to which it is adapted, development is completely controlled by the genic material. Millions of sea urchin eggs grown in their proper sea water develop one like the other; millions of *Drosophila* eggs in their natural food and temperature do the same; and also millions of rabbits in the uteri of healthy does. All this means that the experimental zoölogists interested in interfering with genic actions by changing the internal or external environment may speak of the collaboration of both in controlling development. However, the geneticist as a rule deals with development under normal, optimal conditions and therefore only with genic control. If he finds a mutant which has a different phenotype at different temperatures (including also temperature-sensitive biochemical synthesis as known in *Neurospora*), this does not mean to him a proof for environmental coöperation in control of development but rather a definite type of genic action which has a norm of reaction susceptible to environmental interference. Thus we feel entitled to explain development exclusively in terms of genic action, though using modifying actions of the environment as tools which can help us to understand normal genic action. We discussed this when analyzing phenocopies, and when first using the concept of norm of reaction, but it should be stated again at the beginning of a discussion of genic control of development.

In its most general aspect, animal development consists of an orderly, seriated group of determinations. This means a continuous narrowing down of prospective potencies. In the beginning, the egg is omnipotent. After some time (which might begin with fertilization or, in predetermined eggs, with oöcyte growth), right-left halves are determined; afterward, the location of some primordia for entire groups of organs; then, of individual organs and their parts. The classic methods of experimental embryology have firmly established this sequence of hierarchical steps of successively narrowing determinations of embryonic material, sometimes by abrupt diversification, sometimes (possibly always?) by an intermediate period of labile determination. Genic action is in control of an efficiently timed and spaced series of determinations, followed by specific differentiation. The latter point is of importance. Determination takes place in undifferentiated or little differentiated cells and groups of cells, both in animals and in plants. Visible differentiation follows final determination. The latter fact opens the possibility of different behavior of these phases in regard to genic control. Still another process of embryonic differentiation may play a role, a process which is not directly provided for by genic control. This is embryonic regulation and integration, which means that in an experimental or organically controlled (by a mutant) upset of normal development, the embryo is able to regulate and integrate itself into a more or less perfect whole by means of processes which were not provided for in the normal functioning of the genic material. We shall return to this most important fact.

In order to understand genic action in controlling development, we must find out what the genic material does to control growth, diversification of cell material in regard to prospective potency (i.e., determination and intracellular specific tissue differentiation), the proper timing of these events in relation to each other, the proper spatial arrangement, and the chemodifferentiation. As the actual processes of development take place within the cytoplasm of the cell, additional problems arise as to whether the nucleus remains constant while it controls cytoplasmic diversification or whether the genic material within the nucleus itself diversifies. Further, the qualitative part of nuclear control of cytoplasmic processes, that is, the biochemical meaning of the words "nuclear control," should be established. Finally, independent or at least self-perpetuating cytoplasmic processes have to be considered.

A. THE QUALITATIVE ASPECT

a. Nuclear versus cytoplasmic diversification

It is well known that Weismann conceived of development, as far as genetic control is concerned, as a sorting out of genetic material by *erbungleiche Teilung*. With the rise of genetics and cytogenetics, this idea was abandoned. It became clear that the phenomena of embryonic restitution and of regeneration as well as the presence of the same chromosomes in all cells did not agree with such an assumption. In the case of the salivary gland chromosomes of *Drosophila*, located in cells at the extreme end of development, there is no doubt that in a purely material (not functional) sense the entire genic material is present in its normal architecture. Numerous facts point in the same direction: the most instructive are the existence of cell lethals (Demerec, 1943) and the local effects of somatic crossing over in peripheral cells (Stern, 1936). However, recently some geneticists and biochemists have taken up again the apparently long-settled problem and asked themselves whether there is not also a nuclear diversification in development after all (e.g., Spiegelman, Schultz).

Let us first consider what the question in itself means. Certainly, no independent action of the nucleus is imaginable, since the nucleus always collaborates somehow with the cytoplasm. Even apparently purely cytoplasmic features are known to be genically controlled, as I have stated repeatedly before. I mentioned previously the maternally inherited and simple Mendelian control of the bending of the spindle and spiral arrangement of cytoplasmic particles in the mollusk egg, and the diverse cases of cytoplasmic conditioning. The abnormalities in the formation of sperm tails in *Drosophila* crosses (Dobzhansky, 1933) constitute another example. After all, genic control of meiotic behavior of the chromosomes (see Beadle's sticky and asynaptic chromosomes) also belongs here. Thus, visible cytoplasmic differences resulting in unequal divisions, in regard to both potency and visible differentiation, do not necessarily mean that the genic material is not involved.

But this is not our present problem. What we want to know is whether the genic material remains unchanged during all phases of development, all cells remaining genetically omnipotent. If this is so, we must explain why the action of the different parts of the genetic material in controlling definite steps of development takes place only at definite times and in definite cells. We must explain what has been called the "activation" of individual genes at definite times and places. (The word "activation" includes the idea that genes may remain dormant until they start to function at a certain moment. I use the word here without such a connotation, simply as describing the fact of the orderly timing of genically controlled developmental steps.) The alternative question is whether the genic material itself changes first so as to restrain its genic qualities, select some and discard others by actual loss or inactivation, or changes in whatever other way can be imagined. Though this would not be exactly Weismann's *erbungleiche Teilung*, it would amount to the same thing, because very frequently development uses a single division to produce a specialized from a generalized cell. In all meristematic growth, typical for plants, but found also in animals in the teloblasts of worms, in the production of nurse cells in the ovary, and in other cases, such differential divisions occur: one cell retains all the genetic potencies and the other one is determined to a single fate. The possibility of purely cytoplasmic unequal distribution cannot be denied for this special division. We have discussed the example of the unequal division of the spermatocyte of aphids, in which the smaller cell lacking mitochondria has a fate different from that of its larger sister cell. However, this would not prevent the occurrence of intranuclear change in one product.

Cytoplasmic influence upon chromosomal behavior is well known since Boveri's work on chromatin diminution. Here the location of the nucleus in one or another kind of cytoplasm, visibly differentiated during oögenesis, determines whether or not the chromosomes will undergo diminution. Probably the same principle is at work when in the "segmenting" insect egg a nucleus, entering the posterior, visibly differentiated germ-track cytoplasm, becomes a sex-cell nucleus and henceforth behaves differently, in regard to rhythm of division, for example, from the other nuclei. It is the same thing if, according to Sonneborn (see 1955), the nucleus derived from the last meiotic (equational) division in *Paramecium* becomes a fertilization nucleus only when it becomes located in a definite part of the oral cytoplasm. (Attention is drawn again to Lwoff's findings—see I 1—that certain self-reproducing organelles assume a definite pattern, according to the part of the cytoplasm in which they are located. Though the nucleus is not involved here, the underlying causative chain may be the same as in the former examples.)

Though in all these cases the cytoplasm clearly controls nuclear behavior, it must be realized, first, that there is no reason to assume that the genic material in the nucleus has been affected, changed, or restrained; second, that the differential protoplasm which affects the behavior of the nuclei has been set aside during oögenesis, most probably under control of the genic material in the nucleus, the process being of the type of predetermination. Thus it would be wrong to maintain that any of these cases demonstrate nuclear differentiation during development.

At this point it should be added that some facts show the occasional occurrence of what seems to amount to Weismann's *erbungleiche Teilung*. In the classic case of *Dyticus* (Giardina) the prospective egg cell retains in four consecutive divisions all the heterochromatin, while the prospective nurse cells, the other products of these divisions, have only euchromatic nuclei (see I 2 C *b*). Thus the nuclei resulting from these divisions are differently constituted. However, as our analysis showed, this does not mean an *erbungleiche* division in the sense of our present discussion; though it cannot be denied that a possibility exists that in normal development divisions may occur of the same type, with the same consequences of enhancing or inhibiting future divisions by the control of the quantity of heterochromatin. No such case is known to me, but it would be worth while to check the teloblasts of worms for such an occurrence.

Another example is the division of the fertilization nucleus (or one of its division products) in Infusoria into a future macro- and micronucleus, known since Bütschli (1876). Sonneborn (1955) has made a remarkable analysis of this phenomenon; the results belong partly to the present discussion and partly to the chapter on cytoplasmic heredity, where the important points have already been discussed (see II 2 E *d bb*). It is remarkable that the unequal (in a functional sense) division of the nucleus leads to the establishment of macro- and micronuclei which are definitely different in function and in prospective possibilities, though lying side by side in the same cytoplasm. Nevertheless, both perpetuate indefinitely their characteristics, though originally the macronuclear control of mating type was induced by cytoplasmic specificity (which in turn was under nuclear control). This functional difference of the macronucleus, already said to be self-perpetuating, remains so over subsequent generations. There is, of course, the question whether these interesting features are typical, such as could also occur in the development of Metazoa, thus making *erbungleiche Teilung* a phenomenon to reckon with in the study of genetic control of development. Another possibility is that the processes described are specific for Infusoria, owing to the necessities of the non-cellular organization of the complicated organism. The *erbungleiche* division may be analogous here to any process of segregation of differently determined material in metazoan development. This means that what is accomplished in the metazoan embryo by separating groups of cells differently determined on the basis of cytoplasmic differentiation, is accomplished in the non-cellular organism by intranuclear differentiation, because the lack of cellular subdivision prevents the use of the method chosen in embryonic differentiation. I think that this possibility should be realized when it comes to drawing general genetic conclusions from the facts found in *Paramecium.*

But it must not be forgotten that Nanney (1953*b*) and Sonneborn (1955) showed that in certain cases the location of the nuclei in definite cytoplasm decides their fate as a micro- or a macronucleus, respectively. Even centrifugation can change this fate, obviously by changing the cytoplasmic surroundings. Thus we cannot speak of differential division but only of division products made different secondarily. This would tend to nullify the foregoing argument.

We return now to the problem whether progressive differentiation in development under control of the genic material can be the result of changes of this material within the nucleus, accomplished either by *erbungleiche Teilung,* as discussed, or by some kind of intranuclear differentiation affecting differentially the diverse parts of the genic material, for example, by destroying or inactivating some or by severally augmenting another part, thus narrowing down step by step the possible genic actions.

There is, in my opinion, a group of facts which may be interpreted, after a fashion, in this sense, though this has never been tried, if I am not mistaken. These are the facts relating to polyteny and endomitosis. Since Jacobj (1925) discovered and interpreted the presence in tissues of nuclei of sizes varying according to a 2^n series, and Geitler (1938) found and explained the process of endomitosis resulting in polytene chromosomes, this phenomenon has attracted much attention. (See Geitler's new monograph, 1954.) Apart from chromatin diminution and other specific features of heterochromatin, discussed above, it is the only type of visible nuclear differentiation in Metazoa connected with processes of differential determination. One

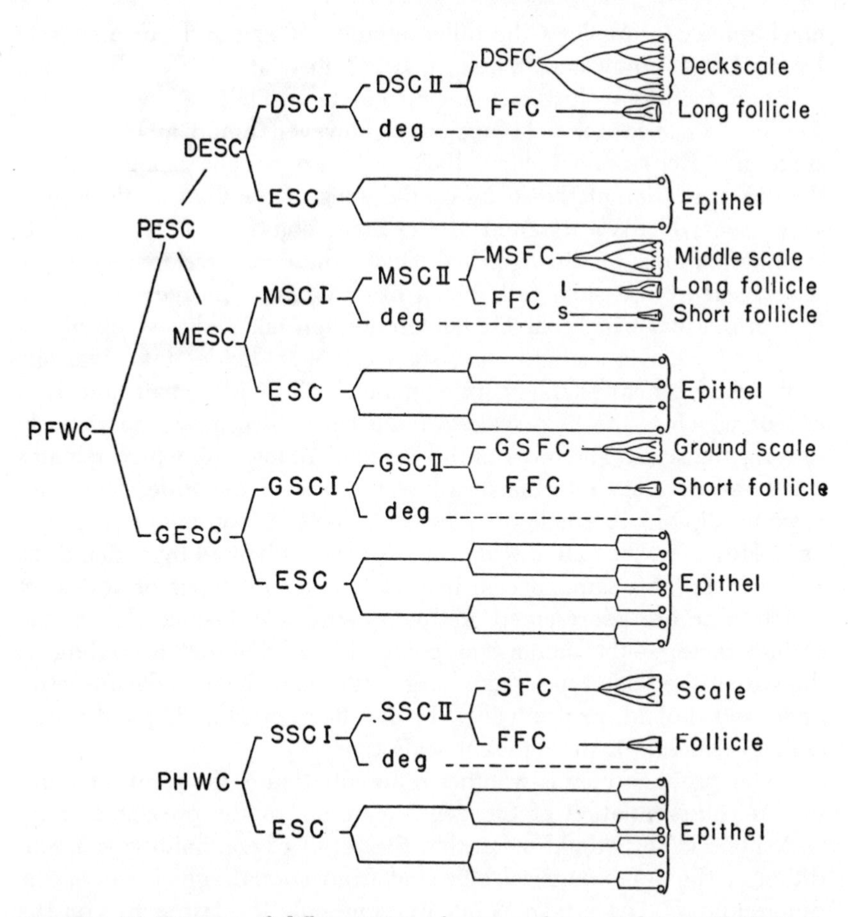

Fig. 17. Diagram of differentiation of wing scales in *Ephestia*. Ploidy is indicated by dichotomic lines in scales. Arrangement of following legend corresponds to vertical columns. (From Henke, 1952.)

PFWC	primordial forewing cell
PHWC	primordial hindwing cell
PESC	pattern-scale epithelial stem cell
DESC	deck-scale epithelial stem cell
MESC	middle-scale epithelial stem cell
GESC	ground-scale epithelial stem cell
DSC I	deck-scale stem cell I
ESC	epithelial stem cell
MSC I	middle-scale stem cell I
GSC I	ground-scale stem cell I
SSC I	scale stem cell I
DSC II	deck-scale stem cell II
deg	degenerating cell
MSC II	middle-scale stem cell II
GSC II	ground-scale stem cell II
SSC II	scale stem cell II
DSFC	deck-scale-forming cell
FFC	follicle-forming cell
MSFC	middle-scale-forming cell
FFC	follicle-forming cell: *l*, large; *s*, small
GSFC	ground-scale-forming cell
SFC	scale-forming cells

much-quoted example is the differentiation of egg and nurse cells in *Drosophila* (Painter and Reindorp, 1939), in which nurse cells, which will not divide any further, develop polytene nuclei by endomitosis. The best material for a discussion is, however, found in Henke and students' (Henke and Pohley, 1952) subtle and painstaking work on the differentiation of the scales on the wing of the flour moth. Figure 17 presents Henke's diagram of the main points. Two types of differentiation must be distinguished. One is the final development of the scale itself from a stem cell, which has a definite lineage going back to a primordial wing cell. This differentiation takes place (top of the diagram) when a scale-forming stem cell first divides into two, one of which degenerates. The surviving stem cell divides again into two, one of which is the final scale-forming cell which grows enormously to form the scale. The other is the sheath-forming cell, which remains small and develops into the sheath at the base of the scale. The latter remains diploid in smaller scales, but becomes tetraploid in larger ones. However, the actual scale cell becomes polyploid by endomitosis up to 32 n. This same is true in principle for all types of scales, of which four are represented in the diagram. But—and this is the second feature—the amount of polyploidy is different according to the size of the scale types (also, large and small sheath cells are tetraploid and diploid, respectively). In the diagram 8- to 32-ploid nuclei are represented for the different scale types.

Our problem now is whether differentiation is the result of intranuclear differentiation of the genic material, in the present case by endomitosis. This would mean that the result of endomitosis is a condition of the genic material, different from normal, which causes the differentiation. If we take as our example only the last steps (on the right in the diagram), the differential division occurs so that one daughter cell develops a polyploid nucleus, and this cell grows, giving rise to a scale; the other cell stays diploid (or becomes tetraploid) and remains small to form the sheath. At its face value, this seems to be a beautiful case of intranuclear differentiation as a cause of divergent determination, but this conclusion cannot stand closer scrutiny. Since the last division always gives one sheath and one scale cell, the differential determination has already been accomplished before growth and endomitosis begins. If we go back in the cellular pedigree, we find the same situation at each differential division. At the time of the first separation (left in the diagram) of epithelial and scale stem cells, the future scale type and therefore the amount of endomitosis already has been determined. Someone might retort that at the time of the first differential division a change could have occurred in the genic material which made it liable to endomitosis in subsequent cell generations. This does not sound very plausible, but, however that may be, it cannot be asserted that determination via intranuclear change has been proved in this case.

We may derive the same conclusions from the work of Wigglesworth (1953) on bugs, though here possible polyteny has been neglected. He showed that the differentiation of epidermis cells into sensory hairs is controlled by a substance in the epidermis needed for determination of a bristle-forming center. Each center drains this substance from the surrounding cells, as is shown by the fact that new centers arise as far distant as possible from old ones. Some results of burning experiments indicate that a certain concentration of the substance suffices for differentiation of gland cells but not of hair. Hair differentiation (or dedifferentiation) of larval or adult type is under the control of the juvenile hormone, all of which amounts to control of cellular differentiation from outside the nucleus.

In plants a comparable situation seems to exist. Geitler and his school have made many contributions to this subject (see Geitler, 1954; Tschermak-Woess and Hasitschka, 1954). In general we may say that the development of trichomes follows the model of the lepidopteran scales. Polyploidy up to 256-ploid is found, while the cells from which such large and specific structures originate remain diploid. In view of the many examples found by Geitler and his school, it seems that polyploidization is clearly connected with differentiation of special large-celled organs. The meaning of this must be the same as in the animal case, and the foregoing and following discussion applies to both.

In view of the importance of the subject, further discussion is needed. In most of the well-known cases of endomitotic polyploidy (including those in plants, the tapetum cells) we are dealing with cells with a single intensive synthetic function. The gland cells, including the dipteran salivaries or the immensely polyploid silk-gland cells of Lepidoptera, muscle cells, secretory intestinal cells, cells of Malpighian tubules, are included in the list. It is certain that these cells, polyploid by endomitosis, have stopped dividing but may grow to very large size, which, in the cases studied (see Kurnick and Herskowitz, 1952), is proportional to the amount of polyteny. We may take it for granted that polytene cells are incapable of regeneration of a whole body, as, for example, leaf cells of *Begonia* can do. (The nematodes with their cell-constant, highly polytenic cells are unable to regenerate.) But the polytene cells have acquired the capacity of synthesizing huge quantities of a single proteinic substance, serin in the silk-gland cell, myosin in the muscle cell, and just protoplasm for growth without division in others. What has happened in these nuclei is just the opposite of intranuclear genetic differentiation. It is actually the stoppage of the genetic activity of the chromosomes which is replaced by a purely functional activity, restricted to one synthetic action. This is also intranuclear differentiation, though of a very specific type and not comparable to what is meant by intranuclear change as a means of genic differentiation.

It is remarkable what happens in this case to the chromosomes. According to new work of Bauer and Beermann (1952), Herskowitz (1950), and Beermann (1952) on salivary chromosomes of *Chironomus* and *Drosophila,* the chromonema of each chromatid (which probably is already a micellar bundle) multiplies this structure immensely by endochromosomal division. The result is in *Drosophila* a calculated number of about 1,000 strands, which thus go down to submicroscopic size (though recent electron microscopic work shows only 16, i.e., 4 for the chromatid). In *Chironomus* these innumerable strands can be seen splitting off in the so-called Balbiani rings and again split down to ultramicroscopic size and an estimated 16,000n constitution. Hand in hand with this multiplication goes the increase in DNA, proportional to the number of strands (in potencies of two), as well as increase in cell size of growth without division (see fig. 3*b*).

From the point of view of cytology—perhaps also of function—it might not seem correct to consider both the endomitotic polyploidy as found in *Gerris,* silkworm glands, and so on, and the so-called polyteny of dipteran somatic chromosomes to be the same thing. In the first case entire chromosomes have doubled, quadrupled, and so on, and the individual chromosome groups may or may not remain separate. Frequently, only the chromocenters and nucleoli indicate the endomitotic groups, the chromosomes themselves being invisible in the resting nuclei. The so-called polytene chromosomes of Diptera have a completely different origin. The four synapsed chromatids retain their individuality, though it is only occasionally visible (see Goldschmidt and Kodani, 1942). Within these chromatids the micellar bundle of the chromonema multiplies immensely; nobody knows whether this happens by division into 2–4–8, and so on, though a 16 group ($= 4 \times 4$) has been claimed in *Drosophila* and also a DNA quantity in potencies of 2, as discussed and illustrated before, so that a bundle of fibrils results which is an enlarged replica of the original micellar bundle. Actually, both the visible behavior in the Balbiani rings of *Chironomus,* where the bundles separate into fibrils varying to submicroscopic size (Bauer, Beermann), as well as the calculation from DNA quantity (Kurnick and Herskowitz), which also leads into the submicroscopic field, show that we cannot call this a bundle of chromosomes, that is, a polyploid structure as in the cases mentioned above. Undoubtedly, there are only four chromatids, which may be separated by specific treatment (Kodani, 1942), but each has a complicated fibrillar structure comparable to the fibrillar structure of a muscle cell (which certainly could not be described as polytene myosin). I should prefer to apply a term like "supermicellar chromosome," and add that recent work by Freire-Maia *et al.* (1953) and Breuer and Pavan (in press) agrees well with my point of view. In the development of salivary cells they found cycles of higher and lower polyteny, which, of course, excludes genuine polyteny. However, it is probable that in one respect the polyploid and the polytene types are alike: both produce a large template surface for protein synthesis. In *Chironomus* the production of droplets at definite points of the salivary chromosomes is visible in vivo.

I think that both types of structure show the nongenic parts of the chromosomes at work and do not permit conclusions concerning intranuclear differentiation as discussed above, though we may call it thus in a limited sense. This, at least, is the way I must look at the facts when taking into account the whole body of information.

But one more remarkable fact should be mentioned which comes as near to chromosomal differentiation in development as can be imagined. Beermann (1952) showed that the giant chromosomes of dipteran cells have essentially the same structure in all different tissues, for example, salivary, Malpighian, and intestinal cells (as opposed to Sengün, 1948; and Sengün and Kosswig, 1947). But individual regions may differ structurally. What is in one cell type a group of clear bands may be in another a "bulb" with diffuse structure. Could it be that these are regions which produce the non-genic specific secretion product, the bulb being a group of bands in the secretive phase? This would be a very important fact, though still in agreement with our former conclusions on non-genic function of these chromosomes. In a sense we might speak here of chromosomal diversification within different cells. But it is very different from *erbungleiche Teilung,* if our interpretation of the background facts is correct.

It might be surmised in this connection that the genic function of the chromosomes in development is bound somehow to mitotic division, that is, opening of the nucleus, as opposed to the non-genic function in polyteny without opening of the nucleus. A major difficulty for such speculations would be the protozoan nucleus with intranuclear mitosis. (See also the discussion in III 4 B.)

In order to gain further insight, we may compare the structure of what we just called supermicellar chromosomes, that is, the salivary type of so-called polyteny with the structure of a large chromosome which is active both genically and metabolically, namely, the lampbrush chromosome in the growing oöcyte of Amphibia, which we have discussed repeatedly (see I 2 A). According to Callan (1952), the stretched lampbrush chromosome is actually of the diameter of a single chain molecule. Guyénot and Danon (1953) find a diameter of only 100–150 A°. It seems to me that we must conclude from such a comparison that the genic action of the chromosome requires (in agreement with Pauling's theory) a fully exposed surface of the proteinic part of the nucleoprotein combination; while the non-genic function of the chromosome (the mass production of a single protein) requires a maximum number of identical templates which must be sought in the DNA moiety of the chromonema. Such a view, which I think is unavoidable in face of the facts, simultaneously disposes of DNA as the genetic material. If Herskowitz (1950) is right that a salivary chromosome is 1,000-stranded with corresponding increase in amount of DNA (to 2^{10}), this alone would suffice to rule out DNA as genic substance. Why should DNA increase immensely in cells with a specialized secretory function, or growing without division, that is, producing more cytoplasm?

I have mentioned the possibility of heterochromatin being involved in an *erbungleiche* division, though I pointed out that this would not be exactly the same as development through intranuclear genic diversification. Schultz (1952) has proposed a rather different type of theory involving heterochromatin and resulting in an argument in favor of intranuclear genic differentiation. This author starts his deductions with the previously mentioned work of Painter and Reindorp on the polyteny of nurse cells in the ovary of *Drosophila.* Here it was observed that at a stage when the nurse cell nucleus is 512-ploid, the heterochromatic Y-chromosome has divided only four times, and other heterochromatic regions the same. Schultz thinks that "thus in at least one case there is a differential multiplication of the various chromosome regions, and the possibility is apparent that concomitant with endomitosis a genetic differentiation of nuclei does take place." This conclusion is, however, refuted (apart from the foregoing analysis of the situation, which shows that completely different problems are involved in endomitosis and genic diversification) by the fact that the total content of DNA in endomitotic nuclei increases with the number of divisions in potencies of two. (See above, fig. 2; also Kurnick and Herskowitz, 1952.)

Schultz now argues that if intranuclear differentiation takes place with endomitosis, it might also occur otherwise (though he himself advises caution). It appears to him that observed differences of heterochromatic parts of the chromosomes may be a case in question. He points to the phenomenon of the variegated position effect in heterochromatic breaks. Since the grade of variegation increases in different tissues with the time of development of the organ, Schultz thinks that a progressive change of the functions of the heterochromatic regions follows. If it is assumed that the heterochromatic regions have a function in the general metabolism of the chromosome, the change of activity of the loci, transposed to heterochromatic neighborhood, could be understood as a transformation in such a way that such loci are able to carry out only the generalized functions of heterochromatin and no longer their own specific activities. If now these variegated rearrangements are regarded as indicative of processes going on in normal development, "the possibility of nuclear differentiation in histogenesis appears." In embryogenesis only the specific genes required for function in a particular type of cell are in an active state. The others are in the heterochromatic state, and carry only the general functions of such regions. This heterochromatization might be irreversible or reversible. Thus far Schultz argues.

Our former discussions of all the facts concerned tend to show that these conclusions cannot be accepted. The variegated position effect probably demands a completely different interpretation, one based upon developmental rather than genic features. Apart from this, Schultz' theory tries to explain differentiation by intranuclear changes, requiring so-called heterochromatization of "genes" with change of their function from a special to a general one. I wonder whether the order of events has not been turned around, just as it was in polyteny. (See the discussion of scale formation, III 5 A *a.*) Assuming for argument's sake that it had been shown that during cell differentiation some chromosomal parts had been heterochromatinized (though there is hardly a more confused subject in modern cytogenetics than the claims for shifting heterochromatization of euchromatic chromosomal regions; a perusal of Schultz' review, 1941, of this subject, as well as our former discussion, will bear out this statement).

Does it follow that this assumed heterochromatization was the cause of differentiation? I would conclude, just as before with polyteny, that the consequence of differentiation, involving the ending of the need for genic activity, becomes visible in chromosomal changes from the specialized structure necessary for genic action to a generalized one adapted for special synthetic action. Schultz' hypothesis demonstrates that models of intranuclear differentiation could be worked out if results of experiments should require such a view. Since this is not the case, we had better not assume that the possibility of stating such a theory in terms of very doubtful and confusing observations increases its chance of being correct.

From a very different angle, the same problem was attacked by the group of researchers interested in the quantity of DNA in the nucleus, the general results of which were discussed (I 2 B *b aa*) in connection with the problem of whether or not DNA is the genetic material. We saw that the authors (reviewed by Alfert and Swift, 1953) considered the constancy of DNA in all cells and the simple ratios in polyploidy and polyteny as indication of such a role for DNA. Lison and Pasteels (1951) found, however, some variation in different tissues, and thought that this is associated with the control of morphogenetic processes, which then may be classed as intranuclear causes of differentiation. Recently R. C. Moore (1952) made extensive measurements, comparing the amount of variation of the DNA content in different tissues of haploid and diploid frog embryos. It was found that the diploid values are always twice the haploid ones, as expected. Furthermore, a considerable range of variability of the DNA quantity was found, first, when comparing the same organ at different times of differentiation, and second, between different tissues. In a general way it was found that a wide range of DNA values is correlated with differentiation. As differentiation proceeds, the range of DNA values is narrowed, and finally they hardly fluctuate. From this it is concluded that if DNA is the genic material, yet is variable in amount in differentiating tissues, an explanation can be derived of how cells with the same chromosome complement differentiate into different tissues. "The genes controlling certain morphogenetic processes may produce different amounts and kinds of DNA at different times, resulting in differentiation." This idea, then, evades the difficulty of genic alterations by leaving the genes unchanged but their activity in terms of "producing" DNA changing, and, in addition, endows DNA with the rather mysterious quality of controlling differentiation by its amount.

Even assuming that the methods of measuring permit the establishing of the facts underlying this theory (which is not generally conceded), it is very difficult to imagine how such vague concepts could be made to account for specific features, apart from the fact that the variability of DNA claimed, but without a clear scheme of distribution, is not of the nature of an agent controlling orderly differentiation. Since the basis of the whole argument is rather doubtful, and since such ideas as genes producing DNA are anything but clear, and are difficult to reconcile with our knowledge of the role of DNA, it seems that the material can hardly be advocated as an indication of intranuclear change as cause of differentiation.

From a very different and rather original angle, P. B. Weisz (1951) arrived at the postulate of intranuclear differentiation controlling (partly) processes of developmental differentiation. His work deals with ciliate protozoa. He starts with Dobell's assumption, now generally accepted, that a ciliate is not a unicellular but a noncellular organism, which, therefore, must be compared to an entire metazoan organism. The macronucleus of ciliates is known to be the product of a differential division of the fertilized micronucleus, the other division product being the new micronucleus (see, however, the variants emphasized by Sonneborn, 1955). It is further known that the macronucleus contains what is assumed to be all the genic material as regeneration, and all other life processes can go on in the absence of the micronucleus, which thus represents only the germ line of Metazoa. (Sonneborn has shown that the macronucleus contains the killer locus; hence the general result applies also to the individual mutant.) The macronucleus, however, does not remain simple, but forms by internal divisions a combination nucleus consisting of many subnuclei, to which may be applied Hartmann's term, polyenergid nucleus, recently demonstrated again in Radiolaria (Hartmann, 1952). This is not to be mistaken for the polytene nucleus discussed above, which never could be unscrambled into single nuclei, as may be done for the polyenergid nucleus. This polyenergid macronucleus contains also, as expected, the proportional amount of DNA. (However, Kimball, 1953, does not find this polyenergid condition, a difference of opinion which will have to be resolved.)

Weisz asked himself whether all these subnuclei (which in cell division are simply split at random) are and remain genetically equivalent. In two species of *Stentor* and *Blepharisma* it was ascertained that the micronuclei are not needed for regeneration. The macronucleus is moniliform in both. By microdissection the individual beads of the macronucleus may be isolated and the cut half animals with these partial nuclei may be tested for regeneration or for remaining differentiated. In early stages after fission all macronuclear nodules are found to be equipotent, each being able to sustain morphogenesis (regeneration) and morphostasis (continuation of detailed differentiations of the body). As the vegetative cycle progresses, the differentiation potential of posterior nodes gradually declines and the more so, the more posterior the location. Midway through the vegetative cycle, the posterior nodules no longer support full regeneration. Toward the end of the vegetative cycle, posterior nodules do not support any regeneration, and intact individuals dedifferentiate the entire oral apparatus. But mid-nodules still support some regeneration, and the anterior nodules never cease to be fully active. During fission the macronucleus is reorganized, and the two fission products are again fully active in their entire length. Relocation experiments (by microdissection methods) show that whatever subnucleus becomes posterior by chance will show the progressive deterioration. Once begun, it cannot be reversed by being put into an anterior position, but it can be reversed by coalescence with normal nodes and re-formation of new ones from the mass. Weisz thinks that it is the cytoplasm with its constant differentiations (the kinetosomes, etc., discussed in I 2 A) which makes the nodes behave as described. (See Sonneborn's work, 1955, on the cytoplasmic positional control of the fertilization nucleus, and Nanney's work on the macronuclear differentiation in *Tetrahymena*, 1953*a*, where anterior or posterior location determines macro- and micronuclear differentiation. Compare Lwoff on similar control of kineties in our earlier discussions.)

It is very important that Feulgen reactions show the macronucleus to be constant in all stages in regard to DNA. However, with the new measuring methods of Pollister and Leuchtenberger, it was found that variations in DNA exist and that near the time of fission a gradient develops anteroposteriorly. Thus it is assumed that depolymerization of DNA takes place in this direction, which is reversed when the nodules coalesce during fission. "In substance, therefore, the data imply that in each somatic cycle, initial subnuclear equivalence gradually gives way to patterned genetic divergence."

Weisz assumes that the autonomous kinetosomes of the adoral zone influence the behavior of the macronucleus. He goes so far as to state that the genic activity of the macronucleus depends upon the function of definite kinetosomes. In the macronuclear gradient just described, the only visible differences of the anterior body part which could produce the gradient are the oral zone and its kinetosomes, which control its morphogenesis. Actually, in *Blepharisma,* anterior and posterior special kinetosomes exist, and here it is the mid-nodules which decline. When anterior nuclear nodes were transplanted in *Stentor* into a posterior position and in *Blepharisma* into a mid-position, they started to show the typical decline.

The relation between kinetosomes and macronucleus may be stated in another way by comparing the effect of "declining" nodules. At a definite level of inactivation, the posterior nodules in *Stentor* cannot support the differentiation of the stomatic organs except that of the ordinary cilia (which do not grow without a macronucleus). In another experiment, partially inactivated nodes suffice for the maintenance of some peristomal structures but not for a gullet and the geometric alignment of the peristome. Thus it is concluded that the subnuclei exist in as many different morphogenetic states as there are possible levels of kinetosomic function.

Weisz thinks that such facts may be explained by the assumption that subnuclei lacking one function of morphogenesis (or another one) lack the genes or the gene products needed. Thus nodal inactivation may be considered to be the expression of progressive and differential inactivation of genes comparable to the assumed parallel processes in the development of Metazoa. An alternative is that the consecutive states of the subnuclei are an expression of a quantitative phenomenon, for example, differential activity of the whole genome which might result in a lowering of quantity or potency of a nuclear product. (This would, of course, involve different thresholds of action for the different affected fields. Though not stated in this form, this is obviously in Weisz' mind.)

Weisz thinks that the second alternative is the correct solution, including an interaction between nuclear and kinetosomal products. This means that origin-specific products of the higher types of more important kinetosomes keep up the nuclear activity at the necessary high level. This concept is used to explain the above-described inactivation of the posterior nodules. He assumes that soon after fission the anterior nodules receive the largest share of the kinetosomal substance, which gives them an initial advantage in the competition for the substance. When the substance becomes short in supply, the posterior nodules first feel the pinch. In detail, then, the relative actions of the macronucleus and the kinetosomes is based upon the need of the autonomous kinetosomes for proper endoplasmic substances as substrates for differentiative syntheses. This might mean that the specific substances produced by the nuclei are enzymatic, permitting proper substrate utilization on the part of the kinetosomes. Vice versa, the same would be true for the kinetosomally produced substances needed for genic synthesis. Inactivation of the subnuclei would then mean inability to produce characteristic metabolites.

Let us now compare these facts and interpretations with the genically controlled, consecutive determination in metazoan development. The most important points for such a comparison are: (1) in the Infusoria, regeneration of exact ectoplasmic morphology with its intricate pattern is equivalent to a restoration of the hierarchy of differential kinetosomes; (2) this is possible only if part of the original hierarchy is left; (3) the necessary specific nuclear substances must be available. An application of these facts to Metazoa must take into consideration the non-cellular nature of the ciliates, as expressed by Lwoff (see I 2 B *b aa*) in the dictum: "A multicellular organism has differentiated cells, a ciliate has differentiated parts." The comparison correctly assumes that each somatic metazoan cell nucleus corresponds to a subnucleus of a ciliate; and the germ-track nuclei, to the micronuclei. Weisz asks now whether it is not possible that the successive segregation of potencies in development might be paralleled by a correlated segregation of nuclear potencies through a mechanism of the type described for ciliates, that is, the interaction of peripheral with nuclear products. It is assumed that in the metazoan cells a similar reduction of genic activities may be followed by reactivation. Finally, also, certain important genes may be completely activated.

We reported this most interesting work in detail because it seems to be the only experimental attack upon the problem of intranuclear differentiation. We note that the author could not convince himself that in the course of morphogenesis the genome is altered by inactivation of individual "genes." The alteration concerned a complicated interrelation between peripheral and nuclear products, the observed changes during "development" being in the nature of quantities in regard to thresholds. Thus we conclude that so far there is no evidence of intranuclear differentiation in development, meaning sorting out and differential activation of genic material. The solution of the problem is clearly one of nucleo-cytoplasmic interaction involving quantities, substrates, and thresholds rather than intranuclear changes within the genome. This, of course, does not exclude the complete inactivation of the entire genome as a consequence of endomitotic polyteny, in itself not a cause but a consequence of differentiation having taken place in the cytoplasm, as derived above with the model of the lepidopteran scale.

b. Biochemical attack

In a former chapter the biochemical theories of primary genic actions as well as those of intranuclear behavior of the nuclear constituents were discussed. At that time we pointed out that we would return to those aspects of the problem which involve the removal of nuclear products into the cytoplasm. Whether the primary products of the genic material are formed at the chromosomal site or not, and whether within the nucleus other than primary genic products appear, the genic control of development requires that such products enter the cytoplasm and in some way control the orderly series of determination processes of which typical development consists, which includes also the possibility that cytoplasmic conditions initiated by the genic material in the nucleus become subsequently self-perpetuating. We have already seen that according to Caspersson at least one derivative of chromosomal material is involved in nucleoplasmic exchange, ribonucleic acid which was derived from DNA and first stored in the nucleolus and finally appears at the nuclear surface. We paralleled these facts with the old ideas of idio- and trophochromatin and discussed the requirements for a genetic meaning of these substances. If RNA released into the cytoplasm is the actual genic product in control of differentiation, there should be as many RNA types as there are different genic materials, and differentiation would consist mainly in their being sorted out.

The role of biochemically characterized substances in the cytoplasm supposed to be in control of its determinative processes has been much studied in the last decades by the experimental embryologists and most prominently by J. Brachet and his school (summaries of Brachet's views in 1949, 1950*a,b*). We are not interested here in the processes of growth and development per se, but only in the question whether or not the chemistry and behavior of genic products reaching the cytoplasm or primary cytoplasmic substances explain the riddle of how the genic material controls orderly differentiation. The geneticist would wish for a solution of such questions as: Are substances known which enter the cytoplasm as genic products? Are they as diversified as must be assumed, if they are in control of all the different processes of embryonic differentiation? In this case does a mechanism for their proper sorting out exist?

Will they be henceforth self-perpetuating or does the genic material continue to supply them? Does previous cytoplasmic differentiation play a role in any of these processes? Is there a cytoplasmic influence upon the genic material, somehow controlling quantity, quality, or release of its products?

It seems very difficult to derive definite answers to these and similar questions from the varied and rather intricate biochemical facts which have been found. The main reason is that a biochemical solution for the processes of genetic determination probably requires an understanding of extreme specificities paralleling the specificities of the genic material; while the methods of study available allow the characterization of only a single substance or a few classes of substances, apart from specificities recognized as serological types. Even if it can be proved that these have something to do with the specific differentiations, we are still ignorant of the real action of the genic material. From the large body of facts, sometimes contradictory facts, we may select those which, first, contribute at different points to the material of the preceding discussions by endowing it with specific biochemical meaning and, second, those most liable to elucidate the genetic problems.

The main fact, according to Brachet, is the existence of granules, microsomes, which consist mainly of RNA and are found in a definite position and relation in the cytoplasm of the egg and the embryonic cells. During oögenesis RNA seems to be concerned with the synthesis of "yolk proteins," mainly at the nuclear surface and in the cortical region of the egg, near the blood supply. (All the data relate to the amphibian egg if not stated otherwise.) In the unfertilized egg the RNA microsomes are arranged in a quantitative gradient which remains when bilateral symmetry is established after fertilization. During development the gradients remain and parallel the morphogenetic activities of the regions; quantitative measurements show larger quantities of RNA in more active regions. During cleavage there is no measurable RNA activity. But at the time of gastrulation, simultaneously with the appearance of nucleoli, synthesis of more RNA begins. At this time, also, protein synthesis starts from yolk as evidenced by synthesis of alkaline phosphatase. The microsomes consisting of RNA proteins, which are synthetized at this time, are *assumed* to have genetic continuity because of their resemblance to viruses, and are even *assumed* to pass from cell to cell. A main argument for the latter assumption is derived from experiments in which development is blocked by heat shocks which are supposed to denaturate RNA. Such a treated piece transplanted into a normal host becomes revitalized. It can be observed that the new synthesis of RNA in the fragment attached to a normal one begins next to the normal cells and proceeds from there on. But this might also be due to a diffusible substance needed, and does not necessarily prove an actual intercellular migration of microsomes. The main function of RNA is supposed to be protein synthesis (refer to Caspersson) and, therefore, Brachet and followers assume that the microsomes are the seat of protein synthesis. Experiments with tagged amino acids are in favor of this assumption.

In the description of the RNA behavior as derived from the work of Brachet, Dalq, and many others, we omitted reference to nuclear activity, which of course is the most interesting point for the geneticist. Brachet considered quantitative changes within the nucleus by measuring the presence of sulfhydril groups. He found their amount variable in different tissues in course of development. Krugelis (1946) found a striking increase in the amount of alkaline phosphatase in the nuclei (and also the cytoplasm) after gastrulation. Very conspicuous intranuclear changes during development were claimed by Lison and Pasteels (1951). We studied before the facts concerning the constancy of DNA in all nuclei of a species when measured by optical methods. The Belgian authors found that this is no longer true after the 4-blastomere stage in the sea urchin egg, the mesomeric quartette having more than the other cells. Later, other and more remarkable differences appear, not following this increase rule; an increase in DNA was especially noticeable in regions of quick cell division. The students of the endomitotic DNA quantities maintain that this result is due to a faulty technique. Whether this is true or not, we may say that thus far a definite relation between intranuclear biochemistry and morphogenesis has not been established.

From another point of view, Brachet attacked the problem of the relations between cytoplasmic RNA and the nucleus during morphogenesis. He starts with the fact that development in most anuran species hybrids stops at the beginning of gastrulation. He concludes that this is due to an inhibition of RNA and protein synthesis by the presence of a foreign nucleus. If this were so, the dependence of the RNA activity upon the nucleus would be proved. When the so-called organizer of such a hybrid is transplanted to a normal embryo, it starts proper differentiation, is revitalized. It seems, further, that at the time of the block, RNA-rich nucleoli are produced and that, simultaneously, the "chromatin" is unusually rich in RNA. Thus the anomaly seems to lie in the alteration of the normal relations between the synthesis of RNA in the nucleus and that in the cytoplasm. The foreign nucleus prevents the passage from the nucleus of the substances which control the synthesis of the cytoplasmic RNA protein granules. Thus it is concluded that the nucleus controls the synthesis of the microsomes, which are the true agents of protein synthesis. Other evidence, such as the quicker uptake of tagged amino acids in the microsomes and the continuation of protein synthesis in enucleated cells, is in favor of the conclusion.

The problems regarding intranuclear and cytoplasmic synthesis of RNA and the question of what passes through the nuclear membrane have found different answers. Very interesting in this respect are data from Brachet's school (Brachet and Chantrenne, 1952; Vanderhaeghe, 1952) on *Acetabularia,* the object of Hämmerling's work, studied previously. The nucleolus is very rich in RNA and most of the RNA is found in the rhizoma near the nucleus. In the non-nucleated stem there is a gradient away from the nucleus. By tagging proteins it is found (in agreement with Hämmerling) that protein synthesis is kept up in the enucleated fragment for a long time at a high rate, which shows that the nuclear control of it is a remote one. Stick and Hämmerling (1953) found that protein synthesis in the cytoplasm is more or less independent of the nucleus. The reason might be the presence of chloroplasts. I wonder whether the decisive point is not the large mass of cytoplasm relative to the nucleus, just as in large egg cells, with the result that the functions of the nucleus are delegated to the cytoplasm in early stages of development, by predetermination. In a single cell with much less cytoplasm, relatively speaking, *Amoeba proteus,* Mazia and Prescott (1955) find that protein synthesis, studied with tagged atoms, is wholly controlled by the nucleus. I expect that all intermediate conditions will be found in different materials.

At this point the relation of the nucleus to the mitochondria also is considered. The respiratory enzymes are attached to the latter; but the mitochondria turn out to be less dependent upon the nucleus than the microsomes. However, work by Mazia and Hirshfield (1951) and others indicates that the nucleus produces a coenzyme for the coupling of phosphorylations and oxidations in the mitochondria. The relation to RNA is established by Marshak (1950), who showed that RNA from nuclei contains more adenine than cytoplasmic RNA does. If nuclear RNA is a precursor to cytoplasmic RNA, a liberation of adenine must take place in the formation of the latter which might be used for the synthesis of coenzymes containing adenylic acid. In all these deliberations, the DNA is more or less omitted.

Thus Brachet considers genetically controlled differentiation to consist of the synthesis of the specific proteins which give rise to histological differentiation under the action of the microsomes and their RNA, which are distributed along well-defined gradients. He directly calls these particles plasmagenes. "One can imagine that the fertilized egg contains an enormous population of particles differing one from another, and that, as a result of competition taking place in the different regions of the heterogeneous egg, certain types will become established in a definite territory of the embryo." However, he also mentions the possibility that the differentiation could be the result of the attainment of a threshold in the concentration of certain substances (an idea which plays a considerable role in my physiological theory of heredity; Goldschmidt, 1927). These substances might be identical with the RNA protein granules. But we are not told how the differences of the regions of the heterogeneous egg are produced. They are certainly controlled genically, and this means before the sorting out of the microsomes takes place. Now which determines which? We shall consider this problem further, on the basis of Brachet's brilliant work, leaving out the unfortunate introduction of "plasmagenes," a concept which can only simulate an understanding, as we emphasized repeatedly before.

In the introduction to the group of facts just reviewed we have pointed out the difficulties encountered when conclusions relating to genic actions are to be drawn from biochemical data concerning the presence and behavior of a few substances. If we take the work on RNA, it is hard to believe that the manifold specificities of genic action could be exercised by a non-orderly synthesis and expulsion from the nucleus of one substance, RNA. Assuming that there are thousands of different DNA protein types making up the genic material, what sense would the orderly structure of the chromosomes make if their different genic products became haphazardly mixed up? Of course Brachet considers a secondary sorting out. However, if this is so, the production of the proper substrates in time and pattern, which take care of the sorting process, would be the real genic actions. If this is true, as it probably is, the microsomes and their RNA become only a chemical apparatus of which the real genically controlled processes (based upon the proteinic moiety of the chromosomes) make use. We refer here to our former discussion of the manifold ways in which DNA can be taken into the growing oöcyte from outside, obviously to be used in protein synthesis (perhaps via RNA), to which no specificity can be attached in these cases (see I 2 B *b dd*). We refer further to the mass removal of RNA from chromosomes without any further function (see I 2 B *a*).

At this point a much-discussed question enters: Does the genic material produce its action in a single determinative act, that is, by extrusion of the specific active gene products into the cytoplasm, followed by autonomous self-duplication which involves all active substances like enzyme systems? Or is a continuous genic function necessary for replacement of such substances? The former idea is more or less that of the plasmagene, produced by interaction of nuclear genes with specific cytoplasm. If general metabolic processes are involved, which may also include morphogenesis of a kind, such experiments as those of Hämmerling (see III 2) clearly show that, after a certain time, the processes cease in enucleated pieces and can be restored by restoring the nucleus. However, it is not easy to draw conclusions from such facts concerning embryonic determination where the difficulty does not lie in the fact of determination but in its spatial and temporal order. This indicates that the problems are of a quantitative and kinetic type rather than of a qualitative type, which in the end is forced to endow the gene products with genic qualities; thus we come to a solution of the problem which is no solution. Discussions of these problems from different points of view are found in Brachet (1947, 1950*a*), Spiegelman (1948), Darlington and Mather (1949), Wright (1945), Marshak (1948), and Mazia (1952). We believe that here the qualitative biochemical outlook will turn out to be secondary to the facts and conclusions from physiological genetics.

Thus I should think that the extremely interesting facts just described, which were brought to light by the most painstaking work, will help one day in the understanding of the growth and synthesis of proteins without shedding light upon the genically controlled processes. The introduction of the very doubtful plasmagene concept (see II 2 E) can only obscure matters by simulating an explanation. I conclude that the qualitative, biochemical study of development has not yet touched the problem of genic action. Sonneborn (1951*a*) recently expressed a similar view (though he was speaking of Protozoa and yeasts as models of genic action) when he said, "It must be realized that none of the models seems yet to touch the master problem of the control of the *pattern* of cellular changes in time and space during the course of development." Thus at the end of all this interesting work we are, as geneticists, still where we were before: the cytoplasm must become differentiated into regions which in some way are competent for specific genic actions, based upon primary or secondary genic products removed from the nuclei. This is, I realize, an unpopular conclusion, since we all long for biochemical solutions of our problems. But when we have hardly learned how to walk, we are simply not yet ready for flying.

B. THE CYTOPLASMIC SUBSTRATE OF GENIC ACTION

We discussed the possibility that genic action in development could acquire its specificity and order in time and space by intranuclear changes which may be described as successive inactivation of no longer needed genic substances, possibly by an inherent cycle of stability and instability, or by the entrance of deactivating products of former genic activity into the nucleus from the cytoplasm. We saw that there is nothing known to support such assumptions and much to discredit them. All facts of regeneration and restitution are opposed to them. The fact that individual cells at the end of development still react typically to new genetic changes like introduction of lethals or mutant loci through somatic crossing over (Stern, 1936; Demerec, 1943) shows the continued activity of at least those genic loci studied. Thus it seems that all the genetic material is present in all differentiating cells, with probably only one exception, namely, the stoppage of all genic activity and potential activity in cells which change to a unique function of mass synthesis through one of the endomitotic processes. Thus we must conclude, with the majority of students of this field, that it is the interaction of the genic material with the cytoplasm which results in orderly, genetically controlled development.

We know from our earlier discussion that genic control of developmental processes has been established (by the finding of mutants) for every step of development from characters of the egg to the very last processes of differentiation. It is true (see the former discussion, II 2 C *c*) that the first stages of development are little influenced by the nucleus, which seems to show no discernible influence in the diverse experiments on merogony and development of hybrids up to the time of gastrulation. However, it is also known that the nucleus controls even prefertilization differences in the egg, and therefore the lag until gastrulation does not mean more than preservicing of this period of quick cell division, in respect to the determining actions of the genic material, which, by the way, is another fact in favor of the idea that genic action occurs during the resting stage of the nucleus. Assuming the general facts of experimental embryology as known, we may formulate the questions posed by that basic situation thus:

1. Is the series of determining processes which take place in development, from the first establishment of polarity to the last bit of histological differentiation, under genic control? Or does the genic control initiate cytoplasmic differentiation which afterward continues under its own steam?

2. What does genic control mean?

3. Why does the proper genic material act only at its proper time and place and others do not act at all, though all of them are always present simultaneously?

a. Basic deliberations

The answer to the last question contains much of the answers to the others. The question has been called the problem of the "activation of the genes," the idea being that all the genes are present all the time without acting, but that at the proper moment, say when some epidermis cells of a *Drosophila* embryo are being determined to form a wing bud, the "wing genes" alone begin to become active in the respective cells and only in these. In the discussions of this major problem there was never a doubt that during development the cytoplasm in some way underwent a differentiation of a chemical type, chemodifferentiation, which made it specifically different in cells or cell groups located in the individual parts of the embryo. It does not make any difference whether this distribution of specificity is a primary one, as in the mosaic type of development, or a secondary one, by means of evocators and inductors in the inductive type of development (with all transitions between the two known). However, this distribution of specificity of the cytoplasm is itself under genic control, as proved by the transplantation experiments with inductors between different genera and families of Amphibia (Schotté, Holtfreter). Adapting an old expression of Boveri, I called the result of such a chemodifferentiation of embryonic regions a "stratification" in order to emphasize both the chemical diversification and the tridimensional arrangement of the different layers. The so-called activation of the genes, then, meant (Goldschmidt, 1927, 1938) that the genic material (as I prefer to say, for reasons discussed before), which is always present and functioning, produces its primary products (and probably releases them into the cytoplasm) all the time; but that they can take up their specific action (as enzymes or producers of specific enzymes, coenzymes, "hormones," etc.) only when the cytoplasm of the cell has reached a certain biochemical and biophysical condition in regard to substrate, hydration, acidity, coenzymes, and so on, to which the specific genic material is attuned. It is the process of stratification which provides—in an extension of Waddington's terminology—the "competent" substratum. It seems hardly possible to form a theory of genically controlled patterning in development without reasoning in general along this line, though the details may be worked out in different ways when an attempt is made to give specific chemical meaning to the whole, as we saw in the last chapter dealing with one of the possibilities.

When we first developed such ideas, we used as models for the process of stratification gradients and especially diffusion patterns like Liesegang rings (today paper chromatography and tube chromatography would serve as comparable models). The idea was that any physicochemical agency like selective diffusion and precipitation which can separate different chemical entities could be the means of the stratification process involving chemically different, specific substances characterizing the locally differentiating substrates (notice that Brachet's microsomes also require such a sorting-out mechanism). Those products of the genic material, always present but probably in subthreshold quantities, for which one or the other stratified specific substrate would be competent, would start reacting with this substrate to produce the specific genically controlled chains of reaction leading to the synthesis of the active determining substances of different kind for which we used the general term "hormones," enzyme systems being only one of the possibilities included. It is these chains of reactions which offer by their rates and threshold conditions a chance to understand the proper timing as well as more or less irreversibility of step-by-step results in regard to determinative processes, a process which Waddington has since called the canalization of development.

Since the time when such ideas were developed, the progress of our knowledge of the biochemistry of enzyme systems, proteins, and nucleic acids, together with such biochemical facts as have already been reported, as well as the facts underlying the ideas on so-called plasmagenes, have led to a number of attempts to express more or less the same type of model in more concrete terms, which are somewhat different if proposed by embryologists than if presented by geneticists. The ideas of one embryologist, Brachet, have been discussed because of their specificity and relation to facts of biochemical cytology. We shall review critically some more work of this nature before trying to formulate a general idea commensurate with today's knowledge, and shall begin with the analysis made by embryologists. The aspect emphasized in Brachet's work will on this occasion reappear.

b. Specific ideas derived from embryology

An elaborate attempt to understand genically controlled differentiation has been made by Paul Weiss (see 1950). He draws on all aspects of experimental embryology, though the genetic side remains rather in the background. The basis of his ideas is the concept of "molecular ecology" within the individual cells. Each cell and cell part consists of an array of molecular species, whose densities, distribution, arrangement, and groupings are determined by their own properties as well as those of their surroundings. Chemical segregation and localization within the cell result from free molecular interplay, as only groups of elements compatible with one another and their environment can form durable unions. Interfaces play a considerable role as segregative factors of molecular mixtures. The fixation of a particular molecular species in a surface is partly due to unspecific factors (like adsorption), but also to selective chemical affinities. Thus morphogenesis, which is the development of structure in space, means the proper segregation of the members of the molecular population within the cell. I think it is evident that this concept does for intracellular differentiation, in terms of molecules, what our concept of "stratification according to the conditions of the system" (i.e., physical and chemical nature of the whole) does for the regional determinations in the developing egg. It is considered safer, however, not to allow oneself to believe that a description in the language of molecules has much meaning without biochemical specification of these molecules and their interrelations. From the genetical point of view, the intracellular differentiation is, however, the minor problem.

We have already seen that specific differentiation like that of the wing-scale cell may be combined with a cessation of the specific genic functions. However, the determination of the embryonic primordia at the proper time and place is the real function of the genic material. Theoretically, this primary differentiation may occur in a differential division of one primary cell in regard to its cytoplasm, but it may also be the result of separation of cytoplasmic qualities over an area of many cells, independent of cell limits. Probably both types occur, the former in the meristemic type of differentiation (see III 5 A *a*); the latter in most organ determinations. In the former, the different fate of two division products of a cell could be described in Weiss' terms of separation of molecular populations. In the latter, a supracellular area would receive different molecular populations from the adjacent one. I cannot see how the description in terms of molecular populations would in either case help us in understanding the genic control of this process and its action according to the pattern in space and time (i.e., the old problem of genic activation). It merely replaces the term "chemodifferentiation" by the expression "diversification of molecular populations." Since differentiation (on all levels) implies in the end an irreversible change (or one reversible only in very unusual circumstances), this must be on the molecular level. But how the genic material affects this differentiation remains the unsolved problem. We still wish to know whether the change in what may be called competence of a cell group is an automatic sorting out of specific constituents of the cellular substratum by a process of "stratification" enforced by the physical and chemical conditions of the cellular system as a result of its past history, that is, initiated at the beginning of development (which would include also possible hereditary cytoplasmic conditions or components); or whether this segregation of materials or physical conditions or both requires its own genic action at the moment it occurs. In other words, does the change in competence between two cells or cell groups, which permits the beginning of specific action of the genic material by providing for it the proper substrate, follow automatically from the conditions reached at the moment as a consequence of former developmental steps, which would be consecutive diversification? Or is it necessary that a genically controlled product starts the "stratification" by producing some initial reaction? As I see it, the idea of molecular ecology does not help us to understand this basic situation, but only circumscribes its existence in different terms. (Lwoff, 1950*b*, seems to have no such scruples.)

We have already discussed the ideas of Brachet and others which solve this problem by assuming a mixture of self-reproducing specific cytoplasmic elements, sometimes, unfortunately, called plasmagenes, which are, in a way, both autonomous and dependent upon the genic material. The change of competence (in the wider sense of the term as used here) of cells or cell groups would have to mean sorting out of these elements, which leaves us again where we were, in need of some kind of stratification. As I stated previously, the underlying facts (the work on cytoplasmic RNA) point more in the direction of growth as the proper function of these cytoplasmic particles. Weiss also discusses this point and comes to conclusions which fit the genetic facts much better, part of which were anticipated in our discussion of Brachet's work.

Weiss argues in the following way: while it is conceivable that differentiation resides in discrete particles, we cannot be sure that the synthesis of the specific macromolecular compounds which make up these cytoplasmic particles actually takes place in the location where they are found (self-duplication). This would imply that growth occurs in innumerable centers throughout the cytoplasm. On the contrary, in the growth of the neurone Weiss showed that protein synthesis takes place near the nucleus, as Caspersson assumed. Therefore, Weiss believes that the basic protoplasmic units are reproduced within the nuclear space in a complex primordial form determined by the whole genic apparatus. (We would say by the non-genic part of the chromosomes; see, above, our discussion on trophochromatin.) They would be alike for all cells of a given individual of a given species. Upon being released into the cytoplasm, they would be subject to conversions and modifications. To quote Weiss, "Especially, upon impact with certain specifically shaped template systems, they would assume conforming shapes and thus perpetuate particular molecular patterns." According to Weiss, each cell strain develops during differentiation its own specific population of template molecules (which is his way of describing stratification—chemodifferentiation in terms of molecules) and, therefore, the same primary nuclear products will assume different types according to the particular molecular populations with which they make contact. "According to this concept, differentiated protoplasmic units would owe their origin and their specific shapes to two entirely different processes, occurring in different places. They would be propagated in the nuclear center and be remodeled in the cytoplasm" (Weiss). What appears to be self-reproducing bodies in the cytoplasm are "model centers of adsorption, aggregation, alignment, and conversion of compounds which have originated in a distant location."

I have no doubt that this way of looking at growth and differentiation is, in principle, far superior to that of the autonomous cytoplasmic particles, and also in much better accord with basic genetic ideas, as has been shown. The geneticist can easily conceive of growth and differentiation being basically separate processes, and has done so (Goldschmidt, 1927, 1938*a*). As we have seen, many facts point to growth, as such, being controlled by the non-specific (i.e., non-genic) parts of the chromosomes. This does not mean that growth is not dependent upon genic control. Growth as multiplication of cell substance is the unspecific feature, but its speed, time, and place are under genetic control, as innumerable facts of genetics prove. However, when we think of the genetics of differentiation, the concept of Weiss is linked to the previous independent differentiation of his template molecules in different cell descendencies (i.e., in our language, to the stratification already having taken place). Thus the concept of Weiss, so useful for following the stages of cellular differentiation, still does not answer the question of primary differences of determination, the production of the differently competent substrates for genic action.

Weiss himself realizes this, though, as it seems, not for the primary divergences between two daughter cells but for the latter configurations of the embryonic patterns in determination fields. (In our opinion there is no difference between the two processes except the status in the hierarchic sequences of more and more specific determinations, i.e., Waddington's canalization of development.) Weiss emphasizes that we know very little about this. But, he says, "it has become ever clearer that growth, as such, is a purely scalar process, producing simply more protoplasmic mass, increments without intrinsic direction. Direction is given to the growing mass not by properties inherent in the chemical mechanism of reproduction itself but by physical properties of the space into which the material issues forth. Physical factors of given polarity, such as tensions, pressures, electric gradients, diffusion currents, fibrous pathways and the like, appear among the factors that guide . . . the growing materials . . ." (i.e., what we formerly called the conditions of the system).

The basic problem to the geneticist is finally touched in Weiss' analysis when he speaks of the most difficult and most neglected of all basic fields of morphogenesis, that of supercellular integration. The basic fact is the existence of patterned field activities in the determination of embryonic events. He states, correctly, that "after all, one has to explain that a determinative field vector causes not just a quantitative change in the activity of a responding cell, but selectively activates in the latter a specific performance from among a whole series of equally possible ones, perhaps by specific molecular segregations. This, it would seem, makes it imperative to concede to the field vectors the property of affecting molecular configuration and constellation, rather than only concentrations and reaction rates . . ." I may add that this is just the situation throughout the entire hierarchy of embryonic determinations (which I developed in detail in 1927), with the genic material controlling the diversification in the field (also within a single cell) by producing stratification as an automatic consequence of the conditions of the system. The next consequence of "genic activation" and its working proceeds by means of rate processes. For the geneticist this remains the primary problem, to which the modern concepts, whether plasmagenes or "molecular ecology," have, I fear, made very little contribution.

The type of penetrating analysis of development and growth just reported leaves the geneticist where he was, specifically where I was in my book of 1927: development consists of a series of hierarchical subdivisions of the embryonic material in regard to its intimate chemistry, a subdivision or stratification which is the consequence of the physical and chemical properties of the whole system and its subsystems. The stratification, an automatic outcome of the genically controlled syntheses of different substances and the direction, order, and place of the genically produced prompters of stratifications, provides the competent material for more and more restricted genic action, otherwise called the activation of the genes, which works mainly by influencing rate processes. Only then do the secondary effects under genic control by means of specific enzymes, hormones, and auxins, and also through contacts, set in. It does not help much if we express any or all of these steps in terms of plasmagenes, macromolecules, and templates. In view of our ignorance about what really happens, the old-fashioned general description is still adequate. This, however, does not mean that, within that frame, more specific notions cannot be developed. We are all anxious to see that done.

Another embryologist, working more nearly to and beyond the borderline of genetics, has repeatedly discussed our present problem. Waddington (1948, 1950) starts from the fact that development is essentially a sequence of chemical changes which, secondarily, are also responsible for the many physical changes like surface tension or permeability. These occur in the cytoplasm of the cell and certainly involve different substances. The differences arise gradually and progressively, not as the simple unfolding of a unified trend but as a series of successive steps. When two groups of cells become different, not much is visible in the beginning. Their determination to different developmental fates must first involve only slight chemical differentials, but once a particular course has been set it is carried along under its own steam. Each progressively increasing differentiation follows a definite pattern leading to a different end result. Thus differentiation is canalized into distinct pathways, and the progressive series of changes is more or less irreversible. The substances involved are mostly active proteins. This general description of development is, of course, the same that we gave before, using the terminology of chemodifferentiation in a hierarchy of determinative steps which distribute specifically different cytoplasmic substrate materials by means of stratification. The additional idea of canalization is new, the assumption that, once a course of chemical differentials has been set, it is carried along under its own steam, though this is only a way of expressing the fact of more or less final determination.

Waddington assumes that the specific cytoplasmic proteins, by which different cell types are characterized, are built from essentially the same building blocks, that is amino acids. This means that before the diversification starts, the genic material permits either type of synthesis, and therefore a competition for these building blocks, the substrate material, exists. (The application to genetics of the idea of competition for a substrate, at present so popular, goes back to Sewall Wright, 1941; and has been especially emphasized by Stern *et al.*, 1943–1946.) Slight changes in the available raw materials may shift the whole system from one path into another. Thus the change in rate of synthesis of any one protein due to a change in the concentration of one or the other raw materials may cause a large change in the collection of final proteins. The differentiation involving many substances may depend upon a single or a few raw materials. Consequently, the fact that some raw materials are used up, altering the concentrations of those remaining, will shift the balance of synthetic rates and even lead to synthesis of new proteins, the beginning of progressive differentiation. The following canalization of differentiation (i.e., irreversible determination) may be due to an autocatalytic element in these synthetic processes which, by necessity, increase the amount of a single product, and, if more syntheses are involved simultaneously, some compatible ones may increase. Such a system would be difficult to reverse, since this would require the restoration of the original concentrations of raw materials. Waddington (1954) has elaborated the same ideas by putting them into the form of kinetic equations, which may or may not prove helpful (in view of our ignorance of the actual reacting substances).

The difference of this point of view from the more generalized one of stratification of substrates should now be emphasized. Both theories endeavor to explain how different chemical entities are sorted out into different cells and cell groups in a definite way, and the role the genic material is playing in the process. The stratification hypothesis assumes that a physical process is involved, comparable to the sorting out of amino acids and also proteins in paper chromatography, primed by what I called the conditions of the system, that is, all physical and chemical features of the cell in its proper surroundings. In principle, this is a mechanistic explanation involving specific movements of materials. Waddington's explanation is a statistical one. It needs a competition for substrate material with a following process of selection, based upon the changes in the amount of the different substrate materials. In my hypothesis the separation (stratification) is an automatic consequence of the type of stuffs (different proteins, etc.) and the physicochemical conditions prevailing at the proper time and place in the system as a whole, and therefore an obligatory one. According to Waddington's hypothesis, we do not know why the competition for the substrate determines one synthesis in one cell and a different one in another cell. In a model he assumes that this happens when another substance is added to the cell. But where does this come from? Why does it enter only one cell? It seems that here a *deus ex machina* is introduced to make the competition-selection idea work. In view of the amazing clocklike precision of development, I have, in addition, misgivings about explanations of a statistical type for large-size material processes of life which can hardly be compared to the elementary processes of physics and their statistical background (which is not acknowledged by all physicists). (See Schrödinger's philosophical discussion, 1944.)

c. Activation of the genes

The problem of what had been called "activation of the genes" in their proper substrate now enters the discussion. Actually there are two phases: (1) the genic control of the primary chemodifferentiation and subsequent sorting-out process; (2) the selective action of the proper part of the genic material with the competent substrate which was produced by the sorting-out process. The first problem is discussed by Waddington in a way similar to our previous analysis of Brachet's work and, still earlier, our discussion of the primary gene products. The genic material synthesizes a product (more or less similar to itself) which, after passing into the cytoplasm, directs enzymatically the syntheses of the materials for differentiation. It is a logical step, then, to renounce the existence of plasmagenes which would independently control such syntheses and which anyhow would at some time be dependent upon the genic material. The second problem, the "activation" of only definite genic actions in the presence of all genic material, is not considered by Waddington to be different from the first, and accounted for by the same idea, which, I think, does not even work for the first problem, as I tried to show. Waddington thinks that it is easy to imagine how competition between genes for substrates, which are required to a varying extent, could lead to situations in which a particular complex of substrates facilitated the activity of some definite constellation of genes. Thus, the generalized statement that genic material becomes active when imbedded in the competent substratum, which I developed (1927), receives a special chemical terminology: activation means better ability to compete for the specific substrate to which the specific genic material is attuned, and the competent substrate becomes a selected assembly of different quantities of various raw materials for synthesis. Though this view has the advantage of being less generalized than mine, it still is more or less indicative of our lack of factual biochemical knowledge.

We come now to the special problems of genic activation, and begin with a recent discussion by Caspari (1949*a*). He uses Hadorn's (1945) term, "manifestation pattern," meaning that organs which are not affected by a certain gene lie outside its manifestation pattern. Two possibilities are given: the genic material may be active in all cells at all times, and the manifestation may depend on differential reactions of different cells on the metabolic changes induced by the gene; or the gene may be active in some types of cells but not in others. Though the discussion is not primarily applied to the problem of embryonic determination, its results may apply to our present problem. Caspari (1933, 1936) studied pigmentation in the flour moth, which is inhibited in the mutant aa; the normal pigment is deposited in the eyes, testes, and brain of the adult and the larval ommatidia and hypodermis. The last character becomes visible in the embryo; testis pigment, at the last larval molt; and the eye pigments, in the pupal stage. The inhibition is based upon lack of kynurenine, an amino acid precursor of the pigment. Almost all organs of the wild type can form kynurenine and release it, if transplanted into aa larvae, but some organs store it and release only a little. From such facts the conclusion is drawn that all genes are active in all cells of the body, though their effect—the morphological reaction pattern—becomes visible only in some cells. Now Plagge (1936) showed that aa testes can form pigment only if supplied with kynurenine before pupation; larval ommatidia lose their ability to react at the last larval molt; different types of eye cells have distinct, overlapping periods in which they react to transplanted or injected AA tissue. This is compared with the embryological concept of competence to react upon induction stimuli. (We previously used Waddington's term "competence" also for the attunement of cytoplasmic substrate to genic action.) These periods of competence in the present sense seem to be related to the sensitive periods for genic and phenocopic action, which themselves are controlled genically in regard to time and duration (Goldschmidt, 1935*a*). In Caspari's case it seems that the competence for forming pigment has to do with the appearance of RNA containing precursor granules. Caspari concludes that genic action is always present in all cells so far as it produces a primary genic product. An organ will react or not to this substance, if it does or does not undergo a period of competence for this reaction, periods which are to be understood as specific biochemical and physiological states of the cell, themselves genically controlled. It is easy to apply these conclusions to the primary differentiating genic actions in development, our processes of stratification and gene activation. Actually, they are a somewhat modernized restatement of the views which I have held for a long time (Goldschmidt, 1927, 1938*a*).

The alternative, differentiation by genic inhibition, or inactivation, perhaps occurs rarely, though there is no convincing proof for it.

The same problem has been attacked in a somewhat different way by Sewall Wright (1941, 1945*a,b*). After dismissing the idea that differentiation is based upon intranuclear changes, he mentions only briefly the possibility that certain genes are transmitted in an inactivated condition and that irreversible activation is induced systematically under special local conditions. It is not clear whether this possibility is meant to include everything we discussed thus far as "gene activation," gene-controlled stratification, competence of the substratum for genic action. Since these theories are neither mentioned nor discussed by Wright, it seems that they are included. But some of the following statements may also be changed into terms of our previous discussion. In one place Wright states that the usual and most probable view is that cellular differentiation is cytoplasmic and must therefore be transmitted to daughter cells by cytoplasmic heredity. An objection to this, according to Wright, is that the germ-line cells do not show differences between daughter cells. A solution for this difficulty might be that evolution has produced a line of cells (the germ track) with plasmagenes lacking in prosthetic groups and hence in specialized activity. The same plasmagenes in somatic cells are capable of combining with such groups emanating from the nucleus, to form molecules that multiply thereafter as plasmagenes of a more specialized sort. Differences in the local conditions may bring about a differential accumulation of metabolic products arising from an interaction of cytoplasm with nuclear products and the environment, and eventually lead to the accumulation of new plasmagenes in particular regions of the organism. Each step in the regional differentiation of cytoplasmic heredity increases the diversity of local environments and so facilitates further differentiation.

Let us consider the essentials of this theory, as compared with the main features of the former discussion, forgetting about the use of the objectionable words "cytoplasmic heredity" and "plasmagenes," both assumed to be changing during differentiation! The main points to be explained are the diversification of the cytoplasmic substrate in the hierarchical series of determinative steps and the fact that specific genic actions are started, or raised above an effective threshold, within these separated regions. The separation (our stratification) is known to be genically controlled or influenced by the setting of what we called the conditions of the system. In Wright's theory the cytoplasmic diversity is not a chemodifferentiation, a sorting out of "molecular populations," in Weiss' terminology, based upon the physicochemical system of the cell and cell group, but the presence of self-perpetuating plasmagenes and the creation of new plasmagenes in the interaction of cytoplasmic environment, nucleus, and plasmagenes. Thus the "conditions of the system" are brought in, not as substrate conditions for a sorting-out, stratifying process but as a help in the formation of new plasmagenes. There is no activation of genic action by supplying the proper substrate for it, but the relation of genic substance and cytoplasmic processes, unavoidable for any theory, is established by the prosthetic groups which are supplied to the plasmagenes. Thus, it seems, the processes to be explained are simply transferred to the hypothetical plasmagenes. I cannot help thinking that this does not aid the understanding and simply shifts one unknown to another, and, in addition, credits plasmagenes with all the accoutrements of a *deus ex machina*.

However, it is only fair to say that Wright (1945) is aware of these objections. In a later discussion of the same subject, he states that persistence (in the sense of embryonic determination) may be based on interactions among constituents which make the cell in each of its states of differentiation a self-regulatory system as a whole. According to this view, the origin of a given differentiated state of the cell is to be sought in special local conditions that favor certain chains of gene-controlled reactions which cause the array of cytoplasmic constituents to pass the threshold from the previous stable state to the given one. This statement (presented as an alternative for discussion) is a somewhat abstruse formulation of what I called the genically initiated stratification via the conditions of the system. But, Wright continues, though there is, no doubt, considerable truth in this idea, the stability of the changed state is easier to understand if there are self-duplicating materials in the cell which can be modified chemically and subsequently multiply by duplicating the new chemical constitution. The whole idea thus amounts to controlled mutation of plasmagenes! Since the existence of plasmagenes is more than doubtful (according to our previous discussion), not to mention their mutations, and since the facts can be completely described in terms of genic actions upon stratifiable substrates, I must repeat that I am not convinced that an interpretation in terms of plasmagenes helps the understanding of genetic determination. Rather, this concept slips in an element of the entelechy type from behind the apparent genetical and biochemical formulation, a thing which Wright certainly does not intend to do. For this reason, other theories involving plasmagenes, which are essentially of the same type as those reported, need not be discussed in detail. Only one more example need be given of what I have just termed the entelechy type of qualities conferred upon the plasmagenes in their interference with genic actions. Spiegelman (1948) proposed that genic action produces a pool of unspecific protein precursors in the cytoplasm which by action of the plasmagenes are transformed into the specific enzymes. Though this idea was proposed as an explanation of adaptive enzymes, it may also serve as an illustration of our point.

All in all, "activation of the gene" may still mean either the segregation of the competent substrate with which only the specific genic material can react; or a continuous function of all genic material on a level which is subthreshold until the proper substratum appears; or the same with a competition for substrate, which is won by the genic material that is somehow specific for the substrate; or an inhibitory action of all substrates, which is locally removed by processes within certain parts of the cytoplasm. All these assumptions are, in the end, the same: a description of the facts of development in terms of genic action and cytoplasmic diversification, whether expressed in general terms or in more specific ones involving unknown molecular configurations.

Up to this point, our discussion of the so-called gene activation has dealt with features of development as exemplified in *Drosophila* and probably in most invertebrates in which the series of embryonic determinations under genic control takes place in the respective areas of the egg and embryo directly (the mosaic type of development). Though we mentioned some of Brachet's work in Amphibia, this was done only in a general way. However, our problem of genic activation appears also in the case of the vertebrate egg (and some insects) where the inductor type of embryonic determination (Spemann's "organizer") is found.

In order to realize the basic difference, we may point out first the results of intergeneric (etc.) transplantation of the inductor tissue (assuming the basic features of this work since Spemann to be known). If frog gastrula ectoderm is transplanted into a *Triton* gastrula, the *Triton* "organizer" makes this group of cells differentiate according to its position, for example, into mouth parts. However, these are typical frog parts, with a sucker and horn teeth, neither existing in *Triton*. Thus the genetic condition of the cells, that is, their genic material, controls differentiation, though the clearly unspecific inductor starts the general features of development. These famous experiments show clearly that the inductor action upon development is basically different from genic control of development. However, the generalized action of the inductor (in the foregoing example, Spemann spoke of the order given to produce mouth parts) must in the end also be under genic control. Thus we may expect an insight into the problems under discussion from a further analysis of induction.

The first important set of facts is the successful induction of axial structures by transplanted bits of any tissue taken from all kinds of animals. Then it turned out that the same tissues after being killed by different procedures also acted as inductors. This was followed by the proof that parts of the amphibian gastrula which, if transplanted, do not act as inductors will become inductors when killed first. It became obvious that there is no "organizer," but that induction must be due to the presence, or production, or release of a substance of rather general distribution.

The search for such substances, mainly by the schools of Needham-Waddington, Brachet, Spemann-Fischer, Barth, and Holtfreter (see Brachet, 1950*a*; Holtfreter, 1951) led to great confusion: Needham and Waddington believed that they had proved certain sterol compounds to be the active substance. Fischer could not confirm this, but found that certain acids, among them DNA, gave positive results if put into the gastrula. Barth again differed and considered protein extracts responsible. Brachet stated that the results are due to traces of nucleoproteins, and succeeded in obtaining induction with yeast and virus nucleoproteins. He further isolated granules, microsomes, from different cell types (amphibian or even mammalian) which contained protein, phosphatases, and RNA, and they acted as inductors, an action which was stopped by treatment of the material with ribonuclease. It was found that methylene blue and cystine also acted as inductors. When Barth found that the toxic digitamine was an inductor, the suspicion arose that toxicity is the common factor of all actions, which would mean that none of these experiments had anything to do with natural induction.

At this time, Holtfreter (whose dramatic presentation of the subject in 1951 we are now following) showed that the insertion of a piece of glass, moving to and fro, suffices for induction; Okada got induction with silica and similar substances. This suggested to Holtfreter that the real action is based upon the destruction of cells with the liberation of products which enter the normal cells and act as inductors. (As far as I am aware, nobody drew attention in this connection to Haberlandt's wound hormones. He showed, 1935, that cells at the surface of a cut potato do not divide when the surface is carefully washed. If it is not cleaned, and especially if it is covered with a brei of broken cells, mitotic divisions start at once. He spoke of wound hormones as instigators of mitosis. Clearly we are dealing with related phenomena.) All the experiments mentioned can thus be explained.

Further progress was made when Barth found that pieces of gastrula (without an inductor region) of an axolotl, cultured in vitro, showed neural differentiation, while similar pieces of other Amphibia would never do so. This led to a series of brilliant experiments by Holtfreter. He assumed that the difference between axolotl eggs and those of other Amphibia is due to differences in permeability, those of the axolotl being damaged by the saline solution used as medium. Actually, axolotl eggs could be made to behave like *Triton* or frog eggs and vice versa by changing the pH of the medium: at 4–5 no induction occurred in the axolotl egg; at 9.2 all eggs possessed induction. Also the reciprocal experiment succeeded. *Triton* gastrulae (the explanted cells of which would produce nothing but epidermis) were treated with a low pH medium, which resulted in disintegration of the cells. By neutralization the cells (in explantate) were made to reunite, and now neural tubes, and so on, were formed; that is, the *Triton* cells now behaved like the axolotl. Obviously, some cytolysis had been produced and the inductor substance had been liberated. Holtfreter calls it the X-substance. By grinding up and centrifuging the cells, Holtfreter showed that the substance must be contained in the cytoplasmic fraction of the centrifugate (not the lipids, etc.). From such a fraction Brachet isolated extremely small granules which also acted as inductors. They contained RNA and their action was inhibited by ribonuclease, from which it was concluded—in harmony with the other ideas of Brachet reported above—that RNA is the inductor substance. Without accepting this as certain, Holtfreter assumes that the active substance X is present in all cells but bound to another moiety. In all types of inductor experiments, the substance X is liberated and can act.

The latest contribution to the subject by Niu and Twitty (1953) agrees generally with all these facts. They showed that an ectodermal explant (in tissue culture) undergoes induction when mesodermal tissue has been present for some time in the drop, without any contact between the two. Thus induction at a distance, by a diffusible substance, occurs; preliminary tests indicate that the substance is a nucleic acid.

These are the decisive facts. Our problem in the present discussion is to put the inductor action in the proper place within the embryonic determination system of genically controlled processes of cytoplasmic differentiation in time and space by a nucleo-cytoplasmic interaction which we called genic activation. We must start with the fact that orderly development in large groups of animals is carried out without the assistance of an inductor system. Thus the latter is an addition to the basic system of nucleo-cytoplasmic relations controlling orderly development which we studied thus far. It is obvious that the inductor method does not replace the ordinary method, which accomplishes differentiation by some action of the genic material upon cytoplasm competent for the interaction. This is proved by the following facts: (1) development of the inductive type takes place with continuous narrowing down of the competences for inductor action, which are first available everywhere and subsequently are restricted to smaller and still smaller areas; (2) induction initiates the general type of organ differentiation, but does not affect the genetic specificity residing in the cells, which differentiate under the influence of the inductor, nevertheless, according to their own genetic origin; (3) the same inductor produces different differentiations according to the region into which it is implanted. The induced organs are, with a certain variation, those belonging to the respective region (e.g., eyes in the head, kidneys in the rump, etc.). This may again be described in terms of competence, established prior to the inductor action. Thus it is clear that the inductor action does not replace the ordinary type of genetic determination, but adds to it a specific feature. In a certain sense we may compare this situation to that of control of sexual differentiation both with and without hormones. In the latter case, an over-all action by a relatively simple chemical substance is superimposed upon the primary genic control of formation of the gonad, which produces the hormones. In the former case, differentiation is under simple direct genic control—"simple" meaning that it occurs in the individual cells after the manner of all genic actions. In the same way, amphibian development is genically controlled by the interplay of genic material and cytoplasmic substrate. But superimposed is the action of probably a single chemical substance, not contained in a single gland but present in all cells, which when released "orders" over-all happenings of differentiation. We might express it by saying that the inductor (X-substance) stimulates something to happen, but what happens is decided by the same method as in non-inductive development. The inductor action, like hormonic action, is a chemical method of integrating processes in many cells simultaneously, but not of determining them. We might also express this by saying it is a technical advance from the condition of the more or less mosaic development, simplifying and also unifying integration of basic developmental processes. Thus the inductor type of development (with the many transitional types found in insects by Seidel, 1936, and his students) does not affect the views on genic cytoplasmic interaction developed previously.

But our way of looking at the facts is not the interpretation given by embryologists like Brachet and Holtfreter. Holtfreter (1951) expresses the relations between inductor and the progressively narrowing competence of the embryonic cells thus. The state of competence of the reactive material determines the direction of differentiation to the same extent as does the specificity of the inductor. In the early gastrula the ectoderm is pluripotent. Which one of these potencies will be realized depends upon the surroundings, especially the adjacent inductor. With increasing age, the competence is narrowed, and finally the ectoderm can no longer react to the stimulus of the inductor. It is strange that the induction works only when it is needed, though the capacity for induction remains in all tissues, dead or alive. It is important that the action of the inductor, at its proper time, is needed only for a short time; afterward, differentiation goes on under its own steam. But some parts of the embryo—and this is important—

never need the stimulus of the inductor but develop just as in mosaic development (e.g., the intestinal tract). Holtfreter then presents some examples of what we considered before as predetermination, and concludes (with others) that there must be self-reproducing cytoplasmic elements, the plasmagenes, originally produced by genic (nuclear) action and identical with Claude's microsomes and Brachet's basophilic granules.

These concepts are applied to the inductor action and the competence for it. The cells of the germ layers contain cytoplasmic elements which are responsible for the various differentiations, which he calls neurogenes, myogenes, and so on. Now the X-substance (the inductor) is present everywhere, but is inactive. In the experiments it is liberated by cutting the cells; in normal development, by separation from what prevents its function; this may be the neurogene N. The X-substance behaves like an enzyme; it makes more X and N dissociate, and the process spreads to adjacent cells. N is now supposed to be the precursor of a plasmagene; by its liberation from X it "mutates" to the functional neurogene, which is self-propagating, and thus fills all cells derived from the induced one. Holtfreter then proceeds to "explain" competence on the basis of this plasmagene concept, namely, the question why the response of a tissue to the inductor stimulus changes in time and is genetically controlled, while narrowing down its developmental potencies. According to Holtfreter, the young cells contain precursors of many types of plasmagenes, which compete with each other for a substrate needed for the synthesis of a functional plasmagene. An external agent or an inductor substance or a nuclear product selectively induces one of these precursors to begin its synthetic activity, and it begins to multiply, taking more and more substrate away from the other latent plasmagenes. Finally, the cell becomes competent only for the one type of plasmagene, which has been selected.

Thus what we called "genic activation," meaning the specific action of genic material only in the presence of the proper cytoplasmic substratum, is replaced by the rather miraculous doings of plasmagenes. It is done by omitting reference to development without inductors, which has all the features of development in common with the inductor type, except for the absence of the inductor. I think that the problem of progressive determination controlled by the genic material must be solved first as such, and that only afterward can the specific features of the intercalation of an inductor be added. If this is done, an explanation of the type presented previously appears infinitely more simple. I certainly do not consider it the duty and also the competence of the geneticist to explain embryonic induction. (See quotation from DeBeer, III 1.) However, so far as embryonic induction is a part of the general problem of genic action and so-called activation, it is within the sphere of interest of the geneticist. I for one am very skeptical in regard to the introduction of the wobbly concept of the plasmagene, with its mysterious competitions and selections, all of which must take place miraculously in the required order and in the proper place to allow a circumscription of the facts of progressive determination in terms of corpuscles. I cannot help disagreeing with such great embryologists as Brachet and Holtfreter in this respect.

Actually, there may be more reason for pessimism in regard to the problem of genically controlled chemodifferentiation of the cytoplasmic component. An immense body of interesting biochemical facts has been accumulated on the chemical processes in embryogenesis, with special emphasis on enzyme systems, to mention only the work of Brachet, Runnström and his school, Lindahl, Ranzi, Spiegelman, and Holter. But when these brilliant researchers stop to look at the general picture derived from the detailed facts, they draw conclusions which show clearly the causes for my pessimism. This is best shown by quoting from a recent synopsis by Hultin (1953), in which he presents a tentative outline of the metabolic background of determination in the early development of the sea urchin egg: "The early development may be interpreted as a gradual, intracellular transformation of a supply of substances of purely maternal origin into metabolic centra and metabolic products of the new individual embryo.

"The rapidly increasing protein metabolism in the microsome fraction during the early sea urchin development may indicate the initiation of a progressive building up of microsome populations. The increased ribonucleotide metabolism during the determination period is in agreement with such an interpretation.

"During the mesenchyme blastula stage populations of newly formed mitochondria appear. This is indicated also in isotope experiments by an increased metabolic rate in the proteins of the mitochondria fraction. Probably the new mitochondria populations are built up from certain kinds of submicroscopic granules . . . As a consequence of the increased mitochondria density, which is first noticed in the animal region, a series of enzymes, associated with mitochondria, show increased activities, and the amino acid metabolism is intensified. Moreover the demands for phosphate-bond energy increase.

"At the same time an intensified production of cell fluid proteins is indicated by the increased incorporation rate of labelled amino acids into the soluble protein fraction. It seems reasonable to suggest that certain microsome populations are induced . . . , by the increased mitochondria activity to a synthesis of specific proteins . . . , needed for the differentiation of the cells.

"The existence of a balanced metabolic interrelationship between populations of microsomes and mitochondria, initiated during the determination period and distributed along gradients, established already during oogenesis, is probably of the utmost importance for a normal development. It is hoped that further experiments will contribute to a better understanding of the nuclear and cytoplasmic conditions, which influence the growing up of such populations and control their functions."

This quotation, together with the work of the Brachet school, gives us a good summarization of the work on biochemical embryology. But when it comes to translate these morphological and biochemical descriptions into terms of genetic control of morphogenesis an embarrassing gap opens. We saw how general embryologists try to bridge it, in a way which appears very unsatisfactory. This is not different when the biochemical embryologist looks at the gap. One of these, Holter (1949), has summarized his conclusions thus: "The indications are that in the stream of chemical and metabolic events that constitute the life of the embryo from fertilization to hatching, the true morphogenetic processes are only like ripples on the surface and their quantitative share in the chemistry of the whole is very small. It seems rather doubtful whether we can hope to reveal the mechanisms which cause those ripples by studying over-all metabolism and general enzyme distribution. We are obtaining very interesting results as to the general biochemistry of the egg and embryo, but the crucial problems of morphogenesis may be beyond the reach of the enzyme chemist."

This rather pessimistic statement is, indeed, worth considering by the geneticist, who looks to the biochemist for a definite chemical meaning of the rather general statements which the geneticist can make about genic action. We all have been too much influenced by the wish to understand genic action in terms of enzymatic action; this is true from Hagedoorn, Troland, and Goldschmidt in the older times to Beadle, Kühn, Wright, and the biochemists and biochemical embryologists in recent times. The quotation above, which is certainly basically right as far as present-day knowledge is concerned (but possibly too pessimistic for the future), might be used as a stimulating cold shower for all of us, who talk more glibly than clearly about enzyme systems and their connection with genic action. There is some reason why many biochemists laugh at what geneticists and embryologists consider to be biochemical explanations. It is rather interesting that the above-quoted biochemical embryologist, after having expressed his views, continues in his search for the biochemical control of embryonic segregation and ends up with a refuge in the unknown, just as the embryologist did, when he states: "It may even be that solutions of the true morphogenetic problems are beyond the reach of enzymes. After all, the enzyme-substrate specificity seems rather crude compared with the degree of specificity involved in differentiation processes. Enzymes can be tools, but scarcely true causative agents in morphogenesis. And I think it is very significant that the substances which in recent years have come into the center of biochemical interest, the nucleoproteids, seem to offer especially wide possibilities with regard to specificity of action. Their connection with the mechanism of gene action, and especially the intensely interesting problem of plasmagenes, offer at present, the most promising approach to the study of morphogenesis." Thus we face the distressing situation that the geneticist expects the solution of his problem from the biochemist, while the biochemist takes refuge in more or less vague concepts of the geneticist.

Hence, the geneticist is left where he was, as all our former discussions bear out. We take it for granted that the nucleoproteins are the master substances in genic action whether they act in the chromosomal, the intranuclear, or the cytoplasmic locality. We saw that none of the real problems of morphogenetic segregation are solved by calling those nucleoproteins within the cytoplasm plasmagenes. Actually, we found that such a terminology is dangerous because it suggests a solution which is no solution. The difficulty of the problem cannot be better illustrated than by the fact that the biochemist gives up and takes refuge in the unknown, the plasmagenes.

It is certainly of interest to see that a geneticist with a considerable inclination toward thinking in terms of plasmagenes, Ephrussi, concludes a brief discussion of the problem (which I have just tried to analyze in more detail) with a statement (1953) that I quote here without endorsing all of it: "After a century of amazing progress in the analysis of the cell and its genetic structure, we just return to the notion of the cell as the ultimate unit of life, lost in the course of our advances. This loss was the inevitable logical consequence of the analytical methods employed.

"The present knowledge of the biochemical constitution of the cell was achieved largely by the use of destructive methods. Trained in the tradition of the theory of solutions, many a biochemist tends, even today, to regard the cell as a 'bag of enzymes.' However, everyone realizes now that the biochemical processes studied *in vitro* may have only a remote resemblance to the events actually occurring in the living cell.

"It is less obvious that the method of genetics, although it involves no 'bloodshed,' is as analytical in its essence. Indeed the 'resolving power' of this method is amazing. It provides us with a picture of the cell's nuclear constitution with unequaled 'definition.' But, so long as the basis of genetics is the study of differences, it cannot be expected to give us an undistorted picture of the cell as a whole. The integrated character of the cell, which is its fundamental property, is bound to escape our notice most of the time.

"These statements are not intended to imply that the current analytical trends and methods are bound to be fruitless. All I want to convey to you is that equal emphasis should be placed on the study of the processes of cell integration.

"Neither should my opinions be taken as a sign of defeatism, for they are based on the belief that ultimately cell integration will find its explanation in terms of knowable, if not known, molecular structures and forces . . ."

C. KINETICS OF GENIC ACTION

The term "kinetics" seems somewhat grandiloquent, if we think of the exactness of chemical kinetics, though there have been numerous attempts to prove that genic action is of the type of a monomolecular reaction. What we mean here is that genic action involves a succession of exactly timed events which implies that rates, velocities, and thresholds enter the picture, whatever the qualitative nature of the reactions and their final products. If we are dealing with the genetic control of development, we can think only very rarely of specific reactions, since we are dealing with the over-all effects of many interdependent reaction chains which are individually not analyzable. Physiological genetics, which attacks the problem of genic control of development, deals mainly with quantitative processes and their over-all effect in time and space. It tries to find the rules of genic action by checking upon phenotypic effects of different genic conditions and, where possible, also to take into account observable features of the timing in development. Thus such studies directly continue our former discussion of the genic control of steps of determination. This former discussion related to the material system which permits the genic material to control the orderly sequence in time, and the pattern in space, of embryonic diversification, a system involving the interplay between nuclear genic material and cytoplasmic substratum. Now we shall attack the same problem by studying the over-all effects of diverse genic setups in regard to their quantitative aspects. This is all that is meant by kinetics in the present discussion.

We first introduced the kinetic point of view of genic action when, in our experiments on intersexuality, a relation between the time of incidence of a developmental feature (the turning point) and an assumed quantitative feature (quantity or potency of sex determiners) was found (Goldschmidt, 1917*a*, 1918), relations which could be best explained in terms of reaction velocities. Sewall Wright (1916) presented similar ideas at the same time. But we must keep in mind that we are trying to explain morphological features and that, therefore, the kinetics of genic action will, in the end, result in some properties of substances and structures. Therefore, I cannot agree with Hersh's (1941) distinction of substance-minded and relation-minded thinking, which I prefer to consider as belonging together as two facets of the same thing. Hersh expresses his views thus: "The substance-minded type of thinking . . . has all the tenacity of original sin. In morphology it has given us representative particles, preformation, the transmission of acquired characters, and such morphochemical hybrids as bristle-producing, facet-forming substances, and so on. The morphologist when substance-minded, thinks of the developmental patterns in terms of the visible structural characteristics from stage to stage. In short, he thinks in terms of a series of pictures. But when relation-minded, the morphologist recognizes that the pattern at any moment is the expression of the events which produce it, and attempts to gain a knowledge of the durations and rates, and relative durations and relative rates, of the component processes in the developmental nexus. Consequently, instead of thinking in terms of a series of pictures, the relation-minded morphologist tends to think in terms of the non-picturable. If the problem of the developmental pattern is similar to the problems of the more exact sciences, then no doubt in time a system of equations will be developed to facilitate our thinking about it."

I am completely in agreement with the trend of the ideas of this "relation-minded morphologist," but we need also the "pictures" of the substance-minded one, because, after all, the relational or kinetic processes lead to real substances at a definite place, in a definite structure. We do not know what, for example, facet-forming substances are. But if injection of a definite substance into a *Drosophila* larva may control facet formation, even through a kinetic process, the substance-minded morphologist and the relation-minded one become the same person.

a. Dosage of genic material

The most obvious method for such quantitative studies, destined to throw light on genic action, is to compare the actions of the same genic material in different doses. If the normal gene is assumed to be a lump of an active substance, we might conclude from the mass law of chemical kinetics that the product of its action is proportional to its dose (Goldschmidt, 1917*a*, 1920*a*, 1927). If a mutant gene is a different quantity of the same substance, it should produce more of the end product if it has a larger quantity, and less if the mutant is a smaller quantity, than the normal locus. (The consequences will be taken up below.) If, however, the mutant is only a position effect and its normal allele the normal chromosomal structure, it cannot be predicted what the change of action of the mutant will be in regard to the end product. It might be the same quantitative relation as in the theory of quantitative mutation of a gene in the classic sense; but the effect might also be a purely qualitative change, which in dosage experiments would hardly lead to results of a simple quantitative type.

aa. Dosage in sex determination

The idea of dosage was to a certain extent contained in the presence-absence theory of Bateson, which may be formulated in terms of gene quantities. However, dosage first seriously entered genetical theory when the mechanism of the sex chromosomes was discovered: the visual demonstration that two doses of genic material, actually two whole chromosomes, determined one sex; and one dose, one chromosome, determined the other sex. But all the attempts to connect this dosage relation with genic action led to impossible consequences until it was found (Goldschmidt, 1912, 1915, 1916*c*, 1920*c*) that the dosage was not acting by means of its own direct effect, but by setting up a quantitative or dosage method for deciding a developmental alternative. This was the balance theory of sex determination, meaning that the sex determiners of one sex are located in the X-chromosomes, those of the other sex outside, and that the quantities of two in the X-chromosomes win out over the action of the ever constant determiners of the other sex, while one quantity does not succeed in doing so: in *Lymantria*, $F > M < MM$; in *Drosophila*, $MM > F < FF$.

In *Lymantria* it seemed possible to link dosages with genic action when it was found that F and M, at that time considered to be sex genes, existed in different states or potencies, called strong and weak. That is, the combination of a strong F with two weak M's made the genetic males intersexual in spite of a normal chromosome complement; and, vice versa, a weak F with one strong M made females intersexual. All grades of these potencies could be found, and their combinations always gave the predictable result: we know that F/MM is a male, but if F_s is a very strong F and M_w a very weak M, the combination F_s/M_wM_w results in a sex-reversal female. If M_{w_1}–M_{w_5} are increasing grades of strength of M, M_{w_5} being identical with a strong M, or M_s, it is possible to replace in the F_s/M_wM_w individuals one of the M's by M_{w_1} or M_{w_2}, and so on to M_{w_5}. The result is, with the exactness of a set of equations, that F_s/M_wM_{w1} is a high-grade male intersex; $F_s/M_wM_{w_2}$, a less extreme male intersex; $F_s/M_wM_{w_3}$, a medium one; and so on until $F_s/M_wM_{w_5}$ is a normal male. (See Goldschmidt, 1930; and fig. 23, below.) As this series—and all other comparable experiments which gave completely consistent results—merges at both ends of the different M potencies into the normal dosage relation F/MM = ♂ F/M = ♀ ($F > M < MM$), the conclusion was obvious that the potencies of F and M are also dosages, different quantities of the sex determiners F and M. As we stated in another connection (see I 2 C *d ee*), today it is certain that F in *Lymantria* is inherited in the Y-chromosome, and that M in the X-chromosome probably is represented by a set of heterochromatic sections. The quantity of M would then be the quantity of this heterochromatin, which agrees with the facts reported previously that quantities of extra-heterochromatin may have corresponding effects in shifting phenotypical features (e.g., variegation). Thus we would still deal with dosages, though not doses of "genes."

In the old *Lymantria* work, the facts of intersexuality permitted establishing what was considered to be a kinetic relation between dosage and effect. In intersexes, development proceeds first according to the chromosomal sex (1X-2X), which probably means, as we saw before when discussing cytoplasmic conditioning, that primary differentiating processes are influenced mainly by cytoplasmic predetermination in the egg. After a certain time, the turning point, sexual differentiation changes into that of the opposite sex. The time of occurrence of the turning point is responsible for the degree of intersexuality: late turning point, low-grade intersexuality; earlier turning point, higher degree, extending finally to complete sex reversal. Thus the timing of a developmental, determinative event is proportional to the imbalance produced by wrong dosages. In the presence of two simultaneous and competing chains of reaction, the normal balance (F/M dosage) controls the process whereby either one or the other product of reaction first reaches the threshold of action (i.e., decision of the sex alternative); the wrong balance, or imbalance through nonnormal dosages, changes the relative velocities of the two reaction chains, with the result that the wrong one (in regard to chromosomal constitution) overtakes the right one at the turning point. In the early days of experimentation, the valencies of M and F were assumed to be genic quantities, thus enabling a kinetic relation between dosage of gene and its action. Though we no longer call F and M individual genes, this dosage effect upon the kinetics of genic action still remains. It is obvious that this analysis led, at that time, to the deduction that all genic actions are subject to dosage effects upon the kinetics of that action; which again meant, within the general idea of the classic gene, that mutants should be dosage differences. Thus dosage became a major problem of genic action.

Within the general sphere of sex determination, the role of dosage could be carried another step farther when actual, not just inferred, dosages became available beyond the 1X-2X relation. Standfuss already had found in pre-Mendelian days that species backcrosses in Lepidoptera produce what I later called intersexes. After Federley (1913) discovered the triploidy of such hybrids, and after I had established the balance theory of sex determination (1912), at that time still believing that in *Lymantria* the F factors are located in the autosomes (they are in the Y-chromosome), Standfuss (1914) realized that his intersexes were triploid ones with a disturbed F/M balance, because three sets of autosomes (3F) were confronted by two X-chromosomes (2M) which gives a balance of 3:2 instead of 2:1. Thus a dosage situation for both F and M factors was established. The most elegant example of this type was found later in *Drosophila* by Bridges (1922), when he discovered in this fly triploid intersexes the explanation of which was similar to that of the lepidopteran intersexes. The *Drosophila* technique allowed combinations of many different doses of both M and F, with the results expected from the F/M balance. As the working of the balance is here demonstrated more easily, at least for the beginner, than in the diploid intersexuality of *Lymantria*, the *Drosophila* example has become very popular in textbooks. This led, unfortunately, to the completely erroneous statement that sex is determined by the balance between the number of autosomes and X-chromosomes. In diploid intersexuality, these numbers are always the normal ones, and the balance is upset either by relative potencies of F and M, whatever this is, or by the presence of mutant loci affecting this balance, as in the different cases of diploid intersexuality in *Drosophila* (see enumeration in Goldschmidt, 1948*a*), or even by environmental action (see later). In *Bombyx* (Tazima, 1943) the F factor in the Y-chromosome is so strong that in its presence a female always is determined, whatever the number of X-chromosomes and autosomes. (A comparable but more complicated situation in the plant *Melandrium* will be analyzed later.) Hence the statement concerning the number of autosomes versus the number of X-chromosomes has no general value. It applies in *Drosophila* to triploid intersexes and the normal sexes (but not to diploid intersexes of the same fly) only, because here the M action is localized in an autosome (see I 2 C *d ee*), thus making multiplication of autosomal numbers identical with M dosage. Altogether, triploid intersexuality is another example of the action of genic material, whatever this means, according to dosage. In *Drosophila* the turning-point idea (the so-called time law of intersexuality) has been established for triploid intersexes (Dobzhansky, 1930*b*) and also for diploid ones (Goldschmidt, 1949*a*); further, for triploid intersexes in Lepidoptera (see discussion in Goldschmidt, 1949*b*). The general relation between dosage of genic material and kinetics of its action is thus established at least for the genetics of sex. Therefore it becomes important to study general genic actions in different dosages, apart from the special situation in sex determination involving a balance.

There is available a completely different set of data on dosage in relation to sex determination, which is, if the observations and interpretations are correct (which is doubted by many), independent of the balance situation (see, however, below) because it takes place in a haploid microörganism. This is true in the much-discussed work of Moewus (see Hartmann, 1943; Sonneborn, 1951), which has not yet been repeated in the same organism or another behaving similarly. The details are rather complicated as far as the problem of sex determination is concerned, and will be discussed in connection with the genetics of sex. We shall show that the genetic facts may have been misinterpreted. For our present discussion we will extract that part of the alleged facts which is connected with dosage, without trying to interpret the sex-determining mechanism and its assumed chemistry.

The main points, leaving out confusing details, are as follows. There are two different, closely linked loci in what may be called an autosome: $gathe^{cis}$ and $gathe^{trans}$. Their function is the control of enzymes or enzyme systems which perform, respectively, the synthesis of cis- and trans-dimethylcrocetinester from the substrate cis- or trans-crocin. These two esters are the + and − substances which permit copulation (the mating types). A female cell must produce more cis- than trans-ester in order to be able to copulate, and a male cell more trans- than cis-ester. Femaleness and maleness as such are controlled in Moewus' scheme by two loci, F and M, not allelic and located in another pair of chromosomes which we might call X and Y. (This point will be contested later.) They are closely linked with some other loci which, in the F-chromosome, produce isorhamnetin; this determines the cell as female. Similar loci in the M-chromosome produce paronin, the male-determining substance. Now F and M are not sex determiners, but they regulate the relative amount of cis- and trans-ester produced by the gathe loci, the relation of which determines the chance for copulation, namely, more cis for the female cell and more trans for the male cell. We assume here that this complicated system has really been found and correctly interpreted in its strange interplay of sex determination and sexual compatibility. (I personally am very skeptical, but Sonneborn has accepted it.) Just now the Hartmann school is repeating these experiments. Thus far they have been unable to duplicate them, and they find a completely different chemism (communication by letter; and Förster and Wiese, 1954*a*).

Now we come to our real topic. F and M are found to have a series of alleles of different valency, or potency, conferring upon the cells the intermediate copulation conditions which Hartmann has called relative sexuality. This, then, is clearly a parallel to the different valencies or strength in the F and M of *Lymantria*, which also act like a set of alleles. Moewus distinguished four grades for both F and M with reciprocal action, as the following table shows:

	cis:trans		*cis:trans*
F_1	65:35	M_1	35:65
F_2	75:25	M_2	25:75
F_3	85:15	M_3	15:85
F_4	95: 5	M_4	5:95

It is this table, clearly a brain child of my description of valencies in *Lymantria* in terms of numerical values, but said to be the result of actual measuring, which has made so many people skeptical.

Now Moewus claims to have crossing-over results which show that two F_1 act like one F_2 and so forth. If this is true, the conclusion is unavoidable that the F and M alleles must be regarded as different quantities of the same "gene," just as we had to conclude for the different valencies of F and M in *Lymantria.* If we accept Moewus' claims, we find a relation between gene dosage and the quantity of two definite stuffs (based upon almost the same precursors and only sterically different). However, these stuffs are not the direct products of the genic action of the F and M doses, but products of completely different "genes," the amount of which has been controlled by the dosages of F and M. Sonneborn (1951*b*) proposes the logical explanation that the function of M is to produce a specific inhibitor of the production of the cis-isomer, in concentration and effectiveness equal to that of the trans-inhibitor, controlled by F_1. Suppose the F alleles control production of a substance which at some point inhibits the synthesis of the dimethylester of trans-crocetin, and that the F_1 allele yields an amount of inhibitor capable of reducing to about one-half the effective amount of the trans-isomer. If doubling, tripling, or quadrupling the rate of inhibition reduces the effective amount of trans-isomer by three-fourths, seven-eighths, and fifteen-sixteenths, respectively, the calculated results very much resemble those in the table. Thus, if Moewus' results are accepted, they provide the best example of genically produced substances in proportion to genic dosage.

Sonneborn adds the assumption that the F and M alleles of different and linear valency are actually duplications of the same chromosome segment or pseudoalleles in Lewis' interpretation. In effect this is not different from our old interpretation of the valencies of the "sex genes" in *Lymantria* as different quantities of genic substance, except for the timely assumption of origin by gene duplication. I refer to our former discussion of pseudoallelism and shall not discuss this phylogenetic assumption, as it does not make any difference for the dosage problem whether it is correct or not. Altogether, I should like to see a confirmation of at least the basic features of Moewus' work, that is, location and crossing over of M and F and the control of the gathe loci.

bb. Dosage within allelism

Dosage effects may permit us to draw conclusions concerning the action of the genic material if it can be shown that different actual numbers of mutant loci exercise a proportional quantitative effect upon the mutant phenotype. To make possible such a demonstration, genic action must be of a type which permits quantitative shifts; that is, it must be of a kinetic type. If we think of the one gene—one synthetic step hypothesis of Beadle, it is obvious that genic actions of this type cannot show dosage effects. If the mutant locus inhibits one synthetic step and thus prevents a definite substance from being present, with the consequent effect, whatever it is in individual cases, then the presence of three or four of these mutant loci cannot make any difference, for the effect is of the all-or-none type. But if the mutant effect were to change the speed of a reaction or, perhaps, any other imaginable quantitative feature of development and differentiation, different doses of the mutant should, *ceteris paribus,* produce proportional quantities of the effect up to a saturation point (threshold for maximal action). The actual existence of a dosage effect for many mutant loci is therefore additional evidence against the assumption that the one gene—one synthetic step theory covers more than a group of special cases.

If we speak of genuine dosage experiments, we exclude dosages assumed on the basis of our former view that mutants are different quantities of genic substance, a concept which was later given up; though we may still hold that a mutant is a change in regard to a quantitative feature of genic action. This idea also permits our considering the relation between normal and mutant action, for example, dominance as a dosage effect, not necessarily dosage of genic material but also (or always?) dosage of action. We shall return to this later; now we are dealing with actual doses of genic material at the mutant loci. In all experiments of this kind an uncertainty factor is involved because more or less large chromosomal sections are always used for the production of different quantities of one locus. But it is a fair conclusion to attribute clear and orderly dosage effects to the dosages and not to interference by other chromosomal parts.

Dosage differences may be produced by means which are in no way completely comparable. In the first type, available without special experimental conditions, sex-linked mutant loci are present in one dose in the heterozygous sex and in two doses in the homozygous sex. However, this is clearly not a simple dosage situation, since the one-dose and the two-dose types to be compared, the sexes, differ otherwise in their developmental systems. Disregard of this fact has led to what I consider serious errors (to be discussed below). Another type of dosage difference is available when a mutant locus is located opposite a deficiency and thus can be appraised in a one-dose condition. Here the difficulty is that we know now that a deficiency may have a position effect, with the result that a deficiency break near the locus may act like a mutant, thus restoring an effect equal to that of two doses. With larger deficiencies this is avoided. The third type of dosage experiment permits studying three and four doses of a locus, when it is possible to duplicate it by appropriate translocations of small chromosomal sections. When these are sufficiently small and the results congruent, we may safely disregard the extra material present. Less certain are the results when dosages are produced by duplication, triplication, and so on, of one chromosome, which affects the entire collaboration of developmental reactions, the so-called genic balance. More reliable are the results in triploids, and so on, though we are not sure what the effects of the physiological changes attached to polyploidy are in each case. Even completely balanced triploids, as in *Drosophila,* are usually not normal flies.

Before using the results of all such procedures to draw conclusions concerning genic action, we may consider the possibilities. We have already mentioned the first possibility: genic action of a qualitative type, with one mutant locus affecting one inhibition of a synthetic step. With such actions no dosage effect could be expected. A second type may be described as an inhibition of a normally occurring process, not as an all-or-none effect but as a quantitative effect. This may be the lowering of the rate of reaction of a process needed for normal development, or the lowering of the speed of growth and cell divisions needed for the normal result, or any such quantitative inhibition which is not of the all-or-none type. The result will be that increase of dosage of the mutant locus increases the degree of abnormality of the mutant. A third possibility is that the mutant locus interferes quantitatively with the production of a substance that is needed for some developmental feature in such a way that the mutant locus produces the necessary stuff, but not in sufficient quantity. Again various detailed effects may result, as long as they are only quantitative deviations from normal. The effect of this type of action would be that one dose gives only the extremest mutant effect, which becomes less extreme with increasing doses up to normal when a certain saturation point is reached.

Muller (1933) proposed names for mutant loci which act in the way just considered, calling them, in the order of the foregoing discussion, amorphic, antimorphic (partly neomorphic), and hypomorphic mutants; he derived the terms from the idea that the mutant loci act in the same way or in an opposite way from the normal gene. I am opposed to the use of these terms because they are linked to the classic theory of the gene, and especially because they might foster the idea that we are dealing with different kinds of genes or mutant genes, while actually the differences lie in the type and kind of developmental reactions which are affected by the mutant loci and their different doses. Moreover, the terminology does not characterize the real differences between reactions of the all-or-none effect type (coincident with Muller's amorphs), and shifts in the kinetics of reactions either by inhibition of determining processes of definite speed (Muller's antimorphs) or by affecting the quantity of reaction products (Muller's hypomorphs).

In the dosage experiments the majority of genic actions were of the last type. Mohr (1923*a*) found that a great many mutants opposite a deficiency showed an exaggerated phenotype, more extreme than the homozygous mutation effect. I proposed (1927) the explanation by dosage: one dose of the mutant locus produces less of the active substance controlling the phenotype than two doses do, and therefore makes the mutant phenotype more extreme. A corollary of this was the expectation that additional doses would make the phenotype more normal. This turned out to be true of most recessive mutants. The proof was supplied in Stern's classic work on the bobbed alleles in *Drosophila* (1929*a*). Bobbed shortens the bristles. By ingenious experimentation Stern could build up flies with 1, 2, 3, 4 doses of bb, and the length of the bristles was strictly proportional to dosage, the wild-type length being the maximum possible (saturation point, threshold effect). Other examples studied since have shown the same result. We may safely assume that wherever the deficiency-exaggeration effect is found, the same type of action of the mutant locus is present. When the exaggeration effect is absent, it may mean either that the mutant action is of the all-or-none type (e.g., one synthetic step) or that the deficiency has a position effect which makes a/— identical in action with a/a. (See above under position effect.) Thus it is demonstrated that the majority of recessive loci in *Drosophila* affect such processes of the kinetics of development which, in a general way, may be conceived as controlling quantities of end products, whatever the direct interference with the kinetics may be.

We return briefly to the former statement that the failure of the exaggeration effect may be due to a position effect of the deficiency. In discussing position effect previously, I pointed out that position effect can be freely exchanged for genuine mutants in dosage experiments, that the combination of two mutant loci plus one position effect produced by a rearrangement near the same locus acts like three doses of the mutant. In the same way a homozygous recessive position effect is identical with the homozygous mutant effect. This shows at once that we are not analyzing the effect of different quantities of genic material, but that of additive action, of whatsoever change at a mutant locus, upon the various kinds of reactions with which the mutant locus interferes in one way or another. Thus the old discussion of gene quantities is out of order here. It is even more so when we accept the modern view that there is no normal gene and that all mutants are position effects. Dosage then means, contrary to our old views (1920*a*, 1927), not dosage of genic substance but dosage of action.

This conclusion must be kept in mind when we turn now to the classic example of dosage, the increase of which enhances the mutant effect away from normal, the case of Bar eyes in *Drosophila*. We have already discussed the basic facts (see I 3 C *c aa*) and have seen that the Bar effect is a position effect of a break involving a duplication; and that double Bar is a triplication in tandem, with two position effects in one chromosome. Originally, when Bar was considered to be a dominant mutant locus reducing the eye-facet number, the dosage series BB, BBB, BBBB could be considered as different doses of a mutant gene. When Bar proved to be the position effect of one tandem duplication, and double Bar that of a series of three repeated chromosomal sections, it could be claimed that here the dosage effect was actually studied with 1, 2, 3, 4 active sections of the chromosome, that is, real doses of genic material. Then it turned out that only position effects were involved, and the apparent real doses of genic material became (as discussed above) additive effects. Again, this dosage series does not shed light upon the nature of the genic material (quantities of genic material as basis of the mutant effect) but involves only the actions. In this case we have the type of action, discussed above theoretically, in which increase of dosage (number) of the causative agent increases the mutant effect, that is, lowers the numbers of facets proportionally (though not in linear progression).

In the bobbed dosage series, we had to conclude in a rather general way that the amount of bristle-forming substance formed by the mutant locus is smaller than normal, but the Bar dosage series permits a more direct approach to genic action. It can be established that the inhibition of facet number by the different Bar dosages follows definite laws. Another Bar allele, infrabar, has an effect intermediate between + and B and also has a dosage effect. We are not concerned here with the problem of what infrabar is in terms of duplication, position effect, or point mutation, since we know it does not affect the dosage problem. Therefore we include infrabar in the dosage series, though it is known to have a completely different reaction upon temperature changes (Luce, 1926; complete references in Goldschmidt, 1938; Steinberg, 1941; Goldschmidt, 1945*b*; DeMarinis, 1952). My original approach to the dosage problem (1927) was this. If the facet-forming reaction (whatever this means) is expressed as a series of curves for the different dosages, and the actual number of facets in the different combinations is plotted on a line parallel to the abscissa, representing the threshold at which the result is decided, the heterozygotes should have curves with an angle intermediate between those of the homozygotes, if simple proportionality to dosage obtains. Actually, the curves plotted from Sturtevant's data of facet number at 25° showed that some exponential relation must be involved. This I assumed to be the number n of cell divisions of the anlagen cells which produce 2^n primordial cells and subsequent facets. Thus the exponent n was calculated from the actual data (e.g., 9.6 for normal eyes). As the number of primary cells decreases with dosage of B, the potency of action of each combination would be inversely proportional to the number of cell divisions, or, in terms of an inhibiting effect, would be directly proportional to it. Calculating in terms of potency of action, we can equate the relative dosage involved to the number of cell divisions needed to reach the actual facet number, in relation to a normal point assumed to be ten divisions. Since $n = 9.6$ for + eyes the calculated dosage (or potency effect) is 10/9.6. Normal is, of course, homozygous +. Therefore the relative potency (dose) of one locus is $10/9.6 \times 1/2$. A table can be compiled for this ideal dose in all the combinations counted by Sturtevant, adding the individual doses for each locus, and this calculated dosage of each combination can be compared with the effect actually found in terms of total dosage, that is, 10/n. Table 3 shows the results.

With few exceptions (9, 13) the order of the two columns is identical. The table shows the simple proportionality between dosage and effect as well as the action of the alleles upon the number of primary cell divisions in the eye anlage.

TABLE 3

No.	*Constitution*	*Calcul. dose*	*Found 10:n*	*No.*	*Constitution*	*Calcul. dose*	*Found 10:n*
1	B B B B	3.28	2.18	9	Bi Bi B	2.02	1.92
2	B B B Bi	3.06	2.18	10	+ Bi B	1.94	1.76
3	B B Bi Bi	2.84	2.08	11	Bi Bi Bi	1.80	1.41
4	B Bi Bi Bi	2.62	2.08	12	+ Bi Bi	1.72	1.32
5	B B B	2.46	1.92	13	B Bi	1.42	1.61
6	Bi Bi Bi Bi	2.40	1.92	14	+ B	1.34	1.18
7	Bi B B	2.24	1.92	15	+ +	1.12	1.05
8	+ B B	2.16	1.82				

Before discussing this result for genic action as revealed in dosage experiments, I must report that DeMarinis and Hersh (1943) have arrived at the same conclusions by the ingenious method of measuring eye mosaics produced by somatic crossing over. They found that the ratio of the white facets to the total number conformed to the relative growth function. The analysis of the data led to the conclusion that the Bar factors control an activator of cell division in the optic disc; the number of facets is the resultant of these divisions. They consider that the additive inhibiting effect may be produced in three ways: secondary destruction of an anlage, which is excluded by Steinberg's (1941) embryological work; or by a failure of size increase in the individual facets, which disagrees with the observed facts; or by lack of formation of facets. From the behavior of the mosaics, in which the time of change by crossing over can be ascertained, this last possibility is explained as a postponement of the time of onset of divisions under the influence of Bar action. Recently DeMarinis (1952) has extended these conclusions by the further use of the mosaic technique. He finds that the anterior portion of the eye anlage contributes a proportionally larger number of cells to the final size of the eye. This happens either by increased rate of cell division or by the prolongation of the period of cell division, which is under control of the Bar series, acting according to dosage. However, the influence of Bar does not reduce the eye anlage as a whole, but affects, quantitatively, a definite number of embryonic cells in the anterior portion of the anlage. The increasing dosages thus reduce the eye from anterior to posterior, and the effect is proportionally greater on the anterior dorsal lobe.

Leaving aside these details, we have Hersh's idea of a different start of cell divisions with simultaneous end, the first, of course, proportional to dosage, compared with our deduction of a simultaneous start, but inhibition sooner or later according to dosage. According to Steinberg (1941), the decisive first divisions in development are not known; they occur before the temperature-effective period. Facet formation (which takes place much later) is delayed in B flies as compared with + flies; later on, the growth curves are identical. Obviously, the Bar effect controls only the number of primordial cells (Steinberg's cell capital). Thus we do not know whether the Bar condition affects the growth substances (hormones) controlling the primordial cell divisions so that divisions begin later in Bar and later still in higher combinations. Since the effect is additive, proportional to dosage, this might mean only an inhibition, for example, of the speed of production of these "hormones," that is, interference with a kinetic feature of genic action. The other possibility is that the production of these hormones always starts normally but is exhausted at different times according to dosage. This could again be interference with the kinetics of production; but it might also be conceived as a direct action upon the control of a threshold condition necessary for continued cell divisions. One of the possibilities of visualizing this would be the assumption that the threshold is set by determination of some of the cells as head epidermis, a process of a completely different kind, interfering with facet formation. In the end, however, this secondary inhibiting action via redetermination would also work in some way via kinetics of a process, as it has to spread with dosage. This would be a third possibility, in general terms, inhibition by an outside process or product proportional to B dosage. There are some facts bearing upon the choice among these possibilities. Thus temperature effects upon facet number can still take place after establishment of the primary differences. This would mean, in a general way, that the processes of inhibition of cell division are of a kinetic type, having a temperature coefficient. Another fact (Luce, 1941; Williams, 1945) is that an experimental increase of developmental time produces more facets. This fact again can be cited in favor of all the possibilities mentioned. Thus we see that it is very difficult to derive one exclusive interpretation of these dosage effects, but, in a general way, they point to action of the genic material upon some phase of the kinetic processes in development rather than to a qualitative chemical action.

However, there are some other facts which lead a step farther. It seems that the number of divisions of the primordial cells is only one factor in the final determination of the size of the Bar effect. It is known that at a much later time of development, when the aggregation of the primordial cells into pro-facets takes place, the number of facets resulting can be greatly influenced (during the critical period) by temperature action, X rays, and other agents, mostly in the direction of fewer facets. Since the primordial division period is already over, this cannot be an effect upon the kinetics of cell division. The decisive experiment is due to Chevais (1943). He found in *Calliphora* larvae an extractable substance which has to do with ommatidia differentiation. If enough of it is injected into Bar-eye larvae before differentiation of the ommatidia, a completely normal eye can be produced. This shows that the primary determination of the number of cells as facet primordia is only one aspect, though certainly the major one. The other side is that the surrounding cells of the imaginal disc which are destined to be determined as head epithelium still retain their potency to develop into facets. Since it is an extractable substance which can enforce this, it might be concluded that the primordial cells or the already grouped pro-facet cells produce a substance which prevents other cells of the head epithelium from developing into facets. This would be another Bar effect, but it cannot be the one which shows the dosage difference.

This interpretation of the facts is, however, not the one preferred by Luce (see Luce *et al.*, 1951). He shifts the emphasis completely to the processes in the critical period, and thinks that the primary difference in cell numbers is of no importance and that everything depends upon the number of disc cells which in the much later sensitive period are determined for epidermis or facets. Therefore, the cells of the Bar mutants are deficient in a substance which is a necessary precursor for the initiation of differentiation into ommatidia. The dosage effect, then, would be one upon the amount of deficiency of this substance, according to Luce. I cannot see any advantage in this interpretation and prefer to consider the processes in the sensitive period as a secondary effect. It seems to me that the majority of facts fit this explanation. However, this discussion shows that the details of the processes between dosage of causative agent and quantity of effect are anything but simple, though, in a general way, they can be described as effects upon the kinetics of chains of reactions.

In recent years, Stern and collaborators (1943–1948) have tried to gain more detailed insight into genic action from dosage phenomena. The large body of facts is anything but simple, and at some points great difficulties arise for a unified explanation, a difficulty which may increase when the still unpublished additional facts become known. We shall try to analyze the facts in close connection with the previous discussion, thus making many points clearer than they would be otherwise. In a general way, the work deals with dosages of the recessive fourth chromosome mutant cubitus interruptus (ci), which was mentioned in connection with the Dubinin effect (see I 3 C *c cc*). The mutant ci removes a segment from the cubital wing vein. The effect can be classed according to the length of the removed piece, thus giving a quantitative appraisal of the effect of the mutant locus or loci. A number of alleles are known of which two, especially, enter the present discussion. One ci^W is a dominant; another, called by Stern $+^3$, is in the usual genetic language a very weak ci "allele" with only a low percentage of penetrance, which is rather subject to temperature influence. In the usual terminology it should be called, say, ci^s. Stern treats it as a low-grade + allele, which in essence is the same but complicates somewhat the description of the results. There are, in addition, two different grades of normal alleles—called by Stern isoalleles—meaning that they produce normal veins, because there is nothing possible above a normal vein, but the grades are distinguishable by a different potency in the hemizygous condition, $+^{ci}/-$, that is, over a deficiency. They are called $+^1$ and $+^2$. All these alleles can be studied in simplex condition, one dose, over a deficiency, or in haplo-IV; in duplex, or two doses; and in triplex, three doses, in a triplo-IV fly; and all of them can be combined in the different dosage experiments. In addition, a number of chromosomal rearrangements, R, are available which have a position effect identical with the ci effect, and they also can enter the different combinations.

Of the alleles mentioned, ci behaves in the way we have already described for the bobbed alleles; that is, the greatest effect upon venation is produced by one dose (the exaggeration effect), and with more doses the vein gap becomes smaller and smaller, though three doses, the maximum available, do not yet suffice to produce a normal vein. Their action may be described naïvely as producing a smaller amount of vein-forming substance than the normal allele. For ci^s, the low allele, this would mean a smaller amount than normal, but not very much less; and for the lower of the two isoalleles, an amount almost sufficient to produce a normal vein in the simplex condition. The dominant ci^W, however, behaves like the dominant Bar effect; with increasing dose the vein is more abnormal, so that the effect must be described in terms of inhibition of a reaction.

For the sake of analysis, we must distinguish three sets of facts, which have to be explained: (1) the elementary dosage relations involving the ci locus and the more or less normal alleles; (2) the dominant ci^W with the opposite type of dosage effect and its compound with the others; (3) the position effect R(+) and R(ci), again in different combinations. The first group of facts seems to be not different from those discussed above for bobbed: relatively simple dosage relations between the mutant loci and some end product responsible for vein formation.

The order of these dosage effects is (including the information obtainable only at low temperature, when the "normal" isoalleles can be distinguished from each other), beginning with the extremest effect, as follows:

1. ci/0	extreme absence of veins
2. ci/ci	considerable absence of veins
3. ci^s/ci	considerable effect varying to normal ($ci^s = +^3$)
4. ci ci ci	not completely normal
5. ci^s/0	small effect visible only at low temperature, otherwise +
6. $+^2$/0	still smaller effect at low temperature, otherwise +
7. $+^{ci}$/0	almost normal at low temperature, otherwise +
8. ci^s/ci^s	normal
9. $+^2/+^2$	normal
10. $+^{ci}/+^{ci}$	normal

Stern's own explanation has been changed somewhat in a more recent publication (1948), which we shall follow without going into the details of his former theory. He first assumes that genic action takes place between the gene and a substrate. As three ci produce more venation, the substrate must be present in excess of the amount turned over by one or two ci. The product of the interaction between genes and the substrate enters a chain of reactions which is positively correlated with the sequence of developmental processes producing venation. Stern thinks that these conclusions are independent of any theory of genic action. Actually, the concept is identical with what we called an effect produced by the stimulation of the kinetics of a process, but it is couched in different language. Stern also mentions the possibility that different alleles use different substrates and thus produce qualitatively different products, and he finds no difficulty in incorporating this into quantitatively arranged results. Thus far the tenets and their interpretation fit into the general scheme which we discussed before.

However, Stern thinks that something new comes in when combinations of different alleles are considered. The intermediate effect of these suggests a simple dosage relationship, each allele acting independently according to its dose, as was assumed thus far in our discussion also. This relation is, however, supposed not to work in the hemizygous condition (opposite a deficiency). For example, Stern's $+^3/+^3$ is normal; $+^3/0$, almost so; but ci/$+^3$ has abnormal veins ($+^3$ is what we called ci^s because it acts at low temperature like a low ci allele with a little penetrance, just as, e.g., vg^{ni} in the vestigial series). Stern calls this an interference between ci and $+^3$. The dosage studies had shown that ci acts in the same direction as + or $+^3$, namely, toward production of venation. Yet, when ci and one of the two + alleles are brought together in the same nuclei, their joint effect is smaller than that of the more effective allele alone. This suggests to Stern some mechanism of competition. If + and ci use the same substrate, present in a limited amount, a competition for it might deprive + of its full share in favor of ci. If ci turned over the substrate less efficiently than + into the product of action P, the joint action may be less than the better one alone. Since it is not known what the reactions are, Stern prefers now the term "interference" to "competition."

We might look at the facts in a somewhat different way, assuming that Stern's $+^3$ is not a + but a weak ci allele with a little penetrance, ci^s. If ci produces only little vein substance, ci/ci more, and ci ci ci almost the full quantity, ci^s also would produce almost the full quantity, much more than ci and ci ci. Therefore, on a simple dosage basis, ci^s/ci should produce an amount between ci^s/ci^s and ci/ci and nearer to the former, which is the case for nos. 1–4 in the enumeration. What is now the expectation for $ci^s/0$? It should be less normal than ci/ci^s on a pure dosage basis, but it is more normal. Therefore, some feature additional to dosage should be involved and, in our way of looking at the facts, it is not an antagonism of ci and $+^3$ (ci^s) which has to be explained in addition to the dosage phenomenon (which is clearly good also for the relation of nos. 5–7 in the enumeration), but rather the action of the deficiency. Thus far we assumed with Stern that ci/0 and so on has only a simplex action. But we know now that deficiencies may have a position effect similar to the mutant effect, as the action of many homozygous deficiencies proves (see I 3 C *c dd aaa*). Thus, if in $ci^s/0$ the deficiency has a position effect not too far below that of ci, normality or almost normality is expected. The simple dosage relation holds thus far, in which the different potencies of different alleles act in the same direction as real dosages. Therefore, neither competition for a substrate nor interference is needed for this group of effects. (A check upon this conclusion could be made by a measuring of $+^3/0$, first with 0 being the small deficiency used in the experiments, and then with 0 based upon haplo-IV, which has no position effect, though it might do some shifting via genic balance change.)

While the basic data do not require any other explanation than one resting upon dosage, or a potency of certain alleles acting in the same sense as dosage, another set of data was presented by Stern in regard to triplex conditions which looks as if in certain combinations ci had not the cumulative dosage effect but an antagonistic effect. The following are the facts ($>$ meaning more normal, 0 being the small deficiency, M-4):

1. ci $+^2$ 0 $>$ ci ci $+^2$
2. ci $+^2$ $>$ ci ci $+^2$
3. $+^2$ 0 $>$ ci ci $+^2$

Thus the presence of two ci with one plus reverses, in all comparisons with the diploid condition, the additive dosage action of ci: this combination is always more abnormal, while such triplex ones as ci ci ci and ci ci 0 follow the dosage rule. We might express the result also by saying that two ci are dominant over +, while the usual behavior is the opposite. Clearly, some new element has entered the group of facts. Stern expresses this by saying that ci has a positive vein-producing capacity as well as a negative one. In the presence of only ci loci, the positive is greater than the negative; in the presence of a + allele the opposite is the case. This, of course, is only an abstract description of the facts. To make it concrete, Stern assumes (as I mentioned when discussing position effect) that each allele has two properties: a combining power (with the substrate) and an efficiency factor. Now $+^2$ and ci have different combining powers, using different amounts of substrate. Regarding the efficiency factor, it is assumed that $+^2$ and ci interact with the substrate to form an identical product P (see above) or two different ones of identical effectiveness. The efficiencies e $+^2$ and e ci mean, in this case, the relative amount of P $+^2$ and P ci formed by the allele per unit of substrate used. If now the efficiency of ci is lower than that of $+^2$, and if the amount of substrate is limited to an amount below that which ci and + together can utilize, the competition for the substrate between the two kinds of alleles of the heterozygote $+^2$/ci/ci will result in the $+^2$ genes not obtaining enough substrate to produce its maximum effect, while the ci genes will use their fraction of substrate less efficiently than $+^2$. Hence the limited amount of substrate present will be utilized less efficiently by the coöperation of $+^2$ and the two ci alleles than by the combination of $+^2$ and one ci allele. Thus the results can be explained formally. I cannot help saying that I do not feel too happy about this theory, which appears to me as a restatement of the fact of non-consistent effects in terms of different qualities of the causative agent. If only nos. 1 and 3 of the enumeration on page 352 were available, we could think of a specific action of the Minute deficiencies, since Minutes are known to interfere strongly with genic actions (see Brehme, 1939, 1941; Goldschmidt, 1949). But no. 2 without a Minute shows the same discrepancy, and therefore the combination ci ci + must be responsible. As we have noted, Stern has recently given up the idea of competition for substrate. Thus, for the time being, the riddle cannot be solved, and there must be some feature of genic action which cannot be described simply in terms of velocities of reaction and quantity of products proportional to dosage.

The second group of experiments by Stern involves the dominant ci^W. It is a strange fact that many multiple allelic series in *Drosophila,* and in maize also, contain a dominant mutant. Frequently, but not always, this is a visible rearrangement like dominant $eyeless^D$. The dominant ci^W has the opposite action from ci, namely, like Bar, an additive action toward abnormality in different doses. We question at once whether or not dominance in these cases is based upon the same causative condition (see below). Thus $ci^W > ci^W\ ci^W > ci^W\ ci^W\ ci^W$, where $>$ means more normal. The difficulties come in again in the compounds:

1. $ci^W/0$ = almost normal
2. $ci^W/+$ = greatly deficient
3. ci/ci^W = greatly deficient, more than $ci^w/+$.

The great difference between 1 and 3 cannot be explained by a position effect of the deficiency, which would make both alike. Stern concludes that here a mutual interference of the alleles becomes visible as the heterozygote $ci^W/+$ is less normal than $ci^W/0$ and $+/0$. If we express the action of ci^W in the same terms used for the Bar series, as an inhibition of the speed of a reaction, while the ci and bb effects control a smaller amount of reaction product than normal, we would not expect that these two effects, involved as they are in different processes of genic action, could be additive. The inhibiting action of ci^W upon a reaction velocity would decide the effect whether an additional ci is present or not. In other words, we are not justified in treating ci and ci^W as if the same action in different directions was involved and neither should we so consider the action of + in the presence of ci^W. Thus, nos. 2 and 3 are expected to be as they are, and no interference is needed. No. 1 presents the real problem. If dosage alone were involved, it should be abnormal. Thus the Minute $M(4) = 0$ must be responsible for counterbalancing the inhibiting effect of ci^W. Once before we had to come to a similar conclusion, which I prefer to the idea of mutual interference. I wonder how $ci^W/+$ would look in the presence of Minutes in other chromosomes.

The third set of facts in Stern's analysis has to do with dosage effects when one of the alleles is the position effect of a rearrangement R, either R(+) or R(ci). We considered this when studying the Dubinin effect, which is just this position effect, meaning that R(+) acts as if + had mutated to ci, but only in the combination R(+)/ci, not as R(+)/R(+) and R(+)/0. We analyzed the basic facts (see I 3 C *c cc*) and tried to explain the distinguishing features of the Dubinin effect without considering the dosage problem and Stern's interpretation. We turn now to Stern's analysis. On the basis of the foregoing data, he states that the peculiarities of the Dubinin effect are of the same type as the relations between the alleles just studied. (I may add that this would be expected if mutants are invisible position effects; but our former explanation of the Dubinin effect was completely free of dosage ideas and based only upon specific features of the position effect at the ci locus.) According to Stern, the specific results are an expression of interference phenomena, which make combinations of alleles less effective in terms of venation than single doses of alleles by themselves. The degree of interference varies with the different R(+) used. Among seventeen R(+) tested, interference was so strong in four of them that R(+)/ci was more deficient than ci/ci. In the others, R(+)/ci was equal to ci/ci or less deficient. One of the R(+) alleles, $R^2(+)$ produced a normal phenotype if hemizygous, but venation like ci/ci in the homozygous condition. I used these facts previously for an explanation in terms of influence of heterochromatin upon the strength of position effect, while Stern sees here the working of interference between the alleles. I prefer my explanation, because it fits into all the other facts of position effect without requiring the dosage concept. This means that all the blame for unexpected results is laid upon the Dubinin position effect, whatever the other allele does.

The next point is the position effect R(ci), the workings of which are found also in the enumeration above. In accordance with the explanation of standard position effect, we might expect such a rearrangement either to be without an effect different from ci or to increase the ci effect. The actual results parallel closely those tabulated for R(+) combinations, and are therefore regarded by Stern as another illustration of interference. There is a final fact: when different R(ci) alleles are put in an orderly series according to the vein-destructive effect in the heterozygote R(ci)/+, and this series is compared with a similar one for R(ci)/ci, the two series do not show the same order.

These are the facts, which are anything but simple. Stern asks now: What distinguishes the position alleles from the ordinary alleles, and what differentiates the different R(+) and R(ci) alleles from each other? It is obvious that the answer involves the theory of position effect as well as of standard mutation, and I have given my own answer previously when discussing the Dubinin effect. Originally, Stern made the assumption that the specific substrate for each gene is present in a specific concentration in the neighborhood of the gene, but in a different concentration in the other regions to which the rearrangement had shifted the gene. Thus the different effects of different "position alleles" would correspond to these different substrates. (This is one form of theory of position effects in terms of gene neighborhoods, which I could not accept in my discussion of position effect.) The details recorded now, however, have convinced Stern that this explanation does not work, partly because the results would be contradictory, partly because they would require close spatial approximation of the two "interfering" alleles within the nucleus, which is not true of some rearrangements. Therefore, interference must be mediated by primary or derived gene products or takes place at a still later stage of the reaction chains inside or outside the nucleus. Thus, on the whole, not much remains of the competition for substrate theory or of the theory of interference, and, in spite of an extraordinary amount of material and a brilliant analysis, the explanation of dosage effects does not seem to have progressed much beyond the general description with which I started the discussion, when presenting my own views. With reference to the Bar case and the conclusions I drew from it (I 3 C *c aa*), I might say that the general features of the ci dosage work agree with a rather simple explanation in terms of reaction kinetics, proportional to dosage, but that also secondary effects have to be considered, the nature of which is not known. In addition, the interpretation of position effect is decisive for that part of the facts which involves the Dubinin effect. All these facts and discussions may be taken as an illustration how little biochemical genetics has helped us so far in the explanation of genic action outside the small group of production of metabolites.

cc. Dosage in sex linkage

The dosage problem comes up most naturally in the cases of sex linkage in which the homogametic sex has two doses of a mutant locus, while the heterogametic sex has only one dose. If simple dosage relations are at play, as we had to assume when comparing homo- and hemizygotes (n/n vs. n/0), the phenotype in the two sexes should show this difference. Actually, the phenotype is frequently alike in the two sexes in regard to a sex-linked mutant. Stern (1929) first considered this situation and came to the conclusion that it must be the result of a selection of modifiers for an identical phenotype of the two sexes, this being of adaptive value. Muller (1933, 1950*b*), who often returned to this problem, speaks of dosage compensation.

There can be no doubt that some mutant loci in the X-chromosome (e.g., of *Drosophila*) act alike in both sexes, but there can be no doubt either that other loci show sexual differences. What is still more important, multiple alleles of a locus with sexual differences of expression may be sometimes more extreme (toward the mutant side of expression) in the homozygous sex; and, in other cases, more extreme in the heterozygous sex; and, finally, some may be of equal expression in both sexes. The best-known example is that of the multiple alleles at the white locus in *Drosophila*. As we stated earlier (I 3 C *c ee ccc*), it has recently been shown that two pseudoallelic loci are involved here, the white and the apricot locus. In all the alleles of apricot, the simplex condition (♂) is darker than the duplex (♀); in all alleles of white, the males are either lighter than the females or they are identical. In this connection, another fact should be emphasized. We showed a long time ago (1921*a*) that melanism (dark wings) in the nun moth is caused by a major sex-linked factor and two minor autosomal ones, all of which act toward increase of pigment according to dosage. In this paper a plate is found with photos of such a dosage series of females and males side by side, and it can easily be seen that the sex-linked mutant (and also the additional autosomal ones) always acts stronger in the males, all combinations of males being one grade of darkness deeper than females of comparable constitution. Now in this case the female is heterogametic, and thus one dose is less strong than two doses, and the additive action of the homozygous autosomal pigment factors does not change this situation. Hence no dosage compensation appears here. This leads to the question how autosomal mutant loci behave in the two sexes. If dosage alone counts, the sexes should be alike. This is frequently so, but frequently, also, the sexes react differently. In a series of mutants producing a plexation of wing veins in *Drosophila,* which I studied in detail (Goldschmidt, 1945*a*), the females were always one grade more extreme than the males of the same constitution. All these facts show that the phenotype in the two sexes may or may not be dependent upon dosage, and that all the different cases should be explained on the same basis (which we shall present below).

Haldane (1932) had already pointed out a somewhat different concept: namely, that sex-linked genes may be of such a high potency of action that even the simplex condition may reach the physiologically possible maximum effect. This condition in the wild type may be the result of selection in the past. The ideas of Stern and Muller follow the same general trend of thinking, but they attribute dosage compensation to modifying genes in the X-chromosome, accumulated by selection. Of course this would also apply to the wild-type condition, assuming that it has an adaptive advantage. The situation for mutants would only reveal what the wild-type behavior would be. There would be a corollary to this: the many sex-linked mutants which do not show dosage compensation would have to be regarded as somehow independent of the dosage modifiers, which does not add to the plausibility of the theory. Muller (1950*b*) has since gone into the problem with more detailed work. He studied mutant loci showing dosage compensation in one dose only in the female, or two doses in the male, obtained through deficiencies and duplications, and found that one dose in the female makes the expression less extreme even than in the male, while two doses in the male produce a higher expression than in the normal female. He even maintains that by photometric methods the same effects can be demonstrated for the wild-type eye in *Drosophila,* which always looks the same to simple inspection. This would mean that the action according to dosage is present but is compensated for by a modifier system, which must be located in the X-chromosome (as first concluded by Stern, 1929, for the bobbed alleles). Furthermore, whereas many loci in the X-chromosome show such behavior, each must have such a modifier system or share in one. It is obvious that this statistical interpretation is based upon the general ideas of Fisher on selection of modifier systems in the heterozygote.

Muller does realize that there is a possibility of an alternative interpretation. This is that the sex-determining genes themselves act as dosage modifiers. To disprove this, he mentions the following facts. There is known a third chromosome recessive mutant, called "transformer," which in homozygous condition transforms 2X females into what look to all purposes like males. If the eye color apricot is present, the transformed males have the same color as genuine males with apricot eyes. By introducing a duplication into a genuine male, it can be made to have two doses of apricot instead of one with the result of a darker eye color. Therefore, the conclusion runs, the XX males-by-transformation should have this darker color if the sex determiners were also the dosage modifiers. Actually, the color is the same as in normal males, which means that not the sex determiners but the dosage compensators within the X-chromosomes are responsible. This argumentation clearly assumes that the normal 1X males and the transformed 2X males are otherwise the same, which means that they have the same developmental system. If the problem had been looked at, not from the point of view of modifiers, but from that of development, it would have turned out that the males-by-transformation have a developmental system which is female in a number of basic features. As a matter of fact, the sex-reversal flies are not males but extreme female intersexes (= 2X intersexes) in which some basic features of growth and differentiation (actually those of early determination) are still female. This is true for size and general growth, for time of development, for many proportions, and for the rhythm of gonad development. In addition, all sex-linked mutants which are sexually dimorphic (i.e., without so-called compensation) show the female phenotype, as Sturtevant (1945) noticed. Thus the behavior of eye color is just what is expected in the 2X intersexes, and the dosage compensation explanation becomes superfluous.

These last facts really show in what direction to look for a better interpretation, namely, in terms of development and not by inventing hypothetical modifier systems where they seem to be needed. I may point out that male and female differentiation take place in very different developmental systems, laid down at the moment of fertilization by the different balance of the sex factors. I point further to the fact that developmental rates in the two sexes are different; that the relative rates for the individual and consecutive phases of growth are different; that times of determination as seen in temperature-effective periods or in times for optimal production of phenocopies are different; further, that the rhythm of differentiation of individual organs, like the gonads, differs in the two sexes. Thus we can understand, on the basis of different developmental systems, why different dosages may fail to produce different phenotypes. We may also expect that some developmental processes might be of such a kind as to produce, in spite of the different developmental systems, different sexual phenotypes, which is known to be true of a number of loci. This means that in the latter case the loci in question act simply according to their dosage. The explanation which offers itself at once is that in both cases threshold phenomena are involved which lead to one or the other type of behavior. The entire problem becomes the same as that of inheritance of sex-controlled characters, for example, when a definite phenotype, sometimes controlled by a single mutant locus, shows up in only one sex (of course, speaking of cases without hormonic control). The sex-determining mechanism, acting through the control of the balance of action of female and male sex determiners, is responsible not only for the course of sexual differentiation but also for all the concomitant differences in metabolism and rate of differentiating processes. These differences are known to occur when other mutant loci produce their special effect. For example: in many moths, males develop faster than females (details in Goldschmidt, 1933*a*, for *Lymantria dispar*). Sex-linked mutant loci may therefore be expected to produce the same effect in simplex and duplex condition when the sex-controlled changes in the developmental system of the simplex sex run parallel to the dosage change of mutant action. If, for example, the reaction produced by one portion of a mutant reaches the threshold of action later than in the case of two doses, the effect of both will be the same if the developmental system of the simplex sex is such as to fit in with later action of the respective locus. If not, the simplex effect will be different from the effect of two doses: lower if the shift is in one direction; higher if it is in the other direction. Such a scheme covers all known behaviors of sex-linked mutants in one or two doses, without recourse to a special explanation (like dosage compensation) for each variant. Thus the action of sex-linked mutants in one or two doses does not lead—for our problem of genic action as revealed in dosage experiments—to conclusions other than those studied before for the Bar, bobbed, and cubitus interruptus experiments. Recently, Cock (1953) has studied the same problem in the barred breeds of fowl, used for autosexing, because the difference in the barring of plumage in the two sexes, based upon a sex-linked dominant, is already visible in the young chick. He shows that dosage compensation (which would exclude autosexing) is not present and that Muller's explanation does not work in this case. Obviously, the barred pattern behaves very similarly to the melanism of the nun moth mentioned above. In both cases an explanation in terms of physiology of development is in order.

dd. Multiple factors and dosage

A dosage phenomenon is certainly involved in multiple factor inheritance. In the first example studied, Nilsson-Ehle's famous work on color in oats, this is rather obvious, because duplicate and triplicate factors are involved, supposed to be the same mutant loci multiplied by polyploidy. The effect appeared strictly proportional to dosage in from one to six doses (= multiple loci). Hence the explanation is obviously the same as in the bobbed case: each mutant locus produces a certain quantity of something which is responsible for a definite fraction of the effect. Thus the information on genic action gained will be practically the same as in the dosage experiments. We should assume that genuine multiple factors would act in the same general way and thus lead to the same conclusion on dosage action. Multiple factors are independently inherited mutant loci all of which affect genically controlled phenotypic properties in the same way (e.g., size). But this might mean very different things from the point of view of genic action. In one group, dosage is certainly not involved. For example, over-all growth of a vertebrate might consist of the additive effect of growth of vertebrae, intervertebral discs, extremities, and so on. Similar examples can easily be found. Certainly we cannot speak here of a dosage effect of multiple factors. But when the individual loci all affect the same chain of reaction, we might consider this a dosage effect, though it can never be excluded that each locus affects different components of such chains, while only the final effect goes in the same direction. Our former example of melanism in the nun moth may serve as an example. One sex-linked and two autosomal dominants control the amount of pigmentation of the wing strictly parallel to dosage (i.e., number of mutant loci present). Since we may assume that production of melanin is a single series of synthetic steps, starting with tyrosine or dopa (see Kikkawa, 1953), and always the same within the same organism, a series of quantities of pigment in proportion to the number of causative loci might mean a simple quantitative influence of each locus upon the kinetics of such synthesis. Actually, it turned out that one of the loci affects the pigment between the bands of the dark wing pattern and the others the pigment within the bands. The over-all effect is simply additive, because it is based upon quantity of pigment, but the paths leading to the ingredients of the total effect are different. This shows how difficult it is to consider multiple factor effects as dosage effects and to draw from them conclusions concerning genic action. The same would apply also to cases in which a definite part effect could be assigned to individual multiple factors. I studied a number of cases (see Goldschmidt *et al.*, 1951; Goldschmidt, 1953*a*) in which it was possible to isolate (more or less) the individual multiple loci by chromosome replacement and to measure their individual share in the total effect. Some had a major share, others only a small one. All of them must have affected a definite process of growth and differentiation (homoeotic transformation of wing anlage in *Drosophila* in one case, number of extra bristles in the other) in the same general direction, although not alike quantitatively. However, there is no way of deciding whether they acted upon the same set of reactions directly or only in some indirect way via necessary but different conditions for these reactions. Thus it is hardly possible to use such material as indicative of dosage actions of genic material.

This would be different, however, if Mather's blocks of polygenes were a reality, whether they were represented by clusters of multiplied identical loci or simply by different quantities of intercalary heterochromatin, as I prefer to assume. In both cases we should be dealing with actual quantities of the same genic material and therefore with dosage experiments. Parallelism of the effects to dosages would give us the same type of information on genic action as gained in the discussion of the genuine dosage experiments. Unfortunately, these polygenic blocks are still hypothetical.

The discussions and interpretations presented thus far are independent, I think, of the general theory of multiple factor inheritance, which has been under much discussion since Mather's work on "polygenes." We have discussed (see I 2 C *d dd*) only that part of the theory which deals with so-called blocks of polygenes of supposed heterochromatic nature. But there is another aspect of Mather's theory which I have difficulty in combining mentally with the one feature discussed formerly (see Mather and Harrison, 1949). From his selection experiments on bristle number, Mather concludes that each quantitative character is determined by many "polygenes," each of small effect upon a single character and distributed over all chromosomes. These polygenes are balanced within each chromosome because they act partly in a plus direction and partly in a minus one. Crossing over then may produce much genetic variability and selection becomes possible. This part of the problem, selection, does not concern us here; neither do we intend to criticize the entire concept, though the unlimited accumulation of impossible numbers of loci is certainly a strain upon the imagination when the concept is applied to all quantitative and selectable characters of an organism. Among those who made experiments similar to those of Mather, but who reached very different conclusions, Robertson and Reeve (1952), and Reeve and Robertson (1953) may be mentioned. They assume that pleiotropy and genic interaction are decisive factors for variation in quantitative characters. Thus selection effects may be due to influences upon the genetic background, which shifts those genic effects. In this case a few major and some minor genes would suffice for explaining the selection results. Apart from the problem of selection, the experiments of these authors lead to the suggestion that the entire range of variability of the character in the inbreeding and selection experiments may be explained by only three or four pairs of genes with a major effect. I have reached a similar conclusion, as did S. Wright (1934*b*, 1935) in his experiments on selection of polydactyly; and, in some instances, I could isolate individual loci the action of which could be measured (see Goldschmidt, 1953*a*). Thus there will be cases in which quantitative inheritance may act on a simple (but not necessarily primary) dosage principle. (Further discussion of quantitative inheritance is not needed for the problems of this chapter, since the major aspects of the phenomenon are involved in the problems of selection and not of genic action.)

Grüneberg (1952*a*) has recently discussed the problem of quantitative inheritance from the point of view of physiological genetics, and has reached conclusions which we might have mentioned in connection with penetrance and threshold effects. He worked with a mutant in mice in which the third molars are absent. The abnormals appear in certain litters in bunches, which indicates an environmental influence upon penetrance. In the same group, the number of molars missing per individual is increased; that is, higher penetrance produces higher expressivity. Though the anomaly is dominant, it hardly segregates in outcrosses. The explanation of this is derived from the fact that in the abnormal lines the existing third molars are smaller and more variable than in normal lines; this feature shows the same characteristics in regard to expressivity and bunching as the absence of the tooth does. The character, reduced molars, has multiple factor inheritance, and complete absence is only the end of a series of genetic variation. Thus the "discontinuous" variant, absence, is a part of "continuous variation." A threshold condition separates the quasi-continuous character from the continuous base. Therefore, here penetrance and expressivity are correlated; further, they are rather sensitive to environment, sex, right-left differences, and single strong enhancers. The conclusion is drawn that multiple factors are genes whose remote effects only are studied. Direct gene effects are considered to be highly specific and acting through different physiological channels (a conclusion shared by Haldane, 1954, in a qualitative biochemical sense). Secondary and tertiary genetic effects are not specific; all or most genes influence ultimately, in progressively indirect ways, many different processes. Gene effects will tend to be additive, if they affect the same process in a similar way, that is, if they are unspecific. Such remote gene effects will tend to be additive also with various major genes with which they enter into modifier relationships. Thus, quantitative inheritance here looks very different from Mather's polygenic systems, if the problem is looked at from the point of view of genic action.

b. Dominance, potency, penetrance

Dominance is one of the basic facts of genetics, the complete understanding of which should shed light upon the problem of genic action. Therefore an analysis of dominance has been tried repeatedly. It is generally accepted as a fact that dominance or recessivity is not a property of a mutant locus, but a result of the action of the mutant locus in relation to the entire system of reactions constituting development. This is clear at the outset because dominance may often be shifted by external agencies, for example, temperature and the interference of other loci, acting as dominance modifiers; both agents are known to shift genic effects by a change in the genically controlled processes and not by affecting the genic material itself. It has been held that dominance of the wild type over most mutant loci is controlled by a modifier system which has been selected in order to keep the heterozygote on the adaptive level of the homozygote. Whether this is true or not does not affect the present discussion, because dominance modification by modifiers must be understood also in terms of genic action upon some feature of the reaction chains constituting development. If we could find out how dominance modifiers interfere with the specific chains of reaction in development, we could draw conclusions concerning the mode of genic actions, which should be the same as those reached from a study of dominance without modifiers.

We may visualize the meaning of the dominant, not dominant, or partially dominant effect of a mutant locus in relation to all the developmental reactions involved in the final effect of the genic action, with the help of a model (see fig. 18), which, I think, can be used for all aspects of the problem. Let us assume we are dealing with a pair of alleles controlling a character which can be measured (e.g., the number of facets in an insect eye). The dominant locus controls a reaction of a certain velocity, expressed in the diagram as the elevation of a curve (for simplicity's sake represented as a straight line). The recessive allele controls a lower velocity; and the heterozygote,

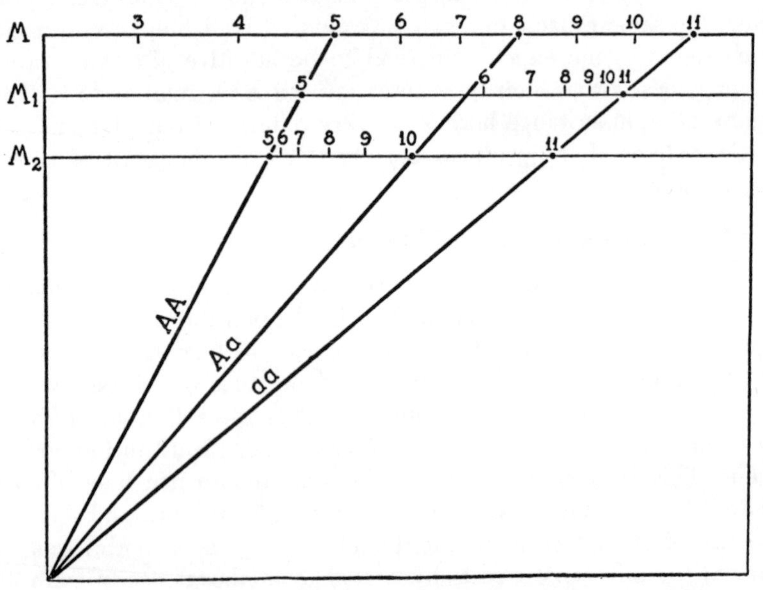

Fig. 18. Diagram explaining dominance in terms of reaction velocities and "buffering." (From Goldschmidt, 1927.)

an intermediate one. The products of reaction attain a determining effect when they reach a certain concentration, the threshold level M. In order to have a very simple model, we assume that the hereditary character is the size of some structure attained by the respective number of cell divisions and that the determining stuff is one that puts an end to further division. Of course, a similar model could be constructed with different assumptions. If the progress of cell division up to the point of stoppage is determined independently, the size of the organ will be smaller the earlier the curve reaches the level M. If all cell divisions proceed in equal intervals, the heterozygote will be intermediate. Let us now consider different systems of cell division caused by different external or genetic environment (the modifiers), which have been represented on the levels M, M_1, M_2 (which should coincide); the numbers indicate the number of cell divisions that have occurred at the different points. In the system M_1, division ceases before six divisions are finished; and therefore the small size is almost completely dominant. (AA is characterized by stoppage after five divisions—line M.) In M_2 we have assumed that cell division proceeds faster at first and later slows up. In this case, dominance of the large size (eleven divisions) results. In this model, the variables responsible for dominance are reaction velocities controlled by the loci according to simple dosage relations, thresholds for morphogenetic effects, the type of effect, and the numerical system of an independently determined process which is involved. It is obvious that the general features of such a model, which permits introduction of whatever variable the facts require, will fit all imaginable cases. From this we may conclude that dominance teaches us, in a general way, that genic action is bound up with quality and quantity of reaction products, with threshold conditions of their action, and with features of the kinetics of the reactions involved. We could also describe such a system as the real, dynamic meaning of so-called genic balance (more correctly called "balance of genic actions") applied to the facts of dominance, but applicable also to all genic actions.

The next question is whether such a genetic system, regulating dominance, may be endowed with a more specific meaning, preferably a biochemical one. Wright (1934*a*) has proposed such a variant of our model. He assumes, as we also do, that there is a chain of reactions between the locus and the end product and that any condition that makes one link of the chain act in the heterozygote as it acts in the homozygote results in dominance. Next he assumes that the gene acts as a catalyst controlling the rate of production of some substance by a chain of irreversible transformations, the intermediary substances being in a flux equilibrium. These reactions may be monomolecular and dependent on the concentration of both catalyst and substrate. In this case the rate varies directly with the concentration of the catalyst, and the curve expressing this will be a hyperbole. Therefore, with increasing activity of the gene, its heterozygous effect should approach dominance. Other similar possibilities are taken into account. All of which can be described as variants of our model with emphasis on different phases. I point out here that the idea of different activities of the gene (which in my former concept were different quantities) is at the base of the hypothesis. (We shall return to this soon.)

At this point I should like to refer to our earlier discussion of biochemical genetics, especially the quotation from Bonner (III 4 C *b*). To those who are greatly impressed by the apparently simple concept of one gene—one synthetic step, such discussions (Goldschmidt, 1920*a*, 1927) must appear rather vague and crude. However, when Horowitz found the temperature-dependent nutritional mutants in *Neurospora*, it became clear that even in those specific and simple cases of genic action, the kinetic element entered, as expressed so strongly in Bonner's words. Thus, biochemical genetics does not lead to a chemical insight into genic action, as was hoped in the beginning, but of necessity returns to the avowedly crude models with which Wright and I approached many problems of genic action.

The best illustration for the derivation of dominance from a system of different variables in the complex interplay of reaction chains in development comes from temperature studies. It is known that different temperatures affect the phenotype of many mutants in the most varied ways. The action must always take place in a temperature-sensitive or critical phase in development, which is typical for individual loci. Without going into the mass of details (see Goldschmidt, 1938), the general fact may be understood as an interference with the kinetics of one process in relation to other simultaneous ones. This results in affecting one of the imaginable variables, like potency of the locus, speed of a reaction, threshold for final action, availability and use of a substrate, or other such possibilities, so long as the all-or-none type is not involved, as in the prevention of a synthetic step. The same applies also to changes in dominance which can be produced abruptly by temperature shocks (Goldschmidt, 1935*a,b;* Plough, Child, and Blanc, 1936) and by X-radiation; and which can be obtained in an orderly sequence by temperature action in the critical period.

Only one thoroughly elaborated example studied by the school of Zeleny, especially Hersh (1930), may be mentioned. It deals with the dominant position effect Bar in *Drosophila* (see discussion in I 3 C *c aa*), the dosage relations of which we have just considered. The number of facets in wild-type eyes and in the mutant series is, *ceteris paribus,* a function of temperature. If the temperature curves for wild type, mutant, and heterozygote are compared, parallelism would indicate that growth rather than dominance is involved. If the curve for the heterozygotes should not parallel that for the homozygotes, conclusions in regard to dominance might be drawn, since a coefficient for dominance would change over the temperature range. Zeleny had proposed (1920) calculating such a coefficient by the formula $Co = \frac{AA - AA_1}{AA - A_1A_1} \times 100$. ($AA$ and A_1A_1 are the quantities found for the homozygote; AA_1, for the heterozygote.) Hersh had found that the rate of change in mean facet number at any temperature is proportional to the mean facet number at that temperature, expressed as an exponential function of the formula $y = ae^{rt}$ in which r is the relative rate of change; t, the temperature; a, a constant; and e, the base of natural logarithms. The instantaneous change in facet number at a given temperature is then $\frac{dy}{dt} = yr$. This value is calculated for different temperatures and combinations, and from these the coefficient of dominance is derived. The results show that the degree of dominance for the number of facets formed at a given moment changes regularly. It decreases, for example, in B/+, with increase of temperature; it increases for dominance of BB over wild type, and so on. Hersh interprets this result as meaning that the more dominant "gene" has relatively greater or less effect proportional to the changes of growth by temperature action, and thus he attributes the results of his measurements to the relative activities or potencies of the alleles. We shall not go into further details as, for example, the strange discovery by Luce that Bar and Infrabar act in the opposite direction in temperature experiments. The main point is that such exact dominance experiments demand the type of explanation exemplified in our model (fig. 18), while it is of secondary importance whether the shift in the experiments is attributed to one or the other of the variables. The decisive conclusion for genic action is then, as before, that a major role is played by the control of the kinetics of developmental reactions in their relation to others which are simultaneous and, perhaps, competing. It is to be hoped that one day this may be expressed in terms of known substances and exact formulations of the kinetics. I have already emphasized that the action of dominance modifiers, which have been studied so much, must be understood in the same terms. A large number of such cases can be found in my book of 1938, and many new ones do not give additional information.

We have used here repeatedly the term "potency of alleles," introduced in early Mendelian days by Davenport and Castle, given a definite meaning in my work on intersexuality, and used later by Wright and Hersh. The term has changed its meaning often. As far as dominance is concerned, we saw that no necessity exists for assuming different potencies of the mutant locus itself, though there are facts in favor of such an assumption. In our work on intersexuality we made much use of potencies of sex determiners, which at that time were assumed to be identical with genic quantities. As I stated previously (I 2 C *d ee*), it seems more probable now that the entire chromosomes are involved in *Lymantria* and that the potencies may be quantities of heterochromatin. The term "potency" should be used in a completely descriptive fashion, not implying any particular notion in regard to different constitutions of genic material, but meaning a different strength of action because of some variable features of the genic material, which might sometimes be the quantity of heterochromatic sections, or else some unknown qualitative feature. The action in question might be a difference in the kinetic processes of the reaction chains, a difference in the quantity of end products, a difference in the substrate utilization which leads to threshold differences, a difference in the time of reaching thresholds of action and, sometimes, also a qualitative difference in the synthesis of a product or in the activation of different enzyme systems. If the term "potency" is used in this sense, it follows that different potencies of mutant loci might act exactly like different dosages if they affect one and the same type of action (e.g., quantity of an active substance). However, if different potencies of the same genic material act directly or indirectly upon different processes of the types just enumerated, very irregular consequences should be expected. It is only in the former case that a conclusion in regard to potencies of genic action will be justified, as is shown by the examples already mentioned.

In the ci case in *Drosophila,* the two phenomena act in the same direction, the dosages and the potencies of some alleles. This is especially conspicuous in what Stern calls isoalleles. One of the consequences of the type of genic action represented in the model (fig. 18) is that any number of genic actions above the threshold for normalcy are possible, a notion which was used frequently in my earlier writings and which appears also in Stern's bobbed work. This is the real meaning of isoalleles. They can best be detected in the hemizygous condition (and in temperature experiments) where actions near the threshold of normalcy, fluctuating also below it, are expected. The potencies thus discovered (see Stern's isoallele $+^3$) turned out to be of the orderly type, that is, acting like dosage and thus acting in different combinations in an orderly and parallel way.

Since such potency alleles or isoalleles are clearly a special type of multiple alleles, namely, those acting near or above the threshold for normalcy, and since the lowest isoalleles, like Stern's $+^3$, may just as well be described as ordinary multiple alleles of lowest action (which we did above when calling $+^{3} = ci^{s}$), it is expected that examples of "quantified" potencies are frequent among multiple alleles. This is actually the case, and formerly led me to the assumption that multiple alleles are different gene quantities because they act like dosage differences. If the theory of the corpuscular gene were correct, this would still be a good hypothesis for cases in which (as in ci) dosage of multiple alleles parallels actual dosage actions and fits in with them. In the discussions of the subject a generation ago, it was emphasized that in the many cases of multiple alleles in which there is a pleiotropic effect upon different traits, the order of the alleles, if grouped according to individual pleiotropic effects, frequently does not coincide with the order of alleles, if classified according to the main action of the gene locus. We shall discuss the present aspect of this problem in the chapter on pleiotropy.

In the same category of facts belongs seriation of environmental effects upon a multiple allelic series, or of modifier effects, when checked for the different pleiotropic actions. However, such facts in themselves do not argue against the existence of potencies paralleling, in their orderly effect, dosage effects. The development of different traits may or may not be determined by the same primary effects of genic action in proportion to potency. In some cases it may safely be assumed that a single primary effect trails automatically behind it a series of consequences in different organs, a syndrome of effects. (See the vast quantity of work in developmental genetics in rodents by Bonnevie, Gluecksohn-Schönheimer, Grüneberg, much of it reviewed in my book, 1938, in Gluecksohn-Waelsch, 1953, and in Grüneberg's book, 1952.) But in other cases, probably more frequently with mosaic development, as in *Drosophila,* the pleiotropic effect may be the result of interference of one reaction chain and (or) its products with other simultaneous ones, an interference which might be orderly, that is, parallel for all of them, or completely irregular, depending upon timing, threshold, and substrate conditions at the point of interference. Thus, on the basis of the facts discussed so far, there is no reason to doubt that multiple alleles act in either case according to their potencies.

But this conclusion is evident only within the classic theory of the corpuscular gene. If more modern ideas of the type discussed above are accepted, mutant loci being changes of the normal order of a pattern, we should have to make special assumptions for orderly potency effects (e.g., that they parallel the degree of scrambling of the normal order). The decisive information would then have to come from multiple allelic action of position effects of visible rearrangements, namely, by discovering some rule for the different actions of different rearrangements, for example, whether they fit in an orderly way in a series of multiple alleles of the respective mutant locus or not. Some of the disconcerting results of Stern's ci experiments in the presence of rearrangements may supply the clues. Potency of a mutant locus is a descriptive fact which still has to be endowed with a definite meaning that fits all cases.

As I have pointed out, potency effects and, implicitly, multiple allelic effects may be dependent upon qualitatively or quantitatively different genic action. In my old work (1916–1920) I had assumed that genic action of multiple alleles is concerned with catalyzing reactions of different speed resulting in production of active stuffs (hormones, including all determining stuffs and enzymes) in corresponding quantities. Haldane (1954) drew attention to a paper of his, written in 1920, in which he said that genes produce definite quantities of enzymes, and that members of a series of multiple alleles produce the same enzyme in different quantities; this is essentially the same as my view was at that time. But in view of the facts of present-day biochemical genetics Haldane prefers a different idea now. He thinks that different alleles make chemically different primary products, for example, enzymes with the same prosthetic group attached to different proteins. Their interaction in heterozygotes is a biochemical matter, different in different organs. The different order of individual pleiotropic effects of a series of multiple alleles might, then, be due to qualitatively different products of each allele, each with a range of specificity, like esterases or adrenaline-like bases.

I cannot help being very skeptical about this qualitative biochemical approach to our problem. Even in the multiple allelic series for metabolites (e.g., pigments) the facts point more in the direction of quantitatively different actions, as Wright's work on pigmentation in guinea pigs illustrates. Bonner's conclusions for *Neurospora* (1951) may again be cited. When it comes to series of morphological characters, I have great difficulty in visualizing the results in terms of qualitative specificities of the genic products.

Therefore, we may end this discussion by presenting an example which simultaneously studies dominance, dominance modifiers, and multiple alleles in the same material in quantitative work, and which permits showing that only a system of genic action involving the kinetics of action, thresholds, quantities of end products, and so on accounts for the orderliness of the data.

The work deals with the mutant vestigial of *Drosophila* (Goldschmidt, 1937; Goldschmidt and Höner, 1937), of which a large series of multiple alleles exist. The vestigial effect consists in reducing the wing substance by more and more scalloping in the different alleles until finally it is a small stump. In this series the reduced wing is not miniature but looks as if pieces had been cut out from a normal-sized wing. This means that the wing edge and wing veins are really absent where a piece of wing spread is missing. The extreme vestigial (and a more extreme No wing), therefore, has in its wing stump only the more or less normal venation of the wing bases of a normal wing and not a reduced venation of a whole wing apart from some minor features of regulation. I found that the lower members of the series had a normal wing at the time of pupation, and only later, when the wing anlage contracts (in all cases), the scalloping appears. I interpreted this as a lysis of already formed wing material in analogy with well-known cases of such lysis in *Lepidoptera* (literature in Goldschmidt, 1940). In the higher alleles (with more scalloping) the wing is already incomplete at pupation time, a fact which I interpreted as owing to earlier lysis. In vg itself even the early imaginal disc is smaller (Chen), which meant to me that lysis had started very early. Waddington (1940*a*) gave a different description of the facts. He thinks that the contraction of the pupal wing is also responsible for the scalloping in the lower grades. To explain the higher ones, he assumes a strange migration of tissue around the edge of the wing, a process which he himself characterizes as rather unbelievable. Actually, this explanation fails to explain the determination of the venation, which is the normal venation for what is left of the wing. Thus the actual happenings must be either as I assumed it or of a comparable type, and therefore the embryonic action may be described in terms of production of a lytic substance or by the absence of a necessary growth substance—an assumption which easily could be modified, while still working in the same direction, if further work showed that another developmental feature is responsible for the effect.

The elementary genetic facts can now be described, following Mohr (1933), by assuming different potencies for the different alleles, meaning the ability to produce different amounts of growth substance, to use the simplest model. Let us assume that the threshold value for wild-type wing is a quantity of 40, and therefore the differ-

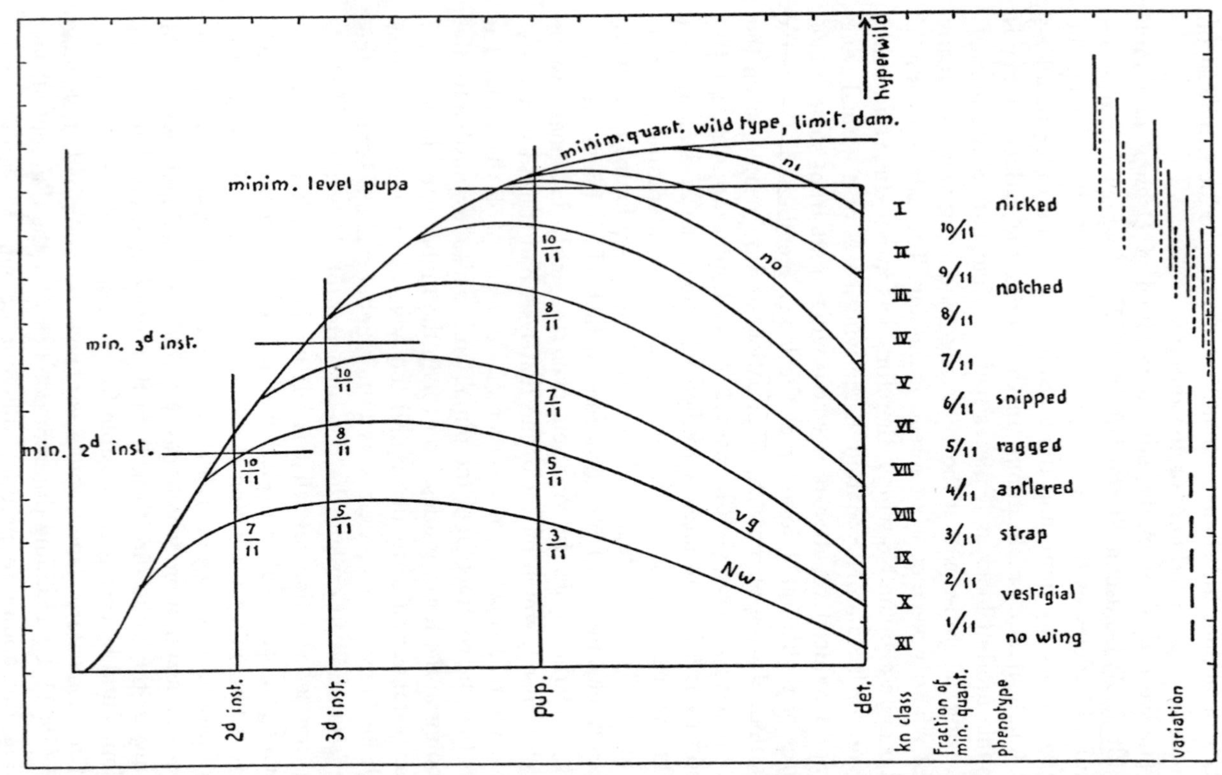

Fig. 19. Interpretation of phenotype of vg alleles in terms of development and gene-controlled reactions. (From Goldschmidt, 1927.)

ent degrees of scalloping are caused by lower quantities. The actual data of Mohr would then give the different allelic combinations and the quantities responsible for them as follows (vg = vestigial, vg^{Nw} = no wing, vg^{no} = notched, an intermediate allele, vg^{ni} = nicked a very low allele, little scalloping):

$\frac{vg^{Nw}}{vg^{Nw}}$	$\frac{vg}{vg^{Nw}}$	$\frac{vg}{vg}$	$\frac{vg^{no}}{vg^{Nw}}$	$\frac{vg^{no}}{vg}$	$\frac{vg^{ni}}{vg^{Nw}}$	$\frac{vg^{no}}{vg^{no}}$	$\frac{vg^{ni}}{vg}$	$\frac{+}{vg^{Nw}}$	$\frac{vg^{ni}}{vg^{no}}$	$\frac{+}{vg}$	$\frac{vg^{ni}}{vg^{ni}}$	$\frac{+}{vg^{no}}$	$\frac{+}{vg^{ni}}$	$\frac{+}{+}$
12	16	20	21	25	28	30	32	36	37	40	44	45	52	60

wild type (40–60)

This shows all compounds intermediate, and the different kinds of normality (wild type) phenotypically alike but of different potencies.

Some other alleles also fit into the series. We shall now consider their effects in terms of quantities of a substance controlled by the respective potencies of the alleles. We saw that, whatever the morphological details of the changes of the wing anlage in development may be, there is certainly a time element in them, since the different alleles produce, at the time of pupation, different degrees of reduction proportional to their known potencies. Therefore, we may consider the different and orderly potency effects of the allelic series in terms of rates of production of the decisive substance. The picture would not change if any other rate process turned out to be the actual one. Thus we may represent the basic facts in terms of rates as shown in figure 19. Compounds of the vg series control the production of the active substance, which must be present at each stage of development in sufficient quantity to insure normal differentiation. In the wild type and all compounds exhibiting the wild type, the rate of production has to be above the minimum. As the production of the substance must keep pace with the growth of the wing anlage, the top curve in the diagram may be taken as the growth curve and assumed to indicate also the minimal level for normality. The minimum levels for all other developmental stages, the instars, are marked to the left. The abscissa gives the time and stages of development; the ordinate, the quantity of the substance in question. As the deficiency of the decisive substance begins earlier and earlier in the course of development in proportion to the decreasing potency of the genic material, the rate curves of production of this substance are presented as dropping at such stages of development. If the size of the anlage at any time of normal development is seen in the normal curve on top, the other curves for the different alleles show the same in fractions of the normal size at the same time. The different mean wing sizes are roughly estimated (e.g., No wing being one-eleventh of the normal size). These values are found at the right ordinate together with the names of the alleles and a classification of the scalloping effect: I is just a small nick; XI, the No-wing type. To the right of this the range of variation for all effects is indicated, as found in experiments at 25° C. I do not maintain that this diagram represents what actually happens; the real causative agent may be something very different from a growth substance. I do claim, however, that it is a model for the type of what must be happening in cases of the kind studied, namely, a regular series of genic potencies leading to a just as regular series of phenotypes. It seems hardly possible that the facts can be explained simply by any theory that does not entail seriated and graduated effects upon the kinetics of genically controlled processes. Thus, this diagram becomes a rather universal model of genic actions that are not of an all-or-none type (see III 4 C), that is, simply biochemical.

Practically all degrees of scalloping from vg to + can be obtained if vg/vg is bred in high temperatures near the temperature shock zone; this fact was known in the early days and has been much studied by Harnly (see 1942). This proves, of course, that the anlage of the vg wing still has all developmental potencies including the complete pattern of venation. Further, speeding up of some reaction by temperature treatment more or less prevents the vg reactions covered in our diagram from taking place, or prevents them from reaching the threshold levels, or interferes in some way with normal growth. It is obvious that the facts fit very well into such a scheme of genic action as that of figure 19, and are very difficult to explain otherwise. Actually this is the same situation as for the temperature-dependent mutants of *Neurospora* (see III 4 C *a*), except that here the parallelism to the allelic series makes it almost certain that the explanation involves the kinetics of a process. As I mentioned before, it was just these temperature-dependent mutants of *Neurospora* that led to skepticism toward the one gene—one synthetic step concept in favor of some action upon the kinetics of chains of reaction.

Only now we come to our experiments, which bear out the correctness of the entire trend of discussion in the present chapter. It is a quantitative study of the vg series in the presence of dominance modifiers. Normal wings are completely dominant over vestigial under standard conditions (25° C). Three dominance modifiers were isolated, located in the first, second, and third chromosomes, respectively, in the presence of which dominance is shifted toward vestigial. If two autosomal modifiers are present in vg/+, only about 1 per cent of the individuals are nicked. The sex-linked modifier alone affects about 0.5 per cent of the individuals. But if all three modifiers are present, all vg/+ heterozygotes are scalloped. (Blanc, 1946, made it probable that at least two of the modifiers are identical with known mutants, facet and purple.) The modifiers have also an additive effect

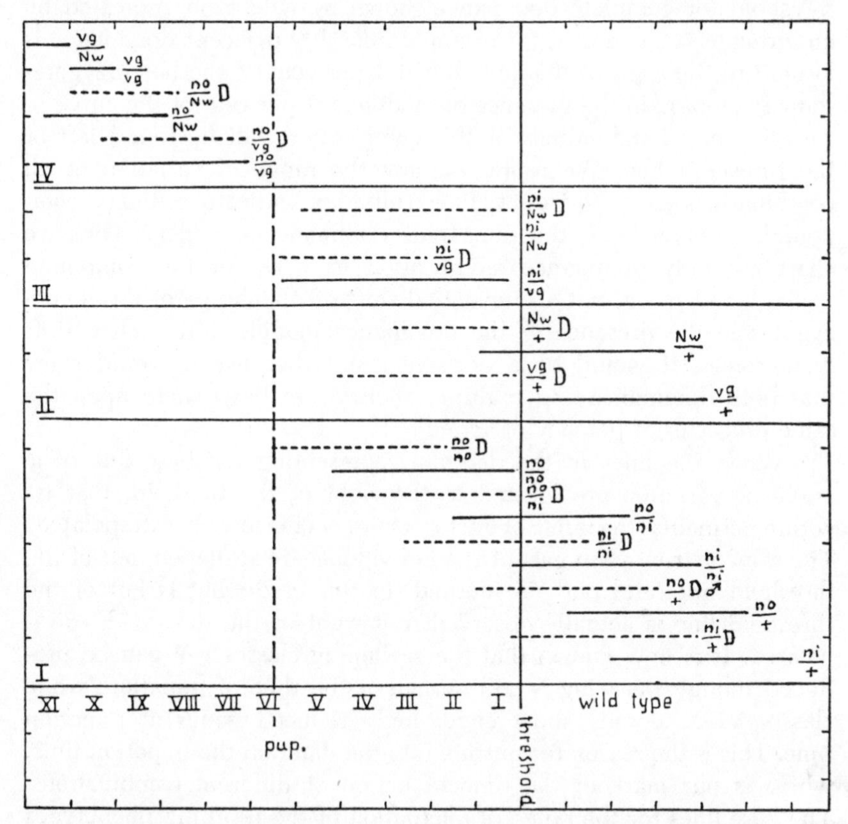

Fig. 20. Action of vg alleles and compounds with and without dominance modifiers and related to development. (From Goldschmidt and Höner, 1937.)

(AA > Aa, AB/AB > AB/ab. Furthermore, the effects are different in the two sexes (see discussion of dosage compensation). We combined many of the alleles and compounds (listed, with their action, on p. 373) with a full set of dominance modifiers, and studied the effects upon scalloping quantitatively. The major body of the results is condensed in a diagram (fig. 20), which simultaneously indicates the explanation in terms of figure 18. On the abscissa we find the classes of scalloping I–XI and wild type beyond I. Since there can be a fluctuation into wild type and, in addition, different (genetic) grades of wild type, the abscissa simultaneously indicates development proceeding from left to right, with the decisive time of pupation (decisive, because we tested the morphology of the anlage at this time) indicated by a broken ordinate. Between scalloping grade I and wild type lies the threshold for complete dominance shown by wild type, indicated by an ordinate. This means, for example, that 100 per cent dominance is located to the right of this line, but if 1 per cent of the heterozygotes show scalloping in the presence of modifiers, 1 per cent of the curve of variation of all individuals of this composition will be found left of the threshold line. We represent now the range of variation of all combinations as a horizontal line; full lines indicate ordinary compounds; broken lines, the same plus dominance modifiers. Thus we chart not only dominance modification in vg/+ or the compound vg/vg^{ni}, and so on, but also eventual shift of phenotype of the homozygotes in the presence of the dominance modifiers. If such a shift were found, it would be a decisive result, because it would show that both dominance and multiple allelism are based here upon the same processes of potency of action.

When the lines in the diagram representing the base line of a curve of variation are located to the right of the theshold, that is, within normality, the range of fluctuation is, of course, only extrapolated. The same is true when part of the individuals are scalloped, left of the threshold line, and part are normal; in this case what is left of the threshold line is actually observed; but right of the threshold, extrapolated. It is now known that the scalloping classes I–V can be produced though the wing is still normal at the time of pupation; while classes VI–X already show increasingly reduced wings at pupation time. This is the reason for putting into the diagram the pupation time, which is our mark of the time of action of different combinations. The base lines for the range of fluctuation of the resulting phenotypes show that for all scalloping classes up to class VI, the dominance modifiers shift all homozygotes, heterozygotes, and compounds in the same way toward the left, that is, toward dominance of vestigial, and so on, as the comparison of the full and broken lines for each type shows, with an ascending order from the lowest, the $vg^{ni}/+$ heterozygote, shifted just beyond the threshold of normality, to the highest combination vg^{no}/vg^{no}, shifted about two classes. In group II, only the shifting of dominance for the vg and vg^{Nw} heterozygote is represented, which shows a still more extreme shift in the presence of the modifiers.

Group III contains the compounds of vg and vg^{Nw} with the low allele vg^{ni} with and without dominance modifiers. Here the same shift is found, but it is very small. The last group, IV, contains the compounds of vg and vg^{Nw} with vg^{no}, all of which show the wing reduction taking place visibly before pupation. Here the effect is no longer clear.

Thus we see that the dominance-shifting action of the modifiers works in a consistent, parallel, quantitative way upon homozygotes, heterozygotes, and compounds of the lower alleles. Therefore, the shift must be based in all cases upon a simple and in its nature identical, quantitative effect upon the processes or reactions controlled by the homozygotes, heterozygotes, and compounds of vg and its alleles. If we turn again to the representation of the vestigial action in terms of speed of reactions and quantities of end products, as represented in figure 19, we realize that dominance is a potency effect, *ceteris paribus,* like multiple allelic effects and dosage effects. I think that so consistent a group of facts requires an explanation in terms of genic action controlling in a quantitative way some phase of the kinetics of production of active end products, whatever their nature.

One additional point should be mentioned. Blanc has demonstrated that two of the dominance modifiers are identical with the mutants purple (darker eye color) and facet (rough eyes); this makes these modifiers loci with pleiotropic action upon completely different characters. (Also in rodents, certain pigment mutants affect morphological traits; see Grüneberg's book.) This again raises the question of qualitative versus quantitative action. The eye color purple is probably a quantitative deviation of pigment formation. The rough eyes of facet do not suggest a qualitative basis, though Hinton and Ellis (1950) could produce the character reversibly by a nutritional deficiency. But practically all phenocopy experiments, with whatever agent, produce rough eyes most easily. Thus the facts mentioned can hardly be cited in favor of qualitative action of alleles.

We are analyzing here the theory of genic action, and therefore the much discussed problem of the origin of dominance enters our deliberations only so far as it has to do with the theory of genic action. Actually, any theory of the origin of dominance can be no more than purely formalistic if a physiological system of genic action controlling dominance is not made the basis of discussion. It is well known that Fisher (1928–1932; see 1935) developed a phylogenetic and statistical theory of dominance of wild type over mutations, involving a selection of modifiers that shift the phenotype of the heterozygote toward wild type, because the wild type has the selective advantage which thus is also conferred upon heterozygotes of the frequently produced mutants. Clearly, such an explanation of the origin of dominance presupposes a type of genic action of the general kind just reviewed, and developed in detail in my book of 1927. If such a system underlies genic action, phylogeny of dominance may be conceived in Fisher's sense but, also, in other different ways. Muller (1933), Plunkett (1932), and Wright (1934*a*) argue, more or less identically, that dominance modifiers may have been selected, to provide a margin of stability and security, to insure the organism against weakening genetic or environmental variability. Quoting Muller: "These modifiers must so affect the reaction set in motion by the primary gene in question as to cause this gene, when in two doses, to be near an upper limit of its curve of effectiveness, that is in a nearly horizontal part of the curve, not so readily subject to variation by influences in general, including reduction in the primary dosage of the gene." Plunkett and Wright express the same idea (the physiological part of which is identical with mine) in somewhat different language.

One of the corollaries of the foregoing discussions is that different wild-type alleles (hyper-wild ones) must exist above the threshold for wild type, though they are distinguishable only in special combinations. Mohr, Haldane, and I have used this notion in theoretical discussions. Muller (1935*a*) discussed it and tried a conclusive experiment, which in principle is of the same general type as Stern's subsequent work with ci isoalleles. He compared in triploid condition white eye mutants of different origin and known to be somehow genetically different (in regard to mutability). He found that the American white locus is less dominant than the Russian, and attributes this to different potency, based upon different levels above a threshold. Thus a very large and diversified body of facts fits together into a single picture of genic action of the type developed in this chapter.

It is only a small step from a discussion of dominance as a dosage phenomenon (or potency phenomenon) to the problem of penetrance, which sometimes overlaps with dominance. Timoféeff-Ressovsky (1927) introduced this term for cases in which a mutant did not produce its phenotype in all individuals, some of the individuals being normal. Thus we may speak of mutants with penetrance varying from 1 per cent to 100 per cent, the last being the "good" mutants, with which the classic geneticist likes to work. The former mutants with low penetrance, though less "useful" for crossover work, are actually of greater importance for the theory of genic action. Many mutants of this type are known. From the point of view of genic action they may be directly compared with some already studied in which different alleles or compounds (e.g., in ci or vg) overlapped with normal. If, for example, vg^{ni}/vg^{ni} was 100 per cent normal, but vg^{ni}/vg^{no} had 0.2 per cent nicked individuals, this was the same phenomenon as penetrance in a homozygous mutant, though we are entitled just as well to say that here notched is a little dominant. The overlap of the two concepts is most conspicuous when we are dealing with a dominant which is a homozygous lethal and exists, therefore, only as a heterozygote. Let us take Beaded in *Drosophila* as an example. The heterozygote Bd/+ has 3–5 per cent beaded-wing individuals. We can call this an incomplete dominance, but since no homozygote exists we may also say that Bd is 3–5 per cent penetrant. We may of course arbitrarily set the rule that we speak of dominance when a heterozygote is involved and of penetrance only in the homozygote. A compound is a heterozygote and therefore vg^{ni}/vg^{no} shows a little dominance. But it could also be justified to treat a compound as partly a homozygote and therefore use the term "penetrance" for the partial effect. All these facts tend to show that the two phenomena have the same basis, namely, dosage (or potency) and threshold effects, and therefore supply the same kind of information on genic action and, incidentally, must be studied from the point of view of physiological genetics as opposed to formal genetics.

Many cases of incomplete penetrance are known and many have been studied quantitatively since Timoféeff's basic work. (Much of this work is reviewed in my book of 1938.) Recently we have studied the phenomenon extensively (Goldschmidt, Hannah, and Piternick, 1951; Goldschmidt, 1952*b*). The details will not be analyzed here, because they would repeat the earlier discussions on dosage, potency, and dominance. I shall enumerate simply the main features, taking the examples from our recent work.

1. Mutant effects of lower penetrance may be based upon single mutant loci which always produce the same incompletely penetrant effect in the same external and genetic environment. However, an incompletely penetrant effect is often based upon a system of multiple factors. It is this type we studied in the so-called podoptera mutants of *Drosophila,* which make a wing bud change into a leglike or haltere-like organ or, partly, into thorax tissue. There are strains with very low penetrance of a small percentage but, nevertheless, controlled by a number of mutant loci in different chromosomes. We discussed some of these facts (I 2 C *d dd*) when I presented my opinion that these are heterochromatic mutants (a point which is not relevant to

the present discussion). In other lines with a much higher penetrance it is possible to isolate the individual multiple factors within their chromosomes and to state that each one alone produces a certain share of the penetrance, which is different for the different loci. The combined effect of these was found to be sometimes additive, sometimes multiplicative. In special cases it was possible to accumulate a sufficiently large number of such loci (or sufficiently potent ones) to accomplish a 100 per cent penetrance. When this was done by selection, it was accomplished by finding a few very potent loci rather than by accumulation of many loci of low potency, which never led very far. In principle, then, penetrance may be treated here like any phenotypic effect which is quantitatively increased by an accumulation of mutant loci of individually insufficient quantitative action (i.e., like any effect of multiple factors), and therefore the discussion of these in regard to genic action (see III 5 C *a. dd*) applies also to penetrance. The only difference is that in multiple growth or color factors the explanation is that different quantities of an end product are the result of the genic actions, that is, more growth substance or pigment; while in the present case there must be an additional feature, namely, a threshold level for normality. The analysis of the details of the effect shows that this threshold condition is set by the time in development at which genic action comes into play, as will be discussed below.

2. Penetrance is affected by genetic modifiers, which themselves are not in control of the same phenotype (as opposed to multiple factors). As in all cases of modifier action, either the modifiers have no other known functions, and may be demonstrated solely by the positive effect of selection experiments; or they may be loci of known visible action, frequently dominants, which in this case act as specific modifiers. This again shows penetrance to be a consequence of the same general type of genic action as that which accounts for the explanation of all modifier action. Many examples are found in the papers on podoptera.

3. Penetrance is more or less influenced by temperature conditions, which may shift penetrance more or less in individual cases. This applies to penetrance of single mutants, for example, in Timoféeff's work, and also to the multiple factor penetrance in podoptera. The details are not different from the temperature action, say, upon the number of Bar facets or the ci effect or any other mutant action which has a temperature dependence, which again means that it must be based on the same dynamic, kinetic system of genic action.

4. Timoféeff-Ressovsky introduced simultaneously with penetrance the term "expressivity," meaning the degree of phenotypic expression of a trait. It is possible that a mutant always (i.e., in all individuals) produces the maximum possible effect; for example, a white eye is always a white eye. Other mutants have a more variable effect, so far as there is a considerable fluctuation in the degree of the effect under identical conditions (i.e., in expressivity). In addition, expressivity is frequently affected by modifiers or by temperature action, sometimes within small limits, sometimes within the entire range from normal to the extremest possible effect. It seems that mutants with incomplete penetrance have a special tendency to variable expressivity. Otherwise great irregularities are observed. We described (Goldschmidt *et al.*, 1951; Goldschmidt, 1953*a*) cases in which no correlation between penetrance and expressivity was found, and others in which there was no correlation up to high penetrance, but complete correlation with the highest grades of penetrance. Bezem and Sobels (1953) found complete correlation for a different, rather extreme mutant of *Drosophila*, Asymmetric. Thus it may be assumed that the type of genic action which accounts for penetrance also may control expressivity, directly or indirectly, except for other interfering reactions. Penetrance, like dosage, dominance, and potency, is probably a rather direct result of the genic effect upon the kinetics of the chain of reactions, together with specific threshold conditions for the action of the reaction products; but expressivity must involve some additional developmental features interacting with the reactions responsible for different penetrance. Such a feature could be the time of competence or labile determination with slowly progressing irreversibility (see III 5 D *e*). The detailed facts of the entire effect of such genic action (i.e., a definite penetrance plus a certain expressivity) would thus suggest a general model of genic action of the types used in figures 18 and 19, with the addition of another variable, the progress in time of irreversible determination of the anlage.

5. Incomplete penetrance is frequently combined with more or less asymmetry of the effect, though the same may be found in certain dominance effects also. Astauroff (1929) has shown that this asymmetry is based upon independent development of the two halves of the body (in *Drosophila*). This means that though right and left are affected independently in regard to the expressivity of the character, thus producing more or less, even extreme, asymmetry, neither side is preferred (or has a bias, as Mather, 1953*a*, expresses it in a statistical study). Our own work bears this out, but we found that symmetry

and penetrance are positively correlated, which could also be stated by saying that the expressivity is more stabilized with higher penetrance. It seems that this feature of penetrance is not based upon the genic action assumed to hold for all the other quantitative effects. This can best be seen by a comparison with similar facts involving dominance. A good example is the scalloping effect upon *Drosophila* wings produced by different mutant loci. In some cases (e.g., cut, Xasta) the effect is perfectly symmetrical. In others, like the vestigial alleles, it is more or less asymmetrical, though never as extreme as in the homoeotic mutants which we studied, where frequently one side is completely normal. A good case can be made out for the dominant Beaded, where the effect is always asymmetrical, but I found a modifier (or group of modifiers) which makes the effect perfectly symmetrical (not published). This shows that the asymmetry is not one of the features of action of the mutant locus but of some independently determined condition of the reacting system. Mather (1953*a*) speaks of chance disturbances of development. In view of the kind of correlations between penetrance and expressivity (negative except at the extreme end) and between penetrance and symmetry (positive), in our case not chance events but definite characteristics of determination must be the cause of the asymmetries. The same can be demonstrated also for incompletely penetrant loci like podoptera, in which there are lines with varying degrees of asymmetry without any visible rule; but there are also lines in which, for example, a majority of individuals show the effect, even the most extreme one, on one side only (see pod K for details). This indicates that independent genetic conditions are involved, which may have to do with the early distribution of cleavage nuclei in the peculiar development of insects, with its migration of the cleavage nuclei within a common cytoplasm. Thus, asymmetric effects must be appraised in regard to their meaning for genetic action in each individual case. (For more details, see our podoptera and tetraltera papers.)

We see that the facts of penetrance give us the same information on genic action as all the other data reported in this section, but they emphasize more the threshold concept and the possibility of fluctuation of the products of reaction near the threshold. They show us, in addition, the interplay with other independently determined developmental processes, especially those concerned with time and progress of final determination of embryonic parts.

c. Dosage via chromosomes

As I mentioned earlier (III 5 C *c*), the least reliable dosage experiments are those which change dosage by means of trisomy, monosomy, and so on, or by polyploidy. In all these cases, different doses of a mutant locus are obtained, but not on one and the same genetical background. This might be irrelevant in some cases, for example, when the tiny fourth chromosome of *Drosophila* is involved, or when the mutant action is so direct that there is little if any interaction with different chains of reaction. The latter might be true, especially when dosage effects upon simple chemical end products are involved. Clear dosage effects in such experiments would lead to the same conclusions as those drawn in the last chapter. The best examples might be expected in polyploids because here the parallel dosage changes for the entire genome might provide a genetic background which is not very different; though this is not necessarily so, as the variable effects of polyploidy upon cell size and physiology of plants demonstrate. The least reliable results are expected for number changes of single chromosomes which may change the entire developmental system considerably.

In view of all this it is surprising that simple dosage effects can sometimes be observed in such cases. Actually, Correns (1900) had already noticed intensification of mutant action in the endosperm of maize (the endosperm is triploid). The best example of this kind was found by Mangelsdorf and Fraps (1931), who studied vitamin A content in corn, using the triploid endosperm. Yellow has a higher content than white, and triploid yellow has the highest. The case is remarkable, because here, simultaneously, dosage by chromosome number increase, by mutation, and by heterozygosis could be checked in the same experiment. If Y = yellow and y = white, the number of Y loci will be in a triploid endosperm 0, 1, 2, 3 in the compositions yyy, yyY, yYY, YYY. The resulting effect on vitamin A units per gram was in the same order, 0.05, 2.25. 5.00, 7.50, an astonishingly exact dosage relation. Obviously, the single genic action here is of the simple type expressed in the one gene—one synthetic step idea, which would permit such exact dosage results in a triploid without interference from other reactions. The same is true when it is found that a homozygote produces twice as much of an enzyme as a heterozygote does. But there are similar examples in which morphological characters are involved, some of which are reviewed in my book of 1938. Here, also, other examples of such dosage relations concerning chemical products are found. (One of them, flower color, will be mentioned below.)

A less satisfactory case will be expected in monosomics, trisomics, and so on, in which a background of disturbed "genic balance" is involved. We saw in the discussion of Stern's work (and the same applies to the extensive work with other loci) that mutant loci in *Drosophila's* fourth chromosome in the chromosomal dosages of haplo-, diplo-, triplo-IV give regular effects in relation to dosage, though the possibility could not be excluded that in some of the irregular results that feature may be involved. The most extensive data available otherwise for different extra chromosomes are contained in Blakeslee's famous work on *Datura*. However, here no individual loci were studied, and the general differences found cannot be attributed simply to dosage differences of loci, and therefore cannot be used for an analysis of genic action.

D. GENIC ACTION IN FOUR DIMENSIONS

The greatest difficulty in the study of genic actions in controlling development is met with when we try to visualize how they are interlocked in order to produce their effects locally, that is, in the three dimensions of space and in the fourth dimension of time, at a given moment. To understand normal development in terms of genic action we must integrate all the individual sources of information on the action of mutant loci and infer the action of the normal genic material. In doing so it should not make any difference what views we hold on the nature of the genic material—the classic gene concept or the modern pattern idea. In any case the information we have is derived almost exclusively from the results of interference of mutant loci with the normal course of development (and the analysis of the factors of development by experimental embryology). Therefore, whatever the constitution of the normal genic material, it must act in the way revealed by mutant interference with its action. The general picture of genic control of orderly (i.e., four-dimensional) development, has been given in the foregoing discussions of individual phases of the process, and some integration of the diverse actions has been presented, wherever there was a need of it. But no attempt was made to offer a complete picture of the interplay of all development-controlling reactions, nor were all groups of facts presented which should enter such an integration. Thus, in trying to visualize the integrated action of the genic material we shall have to add some more relevant factual material.

If we are not dogmatic, we might expect most of the interpretations proposed for individual phenomena to enter the general picture: velocities of reaction chains, threshold conditions, stratification of cytoplasmic differences, self-perpetuating cytoplasmic conditions, substrates, competition for substrates, and everything else mentioned at different levels of the previous discussion. From all this should emerge what a rather plastic German word calls a *Zusammenschau,* a *synopsis* in Greek. A very good model for two dimensions has been used by Goethe, when he poetically compared the fabric of thought with the production of a fabric by weaving:

> Zwar ists mit der Gedankenfabrik
> Wie mit einem Weber-Meisterstück
> Wo ein Tritt tausend Fäden regt
> Die Schifflein herüber hinüber schiessen
> Die Fäden ungesehen fliessen,
> Ein Schlag tausend Verbindungen schlägt.

If this dynamic picture could be extended into four dimensions, it would be a perfect model for genic control of development.

A great many of the individual processes which combine to form a picture of heredity as a whole have been touched upon. But there are still a number of facts which relate especially to the interplay, the fabric of genically controlled processes. The present chapter will deal with their analysis before attempting a general synthesis.

a. Factorial collaboration

Insight into the interplay of genically controlled processes in development should be gained from a study of the interactions of different mutant loci. Such interactions were considered in a general way when we referred to the genetical background, or residual heredity; when we discussed the interplay of genically controlled reactions under the unfortunate term "genic balance"; when we spoke in a more or less specific way of modifier systems; when we found the need for independently controlled threshold conditions for the effect of individual genic actions; when we discussed cytoplasmic substrates and their ultimate genic control; when we mentioned special possibilities like competition for substrates; when we discussed specific interactions like those of dominance modifiers and enhancers of penetrance; and also when discussing the influence of extra heterochromatin upon certain genic actions. The entire body of classic genetics, since the early work on color in mice by Cuénot and that of the Bateson group on different organisms, contains innumerable examples of individual genic interactions in the form of collaborations, modifications, inhibitions, enhancements, suppressions. It is safe to say that all of them will fit one or the other explanation of interaction mentioned before and just enumerated. Therefore, no more examples are needed than those already used incidentally in the discussion of the various problems of action of the genic material.

But there are also a number of special investigations of the problem which are of two types: one deals with morphological characters, which means that the interpretation can be only a more or less indirect one. The other deals with chemical differences, which permit a rather exact interpretation. Only a few examples of each type will be mentioned in order to show that they lead, in a general way, to conclusions concerning genic action of the same types as discussed before.

An interesting attack upon the problem is that made by Dunn and Coyne (1935) and Dunn and Mossige (1937), because they use one genic effect which must be supposed to affect many others, quantitative changes in speed of development. The previously mentioned Minutes in *Drosophila* have a retarding effect upon development (Brehme, 1939, 1941). It is true that Minutes are frequently deficiencies and are suspected of being of heterochromatic nature. But for our present discussion they may serve as models of one possible type of genic action. Dunn and Coyne used the delaying effect in descending order for the Minutes, $M_w - M_b - M_z - M_h - Ml_2$. These were combined with other mutant effects, for example, eye size. In such combinations the eye size was reduced in the presence of Minutes and in degree, corresponding to the retarding effect of the series of Minutes. Whatever the genic action which reduces eye size (see III 5 C *a bb*), the interplay with the independently determined and affected rate of development and its orderliness point to actions and interactions involving some phase of the kinetics of genic action.

Another example which deals with eye reduction, this time by Bar, is Hersh's work (1929). It is not a combination effect with a known genic activity which is studied here, but rather the modifying effect upon one quantitatively measurable genic action (eye-facet numbers) by other mutant loci in the same chromosome which, as such, affect eye structure, eye color, and wing properties. All these, individually and combined, affect facet number, much or little, positively or negatively. One of these modifiers is vermilion, the chemical action of which is the prevention of kynurenine synthesis. In view of the results of Chevais (see III 5 C *a bb*), it cannot be excluded that the absence of kynurenine in the developing eye stalk acts upon the facet-producing reaction, whatever it is. But it is just as possible that the action of the mutant v, which ultimately results in the prevention of a synthetic step between two amino acids, is primarily of a completely quantitative type, for example, one action affecting the rate of some process, which can interfere with the facet-producing reaction. In the wing mutants affecting facet number (cross-veinless and cut), the probability of an interaction of two kinetic conditions is more probable. This example shows the same interactions at work which we met before, and also the same difficulties of identifying exactly the type of interaction. This applies also to some instances in which it is recorded that a mutant locus in control of a definite biochemical situation simultaneously affects a morphological character. Grüneberg (1952*a,b*) recounts a series of mutants for coat color with simultaneous morphological effects of a pathological type, for example, skeletal abnormalities caused by disfunction of osteoclasts, absence of otoliths, or spina bifida. It is quite possible that an abnormal biochemical condition of a pigment precursor directly affects definite embryological processes. But just as well, the indirect type of interference through kinetics may be at work.

Only one more recent example of the type under discussion may be scrutinized. Waddington (1953*b*) combined homozygotes of mutants, all of which affect growth of one or more imaginal buds: aristopedia, which turns antennae into tarsi and also affects legs; vestigial, which affects wings; bithorax, which acts on dorsal and ventral metathoracic buds; and others, all having strong morphological effects. Many types of interactions were found. As I have already pointed out (see paper by my student Csik, 1934, 1936, on such interactions in the *Drosophila* wing and bristles; Goldschmidt, 1938*a*), in such combinations, different results may be expected. The genic actions may be concerned with processes so different that they will not interfere with each other; thus the phenotype will exhibit a combination of the two traits. (Examples are found in Csik's paper.) We could assume that this is so when qualitatively different processes are involved (e.g., processes of the one gene—one synthetic step type), or actions at very different times. It is expected that this is rather rare, since most simultaneous or consecutive reactions should interfere with each other. The other extreme would be that different genic actions concern the same process directly, or, more frequently, indirectly by means of different approaches or points in common. Here the actions may be additive or mutually inhibitive; or sometimes, when the effects are qualitatively different, a compromise between the two effects may result. All intermediates between these two extremes are imaginable, and some were described by Csik. In Waddington's experiments these types occur, but also some more complicated effects which cannot be described simply as "compromise." Thus the effects of loci acting in the same way are, if combined, more than additive. This means that a development which is already abnormal is easier to alter. I think that this is the same phenomenon found in multiple factor inheritance (e.g., in my work on tetraltera, 1953*b*), in which the effect sometimes is not additive but multiplicative. In terms of genic action this may have different reasons which might lie entirely in the type of reaction involved. For exaggerations of the combination effect, Waddington proposes this explanation. Suppose that the sequence of developmental processes involves two steps P and Q; further, that in P a set of reactants k, l, m, n are involved; and in Q, p q r s. One at least of p q r s must have been determined by reaction P, because we started with the idea that P and Q are involved in the same set of reactions. This common step might be p. Then we might distinguish loci which affect reactants belonging to the same reaction (q and r) and those which affect reactants belonging to a different reaction (e.g., k and r). If the reactions P and Q did not involve any tendencies toward the attainment of equilibrium states, the two types of loci would not differ significantly: one affecting k would produce a change in p and, in the presence of the other mutant affecting r, the result would be the same as that of a single mutant affecting q and r. But developmental processes tend to some sort of equilibrium. Thus, in a homozygote for a mutant locus affecting k, the interaction between the other components of the reaction P proceeds in such a way that the result is little altered. Such a mutant might therefore produce a less disturbing effect on the process Q than would be caused by a similar locus acting directly on that process. Therefore, more exaggeration is expected in combinations of mutants acting on the same process at the same time than in a combination of successively acting mutants. If the same things are considered as processes proceeding in time like monomolecular reactions, the differential equations obtained suggest that mutant loci produce changes in the rate constants, while differentiation depends on the composition of the system. If both mutants affect the system, each will have its full effect in altering this composition. Quoting from Waddington: "But if one mutation affects the system and produces a change in the quantity of a_3 [a substance produced by an irreversible reaction which is transported out of the system at a known rate], which passes on to become involved in a subsequent similar system, the composition reached by this second system will, as we have seen, not be affected by this alteration in the initial concentration of one of its components. Another gene altering a rate constant in this second system will therefore have no different effect whether the first mutant gene is present or not. This corresponds to a case of complete 'buffering,' in the development of actual living organisms, the differentiation [= composition] is in general not entirely independent of the conditions outside the system."

We presented this ingenious analysis in order to show how difficult it is to draw tangible and final conclusions upon the interplay of genic action from such experiments. At present we do not seem to get beyond very general statements about interlocking, interference, and attunement of genically controlled reaction chains, preferably involving features of their kinetics.

Much more concrete are the results when genically controlled chemical end products of genic interplay are studied. But it must be realized beforehand that such studies may throw very little or no light on the control of morphogenesis, though they supply models for some kind of interplay of determining reactions. (I have quoted Haldane's more optimistic conclusions.) A good example is the work of Lawrence and Scott-Moncrieff (1935) and Scott-Moncrieff (1936) on flower pigments, especially in *Dahlia.* Since this pioneer work was performed, both authors have made many new additions and corrections (see Scott-Moncrieff, 1939; Lawrence and Price, 1940; Haldane's excellent review of the subject, 1942). We are not interested here in the special biochemistry of the subject but in the general way in which genic actions collaborate in the control of biochemical diversities. Therefore I shall use the original work, antedating present-day biochemical genetics, as an example, because it brings out the points I wish to make. Subsequent corrections in the biochemical details (including controversial points, on which I am not qualified to pass judgment) do not alter the general picture so far as genic action is concerned. Some of this is discussed in Haldane (1954).

Keeping to the original findings, we may consider the following extract, emphasizing the features of importance to the geneticist, who is not so much interested in the individual biochemical facts as in their general trend. In these plants, color may be determined by a number of agencies. If a single pigment is involved, this and the pH of the surroundings are decisive. If more pigments are involved, there are various possibilities: a combination effect, a background effect, a copigment effect (meaning that one is changed in the presence of another). The sap pigments are anthoxanthins and anthocyanins. The former are flavones, of ivory or yellow color, and may be glucosides or not. They may act in all the ways mentioned. As copigments they have a bluing effect upon anthocyanin. The latter are sap-soluble glucosides with colors from scarlet to violet, purple, and blue. The chemical difference between the xanthins and the anthocyanins is mainly that in the flavones an O-atom is substituted in position 4. Anthocyanins are mainly pelargonidins, cyanidins, and delphinidins differing by the possession of 1, 2, or 3 OH groups on the side phenyl ring. More than one of these pigments may be present in a plant, and there are numerous chemical variations, such as methylation of one or more OH groups, changes in the sugar residue, and addition of an organic acid. All these variations and substitutions are under genic control. The most important points are the sugar residues at position 3 or 5: glucose, galactose, cellobiose. Pelargonin, petunin, and others are all 3–5 glycosides of pelargonidin, and so on. Without going into details, we mention from the *Primula* work the action of some loci: K modifies general anthocyanin substrate to the more intense 3–5 oxidized and methylated type; B produces anthoxanthin, copigmenting and suppressing anthocyanin; R produces localized acid pH in the petals and in the red corolla tubes of special forms; D_z produces specific anthocyanin-pelargonidin 3-monoxide; G inhibits anthocyanin in flower center and together with D inhibits the effect of R in petals. From such work with many forms the following known types of genic action are derived:

I. CHEMICAL CHANGES OF ANTHOCYANIN

1. Oxidation of the aglycone at 3 or 3 and 5
2. Oxidation and methylation at the same positions
3. Methylation of the aglycone at the same positions
4. Glycosidic change from 3 to 3–5 type
5. Acylation

II. SAP PIGMENT PRODUCTION

1. Anthoxanthin and anthocyanin
2. Yellow anthoxanthin background and interaction
3. Ivory anthoxanthin copigment interaction and copigment effects
4. General anthocyanin background and interaction
5. Specific anthocyanin background and interaction

III. SAP PIGMENT REGULATION

1. General intensification
2. General suppression
3. Local intensification
4. Local suppression

IV. PLASTID PIGMENT

1. Production of background effects
2. Inhibition

V. LOCALIZED ACID pH

These take care of most colors studied, and the individual known loci may be assigned to one or the other chemical action. Only one specific point should be mentioned: the wild-type color is the most highly oxidized; mutant loci then prevent complete oxidation. Haldane (1935) has drawn from such facts the conclusion which later was called the one gene—one enzyme hypothesis, whereas I pointed out (1938*a*) that different rates of production of the specific enzyme might be at work.

On the basis of such a chemical situation, Scott-Moncrieff studied the interaction of the different loci involved in the coloring of dahlias. The loci involved are as follows: A, necessary for light anthocyanin color produced by either cyanin or pelargonin; B, needed for heavy anthocyanin; I, producing ivory flavone; and Y, producing yellow flavone. A complication, which makes these experiments at the same time dosage experiments, is that these dahlias are tetraploid. Thus, Y and B are completely dominant in simplex condition; A is cumulative from simplex to quadriplex. I is incompletely dominant; when simplex it produces very little pigment; when duplex to quadriplex, the complete amount. There is also another locus H which acts as inhibitor of yellow flavone, with an additive effect from simplex to quadriplex leading to cream and primrose colors.

The interaction of these factors is, generally speaking, such that the pigments suppress each other, but the flavones suppress the anthocyanin more than vice versa, the degree of suppression depending upon dosages. Thus, anthocyanin intensity, controlled by A, is diminished in the presence of ivory flavone (I), with less pigment being formed; the details depend upon dosages. Y acts strongly upon the effect of I and A, suppressing them completely in some combinations; Y and I similarly suppress the action of B; I changes the effect of B to the type of an A effect. To this are added the dosage effects which are not simple and indicate definite threshold conditions.

The authors tried to explain the facts (of which only a short survey was given) in terms of the chemistry of pigment formation and of genic action. As a balance of the different pigments is involved, it is concluded that all pigments are produced from some limited common source for which there is competition. The supply of this source must be so limited that the quantity of each pigment can increase only at the expense of the others (which then is a threshold phenomenon), depending upon the relative dosage of the respective mutants. Anthocyanin may be cyanin or pelargonidin. In *Dahlia* the factors A and B do not control one or the other; the alternative is rather decided by the entire quantitative system of the factors involved. Thus, synthesis of pelargonin, a derivative of pelargonidin, requires the following: (1) presence of A_1B_1Y; (2) two or more B; (3) one or more B with three I; (4) one or more B with two or more I and at least one A; (5) one or more B together with one I and at least three A.

This whole scheme of genic collaboration is visualized by making the arbitrary assumption that the limit of the source of pigment available in *Dahlia* under whatever genic combinations can be stated to be six units. Now B and Y are capable of using the maximum source in simplex condition, and thus contribute at least six potential units. A has a cumulative potential value which in quadriplex condition is less than or equal to the maximal source. Thus unit values are calculated for $Y = 9$, $B = 6$, $I = 1$, $A = \frac{1}{2}$, and their combined action would be, if 8 is the threshold value for pelargonidin, $A_4I_4 = 6$ units, or $B_1A_2I_1 = 8$ units (i.e., only cyanin). $A_1Y_1 = 9.5$ and $B_2 = 12$ units (i.e., only pelargonin). Hence it is concluded that each factor competes for the common source in terms of its potential units, and the total pigment depends upon the proportion and power of interaction of all factors. Also, a chemical interpretation is proposed, namely, that the actions in terms of units are involved in controlling the oxidation of the phenyl ring.

So much for Lawrence and Scott-Moncrieff. For our present discussion of the orderly interplay of genic actions it is not important whether every single point of this analysis is unassailable or has actually been corrected since. The important point is that in a concrete case in which much knowledge is available the interplay of genic reactions points to some of the same physicochemical processes which are met always: velocities of reaction, quantities of reaction products, dosage effects upon both, threshold conditions caused in different ways, nature of the substrate, and competition for the substrate, in addition to the production of the specific enzymes and the precursor substrates of different complexity. Though it is very difficult to visualize such an interplay at the proper places in the four dimensions of embryonic determination under genic control, it helps at least toward forming a vague image, which is the maximum available today, while the straightforward qualitative biochemical approach does not lead very far.

Other examples of a comparable type could be given. One of the best elaborated is Wright's analysis of coat colors in guinea pigs, carried out from 1916 to 1949, involving the interplay of at least seven mutant loci. Without going into the details (which are given in all reviews on biochemical genetics), we may say that again different types of genic actions are involved which must be properly attuned to give the final results. There is present a genic control by a rate process of the quantity of pigment, interfering with the quantity of two different pigments; another control determines which of the two pigments is formed, probably from the same precursors, with competition for a common substrate. This control is assumed to work by conditioning the hair follicles in three different, genically controlled ways; two other processes control the distribution of pigment over the skin (spotting) and within a hair (agouti); this means interaction of the pigment-forming processes with an independent patterning process. This is another system in which an exact interplay of primary synthesis of biochemical precursors, different enzyme systems for further synthesis, rate processes controlling quantities, processes involving competition for substrates, and processes of cellular diversification according to a pattern are found and can be visualized in the way we have frequently discussed before. I do not think that more examples are needed.

b. Pleiotropy

Pleiotropy, the production of manifold effects by one mutant locus, has been mentioned earlier. Strictly speaking, there are probably no mutants in existence which do not affect more than one structure. A close inspection usually reveals such effects, either morphological or physiological (e.g., viability). But if we speak of pleiotropy, we usually mean cases in which manifold effects are rather obvious. We have only to go over Bridges and Brehme's (1944) catalogue of *Drosophila* mutants to find numerous examples of all grades. The same is true for maize mutants. For our present topic, the different examples of pleiotropy are not of equal value; some give us more, some less, or no information on the interplay of genic action.

There is one group which actually should not be called pleiotropy without qualification. Grüneberg (1938) called it "spurious pleiotropy"; I prefer to call it "syndromic pleiotropy," because the effect of the mutant is a syndrome of pathological features which have to be considered as a kind of mechanical consequence of a primary, early embryonic damage. Bonnevie first analyzed a case in the mouse, where, according to her interpretation, the mutant causes a hyperpressure of cerebrospinal fluid in the embryo; this leads to bleb formation, which later causes all kinds of damage to different tissues and organs. Numerous cases of similar type have since been analyzed by Grüneberg, Dunn, Gluecksohn-Schoenheimer, Landauer, and others. (See reviews in Goldschmidt, 1938*a*; Grüneberg, 1952*b*; Caspari, 1952; Gluecksohn-Waelsch, 1953.) It is obvious that these types do not teach us much on interplay of genic action, and we shall, therefore, not go into further details. I drew this conclusion earlier when discussing pleiotropic effects of multiple alleles (III 5 C *b*).

A second, more informative type deals partly with the production of a chemical substance, say a pigment, which affects most conspicuously one process (e.g., production of eye color), but simultaneously acts upon other pigmentation processes at other places and, sometimes, in a qualitatively different way. A well-known example is the effect of light eye color (also body color) mutants of *Drosophila* upon the hue of pigmentation of gonads and Malpighian tubules (see Brehme and Demerec, 1942). We might call this type "pattern pleiotropy." Caspari (1952) has drawn attention to the fact that even Mendel knew an example, namely, a mutant in the sweet pea, which influenced at the same time the pigment in the seed coat, in the flower, and in the axils of the leaves. Some similar cases have been thoroughly studied in the work on biochemical genetics of the Kühn and Beadle schools. For example, in the flour moth (Caspari, 1933) the wild type produces a diffusible substance which is needed for the pigmentation of eyes, testes, and larval hypodermis. In the mutant this substance is not formed (details elucidated in transplantation experiments). The substance is kynurenine (also in the parallel *Drosophila* work of Beadle and Ephrussi, 1936), a precursor for all these pigments.

To this group of "pattern pleiotropy" belong also a number of morphological pleiotropies, in which it is impossible at present to specify a definite genic product. Such, for example, are cases in which a similar type of effect appears in different organs. The mutant podoptera (in *Drosophila*) affects primarily the wing, which grows into a leglike appendage. Simultaneously, the legs are frequently abnormal in different ways (details in Goldschmidt, Hannah, and Piternick, 1951). Both effects are, in a general way, interferences with growth processes, and we may safely assume that the same type of changed genic action accounts for both effects.

All these and comparable cases (which Grüneberg considers also as spurious pleiotropy) contain some information on genic interplay. In the a^+ pigment in *Ephestia* it is safe to assume that kynurenine is, or can be, produced in all cells or not be produced in the case of aa action. However, it will be oxidized further into pigment only in cells which are competent for it (if we use this term, as before, in this wider sense). "Competent" means here an independently determined condition, probably of cytoplasmic differentiation, produced in one of the ways discussed above, but certainly in the end under genic control. Thus pattern pleiotropy shows us the interplay between a genically controlled specific reaction and other, independent ones, controlling a patterning process by means of cytoplasmic "stratification." This cytoplasmic diversification may act by producing different degrees of polyteny, according to Henke's very interesting work (Henke and Pohley, 1952) on Lepidoptera scales (see III 5 A *a*), where both the type and amount of pigmentation are dependent upon the degree of polyteny. If this process were combined with the patterning process of the aa pigment, an interesting series of genic interactions would be visible. (All of them have been individually discussed in previous chapters.)

A third type of pleiotropy, which we might call "dichotomic pleiotropy," is found when some primary reaction of a mutant, usually an inhibitory one, is of such a generalized type that it affects the entire organism simultaneously according to the reactivity of its parts. A deficiency in a growth substance, for example, may affect every growth process, but differently according to its independently determined features. The Minutes in *Drosophila* may serve as an example. Small size and weakness are simple effects. Abnormal shape of wings and abnormal venation are interactions of the same primary defect with the individual steps of independently determined wing development. Shortening of bristles and roughness of eyes may be rather simple interferences with growth processes. (We mentioned earlier, in III 5 C *b*, the relation of roughness of eye facets to definite biochemical deficiencies, which, however, cannot be considered the direct cause.) Abnormalities in the genital region may involve more intricate processes within an imaginal disc and their interactions and compromises through embryonic regulation.

Still another type of pleiotropy might be called "interference pleiotropy." This probably represents the only genuine pleiotropy, namely, one and the same genic action affecting completely different processes. Both Grüneberg (1952*a*) and Caspari (1952) doubt whether such a genuine pleiotropy actually exists, and I agree with this. But I think that the nearest approximation to it, interference pleiotropy, is frequent. We mean by this that a genetically controlled process interferes with other independently determined actions, with the result that they are shifted in a way they could also be shifted directly by independent mutation. The mutant aa may have a pleiotropic action which is based upon a single difference of primary action from that of AA, of any type of mutant action known. The actions of the normal loci BB, CC, DD may require a definite condition at a definite time (model: a definite pH) in order to run properly. If aa affects this condition in the wrong way, the B, C, D reactions may be thrown out of gear; that is, they may run off exactly as if B, C, D had mutated. The result is a change of mutational order in all the end products of B, C, D which looks like (and indirectly is) a pleiotropic action of aa. I think that this type of pleiotropy is present whenever completely unrelated and unrelatable effects are found: for example, in *Drosophila* the effects of Dichaete on wing posture and bristles, of silver on pigmentation, shape of wings, and a pigment-suppressor action. The correctness of the interpretation is borne out by the fact that these different pleiotropic effects may be affected individually in special conditions. I have already mentioned (I 3 C *ee ccc*) my finding that in silver the suppressor action could be separated from the others; for vestigial we found a temperature effect upon the dominance of the pleiotropic bristle effect alone (Goldschmidt, 1935*a*,*b*); other examples could easily be found. To this probably belong the cases of extreme pleiotropic action described by Timoféeff (1931) and Neel (1942*a*).

This leads to another group of facts concerning pleiotropy which contains information on the interplay of genic actions. In a system of the type just assumed for what is actually genuine pleiotropy, it is to be expected that, generally, environmental agents as well as the internal environment (modifier systems) will affect pleiotropic traits differently. Many such facts are known, especially from *Drosophila* literature, and it is hardly necessary to go into details, some of which are found in Caspari's review. But we may return to a related subject (discussed briefly in III 5 C *b*), the behavior of pleiotropic traits in multiple allelic series. (For more details see Stern, 1930; Goldschmidt, 1938*a*; Caspari, 1952.) In most multiple allelic series it is possible to arrange the major effects in a quantitatively increasing series. But if other pleiotropic effects are considered, these may follow the same seriation or they may have a very different order. These facts were much discussed a generation ago, when the problem was whether or not multiple alleles are dosage differences of genes. (See, e.g., *pro,* Goldschmidt, 1927; *contra,* Dobzhansky, 1930*a*; and other material in Stern, 1930.) They are no longer relevant for this problem, since multiple alleles are known to be of very different types, with dosages entering only in the form of potencies of action, as we have seen. However, even if a series of alleles produces its orderly quantitative effect by affecting one and the same reaction differently, for example, by changing the rate and (or) the quantity of the end product, which is probably the rule, other pleiotropic effects will follow the same order only if they are directly controlled by the same reaction. If this is not so, the effects are secondary or are effects of interference. The order of the other characters depends upon the developmental system in which they appear. I once used the following model, which may be varied in many ways (Goldschmidt, 1932*a*): let us assume A, B, C, D to be successive points in development at which the alleles m_1, m_2, m_3, m_4 act. One action determines the quantity of pigment in a linear series proportional to the time of onset (A, B, C, D) of the reaction determined by the alleles. Another consequence (direct, indirect, by interference) of this reaction would be to affect the speed of growth of another organ in a plus or minus direction. Let us now assume—this is "the developmental system" of the case—that normal growth of this part (which is independently determined) occurs in the following seriation at the times A, B, C, D: growth in breadth—in length—in length—in breadth. Now the alleles m_1–m_4 would produce the seriation of length-breadth index in favor of length: $- + + -$, that is, a seriation different from that of the pigment series. Similar models may be constructed also for specific biochemical events, in which a single reaction progressing at a definite rate in different alleles affects different processes of synthesis in an order not depending upon that rate, but upon the substrates available or not available at different times for independent reasons. Thresholds, quantities of specific enzymes, and so on could also come into play. A model of this type was used by S. Emerson (1950) to explain the interrelations of threonin-less mutants in *Neurospora.* Other possibilities of a similar type are mentioned by Haldane (1954): each allele might produce a series of enzymes with different absolute specificities, or hormones stimulating growths in different parts of the body, in different amounts, or qualitatively different products, each with a range of specificity, like esterases or adrenaline-like bases (quoted in III 5 C *b*).

This discussion shows how difficult it is to find a simple explanation for all types of pleiotropy including that in multiple alleles, though, in a general way, we seem to find at work all the different features of genic action we have always encountered. One more example will be added in order to show that our problem might overlap a completely different one, pseudoallelism. I have repeatedly cited multiple allelic series controlling more or less complicated pattern differences, as in coccinellid beetles and in grasshoppers. I mentioned also that in grasshoppers well-known loci, influencing pattern, are located in a small section of one chromosome (Nabours and Stebbins, 1950). The suspicion thus arose that multiple alleles controlling patterns belong to the group of pseudoalleles, meaning, in Lewis' interpretation, different genes, derived by duplication; in our interpretation, effects of chromosomal sections within which any change produces an allelic and similar action. If a pattern effect is involved, we may call it a pleiotropic action upon different parts of an animal or plant and thus understand the result as a combination of pleiotropy and pseudoallelism. If, as in the examples quoted, a pigment pattern is the effect and if the pigment is always the same, the problem discussed earlier for the flour moth enters: the competence or non-competence of different cells for depositing the pigment, the possibility of which is otherwise genetically present in all cells.

Some examples in plants cover the situation just described, for example, Stadler's (1946 ff.) R-r series in maize and the R series in cotton. The latter (following Stephens' review, 1951*a*) involves anthocyanin, which is chemically always the same. This pigment may be deposited at the base and periphery of the petals and in different shades at each place; further, at different places on the vegetative parts of the plant and also upon the anther. In the Asiatic cottons a large series of multiple alleles is known, each of which controls a definite pattern of pigmented parts. As in the other cases mentioned, an orderly arrangement of the effects in one part (e.g., the base of petals) does not parallel the order of grades for another point of the pattern. Thus, while we can explain the pattern as such by the competence of cell groups which is determined independently (including inhibition of synthesis), and the grading of multiple allelic action as such by features of the kinetics of anthocyanin synthesis, the disorderliness of the different effects when listed simultaneously requires another, independently determined developmental system for which we have just presented a model. This would be a purely physiological interpretation, leaving out of consideration the nature of the multiple alleles and considering only their actions and interactions. But a completely different type of interpretation has been proposed, namely, the presence of a set of pseudoalleles, of which at least three (probably more) are needed (Silow and Yu, 1942; Yu and Chang, 1948, quoted from Stephens): one controlling pigment in the vegetative parts; one for a white ghost spot at the base of the petals; and one which, together with the last, produces the basal spot on the petals. The different effects of the allelic series are then a consequence of crossing over between the pseudoalleles. We are not interested here in the details of this explanation (which is not accepted by Stephens), which, after all, is the product of the tendency to circumvent difficulties in the explanation of genic actions by distributing them among different genes (or by splitting a gene into subgenes, as Stadler preferred). The point I wish to make is to emphasize the difficulty of drawing conclusions concerning genic actions when, in cases like those mentioned here, we are not even sure whether or not we are dealing with simple events of a type underlying all genic actions.

In still another way the problem of pleiotropy touches the problem of pseudoallelism. The eye-color locus vermilion (v) in *Drosophila* may be said to be pleiotropic (though not in the usual sense of the term), so far as v produces vermilion eyes and a condition which may be reversed by the presence of specific suppressors. Green (1954) has described pseudoalleles of v which produce the eye color but do not react to the suppressors. From this he concludes that the two pseudoalleles are "different genes" and that my interpretation of pseudoalleles does not hold. He forgets that within a multiple allelomorphic series, individual members may act differently as suppressors, as I showed for the silver series (1945*a*). This situation is the reverse of that in the v alleles, but it shows that suppressor actions as such (active or passive) may differ among multiple alleles, which vitiates Green's arguments.

This subject may one day become important for the analysis of the chromosomal basis of heredity. It is remarkable how many examples of pseudoallelism as well as of accumulation of loci in a chromosomal section are known to be connected with a pattern effect of a pleiotropic type. We find this in the position effect sections of the *Drosophila* chromosomes. The yellow position effect of a break within a well-defined section (as studied above) may affect the entire body, which is yellow, or it may leave the bristles partially or totally unaffected.

The scute mutants and position effects remove definite bristles, but different ones in different alleles, which had led to projecting the phenotypic pattern into a chromosomal pattern in Serebrovsky's theory of step-allelism. We do not know whether the unusually large series of multiple alleles controlling the black patterns on the wings of coccinellid beetles are also based upon a set of pseudoallelic mutants permitting crossing over within their chromosomal section of pigment pattern control. But today we should expect such a condition, also for Nabours' closely linked pattern genes in the grouse locust. Whether the same is true for the color spots in cotton we do not know. But for the parallel case of flower and aleurone color in maize (the a and r loci as studied by Laughnan and Stadler) the separation of "two adjacent genes" by crossing over has succeeded. All these are cases in which non-parallelism of pleiotropic effects among multiple alleles had been observed. This suggests that within the chromosomal section of a definite action (e.g., yellow pigment, removal of bristles, deposition of anthocyanin) the details of the effect (its pattern) do not depend upon independently controlled local competence but are somehow connected with the location of the disturbance within the pattern of the chromosomal section. (This would be clearly the element of truth contained in Serebrovsky and Dubinin's step-allelism; Muller has repeatedly hinted at his belief that after all there is still something left of this discarded theory.) At present it is hardly possible to present a convincing interpretation of this situation. But one thing I consider as certain: such facts exclude Lewis' idea of the subsequent biochemical steps controlled by the seriated parts of the chromosomal section, his pseudoallelic genes, since the biochemical effect is always the same, but not the point in space where it takes place.

c. The time dimension

In all discussions of the interplay of genic actions the dimension of time is of paramount importance. No orderly development is possible if the individual, genically controlled effects are not properly timed. Thus the timing played a considerable role in our earlier discussions of the meaning of genic activation. We met with it in the discussion of temperature-sensitive periods, of the critical periods for the production of phenocopies, and of the timed series of actions of the multiple alleles at the vestigial locus of *Drosophila,* and in many other places. The timing of genic effects becomes apparent with special clarity in the action of lethal deficiencies of *Drosophila* as studied by Poulson (1940, 1945) and Hadorn (1948). Poulson studied the development of *Drosophila* with more or less large and different lethal deficiencies in homozygous condition, in order to find out the time of action of the loci the absence of which causes death. It turned out that eggs without an X-chromosome—the extreme—stopped development during the first hour. The blastoderm nuclei do not succeed in reaching the surface in most parts. If only the right half of the X is missing, death occurs in the second hour and only an incomplete blastoderm is formed. With the other half of the X missing, a blastoderm is formed but no germinal layers, and death occurs in the third hour. With different Notch deficiencies, the stoppage of development occurs after six hours when the first organs are formed. The nervous system hypertrophies; mesodermal organs and entoderm are lacking. It can be shown that these effects are not simply a result of the missing quantity of chromatin. As all Notch deficiencies of very different length give the same result, it is clearly the absence of definite sections which is responsible. From this it is concluded that individual "genes" control the major developmental processes from the very beginning and that each has its definite time of action. Specifically it is concluded that one such locus (facet-Notch) is indispensable for the formation of some of the organ primordia. Another such locus with a lethal action, if absent, is the white locus; all deficiencies containing it produce lethality after twelve to sixteen hours.

Hadorn, who made comparable studies involving transplantations of organs between normal and lethal larvae, proposes the following interpretation. He distinguishes between vital loci, the absence of which is always lethal, and less vital loci which might fall out without major harm. The deficiency effects found by Poulson are always due to one such vital locus: the one which has an irreplaceable function at the earliest time of embryonic development. To each of these a time is allocated at which the deficiency effects become visible; this, of course, is not the same as saying that the locus begins action at this time, but only that the lack of action becomes critical at this time. (This means to me a threshold type effect, conditioned by the other simultaneous genic actions.) Hadorn concludes (now extrapolating upon the normal function) that definite genes are already in specific control of the first processes of embryogenesis, and that the loci in the chromosomes of embryonic nuclei act in a set order, one after the other, upon early differentiation. This is the old problem of "activation of the genes," which we studied previously. As we have seen, it requires much more than an intrinsic order of genic functionality (see III 5 B *c*). Lethality, as analyzed by Poulson, is of course an effect of pleiotropic damage. I refer to the discussion of the subject in the section on pleiotropy, and especially the doubts expressed there that this specific type of pleiotropy contains much information on genic action, except that a mutant (or a deficiency) acts at a certain time in a detrimental way upon something, for example, neural fluid pressure (Bonnevie), differentiation of cartilage (Grüneberg), differentiation of mesoderm (Poulson). What the genic material does in the normal case, however, remains unknown.

d. Short cuts: inductors, hormones

In my old (1920*a*) formulation, genic action was explained as the production or catalysis of chains of reaction leading to the accumulation in quantities up to a threshold of an active substance which was called, in an enlarged meaning, a hormone (*Genwirkstoff,* or determining stuff, including specific enzymes). It is a very remarkable fact that, in the course of phylogenesis, the genic material has developed some kinds of short cuts. In the system of genic actions as it works in typical mosaic development, for example, in *Drosophila,* it is probable that the genic products are synthesized in each competent cell and either do not diffuse or do so very little (barring a few exceptions found by Sturtevant, Whiting, and Hannah; see Hannah, 1953). It seems that evolution has led to the establishment of a simplification of this procedure of determining embryonic parts cell by cell by delegating the determining power to diffusible substances of different kinds, inductors and genuine hormones. The first steps have already been made in some groups of insects other than those containing the most popular materials for genetic investigation, Diptera and Lepidoptera (see Seidel, 1936). In libellulids, for example, a formative center is established in the posterior region of the egg. The segmentation nuclei must be brought in contact with this center in order to start development. Obviously, some kind of inductor substance is produced there and diffuses to the sites of embryonic development. This comes very near to the vertebrate inductor, Spemann's organizer (see III 5 A *b*), of which nothing is left now but Holtfreter's X-substance. It turned out that the inductor substance is not a specific formative substance but a kind of generalized helper in the establishment of the major regions of the embryo. It is exactly what we just called a short cut in the control of development.

At this point a few words should be added about an exceptional case which shows a secondary genic action of a strange type. It is known that spotting in guinea pigs does not behave in a regular way, that is, in showing a fixed pattern (details in Wright, 1925). Many genetic explanations for the action of the spotting factor have been tried. It seems that Billingham and Medawar (1948, 1950) have found a very unexpected solution. They observed in the skin a system of colorless dendritic cells which have a definite arrangement and are in contact with each other. Grafting experiments involving black and white skin show that black cells can "infect" the white cells with what is probably an enzyme system, behaving like a transferable virus. The infected cells form pigment and are now able to infect other white cells. Thus a genic action, production of melanin, is not localized in individual cells as in *Drosophila;* it does not produce a diffusible substance which acts like an inductor over a large area; but it produces a cytoplasmic condition which spreads in a way comparable to an infection. This is so far a unique type of secondary genic action of the inductor or hormonic type, based upon a very different principle, though it might be possible to find analogies with Holtfreter's X-substance (see III 5 A *b*).

There can be no doubt a priori that inductor actions are under genic control as to time and place of release and, probably, also as to some kind of specificity, meaning that a lens inductor is somehow different from an inductor of mouth parts (see III 5 A *b*). But, unfortunately, a genetic analysis of inductor action is not available, if possible at all, in view of the interchangeability of inductors between classes of vertebrates. Thus the genic control of inductive processes can at present be attacked only from the side of the induced features (e.g., competence of a tissue for induction). This side of the problem has been analyzed in a former chapter.

The second type of determinative short cut is by means of the production of hormones. We know that genuine hormones of the vertebrates determine some developmental processes; the classic example is the role of the thyroid (and hypophysis) in producing metamorphosis in Amphibia. In this case also, general genetic differences are known, though not analyzed by genetic methods, showing different genetic reactivity to the stimulus among different species. This requires a system of genic action in which the production of the proper hormones at the proper time enters as one variable with an over-all effect as opposed to the localized effects of the basic genically controlled reactions. A similar case might be made out for the sex hormones in amphibian development, though there are difficulties in interpretation. The genetic analysis of frog races, different in regard to their sex-determining mechanism (R. Hertwig, Witschi), has, it seems, revealed differences only in the genetic sex determiners; genetically controlled differences in hormonic action have not been analyzed, though they can be inferred from the work of Gallien (1954). He showed the existence of a series of different responses to the sex-inverting effect of female and male hormones upon larvae of frogs and newts, according to the species used. In some species, male hormones acted positively, but not the female hormones; in others, no complete sex reversal occurred, but only intersexuality resulted, and so on. Comparable facts are available for sex hormones of birds, as discussed in my book of 1931 and numerous reviews on sex and hormones (e.g., Witschi, 1950).

The best material available deals with insects since Wigglesworth's (1934) famous discovery of hormonic glands and their action, and especially with larval molting. Insects grow by molting (the instars) and the number of molts is genetically determined. The last molt in holo- and hemimetabolic insects is the metamorphosis molt. This molting system is under the control of two types of hormones. First is the hormone secreted by the corpus allatum, the juvenile hormone. In its presence a larval molt occurs. After the last larval molt the corpus allatum ceases to function, and the second hormone, produced by the prothoracic gland, takes over (as it does after removal of the corporata allata), and metamorphosis results. Whether this is the result of absence of the juvenile hormone or only of a superior quantity of the metamorphosis hormone is a special question. There are many detailed facts on the interaction of these hormones (see Wigglesworth, 1952; Bodenstein, 1953*b*) which do not concern us here. However, it should be added that both, number of molts and type of molt, can be influenced and completely changed by external agencies. Temperature action or asphyxiation may induce precocious total or partial metamorphosis; other temperatures and hunger may change the number of molts (literature and details in Goldschmidt, 1938*a*; and Wigglesworth, 1952). Whether this is an effect upon the hormones, or upon the gland, or upon the substrate of hormonic action is not known. However, there is certainly an element of timing contained in the relation of the two types of hormonic action which has something to do with the independently determined growth processes, perhaps through some threshold conditions.

The next important point for this hormonic action is, just as for the parallel direct genic actions, the condition of the substrate, the larval epidermis, or its competence. There is no reason why this competence should behave identically in different forms. If, for example

(Piepho, 1942), pieces of skin of just hatched lepidopteran larvae can pupate in the absence of the juvenile hormone, it seems that here competence of the substrate is not reached by a progressing condition during larval life. But if in *Drosophila* (Bodenstein, 1943) different discs become competent for reaction to hormones in definite order, this clearly shows a phenomenon of independently determined competence. The latter case is of special importance for our analysis of the role of the hormones within the system of genic actions. A very good case has been made by Bodenstein (1953*b*), who showed that in *Periplaneta* the formative material becomes increasingly susceptible with age to the differentiation promoting prothoracic gland hormone up to the adult condition. This is shown when the genital apparatus of an adult female is transplanted into a younger host and actually molts, while remaining adult; whereas a genital anlage of a not yet adult female, in the same situation, molts almost like a larval (nymphal) structure. A number of comparable cases are known, and, under special experimental conditions, it is even possible that the opposite happens: under corpus allatum influence, adult skin may molt into nymphal skin (Wigglesworth).

One more point in the interplay of these hormones is relevant to our discussion. According to Wigglesworth, the prothoracic gland hormone (the differentiation-inducing one) is released before the juvenile hormone in the initiation of molting; consequently the developing tissues are subjected for a short time to the differentiation hormone alone, which provides the stimulus for the progress of differentiation from stage to stage, while the succeeding juvenile hormone inhibits the process up to the time of metamorphosis, when it is obviously absent or in too low concentration. Thus a remarkable interplay of these hormones pulling in different directions is established. There is an interesting corollary to this. We mentioned the extra molt of adult structures (genitalia) under the influence of the molting hormone, but the resulting structure was the same as before; that is, no further differentiation was possible. But Bodenstein (1953*b*) also found organs (the sternum of *Periplaneta*) which molted into a superadult condition, going in the same direction beyond the adult stage. Clearly this is an example of different substrates reacting to the same stimulus.

We come now to what is known on the genetic side. Molting in Lepidoptera is also controlled genetically, since there are races that differ according to the number of larval molts. In the silkworm, races with three to five molts are known (see Tanaka's review, 1953). In

Lymantria dispar there are races that have four molts in both sexes, others with four in the male and five in the female, and others with five in both sexes. In *Lymantria* we know (Goldschmidt, 1933*a*) that the genic control of growth as such is based upon multiple factor inheritance and different setups in different races. The genetics of the molting races has been worked out for the silkworm by Ogura (1931). The details are not very simple, but Ogura accounts for them by a series of multiple alleles plus modifier systems. In *Lymantria* I could account for the facts satisfactorily by a series of three alleles: T_1 produces four molts in both sexes; T_2, four in the male, five in the female; and T_3, five in both sexes. (We might have mentioned this case when discussing dosage compensation. Here is another example of a situation in which the same autosomal mutant acts differently in the developmental systems of the two sexes.) The different developmental systems may be illustrated by the different details of the growth curves. In this genetic system we are dealing clearly with the same type discussed before, involving kinetics of genic action, threshold conditions, and so on; this is demonstrated by the fact that (in the silkworm) variation into the next higher or lower type exists, and that the number of molts can be modified by temperature action (Ogura, 1931; Kühn and Piepho, 1936) or by hunger (Goldschmidt, 1933*a*).

In this case we know that the direct cause of the molts is found in the hormonic system, and therefore its functioning is under genic control. The number of molts is, of course, determined by the occurrence of the last, the metamorphosing molt. This again is the result either of stoppage of the function of the corpora allata or of decrease of their hormonic production with increase of that of the thoracic gland. The role of the mutant loci controlling the number of molts thus can have any of the following functions: (1) to time the ending of corpus allatum secretion; (2) to control the total amount of juvenile hormone which can be synthesized; (3) to control the threshold conditions for the thoracic gland hormone concentration which overtakes that of the other hormone, a function which may be related to relative speeds of two genically controlled processes. (Wigglesworth has pointed out the similarity of such an action to the one at work in the control of intersexuality in *Lymantria* by two competing reactions of different speed.) Whether one of these possibilities, or still another, obtains, certainly the genically controlled reactions are not simply the hormone-producing ones but reactions interlinked with others which in some completely unknown way finally control the function of the hormonic glands.

An interesting fact which shows that the substrates for hormonic action belong somehow to the same genic reaction system is found in the phenomenon of prothetely. This means that parts of the body may be in advance of the development of the rest. One example is the *Lymantria dispar* caterpillar, in which only the antennae undergo the pupal molt while the caterpillar itself may live long beyond the normal span of its life without molting any more. In this case (Goldschmidt, 1923*d*) it was found that the condition was hereditary in a definite line. How this mutant (not analyzed further) localizes the hormonic action and prevents it in the rest of the body is difficult to visualize.

Thus far we have discussed the relations between genic actions and hormones only in animals. Actually one should expect that much more insight could be gained from plants (see Thimann, 1952; Wardlaw, 1952). It seems that in plants, hormones (phytohormones, auxins, etc.) play a role in morphogenesis which is incomparably more important than the corresponding role of hormones in animals. (I am speaking now only of genuine, diffusible hormones.) There can be no doubt that morphogenesis is impossible in plants without such hormonic action and that, therefore, phytohormones should constitute a major subject of physiological genetics in plants. In spite of an immense literature on the subject, it seems that the genetical side of the problem has hardly been touched; this means the comparison of hormonic action under known genetic differences. If a mutant of a snapdragon changes the zygomorph flower into a radiate one, we should like to know whether a different distribution of a phytohormone can be located in the flower primordium. Many types of experiments can be imagined which would link genic differences with phytohormones as morphogenetic substances. Very few are available. For example, in *Hyoscyamus niger* there are annual and biennial forms, differing in a single pair of mutant loci. Melchers (1937; see 1952) grafted shoots of annual flowering plants on first-year biennial stocks, with the result that the latter flowered. The reciprocal graft gave corresponding results. This might mean that the mutant locus was concerned with production or inhibition of a flowering hormone. However, since both races will eventually produce flowers, it might also mean that the always present hormone reaches a threshold level sooner or later. In neither case can we say that the genic action produces a morphogenetic substance, a hormone, which forces development into the path of specific processes leading to a flower. It is more probable that the hormone concentration does not determine a flower but is one of the chemical conditions for allowing the genically determined flower formation to take place sooner or later. This situation may be compared to that of the molting hormones of insect larvae; in both cases the presence of a hormone is needed for the initiation of a genically controlled over-all process of development. Annual and biennial growth would then be comparable to four and five molts in the insect.

A similar experiment was made by Stein (1939). A sterile mutant of snapdragon, forming a non-flowering axis, was grafted to normal stock and developed flower buds. The comparison with the insect case is enhanced by the fact that these "florigens" are not specific, just as with the molting hormones, in both cases demonstrated by grafting. We suggest, further, that Melchers' experiments on vernalization (see II 2 B) point in the same direction and that, *mutatis mutandis,* Hämmerling's work on *Acetabularia* (III 2) can be interpreted in the same way. Another point of comparison between the animal and the plant is the role of timing. Many botanists more or less accept Lysenko's phase theory, which, in zoölogical terms, and stripped of Lysenko's mystical connotations, means that environmental or genic action can take place only when the plant has reached the proper level of competence. However, many facts do not agree with this theory, which interests us here only so far as it means that the time dimension, in the form of successively developing competence, would play a role also in the determinative processes of plants.

The facts just mentioned and the extensive body of facts on phytohormones suggest that what we called the short cut via hormonic action for integrating more complicated developmental processes plays a superior role in the system of genetic determination of plants, a view which is held especially by Went (see Went and Thimann, 1937). We expect, therefore, the most important results for our problem when plant geneticists, following Melchers, will use the physiology of hormonic action to build up the special type of physiological genetics which is accessible only in plants. Unfortunately, thus far the attack has been only physiological and has not yielded much information for the geneticist. Wardlaw (1952) has recently scrutinized the available material in order to find links between hormone physiology, morphogenesis, and genetics. His conclusions are not very encouraging. To quote: "The data . . . make it clear that the inception and subsequent development of the several organs and the differentiation of tissues, are correlated with the presence of growth regulating substances. But how, in any one instance, the specific substance acts as an organ-forming, or as a tissue-differentiating, agent does not emerge from this survey. It may indeed be questioned whether the relationship is one of cause and effect . . . But what can equally be said is, that if the specific substance is not present, the formation of certain organs, or the differentiation of certain tissues, will not (or may not) take place. Viewed in this more general way, the activating substance may be said to be morphogenetic. But we have no definite knowledge of specific leaf-, shoot-, root-, or flower-forming substances . . . The morphogenetic action, insofar as it can be so described, of a substance such as indoleacetic acid is very varied indeed. It is primarily concerned with growth, not with the inception of particular forms or patterns. Hence, Avery [1940] has said that the specificity of response resides, not in the substance applied, but in the tissues of the species being treated [compare with sex hormones in vertebrates: R.B.G.] and Hammer [1938] has remarked that no single tissue, or tissue system, responds either quantitatively or qualitatively in the same manner in the various species investigated. We have also seen that, within a single species, some tissues are considerably more sensitive and responsive to stimulation than others. So, however essential and important it may be, a growth-regulating substance is only one factor in morphogenetic processes . . .

"Whether we are concerned with organs or tissues, the main conclusion from our survey is that biochemical factors must act in conjunction with other factors to produce the morphogenetic effect. But it may well be that the biochemical factor is the master factor in the situation . . . Growth-regulating substances and other important metabolites are probably gene-controlled. Thus, although the supporting evidence is still far from adequate, and the situation to be explained seldom of a simple kind, we begin to see that the new investigations of morphogenesis are likely to be fruitful. This effect . . . is essentially a matter of controlled biochemical activity, activating or growth-regulating substances being specially important in the inception or inhibition of growth in particular regions of the organisms. But such actions alone cannot be said to account for the actual form or pattern which is assumed . . ."

e. Mutational changes of determination; regulation and integration

One of the most interesting chapters of genic interaction relates to the genically controlled changes in primary determination processes.

The best information is derived from the so-called homoeotic mutants in *Drosophila,* in which one type of segmental organ is changed into another: an antenna into a tarsus or a whole leg, a wing into a leglike structure or a haltere-like organ, a haltere into a wing, and so on. Such mutants have been studied extensively in regard to genetics and physiological genetics. A large number of experiments have been performed with aristopedia, a mutant (ss^a) which transforms the arista of the antenna into a part of a leg, a tarsus. In some alleles this transformation is always complete; in others the penetrance is incomplete and the expressivity highly variable from normal through many transitions to aristopedia. The earlier experiments, based upon a simple interpretation which I had proposed, consisting of combining ss^a with other mutants affecting the legs or with mutants changing developmental time, showed that timing of developmental features played a role (Braun, 1940, 1942; Villee, 1943, 1944, 1945, 1946) but that not all facts could be explained simply (Waddington, 1940*a*). M. Vogt (1946, 1947) then showed that a much more complicated system was responsible for the results obtained by combining transplantation techniques with genetical and environmental actions. In development the first visible differentiation (segmentation) of the antennal disc appears before the corresponding process in the legs, and this both in + and ss^a flies. The penetrance and expressivity of the tarsus character of the antenna are increased with lower temperature, and the transforming effect upon the arista, in different degrees of expression, increases from the proximal to the distal. The temperature-effective period lasts from early development into the pupal period, though the quantity of effect decreases during this period of labile determination. Though the tarsal segments of both legs and antenna differentiate late in aristopedia, there is one early difference: in the antenna which transforms into a tarsus, the tip segment of the anlage is larger from the beginning.

It was then found that the transformation of the arista segment into tarsus is linked with an intensive growth of this segment. A proof for the causal meaning of this was found when an explanted disc of ss^a was treated with colchicine to stop growth and was reimplanted; now it formed an arista, no tarsus. The fact that a completely unspecific interference with growth produces the specific effect suggests that the action of the mutant ss^a is also an unspecific effect upon growth of the arista segment. Here it should be mentioned also that the aristopedia phenotype has been produced as a phenocopy by different means (Bodenstein and Abdel-Malek, 1949; Rapoport, 1947;

Goldschmidt, unpublished). Differential growth alone would, however, not explain the specificity of the transformation, and therefore Vogt is forced to assume the presence of a "leg inductor" which is always available and comes into action when growth changes. Vogt assumes that the antennal disc always contains a leg inductor. In the antenna of the wild-type fly the antennal inductor (for arista) is above the threshold quantity, while in ss^a the leg inductor is made to surpass the threshold concentration (which could be expressed also in terms of control of competition for a substrate). An alternative interpretation is that in ss^a the mutant locus produces the extra growth of the end segment, as reported, which in turn results in an earlier or higher reactivity to the leg inductor.

At this point we should discuss how the different grades of penetrance and expressivity fit into this scheme. Exposure to cold in the temperature-effective period increases the higher, tarsus-like classes of expression, which means that at this time the tissue of the end knob still has the potency to react at a different rate and (or) strength to the leg inductor, or to produce or use varying amounts of it. The rate of growth, slowed by cold, has something to do with the effect, while stoppage of growth by colchicine has the opposite effect. The later the action of cold sets in, the lower the expressivity of the tarsus effect; this must mean that the lability of determination is narrowed down progressively during the labile period or, expressed positively, that irreversible determination increases with time (labile determination), which again means some kind of threshold phenomenon. Since, with low expressivity, the basal part of the arista shows a tarsus-like structure for the longest time, while the distal part is arista-like, one might think of some gradient of determination. But the distal end can still be made to become tarsus-like at the end of the labile period, which is not in favor of a simple gradient concept. One might say there is a gradient of determination (determination stream) but not of irreversible determination. (This might be considered an example for Harrison's 1937 contention that there is no real irreversible determination.) Finally, the fact that high classes of tarsus formation cannot be induced after a certain time links the gradient of determination either with a gradient of growth from base to tip, or with a superimposed gradient of more or less irreversible determination in the same direction.

This analysis shows how a mutant locus may interfere with primary processes of embryonic determination by changing one variable in a complicated system, each cog of which is determined independently by genic action. The normal result requires the interplay of at least two determining stuffs with competition for a common substrate or threshold conditions, with timed processes of growth; or timed and directed gradients of determination during a labile period; or timed ending of the labile period and increasing irreversibility. The mutant might possibly interfere with only one of the integrated processes (e.g., initial growth of the end segment of the anlage) in order to produce an orderly upset of the entire determinative system, which probably contains the typical ingredients of all such systems, determining stuffs, gradients, exact timing, threshold conditions.

The topic is so important for the theory of genic control of development that another remarkable example will be discussed: the mutants of the podoptera and tetraltera group in *Drosophila* (Goldschmidt, Hannah, and Piternick, 1951; Rapoport, 1943; Goldschmidt, 1952*a,b*). Here the mutant or mutants (multiple factors, major mutants, and minor modifiers are at the genetic basis) produce complicated structures instead of a wing, leglike appendages, structures resembling a haltere (tetraltera), and transformation of definite parts of the wing anlage into thorax. Again these effects show variable penetrance and expressivity from an almost normal wing through all transitions to the extremest type with no wing and a duplicated thorax.

It is known that the mesothoracic imaginal disc is determined very early (probably already in the embryo; Geigy, 1931; Henke *et al.*, 1941), so that the genic actions to be analyzed occur before any differentiation is visible. The dorsal mesothoracic disc produces most of the dorsal and lateral walls of the thorax and the wings. The wing part of the disc becomes visible first in the pre-pupa, when it separates from the thoracic part and assumes a kind of segmentation by the appearance of transverse folds. This condition might be compared with that of all other appendages so far as the wing starts as a trisegmented rudiment and its growth and differentiation into a wing blade occur mostly in the tip segment.

The series of the expression of mutant action requires the assumption (already anticipated by Berlese on grounds of comparative morphology for the insect wing in general) that the wing anlage has four centers of independent determination for, in an anterior-posterior order, (1) the anterior cubital region of the wing (leaving aside a still more anterior part not relevant for the present discussion); (2) and (3) the rest of the wing blade (2 and 3 being the anterior and posterior halves); (4) the alula, which is rather independent also in the finished wing. The decisive action of the pod (podoptera) and tet (tetraltera) loci consists in disturbing the common differentiation of the four anlagen (centers, fields, territories, in the language of experimental embryology) by forcing them to differentiate separately, with strange consequences. The amount of the final effect, visible as penetrance and expressivity, varies through a series of grades. Clearly there is, as in the former example, a period of labile determination; the earlier the pod and tet action produces the separation of the four embryonic fields, the more extreme are the transformations of the wing. We consider these now individually.

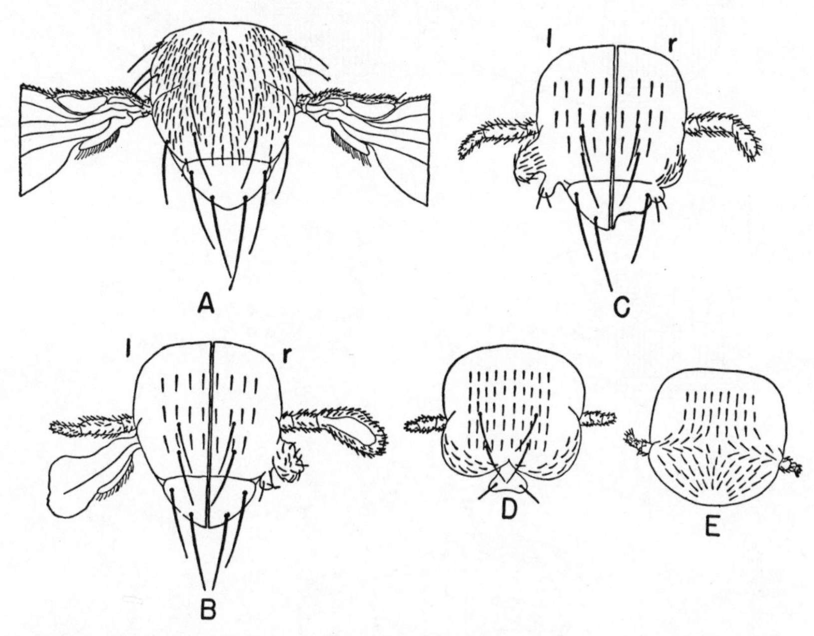

Fig. 21. Series of thorax structure of mutant tetraltera in *D. melanogaster*, including scutellum and wings showing changes of determination in these organs. Semidiagrammatic. (From Goldschmidt, 1952*b*.)

The anterior anlage, the cubital one, may be separated alone (figs. 21, 22); the rest of the wing may then form more or less normal wing tissue. The cubital part, however, transforms into a trisegmented leglike structure, the wing leg of podoptera. The way in which this happens introduces a new feature into our discussion of genic action. At the "raw edge," where the anlage is separated from the posterior end, a mirror-image half of the cubital part with its two rows of marginal hair is formed, thus transforming the cubital part into a symmetrical whole, which assumes the leglike structure. This means, in terms of embryology, that the genic action separating the cubital field with the result of a "raw edge" posteriorly sets in motion the embryonic power of regulation by production of a mirror-image half. This power of regulation is one of the most mysterious properties of development, but a much discussed fact. Here we see it coming into

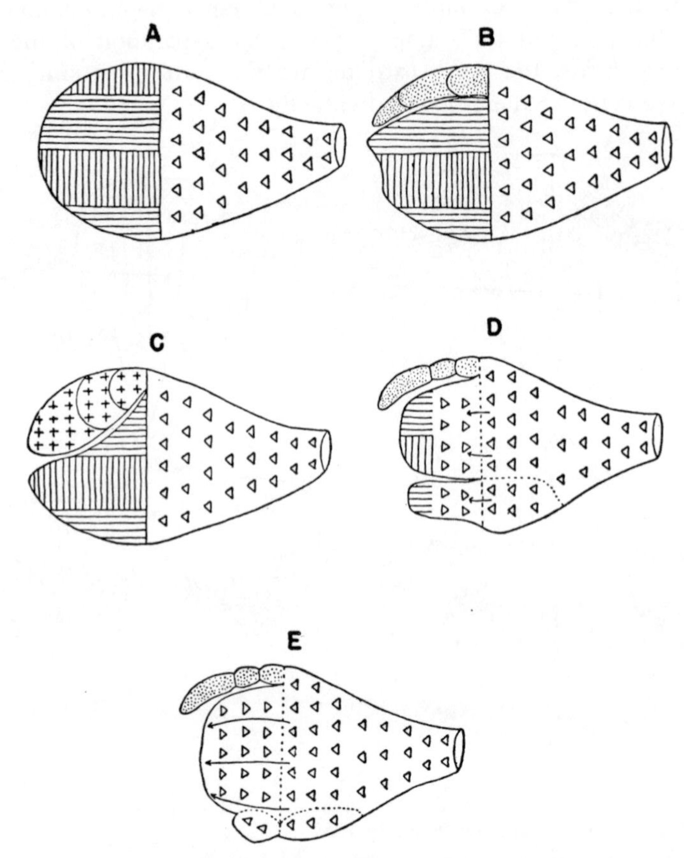

Fig. 22. Diagram of wing (crosshatched) and thoracic discs (triangles) in a series of stages, explaining change of determination in development of tetraltera. (From Goldschmidt, 1952*b*.)

play as a consequence of a genic action which is just the same as if an experimenter had made a cut between the two embryonic fields, a type of experiment known to set regulative processes into motion in numerous cases studied by experimental embryologists.

A variant of the preceding features produces the tetraltera type. If the interruption of the quadripartite anlage separates the cubital field plus the following anterior wing field from the rest, again a mirror-image regulation occurs which now produces a trisegmented structure, the tip segment of which is inflated. If this structure has time (depending upon the time of incidence of the split) to consolidate, the resulting structure greatly resembles a haltere. There is reason for the belief that the normal haltere is homologous only to the anterior half of the wing. The stages of transformation of a haltere into a wing in the mutant tetraptera (Astauroff, 1929) bear this out.

The next grade of transformation of the wing anlage in pod and especially tet is produced when one cleft separates the cubital part (with or without a part of the anterior wing blade) at an early stage, and another cleft separates the posterior wing and alula anlage. If this happens, the parts behind the cubital cleft cease to be determined as wing, but become redetermined as thorax and assume the structure of one-half scutum in mirror image, from the wing blade, and one-half mirror-imaged scutellum, from the alula anlage. It is impossible that material of the thoracic disc takes part in this transformation: the thorax remains always perfect and unaffected. Either the thoracic disc acts as an inductor for thoracic structure in the wing anlage or the wing anlage contains—in strict comparison with aristopedia—both wing and thorax inductors, the latter of which gains ascendancy in the mutant. However, the cubital part never is affected by the thoracic inductor, but always forms its wing leg or a rudimentary segmented palpus or the haltere-like structure. It seems that the anterior part of the wing bud contains cubitus inductor, leg inductor, and haltere inductor; the rest of the disc, wing inductor and thorax inductor. Thus the discussion of aristopedia applies in its general form also to this case. A new factor is that the adjacent thoracic disc influences the redetermination of wing anlage into thorax at least to the extent of determining its laterality (mirror image). But this may be something different from induction, belonging, rather, to the phenomenon of regulation, as mirror imaging is typical for superregeneration (Bateson's law).

The series of tetraltera transformations includes a still more extreme case of embryonic regulation and integration which takes place after the redetermination of wing anlage into thorax. If this redetermination takes place very early, the development of the posterior wing part into an appendix (even one with the structure of a half thorax) ceases. Instead, we find all stages of the incorporation of the wing anlage into the general structure of the thorax. In the end, the wing anlage is pushed behind the genuine thorax and incorporated into a larger thorax, the anterior half of which is real thorax and the posterior half a mirror image of it, the wing origin of which could never be suspected if found alone. In the process both scutella, the real one and the mirror image from alula anlage, are crowded out and disappear. This is an extreme example of how embryonic regulation can make a completely new whole out of two completely different structural parts, once the normal alignment and determination has been changed by a genically controlled action upon one focal embryological condition.

In detail the processes may be of different order, as far as the relative roles of induction, redetermination, and regulation come into play. If we think of the stages in which an appendix of wing type, a pseudo-wing, is formed—anteriorly the histological differentiation (all bristles) being that of a half scutum; posteriorly, of a half scutellum—clearly two things are superimposed upon each other: primary wing determination and secondary thorax determination in the same organ. It might be said that gross morphology keeps some of its original determination, but for stoppage of growth and differentiation. The latter are of the newly determined type. This redetermination might mean the "victory" of an ever present thorax determiner. But it could also mean that the stoppage of wing growth and the eversion of the wing disc in a wrong position with broad attachment to the thorax produces a situation of the type which we called a "raw edge," and that embryonic regulation sets in, transforming the available tissue into a mirror image of the adjacent normal part, the thorax. The "redetermination" would then combine features of mosaic and inductive development plus regulatory processes. It presupposes also something which we called "labile determination." All this fits in with a discussion by Stern (1940) of mosaic development within imaginal discs, where he pointed out that the early fixation of prospective significance of different discs, as wholes, is not in contradiction with a less rigid cell lineage of parts within a disc.

I refrain from discussing further details, which concern experimental embryology more than genetics. For our purposes, the study of integration of genically controlled actions into a unified and orderly development, the main points are obvious. They are the amazing interplay of all the different types of genic action (which we have discussed and which will be enumerated again below) by a rather rigid system of control of quality, timing, direction, threshold conditions, segregations and movements of material, over-all effects of diffusible substances, and so on. To these must be added the setting in motion of the regulatory processes which seem to be a primary property of all cells in contact with each other. These processes, if set in motion in a definite way by genically controlled embryonic situations, might provide another short cut for genic actions, meaning unavoidable (pleiotropic) consequences of these actions which extend and therefore simplify the picture of genic interplay.

Some data relating to the present discussion have been presented by Waddington (1953*b*) in his study of interaction of different mutants. As far as the facts go, they are in general agreement with those found in the studies of homoeotic mutants. A special study of genetics and embryology of some imaginal discs of *Drosophila* by Hadorn (see 1948; and Hadorn and Gloor, 1946), comes still nearer to our discussion, though the details are infinitely more simple. The experiments dealt with the genital disc, which in the female produces a number of internal and external sex organs, visible only at metamorphosis: uterus, oviduct, the single receptaculum seminis, the two spermathecae and parovaria, and further, on the surface, the two vaginal plates and the anal plates. The fields for all these differentiations are finally determined as early as the third larval stage. This was shown by cutting the disc in pieces and reimplanting them: each gave only what it would have given within the whole. At one point, however, a regulation was found possible: when a small exterior piece was cut off, it could produce more vaginal plates and spines than it should. The cut produced a "raw edge" which induced some regulation. The male genital disc, however, is capable of much more regulation.

There is a mutant called "spermatheca" which affects only the organ of its name: either the ducts of the two spermathecae unite; or the paired organs unite in one; or three organs are formed. Each type can be obtained alone by temperature treatment at definite times. This shows that number and form of spermathecae in the mutant are determined finally only in the second half of the third larval instar, though in the wild form the experiments reported above show that the disc was already finally determined at this time. Hence it must be assumed that the mutant spt prolongs the labile state of determination; that is, it acts directly upon a time or threshold element in the system of processes called embryonic determination. Thus, in principle, the system of genic actions is comparable to that described for the pod and tet mutants, though on a simpler scale.

E. SYNOPSIS

In view of the mass of details reported and analyzed, and the variety of genically controlled processes involved, a synopsis of the whole may be attempted. Many of the authors mentioned with their specific work have tried to develop a generalized picture of genic control of development—usually with emphasis on the special group of facts and ideas with which the author is preoccupied. Many of these discussions have already been mentioned, like my own pioneering books of 1920*a* and 1927, and the numerous general papers of Sewall Wright. Many embryologists have taken part in such discussions: Brachet (1950*a*), De Beer (1951), von Ubisch (1952, 1953), Dalq (1941), Weiss (1950), Baltzer (1952), F. E. Lehmann (1945), Holtfreter (1951), and physiological geneticists like Waddington (1950), Stern (1939, 1954), Hadorn (1948), Serra (1949). In all these attempts at synopsis, the individual facts and points of view contained in the foregoing chapters are marshaled with preference given to one or the other aspect. We shall try to apportion the roles of the different views to whatever proved or imagined genic actions may enter the total picture.

The general problem is one of pattern formation, a tridimensional pattern resulting from four-dimensional processes, and this problem is the same for genetics and experimental embryology. I have tried repeatedly to use a simpler, two-dimensional model for the general processes involved (e.g., the pattern on the insect wing; Goldschmidt, 1920*a*, 1927, 1938*a*). The genically controlled actions involved were order, timing and threshold conditions of the decisive processes, centers of diffusion (outlets) of determining stuffs, their path (the determination stream), and relation with growth processes. Many detailed facts have since been added (especially by Henke and his students; see 1935, 1948*b*, 1953), but the general picture, that is, the processes which can be used as a general model for genic interaction, has not changed much. Henke, who has contributed so much to the descriptive, experimental, and genetical analysis of the subject, has drawn the following picture (discussion by Henke in Waddington's 1950 paper). Comparative morphology has led to the conclusion that chains of consecutive processes of diversification occur comparable to the chains of induction in organ development. The first link, the primary patterning in an otherwise undifferentiated blastema, requires definite ideas involving colloid chemistry. (This is what I called stratification and compared to the production of Liesegang rings, which is a colloidal phenomenon.) The next link in the chain is the use of the differentiated areas as centers for further substratification. Diffusible determining stuffs are more or less involved with all-or-none effects upon cells. (This is what I called the determination stream leading to final determination directly or by way of a labile period.) There might be a third link, when the subterritories of the second link work once more as a center (I called it points of outlet) for still another set of determinations. To this system may be added growth processes of a different kind. (For a detailed analysis see Goldschmidt, 1938*a*; and Henke, 1935.)

This model certainly contains some of the main elements of any genic action in control of pattern, and it leaves room for all the individual types of collaborating processes studied before. If we try to form a picture of the entire process, we should first emphasize one important point. The genic control of patterning must not mean that there is genic interference with every single observable process of diversification, as is postulated in some of the more naïve ideas of statistically minded geneticists, who introduce particular genes plus a modifier system for the control of any differentiating action. Actually, in the process of patterning, a great role is played by what we called short cuts, meaning over-all consequences of a single genically controlled process, working like an avalanche when started. These short cuts are found at different levels of development. In most eggs a stratification of cytoplasmic materials of different prospective potency occurs even before fertilization under genetic control (see II 2 A). This predetermination is clearly a self-perpetuating process which lasts for some time in development without further genic interference, as experimental embryology, especially of echinoderms, has shown (e.g., Boveri, Runnström, Hoerstadius, von Ubisch, Baltzer). Waddington has called this the epigenetic momentum. It is this type of fact which led to attributing predetermination to the action of cytoplasmic genes, a concept which was criticized previously, and which is indeed not more than a circumscription of our ignorance. There is no doubt that in later development such self-propelling processes, initiated only by genic action, take place, thus, I might say, alleviating the burden of the genic material in controlling developmental processes. Formation of areas of diversification in the process of organ formation might repeat such processes of epigenetic momentum. The same role of short cut is played by inductors (evocators) and embryonic hormones, as we have seen.

Regulation is another short-cut action the role of which in normal development is little known, though we found it at work in abnormal development. It is quite possible that the position of a cell or a group of cells in the whole necessarily causes (without involving special genic interference) definite features of orientation, planes of division, and direction of growth, which are integral for normal development without being under specific genic control. There is much reason to assume that such regulatory processes take place also in normal development, based upon a primary property of cells, thus far little understood, which exhibits itself beautifully in isolation experiments (Holtfreter). This would be another way of "alleviating the burden of the genic material."

Taking this for granted, genic control of pattern formation requires the interlocking of a basic group of processes with superimposed secondary and tertiary ones. The most important of these is, as embryologists have discussed since the days of His, chemodifferentiation or stratification. Whatever individual opinion one prefers—cytoplasmic stratification as a colloidal or diffusion phenomenon, or as a sorting out of plasmosomes or plasmagenes, or as an orderly sequence of mutation of plasmagenes, or any of the other theories discussed in former chapters—one cannot explain genically controlled pattern formation without localized chemodifferentiation of the cytoplasm, to which I gave a general term, "cytoplasmic stratification." This applies to primary and major differentiation of embryonic regions as well as to such detailed peripheral patterning as the formation of wing scales in a butterfly or moth. It is unknown how genic action produces such stratification. One model would be the crystal in a colloidal solution which initiates the Liesegang phenomenon. Another model would be the setting of a gradient, for gradients certainly play a great role in stratification. But how does genic action initiate a gradient? A more qualitative idea would be that the genic material produces what is probably a replica or partial replica of itself which, when moved into the cytoplasm, catalyzes the synthesis of specific enzyme systems (Spiegelman and others). But why are these sorted out in an orderly spatial arrangement in the cytoplasm? Again the process of stratification becomes more important than the biochemical nature of the products of genic action, the latter of which comes into play only at the next level of pattern formation. I consider this a very important point in view of the great appeal of biochemical and pseudobiochemical interpretations.

The next important genically controlled process is the timing of determinative steps. Differentiation during development consists of an orderly series of determinative steps by which increasingly smaller embryonic areas are narrowed down to single developmental potencies. As we have seen, the facts require a genic action which produces some substance with a definite velocity, thus emphasizing the role of the kinetics of genic action. Furthermore, threshold conditions are involved which must also be genically controlled, and which control the amount of the determining material needed for irreversible action. These basic gene-controlled processes are found to interact with simultaneous and independently controlled gradients of production or of flow of the determining stuffs, and this again is interlocked with growth processes, again independently determined.

The last basic feature is the so-called "activation of the genes," meaning that such parts of the always present total genic material become active, produce or make reactive its special products, for which the specific, competent substrate has been made available by one or the other processes of cytoplasmic diversification (stratification).

In the development of tertiary (etc.) patterns, repetitions of the primary and secondary types of basic genic action may come into play, as well as the other types of genic action I have mentioned. Here the simple biochemical actions of the one gene—one synthetic step type come into play in the control of specific products like pigments or metabolites, actions which are intracellular but allow a chance of diffusibility or migration of their products. Another such tertiary action would be the initiation of polyploidy and its consequence, stoppage of genic actions except definite types of syntheses, probably by a specific cytoplasmic segregant. Here belong also the specific genic actions on growth, initiation or stoppage of cell division, allometric growth by directly affecting the partial growth processes, which are expressed in the constants of the allometric growth formula. Gradients of growth hormones produced under genic control are a part of the picture, and so, also, are the known genically controlled effects upon the place and direction of cell division, cell elongations, and degenerations.

It seems to be impossible to construct a model that would permit us to visualize the entirety of these interplaying processes at once. Such a model would have to contain the features of the Chinese carvings of a set of ivory spheres, one inside the other; each sphere, down to the smallest, would have to contain a set of next grade spheres; and all these, again such sets. Further, each sphere and subsphere would have to contain a tridimensional set of coördinates on which the specific rate processes and quantities of products could be marked. And all this would have to be attached in the proper order to a single time coördinate. It might be possible, fulfilling Hersh's postulate (see III 5 C), to derive differential equations that cover this entire setup. But would such an equation contain any biological understanding of the processes of genic action? I think that an exact knowledge of what "stratification" signifies in known chemical and physical terms would mean much more to the geneticist than a differential equation containing all the general features of genic control of development. Here, perhaps, lies the basic difference between biology and physics, a topic so much and so differently discussed by theoretical biologists from Driesch to Bertalanffi, by innumerable philosophers, and more recently also by theoretical physicists like P. Jordan and Schrödinger. At this point, however, I must draw the line for what, in my opinion, or better, my intention, belongs to the subject matter of this book.

PART IV | GENETICS OF SEX DETERMINATION

1

INTRODUCTION

Sex, as a genetic phenomenon, has frequently been discussed in this book in relation to heterochromatin (see I 2 C *d ee*), genic balance (III 5 C *a aa*), kinetics of genic action (III 5 C *a aa*), and gene-controlled variegation (I 3 C *c dd ddd*). I have no intention of reviewing and analyzing the various details of the problem of sex determination in their entirety, which would require a volume. This has been done by me (Goldschmidt, 1920*b*, 1931, 1932*b*), by Hartmann (1943), by Witschi (1929), and for plants by Correns (1928) and by Allen (1940), not to mention more popular treatments by Crew (1927, 2d ed. 1954), and still more popular books like Caullery's (1941). What we are interested in here is the basic genetic situation as far as it can be generalized without going into the details of all established or assumed variants and, further, the relation of the facts and generalizations of the genetics of sex to those of general genetics. Thus we shall select specific aspects of the problem of sex determination which we consider to be of importance for the general theories of genetics.

The study of the genetics of sex begins with the discovery of the mechanism of the sex chromosomes (McClung, Stevens, Wilson) which established that one sex is heterogametic, the other, homogametic in regard to the X-chromosome and that, as a consequence, two types of fertilization occur, leading to 50 per cent X and 50 per cent XX individuals, the two sexes. The same fact was established on a purely formal genetic basis when Bateson and Doncaster showed that sex-linked heredity is based upon the coupling (or repulsion) of sex determiners and sex-linked genes, making sex determination comparable to a Mendelian backcross. This comparison was further confirmed when Correns found that sex behaved as a Mendelian backcross in crosses between monoecious and dioecious plants, though the introduction of monoecism complicated this example and, therefore, prevented it from exercising a major influence upon the development of the subject. The basic notions were finally established when Morgan and later Bridges proved that sex-linked loci are located in the X-chromosome, thus establishing the cytological and the Mendelian descriptions of sex determination by way of the homogamety-heterogamety and the homozygosity-heterozygosity scheme as one and the same thing.

The modern study of the genetics of sex begins with the discovery of the phenomenon of intersexuality and its separation from gynandromorphism, which permitted giving the sex chromosome mechanism a genetical and a functional meaning expressed in the quantitative or balance theory of sex determination (Goldschmidt, 1911–1920). The basic point was that definite conditions between the sexes, that is, intersexuality, could be produced at will by proper genetic combinations (crosses of subspecies of *Lymantria dispar*) without any change in the mechanism of the sex chromosomes, and this in a typical quantitative series from the female through all intergrades to the male, and from the male through all intergrades to the female, with sex reversal in both directions at the end points. The consequence was: (1) the old assumption that each sex contains the potentiality for the other sex was proved to be the result of the presence of both kinds of genetic sex determiners in either sex; (2) the existence of a quantitative relation, later termed "balance" (though it is actually an imbalance), between the two types of sex determiners decides sexuality, that is femaleness, maleness, or any grade of intersexuality; (3) one of the two types of sex determiners (male ones in female heterogamety, female ones in male heterogamety) is located within the X-chromosomes, the other one, outside of them; (4) as a consequence of this, the same determiners of one sex are faced by either one or two portions of those of the other sex in the X-chromosomes; (5) the balance system works so that two doses in the X-chromosomes are epistatic to the determiners outside the X, but one dose is hypostatic; (6) intermediate dosage (or potency) conditions in favor of one or the other of the two sets of determiners result, according to their amount, in females, males, intersexes, or sex-reversal individuals in either direction; (7) the action of these determiners in the two sexes can be understood in terms of the kinetics of the reactions controlled by the sex determiners, namely, by the attainment of a threshold of final determination by one or the other chain of reaction in early development; while in intersexuality the primary determination, owing to the 1X-2X mechanism, is overtaken sooner or later—meaning in higher or lower intersexuality—by the opposite one, so that sexual determination finishes with the other sex after this turning point. The last point is, of course, a problem of genic action.

These basic facts, which have since been established in all other comparable cases, pose a series of problems. Where are the determiners outside the X-chromosomes located? Do different types of these locations exist? How is the mechanism of balance influenced by genetic or external environment? In what way does the balance mechanism affect the control of all the different sexual attributes? Can the balance mechanism be explained in a different way? Is it possible to explain the facts without the idea of balance? Is the balance mechanism of sex determination widespread or restricted to special organisms? What other types of sex determination have been established? These and other general questions will be the subject of our discussion.

2

PRIMARY GENETIC POSSIBILITIES

If the phenomenon of genetically controlled intersexuality were not known, the mechanism of the sex chromosomes could be given a very simple, I might even say naïve, if not even primitive, meaning. We could assume that in the autosomes a number of determiners for all individual female and male traits were represented, meaning, in animals, for ovaries and testes, for female and male external and internal sex organs, for sexual differences in any part of the body (e.g., in insects, color, segmentation, size and shape, behavior, and almost every type of structure). The X-chromosomes would not contain any sex determiners but only something which simultaneously inhibits the action of one set and enhances that of the other set of determiners. This something, in terms of genes, would be realizator or trigger genes, which in one dose can act in favor of only one group of the basic autosomal sex genes; and in two doses, in favor of the other group. We could express this differently by saying that in male heterogamety (vice versa with female one) the male autosomal sex genes are more frequent or more active than the female genes, and therefore two doses of the trigger genes are needed in order to suppress this superiority. It seems that such an idea is still entertained by Westergaard (see 1948, 1953), *mutatis mutandis,* for the specific features of his material where the trigger action is assumed to involve partly the Y-chromosome. This means that the balance idea is discarded or used only in explanation of some minor features.

This interpretation, which does not work when applied to individual cases and assumes what I would call a naïve genetic idea, has two different aspects. One is the assumption of individual genes for every possible character, which in the case of sex would mean for every female and male character, extending in some cases to each cell of the body (a naïve or even primitive concept); and the other is the trigger idea. Since the first part of the interpretation enters all other genetic theories, we may dispose of it first. I myself started with this assumption when in my early work (1911*b*, 1912) I assumed the presence of a set of genes for secondary sex characters, which I called A and G, and assumed that they were linked with the real sex determiners. I gave up this idea when it turned out that in intersexuality all characters behave in a parallel way to those in the separate sexes themselves, with definite rules. Thus I concluded that sexual differences, extending to differences in practically every cell, are not based upon two sets of genes for male and female development, sometimes called the sex-promoter genes; but that any genetically controlled character may have an alternative norm of reaction which is decided by the real primary sex-determining mechanism. There are many facts available to prove the correctness of this assumption. Differences of this type in the two sexes may mutate individually, with the result that after crossing the mutant with the original form a simple Mendelian segregation occurs, but only in the proper sex; that is, mutants of male characters segregate only in the male. (I called this sex-controlled inheritance; details in my book 1920*b*, and a recent discussion, 1953*a*.) The best illustration of the interpretation is found in *Lymantria dispar*. The male has dark wing color and the female a whitish one. Mutants of the male color exist which Mendelize simply in the males but do not affect the females. However, if these females become intersexual, in specific experiments, they show the same segregation of wing color as the males. Since these intersexes are of the lowest grade, being actually fertile females with only male wing color and partly male antennae, the sex-deciding mechanism is hardly affected. It is very difficult to imagine that only the wing-color gene and its mutant of the male type are picked out for enhancement with suppression of its female partner, while everything else remains female. It is simpler to assume that wing color in both sexes is determined by the same genetic determiners, which act with an alternative norm of reaction according to the presence of the sex-determining stuffs of one or the other sex.

A powerful support for our interpretation comes from a number of facts concerning environmental action. The antennae of females and males are very different in *Lymantria*, and the development is also very different from the beginning (Goldschmidt, 1922). But when females are treated with temperature shocks in a sensitive period of the pupa (Kosminsky, 1909; Goldschmidt, 1922), the antenna becomes more or less male. Or one part of the genital armature in *Lymantria*, the uncus, is a single structure developed from a paired anlage. It is homologous to a paired structure in the female genitalia, the labia. In development the first anlagen are paired in both sexes but concresce later only in the male to form the single uncus. If a female becomes intersexual through F/M imbalance, the labia concresce into a single unpaired structure of the uncus type. If a male becomes intersexual, one of the first effects is duplicity of the uncus. If a normal male pupa is exposed to temperature shock, the same paired uncus results (Goldschmidt, 1922; Kosminsky, 1927). This might be called a phenocopy of the intersexual condition. Comparable phenocopies in wing color and pattern have been produced by Standfuss in pre-Mendelian days and are available also in *Lymantria* (Goldschmidt). These facts clearly require an interpretation in terms of an alternative norm of reaction, and cannot possibly be reconciled with the promoting genes and trigger idea, except by rather wild assumptions.

Thus the assumption of separate autosomal genes for all individual female and male characters is disproved by the facts of intersexuality as well as by those of phenocopies of sexual characters; this disposes also of the trigger genes and requires a genuine balance system of sex determination plus an alternative norm of reaction. Nevertheless, Correns, followed by Wettstein and Hartmann (see Hartmann, 1943), tried to introduce the "naïve" AG system into the balance theory, so that primary sex determination is based upon the F/M balance which simultaneously triggers the inhibition of the mass of A genes and enhances the G group. I think this is an unnecessary complication for which no genetic facts can be adduced, and leads only to making the genetic formulations more onerous. Hence I shall leave the AG system out of the discussion, under the assumption of an alternative norm of reaction for some or all genetically controlled processes, as the case may be. I shall mention the AG idea only in connection with very specific features of sex determination in plants (where we shall also discuss a proposal of a balance between trigger and promoter genes, which, I think, is based upon a misunderstanding of the facts). We come to the conclusion that the "naïve" theory which requires the unspecific trigger in the sex chromosomes can be absolutely excluded in *Lymantria,* and therefore in other animals and plants which follow the same scheme. Apart from the basic experiments on production of intersexes in an orderly way after appropriate crosses, which require the simple balance theory, three more sets of tests exclude any but the balance interpretation and establish the fact that normal sexes as well as all types of intersexuality are exclusively the result of the balances and imbalances between female determiners in the Y-chromosome (in *Lymantria!*) and male ones in the X-chromosomes (not using the W-Z designation in this case of female heterogamety). This, of course, does not exclude modification by genetic or environmental action.

The first set of experiments consists of multiple crosses. For example, in the races A B C (etc.) female and male determiners have different strengths or potencies (whatever this means in detail; see III 5 C *a*), as evidenced by the results of crosses in regard to production of normal offspring or any definite grade of female or male intersexuality, including both kinds of sex reversal. We might now cross A × B, and the hybrid from this cross to C, that is, (A × B) × C (mothers given first). In this way we might finally come, for example, to the following cross: ♀ (((A × B) × C) × ((D × E) × (F × G)) × N))) crossed with ♂ (((B × D) × (F × G)) × N))) × N. In such crosses all kinds of autosomes are brought together, and the most varied combinations are expected. If "sex-promoting" genes in the autosomes were responsible for the effect, unpredictable results would follow. Actually, at every step of such a buildup and also in the end, and this in the most varied combinations of races of known potencies, the result is exactly the same as if a female of race A (in the example), which supplied the Y-chromosome for all further combinations including the last, and a male with one X-chromosome from the mother, that is, N, and another one from the father, which in the example can only be N, were crossed. In the example the result is the same as A × N, without any influence of B, C, and so on. Thus no explanation of this result other than by the balance of F(Y)/M(X) or F(Y)/M(X)M(X) is possible.

The second example, which leads to the same conclusion, is the so-called Hokkaido replacement series, also briefly mentioned above (details in 1930). The basis of this experiment (fig. 23) is that if a Y-chromosome = F from a very strong race (e.g., Tokyo) is combined with two X-chromosomes from the very weak race Hokkaido into the formula $F_{st}(Y)/M_w(X)M_w(X)$, with st and w representing strong and weak, the resulting individual is a female by sex reversal in spite of possessing two X-chromosomes. By appropriate crosses, genetic males (i.e., with two X's) can be obtained from eggs with the strong Y and one weak Hokkaido M, if the other M(X) is taken from races with ascending strength of M up to the very strong M_{st}. (We must keep in mind our discussion on predetermination, in II 2 A, meaning in this case that the Y of an egg to become a male or male intersex already has acted before fertilization.) In figure 23, six such combinations are represented. All have the strong F from Tokyo and one very

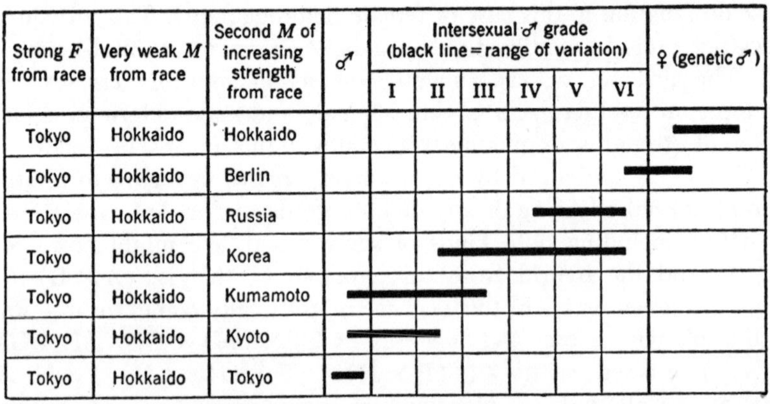

Strong *F* from race	Very weak *M* from race	Second *M* of increasing strength from race	♂	Intersexual ♂ grade (black line = range of variation)						♀ (genetic ♂)
				I	II	III	IV	V	VI	
Tokyo	Hokkaido	Hokkaido								
Tokyo	Hokkaido	Berlin								
Tokyo	Hokkaido	Russia								
Tokyo	Hokkaido	Korea								
Tokyo	Hokkaido	Kumamoto								
Tokyo	Hokkaido	Kyoto								
Tokyo	Hokkaido	Tokyo								

Fig. 23. Replacement of very weak Hokkaido determiners by a series of stronger ones and result upon grade of intersexuality in males of *Lymantria dispar* crosses. (From Goldschmidt, 1938*a*.)

weak M from Hokkaido. In addition, the XX individuals have one M(X) from a set of races known from other experiments to contain M's of ascending strength. The perfectly consistent results are given, with the range of variation of each combination. Again quite different groups of autosomes are brought together, for example, in the second combination made by crossing (Tokyo × Hokkaido) ♀ × Berlin ♂. Nevertheless, the result is determined only by the Y and the two X's, the latter acting together in a strictly additive way.

The third proof can be derived from the following fact: if the same weak race Hokkaido as mother is crossed to the strong Tokyo father, all potential female offspring are transformed into males. Occasionally, however, one or a few real females appear. If they were ordinary daughters (owing to a failure of sex reversal for unknown reasons), they would have the weak F(Y) from Hokkaido. But actually they behave like strong females. The only explanation is that a strong F(Y) transmitted occasionally to a Tokyo male, owing to non-disjunction in his mother, enters a sperm which, upon union with an X-bearing egg from the Hokkaido female, gives rise to a strong female, that is, $F_{st}(Y)M_{w}(X)$. It was this analysis which first suggested that F is located in the Y-chromosome (1920*c*). (Later I thought for some time that F was a cytoplasmic property, which left the present case unexplained. I finally returned to the old interpretation; see 1942*b*.) Here again we face the same situation for our present problem. Only the F/M balance agrees with the facts, and the sex-promoter genes-trigger mechanism is ruled out.

The same conclusion can be derived also from the facts of triploid intersexuality in moths and especially *Drosophila* (Bridges, 1922). We have already mentioned the loose way of describing the facts by saying that sex in these triploids is determined by the relative number of autosomes and X-chromosomes. This is a confusing way of saying that in *Drosophila* the X-chromosomes carry the female determiners, and one or more autosomes (see I 2 C *d ee*) the male determiners, and that the normal balance mechanism M(autosomal)/F(X) or M/F(X)F(X) can be changed, for example, by multiplying the autosome sets and (or) X-chromosomes, with the balance undisturbed or disturbed, as the case may be. The result, normal sexes or intersexuality, does not follow the multiplication of autosomes, as the trigger theory requires, but exclusively the balance or imbalance between autosomal and X-determiners. It follows that only our F/M balance theory can explain the result, as both Standfuss (1914) and Bridges (1922) concluded correctly. Thus we may regard the idea of sex determination without F/M balance, according to what I called the naïve theory, as disproved. This also entails the idea, expressed by Westergaard (1948), that the balance is between sex-chromosomal trigger genes and autosomal sex-promoting genes. All the facts are opposed to this, including those which Westergaard himself established. To these we shall return later.

3

DIFFERENT GENETIC POSSIBILITIES WITHIN THE BALANCE THEORY

The general facts of genetics make us expect that within the general features of the F/M balance, variants in detail will be found. Thus we know that in *Drosophila* or man, sex-linked loci are numerous, while they are very rare in rodents. Further, the Y-chromosome in man and fishes has a considerable pairing segment which can cross over with the X-chromosome, while *Drosophila* does not have much of it. Also, certain traits of similar type may be inherited in one species as simple Mendelian traits; in another one, on a multifactorial basis. Thus we cannot be surprised to find variations of the same theme for sex determination also.

A. VARIANTS IN REGARD TO SEX DETERMINERS

Such variants may first be found in regard to the sex determiners themselves. I had originally assumed that F and M in *Lymantria* are single loci, since no facts were found which could be interpreted as pointing to a group of linked loci. (A few extremely rare exceptional intersexes where none were expected were interpreted by others as results of crossing over, but without any proof.) However, Dobzhansky and Schultz (1934) showed that the X-chromosome in *Drosophila* does not contain a single F locus, but has female action in many sections of its length, which was interpreted as a set of multiple sex factors. The details do not concern us here. Actually, Pipkin (1942) found facts which do not agree with the simple conclusion. There are modifying actions of small fragments which can be distinguished from primary sex determination. The latter was established only for sufficiently large segments at either end of the X, without any intimation as to what acted in these segments. "Multiple sex factors," in this case, does not mean much more than a statement that no single "F gene" was found. As I have already stated (I 2 C *d ee*), I feel that we are entitled to assign the F function here to the intercalary heterochromatin. It would, however, be wrong to conclude that, therefore, in *Lymantria* also the X must contain multiple sex factors or that all sex chromosomes must harbor such sets. It is possible that in individual cases only a single F or M locus exists, or a block of completely linked loci or a more or less large set of individual loci (locus being meant either in the classical sense or in the sense of heterochromatic sections, if our interpretation turns out to be true). Thus the question of one sex determiner versus many sex determiners, which once seemed very important, is no longer of theoretical importance so far as sex determination alone is concerned. We have already discussed an example of assumed single sex determiners (III 5 A *b;* Moewus' work), to which we shall return.

These remarks apply to sex determiners in the X-chromosome; they may apply to the Y-chromosome also, as we shall see. (Tazima, 1943, found that in *Bombyx* only a small section of the Y was female-determining.) These remarks should apply also to autosomal sex determiners. A good example is *Drosophila,* in which Bridges (1922) first assumed that M determiners were distributed over all autosomes. Later he found that haplo-, diplo-, triplo-IV did not affect sex or grade of intersexuality, so that the fourth chromosome fell out. Then S. Bedichek Pipkin showed, with the same method used by Dobzhansky and Schultz (1934), that none of these are present in the second chromosome, as far as the experiments go. Thus only the third chromosome is left, and nobody has thus far located the M factor or factors there. In spite of these clear-cut facts, the multiple sex factors over all the autosomes of *Drosophila* continue to be presented as a fact in general discussions and in textbooks; even the presence of both F and M factors in the autosomes are claimed without any factual basis.

B. VARIANTS WITHIN THE BALANCE SYSTEM

Much more important are the variants in regard to the chromosomal setup of the balance system. Basic differences are expected here between forms with female and those with male heterogamety.

a. Female heterogamety

In female heterogamety, each egg before maturation contains a Y-chromosome. Genetic properties of the Y can act in the growing egg via predetermination through the cytoplasm. Thus an egg that later will develop into a male was exposed to Y action during the period of predetermination. Therefore, it is possible that the Y contains female determiners which in the male without a Y take part in the balance system because of their action before fertilization. We have seen that this is so in *Lymantria,* where autosomal sex determiners (but not modifiers!) have been completely excluded. (Winge, 1937, once tried to interpret the facts with autosomal determiners of both sexes, but we have seen that the experimental data disprove such ideas.) In female heterogamety in animals with large eggs, showing considerable predetermination, the balance mechanism can use F determiners located solely in the Y-chromosome. This is probably the case in the silkworm also, though a final conclusion cannot be drawn in the absence of intersexes. Tazimas' (1943–1944) results are based upon the production of different polyploid and aneuploid conditions in the silkworm egg. Table 4 contains the following important combinations (as assembled by Kihara, 1953): A, autosomes; X(Z), Y(W), sex chromosomes; −L, −M, −R, deficiencies in the left, middle section, or right arm; X(L) and X(R), only the left or right arm, respectively, present; X(R)Y, the attachment of X(R) to Y.

TABLE 4
(From H. Kihara, 1953)

Autosomal sets	*X(Z)*	*Y(W)*	*Sex*
2A	X	—	♂
2A	XX(-L)	—	♂
2A	XX(-M)	—	♂
2A	XX(-R)	—	♂
2A	XX	—	♂
2A	X	Y	♀
2A	X	XRY	♀
2A	XX(L)	Y	♀
2A	XX(R)	Y	♀
2A	XX	Y	♀
3A	XX	—	♂
3A	XXX	—	♂
3A	XX	Y	♀
3A	X	YY	lethal
3A	XX	YY	♀
4A	XXX	Y	♀
4A	XX	YY	♀

The table shows that the presence of a Y (= W) produces a female in whatever combination. This could mean that the Y contains a very strong female determiner. But this could not act via cytoplasmic predetermination: otherwise, all males should be intersexes (at least). Another possibility is that the basic genetic mechanism is the converse of that in *Drosophila,* F in the autosomes and M in the X, but with the addition of a powerful female enhancer in the Y. We shall find later this situation (*mutatis mutandis*) in *Melandrium*. If this were so, 3A 2X should be an intersex (male intersex), though it is possible that the F factors in the autosomes are so weak that 3A would still not affect the 2X action. If 4 or 5A with 1 or 2X could be obtained, the problem could be answered. Regarding the M factors in the X-chromosomes, we may postulate them, but the data of the table do not prove their existence. It would be proved if 2A 3X or 4X and Y turned out to be female intersexes. So far, we know nothing more but that the Y in *Bombyx* has an overwhelming female influence, while the rest of the genetic system is still unknown.

It would be of great interest to know the genetic situation in plants with female heterogamety like *Fragaria*. A cytoplasmic predetermination in the plant egg is very improbable in view of the type of determination in plant development, which is so different from that in animals. However, thus far (see Staudt, 1952) nothing is known about localization of F and M.

b. Male heterogamety

Very different are the expectations in male heterogamety. Here the egg has no Y-chromosome, which is present only in the male line, and therefore a straight balance system between X- and Y-borne sex determiners is impossible. This means either that sex determination works without a balance system or that the balance is between X-chromosomal female and autosomal male determiners, as in *Drosophila*. In some dioecious plants, male determiners in the Y seem to exist. We shall see later that the facts require a very different explanation from that assigned to them and that they fit perfectly into the point of view which we are developing here. There is also another possibility, a plasmatic action of the M type, conditioned by autosomes or acting like a plasmon. (This will be discussed later for certain examples in plants.)

These primary conclusions are very different from those which Correns originally drew for plants. He thought that in male heterogamety, F is located in the X-chromosome and M in the Y-chromosome, M being epistatic to F. We have seen that this is impossible when intersexuality is involved. Hartmann (1943), who tries in his book to revive Correns' antiquated views in this and other respects, thinks that they have been proved by the special conditions found in *Melandrium* (which will be discussed later). Actually, otherwise not a single well-studied case of genetic intersexuality, including those in plants, can be explained by the formulations of Correns. As the foregoing discussion showed, it is a basic error to treat female and male heterogamety alike, and this applies also to plants. In one of the best analyzed cases of intersexuality in plants, *Rumex acetosa* (Ono, 1935), with male heterogamety, it is completely certain that sex determination is identical with that of *Drosophila.* Here, also, combinations with different numbers of autosomes and X-chromosomes show that the F factors are located in the X-chromosomes; the M, in the autosomes; that the balance F/M decides sex or intersexuality; that the Y-chromosome here does not take part in the balance mechanism; and that probably only two autosomes contain the male determiners. If it should turn out, as will be demonstrated later in detail for *Melandrium,* that the Y-chromosome may enhance the F/M balance, based upon X and autosomes, in favor of M, this would be an additional problem paralleling the influence of Y heterochromatin upon other genic actions, as discussed in detail in the chapter on heterochromatin. Thus it is considered certain that with female heterozygosity the F determiners may or may not be located in the Y-chromosome; but this in no way favors Correns' old formulation (which was made for a case of male heterogamety), since the analysis of intersexuality shows that the F/M balance is decisive with both F and M present in each sex, and is not a simple dominance relation, as Correns assumed. It is further certain that in male heterogamety, M must be located in the autosomes (or eventually in the cytoplasm), which does not exclude male enhancers in the Y, as we shall see.

In discussing the genetics of sex determination in some dioecious flowering plants, it must be kept in mind (as also Hartmann and Westergaard intimated) that we are dealing with a situation which is basically different from that in *Lymantria* and *Drosophila,* and many other animals. These are real sex-dimorphic species in which each cell at any stage of life is either completely female or completely male. Intersexuality therefore means stoppage of female determination during the individual development and replacement by a male one, or, as I have called it, a mosaicism in time. But the plants in question are basically hermaphrodites in which the anlagen for both types of sex organs are present in different positions in the flower, and frequently are even visible as rudiments in the intersexual flower. In a female the female organs will always occupy the place they would occupy in a monoecious flower, and vice versa, also the male parts. A somewhat parallel situation is found in the vertebrates, where both gonads and ducts are first laid down with the anlagen for both sexes, and one set or the other is more or less suppressed during development. It is to be expected that such a system is much more subject to variation than the one in *Lymantria* and *Drosophila.* The F/M balances in the two sexes of such organisms may be very little different and, therefore, additional genetic and environmental features may shift the sexes more easily. Thus indeed in fishes and amphibians, external conditions like temperature and internal ones like age, hormones, and overripeness of eggs may easily supersede the primary balance system; so also may genetic modifiers located in autosomes and, in male heterogamety, even in the Y-chromosome. These facts are probably responsible in large part for the different, often complicated explanations of genetic experiments, in which the only slightly different primary balance condition in the two sexes was not or could not be clearly separated from the additional modifying genetic properties. I may point to the discussion of sex determination in fishes by Kosswig and Breider (see Kosswig, 1939) and the very different conclusions of Hämmerling, Goldschmidt, and Hartmann. The Kosswig group thinks that sex determination is dependent upon multiple factors in the autosomes, with little effect of the X-chromosomes and different types of Y-chromosomal action. I agree with Hartmann that the facts can be accommodated in the general F/M scheme together with different modifying actions, though Hartmann thinks only of the FF-FM scheme of Correns without clear application of the balance system, which is known to work in Amphibia and therefore is supposed to work in fishes also. There is the additional fact that different species of the same fish genus may be male-heterogametic or female-heterogametic and that some genera are actual hermaphrodites. A detailed discussion is beyond the scope of this book, but the basic genetic principles involved are apparent, I think, in this brief discussion.

c. The Melandrium case

This leads finally to the extremest variant known, extreme because it seems at first glance to deviate farthest from the simple balance scheme, the facts found by Ono, Blakeslee, Warmke, and Westergaard in *Melandrium* (literature in Westergaard, 1948). Sex in *Melandrium* involves both Y-chromosomal action and sex dimorphism derived from hermaphroditism. *Melandrium album* is dioecious and has the classic sex-determination scheme of XX = ♀, XY = ♂, the Y-chromosome being very large. This plant, as is well known, was one of the first in which not only the sex-chromosome mechanism but also the first case of sex-linked heredity was demonstrated in plants. Only *Melandrium album* and *rubrum* are dioecious; other related species are monoecious.

However, a number of cases are known in which XY individuals become more or less hermaphroditic (subandroecious) and, as it seems, more rarely, XX individuals may show male characteristics, are subgynoecious. In addition, it was found a long time ago by Strasburger that females infected with *Ustilago* will develop male characters, which is a very important fact to be kept in mind.

The authors mentioned above studied sex determination in this plant with the aid of polyploid combinations, thus paralleling Bridges' work in *Drosophila*. Without going into the genetic technique for producing the combinations, we give the results in table 5, in which the corresponding *Drosophila* combinations are entered (A = set of autosomes; ⚥ = intersex in *Drosophila*, subandroecious in *Melandrium*).

TABLE 5
(From M. Westergaard, 1953)

No.	*Chromosomes*	*Melandrium*	*Drosophila*
1	2A + XX	♀	♀
2	2A + XXX	♀	♀ (hyperfemale)
3	3A + X	?	♂ (sterile)
4	3A + XX	♀	⚥
5	3A + XXX	♀	♀
6	4A + XX	♀	♂
7	4A + XXX	♀	⚥
8	4A + XXXX	♀	♀
9	4A + XXXXX	♀	?
10	2A + XY	♂	♂
11	2A + XYY	♂	♂
12	2A + XXY	♂	♀
13	2A + XXYY	?	♀
14	3A + XY	♂	♂ (hypermale)
15	3A + XXY	♂	⚥
16	3A + XXXY	♂	♀
17	4A + XY	♂	?
18	4A + XXY	♂	?
19	4A + XXYY	♂	?
20	4A + XXXY	♂	?
21	4A + XXXYY	♂	?
22	4A + XXXXY	⚥ = ♂ → ♀	?
23	4A + XXXXYY	♂	?

The table shows that in *Drosophila* the balance of male determiners somewhere in the autosome set versus female determiners in the X-chromosomes controls the sex; the Y-chromosome is not involved. In *Melandrium*, in contrast, the presence of a Y always determines males, and its absence, females, whatever the autosomes and X-chromosomes (except no. 22). Thus the Y-chromosome is here so strongly male-determining that it looks as if the autosomes and X-chromosomes do not play any role, and no balance mechanism is present. But no. 22 (from Warmke) shows that the X-chromosomes do contain female determiners of such weakness that, in the presence of Y, four of them are needed to make this influence felt. Hence the decisive fact that was missing in *Bombyx* is established here.

The presence of female determiners in the X-chromosomes without a balance mechanism seems queer; we know (see above, Strasburger; and below, gynomonoecism) that females (without Y) can develop male characters. Relevant for the solution of these contradictions are further data by Westergaard. From crosses between triploids, females and males were obtained as before, and in addition some hermaphrodites (intersexes; see below regarding this nomenclature) having a Y-chromosome. These, then, are andromonoecious: usually the first flowers are intersexual (hermaphroditic); the next ones, low intersexual; and the last, male. It was noticed that this result was found mostly in the presence of three sets of autosomes. Since all these intersexes could be selfed, analysis of many combinations became possible. One important point is that by selection of "androhermaphrodites" (or weak male intersexes), real hermaphrodites (or higher grade intersexes) could be established. Without going into further details, the conclusion was reached that bisexual plants, that is, subgynoecious males in the presence of a Y-chromosome, are determined by the number of X-chromosomes and the combination of the autosomes. Table 6 illustrates this.

The table shows that the percentage of "intersexes" increases from 0 to 100 per cent when the number of X-chromosomes increases from 1 to 4. Since plants with identical constitution in regard to sex chromosomes may develop into males or intersexes, the cause must be sought in the only variable left, the combination of autosomes. Thus it follows that the X-chromosome acts in the female direction, and some autosomal combinations can enhance the pull in the female direction. Westergaard thinks that this role of the autosomes means that some autosomes are female-determining. Further, he assumes that the more female-determining combinations in the aneuploid types are originated by a "changed individual equilibrium" between female- and male-determining autosomes. Such an equilibrium change could occur in

TABLE 6
(From M. Westergaard, 1948)

Sex chromosomes	*Number X*	♂♂	♀	*Percentage* ♂
XY	1	15	0	100
XXY		25	3	
XXYY	2	37	5	89
XXYYY		1	0	
XXXY	3	73	133	36
XXXYY		7	5	
XXXXY	4	0	8	
XXXXYY		0	1	0

the offspring of the triploids if female-determining autosomes occur as aaaa and so on, and male ones only as aa.

Westergaard thus draws the final conclusions: *Melandrium* is endowed with two different mechanisms of sex determination, a primary sex-producing mechanism and a secondary sex-deciding one. Female and male primary genes control the development of female and male sex organs. These genes are located in all autosomes, some of which contain more male genes and others more female genes. If this mechanism were present alone, it would produce a hermaphrodite. In the dioecious organism this primary sex-producing mechanism interacts with a secondary sex-deciding mechanism which permits only one group of genes to function in one individual. The secondary mechanism is located in the Y-chromosome. The X-chromosome of *Melandrium* has indeed female determiners, but these are only some of the primary sex genes and have nothing to do with sex decision. In addition, the female-inhibiting function of the Y-chromosome may be prevented by an accumulation of female-determining X-chromosomes and autosomes, while the male action of the Y cannot be replaced by an accumulation of male-determining autosomes or diminution of the number of X-chromosomes. (Parenthetically I may mention that Hartmann tried to explain these facts by the obsolete formula of Correns, FF = ♀, MF = ♂, which fails here as everywhere else to explain the details.)

Westergaard's interpretation is not only cumbersome and full of *ad hoc* assumptions but also has the disadvantage of being developed only for the interpretation of a single aberrant case, and is completely inapplicable to the well-established cases of intersexuality through genic balance. I wish to raise the question whether we are not faced here by one peculiar variant of the general balance scheme, which means, in the presence of male heterogamety, the same basic mechanism, X-chromosomes: autosomes = F/M balance as in *Drosophila,* with the additional unusual feature of specific behavior of the Y-chromosome. In my opinion all the facts (omitting, for the moment, the Y-chromosome) point to the presence of the usual balance mechanism between autosomal male determiners and X-chromosomal female determiners. When this mechanism gets a chance to work, as in the case of accumulation of X-chromosomal female determiners, it works just as in other cases, producing male intersexuality (subandroecious flowers). So far, no analysis of the opposite condition is available—autosomal male determiners being conditioned to produce female intersexuality (subandroecious flowers). But the fact of Strasburger's *Ustilago* case and the perhaps rare occurrence of natural subgynoecists show that this is a possible situation. Thus the only fact in the *Melandrium* case which, in my opinion, requires a new interpretation is the overwhelming male action of the Y-chromosome. I conceive of this as a specific modifying action upon the otherwise normal balance mechanism, superimposed for unknown reasons in this species upon the standard type of sex determination, and working in the same way as known modifiers in *Drosophila* and *Lymantria.* (These will be discussed in the next chapter.) If in *Drosophila* a mutation in the Y-chromosome should appear, acting as a strong modifier for maleness, the same situation would result; and such mutants in autosomes are well known.

These deliberations lead to further discussion of the Y-chromosome of *Melandrium.* Some interesting facts, not mentioned thus far in the interest of clarity, are known about it. As in other X-Y pairs of sex chromosomes, the Y-chromosome contains a segment which is homologous to a segment of the X-chromosome, with which it pairs and produces a chiasma. Actually, X-chromosomal loci are known (Baur, Shull), also Y-chromosomal mutants (Winge), and crossing over between Y and X loci (Winge) in the pairing segment. The rest, the differentiating segment alone, contains whatever sex determiners or modifiers there are. Westergaard (also Warmke before him) have found Y-chromosomes in the polyploid strains in which parts of the Y are missing: in Y^1 a part of the left half is missing; in Y^3, a part of the right half. Y^2 probably contains only the right half plus a translocated piece from X. Plants with Y^1 or Y^2 are always genuine hermaphrodites with fertile ovaries and anthers (euhermaphrodites), as opposed to the intersexes or, more correctly, andromonoecists, which show all transitions from hermaphrodites to males. The Y^1 or Y^2 hermaphrodites selfed produce females without Y and hermaphrodites with Y^1 or Y^2. From this Westergaard concludes that the missing left segment normally prevents the formation of female organs and contains no important male determiners. In Y^3 the other end of Y is missing. Plants with Y^3 are always rudimentary (sterile) males. From this it is concluded that the "genes" contained in this segment control the last stages of pollen formation without an effect upon the female organs. Thus the differential segment of the Y-chromosome is assumed to have three different functions. Segment I exclusively has the function of preventing the normal development of the female organs; segment III contains the genes needed for complete development of pollen; segment II, in between, "must" therefore contain the genes controlling the formation of anthers, since, in the absence of the entire Y, anthers are "never" formed. But Westergaard himself mentions spontaneous 2X hermaphrodites found by Åkerlund, but dismisses them on the assumption that one X is really a rudimentary Y. However, he should also have mentioned Strasburger's intersexual females by *Ustilago* infection, which cannot be interpreted in such a way.

Actually, these facts lead to an interpretation which I consider to be far superior to Westergaard's, because it fits the facts into the general well-established system of sex determination by F/M balance, instead of denying the proved method of sex determination in animals on the basis of a single case, only slightly aberrant, and, in my opinion, misinterpreted. In *Drosophila,* where the balance system has been established beyond any doubt, the Y-chromosome also consists of sections of different functions (Stern, 1929*b*); some of them are responsible for "fertility," since their absence results in male sterility. Westergaard considers this a proof of the presence of male factors in the Y-chromosome after all! But Stern and Shen (see Shen, 1932) showed that this "sterility" is nothing but the absence of motility of sperm.

Since in both *Drosophila* and *Melandrium* a definite section of the Y-chromosome is needed for the accomplishment of a comparable last step in male gamete formation, the explanation is expected to be the same. In both cases, without Y in *Drosophila* and without Y^3 in *Melandrium,* the sex is completely male in every respect. What is missing is only a physiological condition of the male gametes enabling them to function. In insects we have some knowledge what this means, namely, the need of a hormone-like stimulus for sperm motility. In Lepidoptera this substance is secreted in the female organs where sperm is stored and, therefore, is certainly not a part of male sex determination. Growth of the gonads in insects is also dependent upon a known hormone. These physiological features have clearly nothing to do with sex determination as such, but act in a definite physiological way upon the genetically determined sex cells. Thus I conclude that the right section of the Y in *Melandrium* does not have a partial function in sex determination, but controls some physiological action upon the fully determined male sex cells that is needed for finishing their cycle. The left end and the middle part of the Y remain alone for assaying.

According to Westergaard, the left segment of the Y contains only genes for the suppression of the female organs, because its absence results in fully developed hermaphrodite flowers. From this the inference is made that the middle segment contains the male determiners for anther development. This conclusion cannot stand close scrutiny, if all the facts are taken into account: subandroecious and subgynoecious flowers and the *Ustilago* effect. I can only conclude that the left and middle sections of the Y contain powerful suppressors of the female primordia, so powerful that they win out even in the presence of as many as three F-carrying X-chromosomes, that is, a powerful shift of the F/M balance in favor of F. The anthers are clearly always formed when only one X-chromosome is present, a balance F(X)/M(autosome) strongly in favor of M. There is absolutely no need and no proof for assuming male determiners to be in the Y-chromosome, but the suppressors of the female anlagen may also be called enhancers of maleness, if we realize that the dioecious plants are actually monoecious with suppression of the anlagen of one sex.

Thus the problem of monoecism enters. Westergaard himself has emphasized that it must not be forgotten that the only two dioecious species of Melandrium must have been derived from monoecious ones. This is indeed a decisive point. If they are basically monoecious with a secondary suppression of female organs in the male (and vice versa), and these organs, as we have seen, can reappear in definite genotypes, the basis of sex determination is a F/M balance which is very near equality and is shifted only inadequately by the 1X-2X mechanism. This means that MM is only a little superior to one F, while MM is much inferior to FF, as the greater rarity of subgynoecious plants shows. In the transition from monoecism to dioecism, the relatively unstable A(M) A(M)/X(F) condition, alone capable of producing anthers, but not of suppressing ovaries, is shifted by the appearance of a modifying action in the Y-chromosome which so strongly suppresses the female anlagen that it overrules the F/M balance in all genotypes possessing X(F), XX(FF), or XXX(FFF) chromosomes, but not 4X(4F). This alone suffices for the explanation of all the facts, and no male determiners in the Y are needed.

This simple solution, which takes from the *Melandrium* case all the features that seem to require a genetic system different from all other well-explored ones, is in harmony with important facts known in regard to the Y-chromosome in *Drosophila* outside the sphere of sex determination. We found that the heterochromatin in the Y-chromosome has a considerable modifying action (probably proportional to quantity) upon other genically controlled developmental processes, which are sometimes enhanced, sometimes inhibited, as the case may be. We refer especially to the extreme case of podoptera K (see I 2 C *d aa*), in which a remarkable and extreme mutant action is realized, not in the normal female but in XXY females. Hence it is in no way unusual to find that Y heterochromatin has a strong effect upon other genic actions. In *Melandrium* this means that in the transition from monoecism to dioecism via dropping one female-determining X-chromosome, an additional modifier has appeared, namely, a mass of heterochromatin suppressing still further female action. *Melandrium* thus has the same sex determination as *Drosophila* plus a powerful antifemale modifying action of Y heterochromatin.

d. Dioecism derived from monoecism in other cases

We might expect to find a comparable situation in other cases where dioecism is derived from a monoecious condition. This is indeed so. The classic example is sex determination in frogs with its great modifiability and lability from a more or less monoecious basic condition. Witschi (1914 ff.) showed in classic papers that the basic condition is the F/M balance system, but, in addition, some action of the Y-chromosome must be introduced in order to explain all the detailed facts. (See full discussion in Goldschmidt, 1931; and Witschi, 1939*a*.) This condition is assumed to be a weak female factor in the Y-chromosome. We might well describe it as a modifier acting in the opposite direction from that in *Melandrium,* namely, enhancing femaleness, with the result of producing a very labile, almost monoecious condition in the 1X males. The many races of frogs, in regard to more or less labile sex determination, extending to complete dioecism, represent different valencies of the F and M factors, just as in *Lymantria,* and, in addition, different conditions of the Y-chromosome modifier. It is remarkable that P. and G. Hertwig (1922) were led to adopt Witschi's formulation in their study of crosses involving natural subandroeciousness (male intersexes) in *Melandrium.* They used different valencies of the F factors in the X-chromosomes and the Y-chromosomal factor (or modifier in my terminology, a weak F in Witschi's = f_1f_1) to explain all the individual results. The decisive point is that they needed the F/M balance, different F valencies in different strains, and a special modifier in the Y-chromosome. Another problem enters all these discussions: the relation between andro- or gynodioecism and intersexuality, terms which were used indiscriminately in the discussion of *Melandrium.* This is actually a problem of great theoretical significance when it comes to finding a general solution of the problem of sex determination which fits all the different cases already analyzed and still to be analyzed. (A separate chapter will be devoted to these questions.)

We discussed the more complicated developments in *Melandrium* without much reference to the simpler genetic facts, because Westergaard has used the results to cast doubt upon the basic tenets of genetics of sex in animals, which made it imperative to show that the facts actually fall in line with others. We should now add a few words on simpler cases, for they show the relations of monoecism and dioecism at a less complicated level. As is well known, Correns (1907) made the first crosses between monoecious and dioecious species, which led to the formulation FF = ♀, FM = ♂, plus something additional for an explanation of monoecism; he could not analyze the latter because of F_1 sterility. Galan (1946; see 1951) has since finished this analysis in another form, *Ecballium elaterium,* which occurs in monoecious and dioecious races that cross freely. The crosses in F_1 and F_2 (together with interesting changes occurring in the same plants flowering the second year) lead to a simple genetic interpretation which is borne out by all experiments. Decisive are three "genes" of a multiple allelomorphic series, a, a^D, a^d, and the effect of their combination is tabulated (see overleaf).

1. Pure races	2. F_1 and F_2 combinations
$a^+ a^+$ = monoicum	$a^d a^D$ = ♂
$a^D a^d$ = dioicum ♂	$a^+ a^D$ = ♂
$a^d a^d$ = dioicum ♀	$a^+ a^+$ = ⚥
	$a^+ a^d$ = ⚥
	$a^d a^d$ = ♀

It is easy to fit these facts into our former discussion. (Bridges, 1939, tried to explain the analogous results of Correns on the basis of his views on sex in *Drosophila,* assuming that females are XX AA; A = autosomes with a male tendency. The details of Galan's crosses do not agree with this interpretation.) It is obvious that in the formula M(A)M(A)F(X)F(X) = ♀, M(A)M(A)F(X)Y = ♂, with the Y-chromosome acting as a modifier, as shown in *Melandrium,* the a of Galan is a condition of F with the potency F = M (a^+ = F) in the dioecious plant. Galan's a^d is then the F in the dioecious form, which has a higher potency than the one (a^+) in the monoecious form, say F^1, so that F^1F^1MM or a^da^d = ♀; a^D then becomes the Y-chromosome, absent of course in the monoecious form and always present in males. Since a^+a^d = F(X)F^1(X)MM is monoecious, just as a^+a^+ = F(X)F(X)MM, the F^1 of the dioecious form (= a^d) has a potency (pull in the female direction) which is not far above that of F = a^+. Thus, in Galan's terminology, what looks like a completely different story is in fact identical with the *Melandrium* case as we expounded it. But we cannot say whether the Y in the male acts as a male enhancer as in *Melandrium,* or only as the absence of one F^1 as in the standard case. Only polyploidy experiments like those made with *Melandrium* could decide this point.

e. Once more the Y-chromosome

All these facts and interpretations lead us to consider the problem of the modifiability of the sex balance system. Before doing this, one more point should be made in relation to the present discussion. I emphasized above that in male heterogamety no room is left for genuine sex determiners in the Y-chromosome, whereas in female heterogamety the Y(Z) can carry a female determiner, at least in animals where predeterminative action of the Y(Z) in the immature egg permits the production of intersexuality in the XX sex. There are now available some interesting facts concerning sex determination in the silkworm (Tazima, 1943 ff.), in which the female is XY(WZ), which we have already presented (IV 3 B *a*). A brief repetition at this point will serve as the basis for further discussion. Tazima found that the female determiners are located in the Y-chromosome, as in

Lymantria, but they are so strong that any egg with a Y will be female, whatever the number of X, which contain the male determiners. As XX individuals are males, the strong Y which is present in all eggs before fertilization cannot have a predeterminative influence, for otherwise all males would be intersexual. Thus the old Correns formula (changed for female heterogamety), MM = ♂, MF = ♀, F > M, could be employed here so long as no male intersexuality is known. This problem awaits further clarification.

We might attempt to explain both the *Lymantria* and the *Bombyx* situation in the same way we tried to understand that of *Melandrium,* forgetting for the moment the potential monoecism of this plant. This means the assumption that F is an autosomal property; M is located in the X-chromosomes; and a strong enhancer for femaleness, in the Y-chromosome. In favor of such an assumption could be cited the fact that triploid intersexuality in moths possibly follows the *Drosophila* scheme (of course, with the changes due to female heterogamety). I said "possibly" because we do not know much about the Y-chromosome in most cases. But where no Y is present (the XO type in *Solenobia*), the *Drosophila* type must obtain. The facts regarding the silkworm may be expressed in the same terms as in *Melandrium,* that is, with a strong Y-chromosomal enhancer. In this case, the assumption of a predetermining action of the Y in the eggs destined to become males is superfluous, because autosomal F (female determiners) are present, though they have not yet been demonstrated. However, in *Lymantria* such a theory would be very difficult. In order to explain the experiments on the production of male and female intersexuality, we need both male and female determiners of different valency. If F were located in the autosomes, and the Y carried an enhancer for femaleness, the autosomes would have to carry F's of different potency in order to explain male intersexuality in the absence of a Y. But the facts of female intersexuality require different potencies of the female "enhancers" in the Y. Finally, the facts of the complex crosses and the Hokkaido replacement experiments (discussed in IV 2) exclude a participation of autosomal female determiners (although autosomal modifiers have been demonstrated). Thus the genetics of sex determination is probably of the *Lymantria* type, as described, wherever female heterogamety exists with the presence of a Y-chromosome; of the *Drosophila* type, in male heterogamety and in female XO heterogamety; and of the *Drosophila* type plus Y-chromosome enhancers, in special cases like *Melandrium.* There is, of course, no reason to expect that the details are the same in all organisms, in view of the fact that many features of general genetics, like dominance, maternal inheritance, heredity within the Y-chromosome, and crossing over in one or both sexes show specific features from case to case. But the underlying principle, the F/M balance, is always the same.

4

BALANCE AND MODIFICATION

It is obvious that a genetic system of the F/M balance type must be rather easily modifiable by environmental and genetic actions, since time relations and similar features of the kinetics of the genetic systems and also threshold conditions are involved. If the balance is effected by a 2X-1X system, it is to be expected that it is more easily upset by modifying action in the homogametic sex. If we use arbitrary measures for the genetic actions, for examples, for *Lymantria* $F(Y) = 10$, $M(X) = 6$, the female imbalance is in favor of F 10/6; the male one, in favor of M 12/10. That is, in the homogametic sex, maleness outbalances femaleness by only one-fifth; in the heterogametic sex femaleness outbalances maleness by two-thirds. Modifiers acting upon the thresholds will therefore more easily affect the homogametic sex, especially in intersexes with already impaired balance. However, this does not mean that the homogametic sex more easily becomes intersexual. Haldane's rule that the opposite is true applies to many cases, for a special reason. If we take *Lymantria* as an example, with the balance $F(Y)/M(X) = ♀$, the facts prove that an increase in the potency of M (as found in different races) produces female intersexes in F_1 of a cross of a weak race with the male of a strong one. But for the males $F(Y)/M(X)M(X)$ the reciprocal cross transmits only one weak M to the F_1 males, which then become intersexual only when strong F and weak M are very different. Otherwise two weak M's will be needed to produce intersexual males which will occur only in F_2 or RF_2. Thus we may say that in this sense females become intersexual more easily. Of course, this derivation is not a theory but a description of an extensive set of experimental facts involving all possible combinations.

When in such combinations the males of the formula $F_{st}/M_{st}M_w$ are normal, and those F_{st}/M_wM_w just a little intersexual, the proper setting for the action of the modifiers is given, which may act in either direction. Actually, two pairs of such dominant autosomal modifiers were found, both acting in favor of M; as a result, only the homozygous recessive segregants for one or both of these modifiers showed low male intersexuality (details in Goldschmidt, 1923*a*). In the triploid intersexes of *Drosophila* it was shown by Bridges (1925) and Dobzhansky (1930) that modifiers for the degree of intersexuality can be selected, though the case is not as clear-cut as in *Lymantria*, where individual Mendelizing loci were demonstrated. Pipkin (1942) found also in *Drosophila* dominant intersex modifiers in the X-chromosomes of wild-type stocks of different geographic provenience. The latter fact strongly suggests the parallelism with *Lymantria*, as does also the *repleta* case to be discussed later. We meet frequently with the statement that these modifiers are autosomal sex genes, an interpretation which has led to much confusion and the assumption of multiple sex factors located all over the chromosomes. This would, indeed, be a strange mechanism for accomplishing a simple genetic alternative in the absence of complete linkage of all these autosomal loci. The production of the two sexes in equal numbers would be a very rare and improbable event, and if autosomal multiple sex determiners for both sexes are assumed, as has been done, only a miracle could lead to the regular production of the two sexes. From the point of view of genic action, such theories are even worse than from the purely statistical aspect. The serious error in this confusion of the sex-determining mechanism and the possibility of modifying effects upon the action of the primary F/M balance can be made most obvious by comparison with facts outside the realm of sex determination.

In a former section I mentioned dominance modification. Among innumerable examples (all the inhibitors, suppressors, enhancers in genetic literature) are the accurately studied dominance modifiers for vestigial wings in *Drosophila* (see III 5 C *b*). One of them, which shifts all combinations and compounds in the direction of more wing destruction, is the mutant locus purple, so called for its effect on eye color. Shall we now say that purple is one of the wing-determining loci, or is it not rather true that the action of purple collides at some point with one of the processes or reaction chains which take place in wing determination? This collision may mean a common substrate or precursor substance or condition for the kinetics of the reaction. Exactly the same situation is known from the realm of sex determination. Thus Winge and his successors showed that certain mutant loci for pigmentation act as modifiers of sex expression in fishes. Such cases are bound to be found whenever there is a labile balance which can be pushed out of gear by effects of loci and the genetic background, within which the balance system works, but works differently when one or more of the variables of the developmental system are changed. It is therefore to be expected that environmental actions like extreme temperatures, hunger, and parasitism may have the same effects, producing intersexuality. We have mentioned (in III 3 B) the phenocopies of intersexual features in *Lymantria*. Examples, some very remarkable, of similar action of other environmental factors (e.g., parasitism) can be found in my book on sex intergrades (1931).

With these facts as a background we shall have no difficulty in assigning the proper place to genetic modifiers producing, if mutated, intersexuality in the presence of the normal F/M mechanism. We meet here with the same error of interpretation as the one mentioned above. We remember, for example, that in *Drosophila* sex determiners in the second and fourth chromosome were ruled out (see I 2 C *d ee*). If a mutant locus which makes one sex intersexual is found in the second chromosome, it is said that this shows that sex determiners are nevertheless present in the second chromosome and that a multiple factor sex determination is demonstrated. Actually, a mutant has been found which changes the genetic system of development so that the usual F/M balance works in a different system of coördinates and therefore has a different effect. Thus it is not surprising that in *Drosophila* species a number of mutant loci which alone produce intersexuality have been found; further, that combinations of ordinary mutants exist which make the carriers intersexual, for example, the low-grade intersexual males produced by the Beaded-Minute combination (Goldschmidt, 1949*a*, 1951*b*). New cases of one or the other type are being found continually. Whatever their specific features—and these are expected, since they probably act through different coordinates of the developmental system—their interpretation is always the same in principle. All these facts may, in addition, be used as material to support the correctness of our interpretation of sex in *Melandrium*.

5

MONOECISM AND INTERSEXUALITY

a. Introduction

In our discussion of *Melandrium* we used the terms "subandroecious," "subgynoecious," and "intersexual" in the same sense without much explanation. When we analyze sex determination in animals and flowering plants in terms of identical genetic ideas, we must, however, realize the differences. Correns used the term "euhermaphrodites," for example, for a *Melandrium* species or race or experimental product in which both female and male organs are functional. When we considered before such conditions, produced by the presence of four X-chromosomes, it could be described as one step in the change from maleness to femaleness, that is, intersexuality. But if we use such a term, we must realize that it means something different from intersexuality, say, in *Lymantria* or *Drosophila*. In the monoecious flower, whether it is primarily monoecious or secondarily by a sexual shift away from a male (or a female, if found), there are two spatially separated anlagen for complete male and female organs, both of which can be evoked alone or simultaneously and become functional together. This situation is then comparable in animals to a genuine hermaphrodite like a trematode with two complete functional and spatially separated sex organs. The trematode parallels *Melandrium* so far as all members of the order are hermaphrodites except one genus, *Schistosomum*. My student, Lindner (1914), could show that this exception involves the establishment of a 2X-1X mechanism. This shows, as do the facts in *Melandrium,* that hermaphroditism (monoecism) is based also on the sex-determining mechanism of F/M balance with F = M. However, there must be an additional genetic system which causes the spatially separate anlagen, that is, a definite primary developmental pattern. Needless to say, such a genetic system also permits shifts by genetic or environmental means, which then could be called intersexuality, just as in frogs or in *Melandrium.* Actually, Buttner (1950) found that in a host containing only male *Schistosomum mansoni* their testes may degenerate and rudimentary ovaries appear.

We spoke of a primary determinative pattern controlling the spatial arrangement of the female and male parts in a hermaphrodite. In animals this patterning part of the determinative process can show many variations: separate gonads or a single gonad with separation of sex cells, consecutive functioning of the female and male parts of the gonad with and without much modifiability. (See all the variants in mollusks, especially studied by Coe.) In plants it is probably the specific aspect of differentiation at a vegetative point which causes the always more or less identical spatial relationships.

b. Shift of sex expression in maize

This situation, and simultaneously the correctness of the interpretation used, comes out best in the well-known work of Emerson and especially Jones (1934) in maize. Maize is monoecious, with the additional feature—based on a genetic condition, which is independent of sex determination itself—that the apical flowers (the tassel) have normal anthers and a rudimentary gynoecium, thus being male functionally. This means that something suppresses female differentiation, though all flowers are genetically monoecious, in the language of balance, F/M, F = M. The lateral flowers (where the cob develops) are functionally female, while the anthers are rudimentary, the interpretation being the opposite from that of the tassel flowers. Emerson and Jones found and analyzed modifying mutants which specifically counteract the local suppressor action upon the anlagen of one sex in the genetically monoecious flower and enhance the other sex. (I present only the interpretation of the facts which I favor and which fits into the entire genetic picture of sex determination in monoecists.) One recessive locus, tassel seed, affects the terminal flowers in which anther development is suppressed and gynoecium development enhanced so that real seed can be formed. Such a ts_2 ts_2

plant might be called a female, because it has no functional male organs, but this would be an incorrect name, because there is still a tassel, only it is modified in the female direction. This means that the plant is a female as much as a normal plant after cutting away the tassel. The plant is actually a monoecious plant with a shift of expressivity in one group of flowers by a homozygous modifier. It can, of course, breed true to this condition, being homozygous for the modifier, thus mimicking a dioecious female condition (of a type unknown in nature) without really being a female.

A second mutant in another chromosome, silkless (sk), specifically suppresses the gynoecium in the lateral flowers without affecting the tassel. Thus it produces what functionally is a male plant but genetically still a monoecious one with sterilization of the gynoecium in the female flowers. It would be comparable to a normal monoecious plant which has been castrated for all ovaries in the lateral flowers. This is certainly only an imitation female, though with both modifiers combined a line can be established with "female" and "male" plants, but only in regard to function, not to sex determination. This is due to the fact that ts_2 homozygous is epistatic to sk sk, and therefore in both locations "female" flowers are formed. As ts_2 does not act so in heterozygous condition, Ts_2 ts_2 sk sk is male, like sk sk alone. Thus a true breeding dioecious line is established when Ts_2/ts_2 sk/sk is crossed with ts_2/ts_2 sk/sk. It is not surprising that these facts, which are easily understood when put in their proper place in the general theory of sex determination, have led to the most confusing interpretations when the general setting has been disregarded: confusing functional sex with genetic sex, sex determiners and modifiers of expressivity, monoecic F/M balance (where $F = M$) with epistatic effects of modifiers. This, then, is clearly something completely different genetically from real intersexuality.

c. Monoecism and intersexuality in Streptocarpus

In view of this, special importance is attached to flowering plants in which androecia *in situ* are transformed into gynoecia (or vice versa) in a series of real intersexual transformation. The fact that such cases seem to result frequently from species crosses, like diploid intersexuality in *Lymantria* and a few cases in *Drosophila* (see II 2 A; discussion of crosses in the *repleta* group), suggests that a similar method of sex determination is working within the setting of monoecism. This might permit us to assign each mechanism to its proper place, the sex-determining and the monoecism-controlling mechanism, the latter of which we described as a patterning of primordia within a flower bud.

The *Streptocarpus* crosses (Gesneriaceae) of Oehlkers (1938–1952) represent the best analyzed case. The species are monoecious, with two functioning and three rudimentary anthers (staminodia). Of the six species investigated, four species behave alike and the other two form a separate group. As examples, the crosses between *Rexii* and *Wendlandii* are presented (W = *Wendlandii;* R = *Rexii;* ♀ always given first place).

F_1 R × W	dioecious, like parents
F_1 W × R	anthers reduced to staminodia
RF_2 (W × R) × R	half like F_1, half normal gynoecia, but, instead of anthers, all transitions from anthers to carpels
RF_2 (R × W) × W	half normal monoecious, half externally the same, but with rudimentary ovaries

To this group were added later crosses with another monoecious species, *polyanthus* (P). The results are as follows:

F_1 P × W	like parents
F_1 W × P	like parents
F_2 $(W \times P)^2$	3 like F_1 : 1 without anthers, i.e., like F_1 W × R
RF_2 (W × P) × P	1 like F_1 : 1 without anthers
F_2 $(P \times W)^2$	all like F_1

The following formal explanations have been proposed for the first group of facts (the second group to be considered later). Oehlkers follows Correns in assuming that the genome contains a general AG complex of female and male sex determiners. In *Rexii* the G factors are superior to the A factors and vice versa in *Wendlandii.* The plasmon in either case must pull in the opposite direction, because both forms are monoecious. Thus R plasmon pulls in the male direction; W plasmon, in the female direction. In the backcross (W × R) × R, the W plasmon, pulling in the female direction, becomes combined with genomes working in the same direction; therefore, female intersexuality occurs in half of the offspring. This requires, of course, that the assumed AG complexes segregate like single loci. If we try to visualize this in detail, insurmountable difficulties arise. However, discarding this unworkable AG hypothesis, we may postulate a single pair of Mendelizing alleles and a modifier, present in the R genome, which pulls, if homozygous, in the female direction, but only in a proper plasmon, which is found in W. One could mention in favor of such a modifier that Oehlkers found in the same crosses a modifier for flower form which acts in exactly this way; and, further, that the second group of facts (W × P, etc.) fits into such a scheme, assuming a lower action of this modifier. Thus, while the AG explanation is unworkable, a single Mendelian modifier, comparable to those found in *Drosophila* (e.g., Sturtevant's *repleta* crosses), could account in a general way for the results, together with a plasmonic difference and an action within the system of independently determined monoecism, that is, a pattern of development of the flower primordia. This modifier would, then, act upon sexual differentiation, independently of the primordia, shifting any development toward femaleness. We could describe this as a case of intersexuality superimposed upon monoecism. In view of the great confusion found in the discussions of sex determination, monoecism, and intersexuality in plants, I consider the present discussion to be of major importance.

Monoecism, then, would be here, as everywhere, a genetic condition of equal F/M balance, F = M, in the absence of an X-Y mechanism. All individuals are FF MM, and the FF chromosomes have not yet reached the status of X-chromosomes which they accomplish only when one F drops out (XO or XY) or changes into a weaker F, as discussed before for *Melandrium, Ecballium,* and frogs. The completely independent genetic condition which controls the pattern formation of the flower primordia supplies in different places primordia for androecia and gynoecia, which, with the balance F = M, differentiate independently. The establishment of an X-chromosome mechanism could make the flowers andromonoecious and gynomonoecious by enhancer-suppressor action, and the establishment of modifying Y material could affect the balance effect in a still more extreme way. But the flowers would still be morphologically potential monoecists with more or less extreme suppression of one type of organ. Monoecism is thus a floral developmental pattern in the presence of F/M equally balanced and dioecism developed from it as the result of a shift in only one of the two components, the F/M balance via production of a sex chromosome mechanism and (or) a change in the potency of F or F and M.

Intersexuality, in which an androecium transforms into a gynoecium (male intersexuality) or vice versa (female intersexuality), could be superimposed upon monoecism-dioecism either by introduction of a modifier which enhances F or M in both types of primordia, which means intersexual transformation for one and reduction for the other, and vice versa; or by the development of a plasmon condition which has the same modifying effect; or by a combination of both; or by the existence of weak and strong races, meaning different potencies of F and M which may be recombined in an abnormal way after crossing. I had formerly assumed that the *Streptocarpus* case follows the last alternative (Goldschmidt, 1938*b*). But the new results of Oehlkers with *polyanthus,* giving a 3:1 F_2 segregation, requires an autosomal action, a modifier of the type found in the *Drosophila* cases mentioned. However, this alone does not suffice for the explanation of the R × W crosses; an additional interaction between a plasmon and the autosomal modifiers is required. This puts the modifier system on the same plane as that discussed above for male sterility, which then might be a beginning intersexuality superimposed on monoecism (though this is improbable, as discussed in IV 3 B *c*). The modifier in *Drosophila repleta* worked by means of the cytoplasm as did also the Bd M intersexuality (see II 2 A), though no separate plasmon existed. However, there still remains this riddle: Why does the change in F(X) (plus the Y-chromosome modifying action) in *Melandrium* produce only a shift in the development of the flower anlagen in the way of suppression-enhancement, while the modifier in *Streptocarpus* affects both anlagen in their actual sex differentiation, in the presence of the proper plasmon? The nature of monoecism cannot be involved in this difference. It must therefore be the presence of different plasmons interacting with the genetic modifiers of F/M balance which is responsible for the genuine intersexual effect in *Streptocarpus.* A more specific meaning will be given at once to this conclusion.

Facts resembling those in *Streptocarpus* have been described in other plants after species crosses, though they could not be analyzed genetically as well as in *Streptocarpus.* In these cases even the F_1 showed the intersexuality, as in *Lymantria.* This might suggest that the genetic basis is different, more as in *Lymantria.* But it is of no use to speculate on this, in view of the meager information. Good examples are the *Salix* crosses of Rainio (1927) with complete series of female and male genuine intersexuality, and the comparable *Solanum* crosses of Koopmans (1952). It is remarkable that in the latter, also, similar anomalies of the flowers themselves (petals) were found, like those studied by Oehlkers in *Streptocarpus,* and explained by a recessive mutant collaborating with a definite plasmon. In view of the fact that certain color mutants in fishes act as modifiers of sex determination, one could expect the intersexuality modifier in *Streptocarpus* (and also in *Solanum*) to be identical with the flower modifier for choripetaly. If this were so, an explanation of the dilemma mentioned above would suggest itself: the sex modifier in *Streptocarpus* and *Solanum* acts upon the flower bud *before* the determination of the pattern of a monoecious flower; while in *Melandrium* and *Ecballium* the X-Y system works only after the anlagen of the flower parts have been determined. In favor of this solution is my work (see II 2 C *a*) on the cytoplasmic effect upon the pigment-forming process in *Lymantria*, where it was shown by a study of the pigmentation process in development that the cytoplasmic interaction with a pair of alleles affects the speed of the process.

d. The embryological side of the problem

At this point we must return again to intersexuality in animals, in order to show that complications exist, which make a kind of bridge between monoecism and intersexuality by combining some features of each in the same individual. The facts relate both to the genetic basis and to developmental control of sexual differences. I have emphasized repeatedly that the genic control of sexual differentiation works with an alternative norm of reaction, meaning that a group of cells, which may be so large as to include all cells, are able to develop in the female or male way, according to the genetic situation. This includes also the "short cut" of hormonic actions, which are genically controlled. It includes also the corollary that the decision of the alternative norm of reaction may be brought about or superseded by genetic, environmental, or hormonal action in proper experiments.

To this basic solution we must now add that the morphological basis for the developmental alternative is not simply a cell or group of cells with the potency for alternative differentiation. Actually, in animals we meet with two primary types. Some sexually different organs are homologous in both sexes, which, in this instance means development from the same primordia. Other sexually different organs develop from different primordia. Examples of the first type are the gonads and parts of the ducts in insects. Examples of the second type are some parts of the ducts and external genitalia in insects which are formed by different imaginal discs; the ducts in vertebrates, developed from different anlagen (Müller's and Wolf's ducts); and the vertebrate gonads developed from different parts of a primary anlage (cortex and medulla).

The results expected from this situation, in intersexuality, are different accordingly. Intersexuality results in development first with the chromosomal sex and later, after the turning point, with the opposite sex, as proved for *Lymantria* (Goldschmidt, 1916 ff.), *Dro-*

sophila (Dobzhansky and Bridges, 1928; Dobzhansky, 1930*b*; Lebedeff, 1939), Amphibia (Witschi, 1914 ff.), and, of course, all cases of the freemartin type. This means for homologous anlagen that the anlage changes its developmental path during development with the result that the features laid down early are those of the primary sex, and the later features are those of the new sex. The result is the "mosaicism in time" of which so many beautiful examples have been shown for the gonads and genital armature of *Lymantria.* The developmental situation is, however, different for non-homologous anlagen. In the normal sexes only one of the cell groups (male or female) may develop at all (e.g., the imaginal disc for definite female or male parts), while the cells at the other location do not form a disc at all. After the turning point in intersexuality, the primarily absent disc of the other sex begins to differentiate. The result would be a rudiment of the organs of the primary sex and more or less development of the organs of the other sex after the turning point; the details depend upon the time of incidence of the turning point, that is, the degree of intersexuality. In this case, however, the turning point may occur at a time when the determination of the primary disc is already final, which means that it continues differentiating in spite of the turning point. The result is that more or less complete organs of both sexes are present. Minor examples of this are found in *Lymantria;* more extreme ones, in *Drosophila* diploid intersexes (Lebedeff), and in the triploid intersexes of *Solenobia.*

Finally, if the alternative is based upon primarily different anlagen, both present in either sex, as in Amphibia, different conditions of development of both anlagen and different types of suppression of the other result, as Witschi's work on frogs demonstrates. But in vertebrates (see the work on birds and mammals reviewed by C. R. Moore, 1944; Witschi, 1950; Ponse, 1949), the complicated interference of hormones makes the details much more variable than in insects. These, then, are the basic features of the morphological consequences of genetic or induced intersexuality.

The most elaborate work on the morphology of intersexes (apart from Baltzer's work on *Bonellia,* which is not strictly comparable with the material of the present discussion as analyzed in detail in Goldschmidt, 1931, 1938*a,* 1946*a,* 1949*b*) is the work of Seiler and his students (full literature in Seiler, 1949; and Ammann, 1954) with the triploid intersexes of the moth *Solenobia.* It is unfortunate, in my opinion, that this very elaborate and devoted work has led to interpretations which cannot stand a critical scrutiny. For a long time

Seiler insisted that the development of these intersexes did not follow the time law but was an intersexual development, that is, intermediate between the sexes. Only for the gonads the time law was accepted more or less reluctantly. But recently Seiler (1949, 1951) has convinced himself that there is no such thing as intersexual development but that differentiation is exclusively male or female for each cell or group of cells or organ. In view of the existence of a graduated series of intersexes, also in *Solenobia,* this new solution demands the acceptance of the time law. But Seiler still thinks that the facts do not agree with this. His first objection is that there is a greater tendency for a mosaic type of organization in the *Solenobia* intersexes than in *Lymantria:* organs which are homologous in both sexes (i.e., based upon an alternative norm of reaction of the same anlage) do not show a structure of the type described for *Lymantria* (and also *Drosophila*) as a mosaic in time but an actual mosaic of female and male parts. This is even now assumed for the gonads, though these show, just as in *Lymantria,* only a tendency in one or the other of the eight compartments not to undergo the intersexual change. The mosaic condition is most conspicuous in the ducts developed from homologous anlagen. We have already discussed the details in a different context, namely, variegation (see I 2 C *d ee*). For the present discussion the important point is that in such organs the mosaic of low-grade intersexes means the addition of small cell groups of the other sex; with increasing intersexuality, these patches increase in number and size up to final prevalence. When we discussed the proper embryological interpretation of this fact and compared it with the situation in *Lymantria* (see I 2 C *d ee*), we saw that this is clearly a consequence of the working of the time law in the presence of a definite type of embryonic determination. Seiler, however, proposes a very different explanation, which to my way of thinking is very unfortunate: in the intersexes that he himself had proved to be 3A 2X (no Y), he assumes that the F and M factors are equally balanced and that the local environment decides the alternative. Apart from the fact that such a view is genetically unfounded and irreconcilable with all other knowledge on intersexuality, it does not account for the graduated series of intersexuality.

The second point in the morphology of the *Solenobia* intersexes is that, just as the gonad does, the products of the so-called Herold's organ behave exactly as the time law requires, as Seiler's student Nuesch has shown (detailed discussion in Goldschmidt, 1949). But Seiler regards this as less important than the fact that sexual characters which are developed from *different* anlagen may both be present in a mosaic way within the same individual. I have already presented what I consider to be the proper explanation of this fact. Thus I cannot help concluding that the triploid intersexes of *Solenobia* are to be explained in the same way as all others; though a certain variability in detail, based probably upon the unbalanced triploid condition as such, may lead one to overlook the orderly background of main events behind the sometimes disturbing details.

In dioecious animals the sexual alternative based upon different anlagen may be called a transition between monoecism and intersexuality as far as the spatial separation in the anlage pattern is concerned. The condition in insects and in Amphibia would be different grades of such approximation to the monoecic pattern—approximation only because in these dioecious animals both sexes are never functional in the same individual. This condition of approximation to monoecism is itself genetically controlled by modifiers in control of developmental patterns which affect sexual development without being sex factors. This can be demonstrated best in *Lymantria.* Kosminsky (1930, 1935) found a local race of this moth in Russia which, crossed to other races, produces male intersexuality of a completely different type from the usual one. Even organs developed from the same anlage with alternative norm of reaction, like gonads and antennae, show a spatial mosaic instead of the typical mosaic in time. I could show (Goldschmidt, 1938*c*) that these special features are due to the presence of some simple Mendelizing modifiers, which somehow affect threshold levels in the development of these organs in the intersexes, a close parallel to the (genetically unanalyzed) situation in *Solenobia.*

6

DIFFERENT TYPES OF SEX DETERMINATION

A. SO-CALLED PHENOTYPIC SEX DETERMINATION

In the work of Hartmann (see 1943) and his students, the term "phenotypic sex determination" plays a considerable role. The idea is that internal or external environment alone decides whether a female or a male is formed. However, this deciding action is supposed to work upon the complicated genetic setup which Hartmann assumes under the influence of Correns. An animal or plant with phenotypic sex determination is supposed to have all the female and male determiners A and G and, in addition, the female and male realizators or trigger genes MMFF, these in equal potencies so that none of them controls sex. The environment determines the suppression of either A or G, with the result that either females or males are produced. In other words, we need a complicated genetic mechanism of sex determination, which, however, cannot function unless the environment gives one of the component genetic entities a lift. I prefer to say that the norm of reaction of the genetic determiners is such that they produce their effect only in a definite environment, which is nothing but an application of the classic definition of genic action. The term "phenotypic sex determination" is thus not only unnecessary but completely confusing. It is still more so when we realize that the true sex determiners F/M are completely balanced but that the A and G factors alone are affected by the environment. I showed above that the A and G factors are a complicated assumption completely unwarranted by the facts. Thus we have the old story of an equally balanced F/M action in the absence of the 2X-1X mechanism, and a norm of reaction for the action of F and M that allows a shift in the amount of their activity which can be brought about by factors of the environment. This is, as far as the effect is concerned, the same as such a shift by the presence of specific modifiers, or by a change of potency of F and M, or by the interaction with different plasmons, examples of all of which we have discussed. We have (1) genetic sex determination without a 2X-1X mechanism to shift the balance; (2) a norm of reaction of F and M which is more than usually sensitive to definite external conditions, for example, position of sex cells in gonads, age of the individual, metal ions (*Bonellia*), hormone-like secretion (proboscis secretion in *Bonellia,* etc.); and (3) any one of the possible variants that can influence the genic action of F and M. The sooner the term "phenogenetic sex determination" disappears from genetic literature, together with the superfluous A and G factors, the better for the clarity of our understanding.

The correctness of the conclusion can be illustrated by the realization that all imaginable conditions of transition exist within the phenomenon of monoecism or hermaphroditism, which is the genetic basis of Hartmann's group of phenotypic sex determination. Let us take a monoecious plant, that is, a plant in which F/M is in sufficient balance to make the plant as a whole a hermaphrodite. However, within the flower anlage the local internal conditions (probably of genically controlled hormonic type) are such that the inner circle of anlagen produces only gynoecia; the outer one, androecia. In another such hermaphrodite, only a few of the outer circle anlagen produce androecia; the rest, staminodia. Again, in another hermaphrodite the internal environment (hormone titer?) in some flowers is such that the outer circle anlagen are more or less suppressed in their differentiation, while in other flowers it is the inner circle which is suppressed. Now we know genetic monoecists in which comparable suppressions are produced by modifiers, that is, by the genetic environment, or under the influence of a definite plasmon, or by the interaction of modifiers and plasmon (as discussed in the foregoing chapter). Finally, the sex of the anlagen can be shifted independent of their position when such modifying genetic conditions produce intersexuality superimposed upon monoecism. Where does phenotypic sex determination belong in this series? Why is a modification of genic action by, say, a hormonic titer or another gradient and the same effect by the action of a genetic modifier, possibly by way of the same chemical channel, different in principle? The only clear-cut difference is between genetic monoecism, that is, F = M, and genetic dioecism by development of the 2X-1X mechanism, that is, MM F(X) or MM F(X) F(X). However, even here transitional conditions are found.

The same argument applies to animals. There are true hermaphrodites which we can understand only as based upon a F/M balance, where F = M. The differentiation of the male and female apparatus is a problem of embryonic differentiation through diversification of areas, just like any other differentiation. Thus we would have to speak of two types of phenotypic sex determination within the same individual. This again may show any number of variants. I drew attention in my books (1920*b*, 1931) to such cases as the trematode *Wedlia,* where, according to Odhner, one egg divides and the two daughter cells of the same genetic, hermaphroditic constitution become encysted. One develops into a small functional male with rudimentary female organs; the other, into a large female with rudimentary male organs. The internal environment (e.g., growth substances, oxidation systems, and the like) thus affect developmental features within the same genetic system. *Mutatis mutandis,* this is exactly the same as if in a hermaphrodite maize plant lateral shoots had female flowers; and terminal ones, male flowers, that is, hermaphroditic flowers with suppression of one set of anlagen. In plants we know genetic modifiers which can affect primary differentiation, producing superimposed intersexuality. In trematodes no intermediate steps are known; only the final one, development of a 2X-1X mechanism (*Schistosomum:* Lindner, 1914).

In view of these facts it is not surprising that in animal monoecists also, all types and grades of modification, on the same genetic basis, are found, produced not only by all kinds of norms of reaction but also by genetic modifiers in cases where only one definite effect occurs (e.g., obligatory protandric hermaphroditism). Certainly no borderline can be established between simple norm of reaction and genetic modifiers. The details of these modifying conditions in different monoecists (e.g., control by position in body, by age of individual, by chemicals and hormone-like substances, and by genetically controlled cycles) are very interesting. Many types are discussed and classified in my books (1920*b*, 1931), and new ones have been added especially by Coe for mollusks and Hartmann and students for worms. But nothing has changed the fact that we can differentiate only between monoecists with F/M in equilibrium and dioecists with a 2X-1X mechanism for controlling two equilibria, though transitions between the two (Amphibia) are not missing. All this shows that the idea of phenotypic sex determination is not only vague but actually harmful, because confusing.

The correctness of this conclusion may be witnessed even by work from the Hartmann school. C. Hauenschild (1953) studied sex in a polychaete annelid, *Grubea clavata.* The main facts (which may be taken as a model for many more or less similar ones) are these. In different cultures of the worm 0–69 per cent of females are found, but never hermaphrodites. The males always remain males, but 37 per cent of the females, after laying eggs, transform into males and remain so.

Crosses of females with such secondary males give no different result from ordinary matings. But in one case males could be transformed into females by amputation of the sex segments and regeneration. Females can easily be changed into males by amputation of the posterior end or the head. In younger stages they even change sex as a consequence of hunger or high temperature. Isolation of females (prevention of copulation) also makes them change into males. This, then, is considered a typical example of phenotypic sex determination.

In discussing the facts the author states first that the finding that the monoecist never forms egg and sperm cells simultaneously requires a special genetic condition, in addition to the F/M balance which controls sex. However, he thinks that in other worms or mollusks, where both sexual products are formed simultaneously or consecutively, real phenogenetic sex determination occurs. In *Bonellia* or *Grubea,* where only one sex functions in one individual, we are near to the situation in Amphibia with a little F/M imbalance and secondary modifiability, that is, a transition between genotypic and phenotypic sex determination. It seems to me obvious that in all the examples here discussed (*Bonellia,* with two alternative sexes decided by the presence or absence of a chemical action upon young larvae; *Sagitta,* with both sex cells present simultaneously; *Ophryotrocha* and mollusks, with a more or less complicated consecutive change from suppression of one sex to that of the other by external conditions, age, or an inherited order; *Grubea,* with the mentioned limitations of sex change) specific genetic determiners control the special type of internal environment in space and time which sets the norm of reaction of the F and M determiners. To call this phenotypic sex determination is rather absurd and can only lead to confusion. Hauenschild, after breaking a lance for phenotypic sex determination, tells us further on that the different reactions of females and males in individual cases are based upon a whole complex of factors which enhance female or male determination and the equilibrium of which can be shifted by external conditions. Finally it is admitted that it could also be possible that not all individuals are real monoecists but are genetically weak males. Or the possibility exists that certain genic combinations shift (by some physiological process) the equilibrium of non-hereditary factors. Again we see the lack of usefulness of the idea of phenotypic sex determination when nothing is visible (and discussed) but a monoecic, hermaphroditic genetic constitution with all kinds of genetic and non-genetic influences upon the internal environment which is the partner of genic action in a norm of reaction;

a system which often works just as well in dioecism as in Amphibia and *Melandrium*-like types.

One word should be added about the most aberrant case known in animals, the classic case of *Dinophilus* (Korschelt), which Hartmann also terms "phenogenetic sex determination." The female of the primitive worm *Dinophilus apatris* lays egg capsules containing large and small eggs. The large ones develop into females; the small ones, into males. Thus fertilization (i.e., the nature of the sperm) has nothing to do with sex determination, which is already fixed in the eggs before meiosis. The two types of eggs develop somewhat differently. Both are formed by union of a number of oöcytes with resorption of all but one nucleus (the details are a little different for male and female eggs). The future female eggs add a growth period, which the future male eggs do not have. If females are prevented from being fertilized (which is possible in some species by using a trick invented by Beauchamp, 1910), the two types of eggs develop parthenogenetically and again into females from large eggs and males from small eggs.

Though there can be hardly any doubt that here the two pure sexes are not determined by a chromosomal mechanism, it does not help much to call this "phenotypic sex determination." It cannot be excluded that the female is XXY with a strong female determiner in the Y, and that in oögenesis the Y is removed in future male eggs, since the orderly removal of definite chromosomes (heterochromatic in *Sciara,* sex chromosomes in aphids, etc.) is a known phenomenon. It could also be possible that in an XY female the small eggs have a directed first maturation division, always removing the Y, just as Seiler (1920) was able to do in *Talaeporia* by temperature action; while the unknown different chemical condition of the large eggs is responsible for always pushing the X into the first polar body. Also in aphids we know of definite cytoplasmic influences upon the maturation division in the sexuparous females (directed meiosis in aphids not yet found). Parthenogenesis may or may not affect such a mechanism, depending upon the type of parthenogenesis (e.g., diploid, haploid, with and without autogamy, etc.). Before accepting the pseudo-explanation of phenotypic sex determination, I am willing to wait for a detailed cytological study.

The best case known to me which could be claimed for phenotypic sex determination is Buchner's (1954) work on the symbionts of a coccid. Here the amazing fact was found that embryos which are invaded by the typical fungoid symbionts of the species develop into females; without symbionts, into males. Schrader's work in related species shows there is no 2X-1X mechanism present, and thus a F/M balance of the monoecic type may be expected. The change of metabolism by presence or absence of the symbionts provides the interior milieu for the change of F or M action according to its inherited norm of reaction with the two different environments. All former discussions of this situation apply also to this extreme case.

B. MULTIFACTORIAL SEX DETERMINATION?

Another unconventional type of sex determination (we call the standard F/M balance mechanism the conventional one) has been claimed for isopods. In diploid species, Vandel (1938–1947) found the existence of females which produce both sexes among their offspring, others with only daughters, and still others with only sons. As the father does not seem to affect this result, Vandel concludes that the females are XY and that directed maturation divisions occur, just as we discussed above as a possibility for *Dinophilus*. In addition, a cytoplasmic factor controlling the directed meiosis is assumed, since the monogenic behavior (only sons or daughters) is inherited without participation of the father. Actually, an XY or WZ group was never found cytologically. A tendency to hermaphroditism is also present in the isopod groups. A priori, one would expect Vandel's explanation or a similar one to be correct, because neither total nor partial monoecists or intersexes occur in the crosses, but only the pure sexes in ratios from more or less normal up to extreme (100:0), and because some constitution of the mother is responsible. Since we know that all these conditions occur in aphids with a proved X-chromosome mechanism plus cytoplasmic controlling factors, we need not look for another type of explanation. But de Lattin (1952) has studied some other genera of oniscoids and asserts that he has disproved Vandel's explanation and substitutes for it a system of "multifactorial sex determination," derived from Kosswig's interpretation in fishes. Since I consider the entire idea of multifactorial sex determination a fallacy (see IV 2), except when it is only an unfortunate term for describing modifiers of the action of the F/M balance, more details must be discussed.

Vandel called *Trichoniscus* females with ordinary offspring in the ratio 1 ♀ : 1 ♂ the "amphogenes," and different types of females with offspring either wholly or partially of one sex, the monogenes. The latter fell into six groups: (1) complete arrhenogenes, producing only sons; (2) incomplete arrhenogenes, with a few exceptional daughters; (3) complete thelygenes, giving only daughters; (4) incomplete thelygenes, producing only a few sons; (5) allelogenes, meaning females which produce sometimes only daughters, sometimes (in different egg batches) only sons; (6) mixed females, meaning amphogene offspring, though the mother is derived from a monogene ♀; their granddaughters may again be monogene. De Lattin finds in *Cyclisticus* the same classes, except for no. 5. While Vandel's incomplete monogenes contain relatively high percentages of exceptions, de Lattin uses the term only when few exceptions are found.

The main facts on heredity in Vandel's experiments are as follows. Amphogene females with males of amphogene origin produce half daughters, half sons. Females of thelygene origin crossed with any kind of male produce only monogene daughters. Thelygene females produce either only thelygene females, or arrhenogene females, or both. Exceptional females, daughters of an arrhenogene mother, have preponderantly arrhenogene daughters, but occasionally also thelygene or mixed (no. 6) daughters. Allelogenes (no. 5) sometimes have only arrhenogene daughters, sometimes both arrhenogene and thelygene ones. "Mixed" females (no. 6) may have arrhenogene, or preponderantly thelygene, or both types of daughters. All these facts agree with Vandel's explanation of directed meiotic division in female heterogamety (the possibility of which had been proved by Seiler in *Talaeporia*) and a cytoplasmic control of this (known to exist in aphids).

De Lattin's main objections to Vandel's theory are as follows. (1) No female heterogamety is proved cytologically or genetically, that is, by sex-linked inheritance. This means very little. In *Lymantria dispar* the XY group is cytologically not discernible, and no sex-linked mutants are known. But its cousin *L. monacha* has cytological differences of the sexes (Seiler and Haniel, 1921) and also the correct case of sex-linked heredity (Goldschmidt, 1921*a*). (2) In the offspring of monogenic females, amphogenic females occasionally appear. However, there is no reason why the cytoplasmic control mechanism should not be susceptible to occasional genetic or environmental modification. Actually we would be surprised if the directive mechanism always acted like clockwork. (3) Arrhenogenic females are derived frequently from thelygenic mothers, actually as half or more of the daughters. Thus the cytoplasmic feature which is assumed to control directed meiosis cannot control the alternative, thelygene-arrhenogene. This difficulty would not be hard to overcome. If the cytoplasmic factor decides that all eggs of a given female are monogene (i.e., have a directed meiosis), other environmental or genetic modifiers could decide which alternative happens on the basis of threshold conditions.

De Lattin finds in his own material other difficulties for Vandel's hypothesis. Monogene females may appear among the daughters of an amphogene mother, also amphogene females among the daughters of thelygene mothers; further, nearly 50 per cent of monogene females appear among the offspring of females from amphogene mothers, and fathers of arrhenogene descent. The conclusion which we could draw from such special facts is that within the system of directed meiosis of an XY egg, which accounts for monogenesis, other modifying features must be present affecting the completeness of control of Y movement in one direction, the threshold for working or not working of the control, and other imaginable interferences with the basic mechanism of meiotic control. But de Lattin concludes that we must renounce all explanations on the basis of an XY mechanism, and that only two possibilities remain: either phenotypic or multifactorial sex determination. This is proposed without realizing that the existence of an XY mechanism and its control is not at stake but only the variability of the control mechanism, whatever it is.

The "polyfactorial" scheme proposed is this. There are realizator complexes F and M which are spread over all the autosomes and are in an approximate equilibrium. But because some of them are still heterozygous, the equilibrium is only relative and thus works only for the average, not for the individual that may digress considerably from equilibrium conditions. (We would have to call this a somewhat labile monoecism.) To explain the monogenic animals, two other pairs of alleles are added: a dominant F^1 which is one of the realizators of the F complex and has a predetermining action, assumed to be via a stuff phi which may come from the mother in F^1 and f^1f^1 individuals. Then the author adds another gene, I, that does not belong to the realizator complex. It is supposed to increase the feminizing action of F^1. When its products are carried over to the next generation, absolute feminization results. Thus animals containing I and F^1 (or phi) will "almost always" be females, independent of other realizators over which F^1 is epistatic in the presence of I. The gene I may act in the mother with the result that all offspring receiving the intensified phi become females, even if they are themselves f^1 f^1 i i. But the I may act only in the zygote if a maternal phi is combined with a paternal I. The constitution of thelygene females is then F^1 f^1 I I. The pairing of two such individuals will produce only daughters, which are half F^1 f^1, half f^1 f^1. The first will propagate like their mothers; the second, which become females only by the combined action of phi and I, will produce with males from arrhenogene mothers an arrhenogene offspring, since these males have the same constitution as the second type of females except for the absence of phi. But this complicated system still does not suffice to explain amphogenic offspring of monogenic mothers. The proposed explanation is that the penetrance of I is less than 100 per cent, and in the absence of penetrance the other realizators again act alone. Even this does not suffice: in addition a monogenic line must have a weak F and a strong M complex and, in order to explain all details, still other assumptions have to be made.

There is no need to enlarge on the utter artificiality of this "polyfactorial theory" of sex determination, which in the end must go back to the F/M balance plus all kinds of modifying actions. I have no doubt that Vandel's explanation covers the facts in principle, though some modifying actions will have to be explained in terms of plasmon, predetermination, and modifiers. But this is nothing unusual, and is within the facts known for both the sex determination via a 2X-1X mechanism and for many other known genetic actions. It would, in addition, be very odd to assume that nature had invented (i.e., built up by selection or fortuitous drift) such an unmanageable, unreliable, and queer system of producing sexual dimorphism when the simple mechanism of F/M balance through the 2X-1X mechanism is available. Such considerations will excuse me from reporting and analyzing other cases which have been claimed for—to be frank—the monstrosity of so-called polyfactorial sex determination. This must, of course, not be confused with the already discussed problem of whether F and M are single loci or linked groups of such or what else. Even the AG idea—the sex-promoting genes—which we discarded above, is a completely different problem.

C. SEX IN HAPLOIDS

We have discussed thus far only the theory of sex determination in diploid organisms, and have found that no types could be established different from the standard type of F/M balance, regulated by the 2X-1X mechanism, including its variants and, from case to case, special modifier actions. The same is also true for the haploid lower plants or the haplophase of others, as I tried to show a long time ago (1929*a*). The work of the Hartmann school (see 1943), especially, has established that the same genetic setup as in diploids is at work in principle. The difference in detail between the explanations based upon Correns' scheme, used by Hartmann, and my point of view is more or less the same as for diploid sex determination. Hartmann insists upon the need of the AG factors. I think they are superfluous, and the argument is the same as discussed above. Also in haploids a F/M balance must be present, and both F and M can occur in different potencies or valencies, as shown in what Hartmann termed "relative sexuality;" this, in unicellular haplonts, which are simultaneously sexual organisms and gametes, is the condition parallel to strong and weak races in *Lymantria,* producing intersexuality in crosses. Correspondingly, the explanation of relative sexuality is derived from the *Lymantria* case, of course with the difference that the haploid cells are both gametes and sexual organisms. The chemical mechanism which Moewus and Kuhn claimed for the action of F and M of different valency has already been discussed (see III 5 C *a aa*). The "valency" was a definite mixture—variable with different valencies—of two sex-controlling stuffs (if this is true). Thus far, then, the genetic theory is identical for the higher diploid organisms and the haplonts. This includes also what Hartmann called "phenotypic sex determination," since my criticism of this concept is directly applicable to the haploid organism. The same applies also to the modifier actions studied in haploids as mutant effects. Therefore there is no need to go into the many details assembled in Hartmann's book, which is not easily read on account of the cumbersome terminology, derived from Correns' ideas and the failure to draw a clear line between sex determination and sex attraction (mating type).

However, at one important point Hartmann's theoretical interpretation, based upon the AG and realizator concept, is basically different from what I believe to be the correct solution in harmony with the theory of sex in diploid organisms. If Hartmann's interpretation is correct, the lower plants use a different mode of sex determination from that of the higher plants and animals. In order to understand this, let us try first to derive the consequences for haploids (or haploid phases) from the previous discussion (see Goldschmidt, 1929*a*). Assuming that the F/M balance mechanism works in the same way as in diploids and that male heterogamety is present, we see that the X-chromosomes can contain only F factors; and the autosomes, M factors. If the diploid condition were female, MMFF, the haploid would be MF, just as in the post-meiotic eggs; that is, the same balance makes this haploid a female. (This has been proved for *Drosophila* by Bridges, 1925.) From the diploid male MMFf (f = O or Y-chromosome) two haploids would be derived (like gametes of a diploid), MF = ♀ and Mf = ♂. Here the male haploid would have no female determiners, could not show relative sexuality or intersexuality. But haploids may show intersexuality: the male haploid must be derived from a more or less hermaphroditic diploid of the type Witschi has established for frogs, $MMFF^1$, F^1 meaning an X-chromosome with a weak F factor. Haploids, then, would be either MF with $F > M = ♀$, or MF^1 with $M > F^1 = ♂$. In both cases, shifts (relative sexuality) would be possible by means of modifiers or different valencies of F and M. The diploid phase would be hermaphroditic or almost so, and liable to easy genetic shift, just as in frogs. Both sexes of the haploid would contain both F and M factors with the F/M balance deciding the sex.

Hartmann derived (many papers and reviews quoted in 1943) a different interpretation from strict adherence to Correns' formulation. I once called this naïve and primitive, meaning that it tries to explain everything within the limits of elementary Mendelism. Correns first found (1907) that in crosses between monoecious and dioecious forms of *Melandrium,* sex behaves like a Mendelian backcross, which had been known before to zoölogists from the work on sex-linked heredity and the X-chromosome mechanism. At that time the cytological meaning of sex-linked heredity was not yet known; so the backcross explanation could not be brought in line with the chromosomal mechanism. Thus the formula FF = ♀ and FM with M epistatic = ♂ was developed. However, since it was known that females could develop male characters, another set of genes had to be invented, the A and G groups of genes, for every character which could be sexually dimorphic; the role of F and M came to be decisive in determining whether A or G became more active and the other group inhibited. Wettstein later called this the realizator function. Later, when the location of the sex determiners in the sex chromosomes became known, F had to be located in the X, and M in the Y-chromosome, which of course left all cases of XO in the air, as well as *Drosophila* without a sex determiner in the Y. Then came intersexuality and the balance theory, which required only F (M with female heterogamety) in the X-chromosome and M outside, which in male heterogamety could only be the autosomes, but in female heterogamety, also the Y-chromosome, as we have seen. Thus AG became a superfluous notion, FF = ♀, FM = ♂ did not work; and, in order to explain intersexuality, the different valencies of F and M, the balance idea, and the epistatic minimum had to be introduced. All this means that the formulation of Correns which was good in 1907 (though even at that time it neglected the sex chromosomes) ceased to be useful after 1910–1912.

Nevertheless, Hartmann derives from it the mechanism in the haploids. According to him, there are no autosomal sex determiners (realizators) but only both A and G genes distributed all over the autosomes in equilibrium (but when the facts make this equilibrium improbable, he has no hesitation in assuming that there are more G than A genes). The sex chromosome of the haploid contains the "realizator" either F or M, haploids with F being females, or + forms, with M being males, or – forms. The diploid phase will be hermaphroditic. But now the female haploid may show male characteristics and vice versa. Since only one realizator is present, the relative number or activity of A or G genes must be variable. Then relative sexuality is found which now requires different valencies of F and M but without a F/M balance.

Apart from the a priori improbability of this scheme (on which different minds may have different opinions), we must ask whether the existing facts permit a decision. Most of the facts and variants found in Hartmann's book and discovered since may be formally explained in both ways, with more or less additional assumptions. But there are a few facts which may be considered decisive and are also recognized as such by Hartmann. The decisive experiments in favor of my view have been made by Knapp (1936) and Knapp and Hofmann (1939). By X-raying of spores and vegetation points of female thalli of *Sphaerocarpus,* a certain number of male gametophytes were obtained. According to Hartmann's theory, the chromosomes should be 7A + 1X, and the X should contain only the female determiner F (realizator). Knapp proved in an excellent genetic and cytological analysis that the X rays had knocked out a piece of the X-chromosome and that maleness resulted even when a small piece was removed, and the number of male plants increased with increase in the size of the deficiency. This deficiency must have contained the F factor or factors, and therefore the M in the autosomes took over. It should be added that these mosses (Allen, 1917) have a visible XY group of chromosomes.

A still more powerful proof for the correctness of my conclusions is the following (discovered by Rizet, 1952). In the mold *Podospora* the haploid plant can be made diploid by so-called heterokarya (union of two plants) or by homokarya (diploidization of the same plant). In the latter, if Hartmann were right, the homokaryon should be of one or the other sex containing only FF or MM. Actually, the homokarya are hermaphrodites producing both sex organs. This is possible only if my interpretation of the genetic constitution is correct. It is important that the mating type is either − or +, as expected in a homokaryon, if mating type is independent of the F/M mechanism. We do not intend to discuss here the latter problem, which is one of physiology of fertilization and self-sterility. However, I may point out again that the inclusion of this problem in that of genetic sex determination by Hartmann and his school has led to much obscuring of the genuine genetics of sex and will necessitate one day a critical analysis and an unraveling of the separate problems. But let us return to the localization of F and M in haploids.

In favor of Hartmann's hypothesis are the claims that the assumed F and M realizators in the sex chromosome of female and male haploids are located at different loci and can be brought into one chromosome by crossing over, with the result of a hermaphrodite FM. This would be a proof if the other hypothesis led to a different expectation, which it does, as MF + F should not be a hermaphrodite but a hyperfemale. But Moewus says (see III 5 C *a aa*) that with F and M in one chromosome, the haploid is a hermaphrodite. If we could accept this as proved, Hartmann would be right in assuming a different sex-determining mechanism for at least this haploid organism. Unfortunately, the crossover experiments of Moewus have evoked much criticism, and, for the time being, I am not inclined to base such a far-reaching decision upon them. Recently the Hartmann school itself repeated Moewus' experiments, and in a sufficiently large sample no such crossovers could be found (Förster and Wiese, 1954*a*). A few other such examples have been claimed. Among them is a case (see Hartmann, p. 142) in which both haplonts, one with FM in one chromosome and the other without any "realizators," developed into monoecious plants. This makes me very skeptical in regard to the explanation as well as the experiments, though markers of the chromosomes were involved here. The crossing over is clearly not proved but is assumed on the basis of the general theory. Thus, on the whole, I do not think that it has been proved that haplonts have a radically different mechanism of sex determination from that of diplonts.

D. THE HYMENOPTERA TYPE

This leads to what is probably the most complicated situation. In a number of animals, especially all the Hymenoptera, males are developed from haploid parthenogenetic eggs. Females may be produced from fertilized eggs, but also sometimes from parthenogenetic ones, and thus are always diploid. In special cases, males may be derived from fertilized eggs. There is an immense variation in detail in individual cases, and the cytological mechanisms may be of many different kinds. (See the reviews by Vandel, 1931; and Whiting, 1945.) But it is not necessary to go into details, since the result is always controlled in these diploid females and males of whatever origin (e.g., parthenogenesis with subsequent autogamy or with doubling of the chromosomes, etc.) by the standard 2X-1X mechanism and the F/M balance. Only the haploid parthenogenetic males in Hymenoptera and other groups (haploid arrhenotoky) seem to be unexplainable on the basis of the general theory: their balance F/M must be the same, for example, as in parthenogenetic females produced by whatever kind of doubling of the chromosome set, developed possibly from the same unfertilized egg, which could have developed into a parthenogenetic male. The fertilized eggs are the same eggs which would have produced males if unfertilized.

A remarkable experimental attack upon this problem has been made by Whiting and his school (quotations in Whiting, 1945). He worked with the ichneumonid wasp, *Habrobracon juglandis,* in which all eggs are facultatively parthenogenetic, and, as a rule, unfertilized (and haploid) eggs produce males in the classic way, as one can also make certain by the use of genetic markers. But, if the parents come from the same parental stock, some diploid biparental males (as the markers prove) are also produced. They are of low viability, almost sterile, and not intersexual. Their viable sperm are diploid and, with normal eggs, may produce triploid daughters. The crosses show that a number of X-chromosome types act as multiple alleles in regard to sex determination, though sex-linked traits cross over. One might compare this series of multiple allelic X-chromosomes to the X- and Y-chromosomes of different potency in *Lymantria*. Whiting found nine such types Xa, Xb, Xc, and so on which, then, may exist as hemizygous (haploid) $\frac{\text{Xa}}{\text{O}}$ ..., or as compounds in diploid condition, $\frac{\text{Xa}}{\text{Xb}}$ ..., or as diploid homozygotes $\frac{\text{Xa}}{\text{Xa}}$ .... The hemizygotes are always males, the homozygotes are diploid males, and the diploid compounds are females. This is explained by the assumption that the so-called multiple alleles, Xa, Xb, . . . , are in fact chromosomal sections in which no crossing over occurs and in which a dominant female sex determiner is always present, F_a F_b, . . . , and a number of recessive male determiners m_a, m_b, m_c, . . . , or their normal alleles +. Thus a diploid heterozygote (compound) always has two dominant F, which are epistatic to the homo- or heterozygous m. A haploid has only one F and possibly many hemizygous m, which then are epistatic to the F. The same is true for the homozygote: an FF is not acting differently from one dominant F, and a number of homozygous m are present. Whiting calls this "complementary sex determination." If we would express this scheme in terms of the former discussion, we would have to say that here a unique condition obtains: the M and F determiners are not located in different chromosomes, but both within the X-chromosome; further, they are completely linked here; and the F/M balance is such that F has a high potency which is additive in compounds but not in homozygotes; the M potency is such that it has no action in the heterozygous condition (recessiveness of m) but an additive one in hemizygotes and homozygotes, so that MM (= m o, or mm, or m_a m_a m_b m_b) is epistatic over F or FF. If this remarkable scheme turns out to be correct, we could conclude that here also the F/M balance system is at work, but, by changing place so as to be confined in an X-chromosome, it permits the variant of sex determination by haploidy. This might be called a new type of sex determination, but I prefer to consider it only an extreme variant of the general scheme. Thus the general genetic theory of sex determination is, in spite of all variants, unified and rather simple.

PART V GENETIC THEORY AND EVOLUTION

1

INTRODUCTION

The title of this short chapter is not "Genetical Theory of Evolution" or "Genetics and Evolution" but "Genetic Theory and Evolution." The title indicates that I do not intend to discuss the genetic basis of evolution or evolution as such. In this book we are concerned only with the question whether the *theory* of genetics leads to ideas on the theory of evolution, or demands certain basic assumptions in regard to evolution. I have previously treated theoretical genetics under the headings of (1) the nature of the genic material, and (2) the action of the genic material. Thus the present problem is whether the views on the nature of the genic material and its action, as developed here, lead to definite conclusions regarding the theory of evolution.

In order to see at which points theoretical genetics affects our views on evolution, let us review briefly the elements involved, without details. The classic theory of the gene from Mendel, De Vries, Correns, Bateson, and Johannsen to Morgan gave a definite meaning to what Darwin had called variation. Genic mutation became the cause of hereditary variation; and genic recombination, in the widest sense, the manner in which variation was effected. Selection became the isolation of definite genic combinations. The continuous variation with which Darwin worked (though his proofs for selection taken from domestication were based largely upon discontinuous variation) became a matter of phenotype, while genetic variation was discontinuous. Such a system makes it rather difficult to lead evolution beyond the reshuffling of the mutated genes, that is, limited permutation or variations on the same theme. The early Mendelians felt this rather keenly and assumed a skeptical attitude toward evolutionary speculations, which found its extremest expression in Bateson's Australian address (1914) with the embarrassing idea of evolution by loss of inhibitors.

At this time a genetic attack upon the problem had already been attempted. Punnett (see 1915) and his student Fryer analyzed genetically a case of major evolutionary adaptation, mimetic polymorphism, which they found to be based upon Mendelian differences (as de Meijere had done before). This led Punnett to ask how such differences would be distributed in interbreeding populations and how selection could work on them. The mathematician Hardy worked out for him what is now known as the Hardy-Weinberg law, the basic fact of population genetics. At the same time I analyzed the genetics of industrial melanism in the nun moth (Goldschmidt, 1921*a*; see also 1948*b*), in which a melanic mutant form had replaced a white one in industrial areas within a known number of decades. After analyzing the genetic differences between the two types (three pairs of alleles, one sex-linked) I made a calculation of the mutation pressure needed to replace one form by the other in the known time. As the required mutation rate was too high to be possible, I concluded that the dark form must have a selective advantage. This, then, was a simple case of population genetics at the lowest level of micro-evolution.

At the same time it was realized that the first attack upon the genetic solution of evolutionary problems should be made by analyzing what Darwin had called "incipient species," the subspecies, which contemporary taxonomy had again pushed into the foreground in the Rassenkreis concept of the species (Kleinschmidt, Jordan, Rensch), a fact which most geneticists realized only decades later (the "new" systematics). Sumner started the genetic and ecological analysis of the subspecies of *Peromyscus* (final review, 1932), and I did the same simultaneously for *Lymantria dispar* (final review, 1934*c*). Both found that the subspecies differed from each other in definite Mendelian combinations. It was further established that some if not all of these genetic differences were of an adaptational nature, directly or indirectly. In 1917 and up to the early 20's I had already come to the conclusion—shared by Baur and East—that genetics leads back to Darwin and that especially numerous small mutants, accumulated by selection for the sake of adaptation, will account for speciation, exactly as Darwin saw it. (One non-technical article of mine had the title "Return to Darwin.")

A new period of genetical analysis of evolution below the level of the species—the only part accessible to genetic experimentation, not counting a few exceptions—began when Fisher (1919) and Wright (1921) worked out the statistical consequences of Mendelian breeding within populations under all types of mating; while Haldane (1924) added all the consequences for selection. Subsequently, Haldane, Fisher, and Wright explored in detail what happens in interbreeding populations from the point of view of distribution, isolation, selection or discarding of genic combinations, with and without selection. The general result was that shifts in genetic constitution and isolation of new recombinants leading to adaptation to diverse environments could be understood as statistical consequences of the classic theory of the gene and its mutation, together with the work of selection or drift upon the genotypes in interbreeding populations, especially by selection of modifier systems. There is no doubt that population genetics can explain all evolutionary happenings within a species, its diversification, fluctuation, adaptation to local environment. From the point of view of theoretical genetics, discussed in this book, population genetics and its results do not require further consideration. The actual problems (e.g., the relative importance of drift in S. Wright's sense) are evolutionary problems, frequently more or less problems of ecology and not problems of genetic theory. Genetic results and points of view enter the picture in special cases: the role of heterochromatin, the theory of polygenes, the consequences of chromatin rearrangements, the role of cytoplasmic diversification. We have already referred to these special problems in their proper places. As far as genetic theory is concerned, population genetics deals only with elementary Mendelian genetics based upon the classic theory of the gene and its mutation.

However, problems of genetic theory are bound to enter the picture when the question is raised whether or not the genic permutations of all kinds, together with selection and drift, suffice to explain evolution beyond the level of adaptive or non-adaptive diversification within the species in interbreeding populations. Neo-Darwinian evolutionists take it for granted that the findings on the intraspecific level can be simply extended to cover all evolution. This means that the diversification by selection of small mutant deviations and their accumulation slowly builds up species from subspecies, genera from species, and so up to phyla. I have repeatedly discussed this conclusion and tried to show the numerous difficulties with which it meets (see Goldschmidt, 1940, 1945*b*,*c*, 1948*c*, 1951*a*). We are not concerned here with most of these objections. If we look at the problem purely from the point of view of theoretical genetics, we realize that the classic theory of the gene in itself, that is, without additional assumptions, would limit possible genic permutations by reshuffling of mutant loci within the confines of the species. The maximum that could be accomplished would be the reproductive isolation of one or the other permutation, which then might be called a different species. However, this new species could only supply more of the same permutations and certainly nothing really new. It was the realization of this situation which made me renounce my former Neo-Darwinian ideas, when the analysis of the adaptive subspecies of

Lymantria showed that they varied within a blind alley so far as the origin of genuinely new traits is concerned. Thus I had to deny that subspecies are incipient species, which does not mean that sometimes a subspecies may reach the taxonomic value of a species, but rather that evolution does not, as a rule, use the subspecies as the first step. It is gratifying to see that this much criticized conclusion is now in large part accepted by so prominent a Neo-Darwinian as Mayr (1951), who finds that most subspecies, especially those arranged in clines, are not incipient species and may become such only when isolated (e.g., on islands at the periphery of the range).

It has been claimed only once that a permutation in the segregants of species crosses actually produces a completely new form. This was thought to be true in Baur and Lotsy's *Antirrhinum* crosses. But Stubbe and Wettstein (1941) and Stubbe (1952) have since shown that these authors were deceived by the presence of a remarkable but not rare macromutation. Thus it must be taken for granted that something really new in evolution cannot be produced by the permutations of small mutants with which population genetics deals so successfully. This may mean that evolution requires such profound changes of the genic material as the origination of new genes, if we stay within the classical theory, and (or) a type of mutant change which is different from the small variants of genic effects with which Neo-Darwinian theory deals. The solution of the problem of the origin of new genes is clearly dependent upon insight into the nature of the genic material; while the type of mutational action is a part of the problem of genic action. It is thus within these two spheres that the problems of evolution come in contact with theoretical genetics.

2

EVOLUTION OF THE GENIC MATERIAL

Most of the facts pertaining to this chapter have already been mentioned in connection with the theory of the gene. The first group we shall consider here deals with the evolution of the chromosome set. It is one of the surprising features of cytogenetics that the chromosomal cycle and the karyotype have not changed much in the phylogenetic tree. Some chromosomes of Protozoa have the same size, form, number, and finer structure as those of the highest organisms, for example, *Monocystis* (gregarines) and the large symbiontic flagellates. If we accept Moewus' work on the linkage groups in *Chlamydomonas,* the genetic structure of chromosomes in Protista—not to mention bacteria—closely parallels that of higher animals and plants. If we assume that the chromosome has been "invented" to make possible the exact duplication of the genic material (Roux, 1883), the lack of visible evolutionary changes in this mechanism indicates that whatever evolutionary changes took place within the chromosome, they were changes that did not affect the visible features of the chromosome.

Within this constancy of the general features of the chromosomal apparatus, some diversification has taken place for which it is very difficult to find an explanation. If we say, as has been done, that the chromosomal configuration (the karyotype) is just a morphological character like all others, we do not gain much insight. Other morphological characters are the result of mutation and selection in some way. But how selection could produce the characteristic karyotype of sauropsids or of most Lepidoptera is a question which seems unanswerable. A number of larger or smaller taxonomic groups have karyotypes so characteristic that the group could be diagnosed from a metaphase plate. All birds and reptiles have a circle of large chromosomes with a number of small ones in the center; and it is most suggestive that the Monotremata have the same karyotype (see Matthey, 1949). The majority of Lepidoptera have a group of about 60 dotlike chromosomes arranged in a very characteristic way. Many urodeles have about 24 very long, looplike chromosomes. Many Orthoptera have very large and typically arranged chromosome sets, frequently around 2n = 24 individual ones. Crabs tend to possess very high numbers (over 100) of small, dotlike chromosomes; and Diptera, a few (down to 6) chromosomes arranged in pairs. I cannot think of any reasonable explanation of this, since all types certainly work equally well from the point of view of the mechanism of meiosis and heredity; and since the organizational differences, say between Diptera, Orthoptera, and Lepidoptera, are not of a magnitude that requires different cellular mechanisms.

Not less enigmatic are the much studied (see White, 1945, 1951 for animals; and Babcock and students' extensive work on *Crepis,* 1947*a,b*) relations between karyotypes of species of the same genus or nearly related genera. Sometimes a large number of species have the same or almost the same karyotype (e.g., shorthorn grasshoppers). Even nearly related species sometimes have different karyotypes (e.g., some grasshoppers), and there are even subspecies with different karyotypes (e.g., domestic and wild silkworms, some *Peromyscus*). Much work has been done to find out whether these different karyotypes can be derived from an ancestral one, and this is frequently so. The methods of change seem to be, in most cases, division of the centromere with breaking apart of two arms, union of terminal centromeres with the opposite effect, all kinds of translocations, and pericentral inversions. We have already mentioned the well-worked-out example of the *Drosophila* species (see I 3 C *d bb*), in which many different karyotypes can be derived in this way from a basic configuration. Numerous examples for all this can be found in the books by White (1945), Matthey (1949), Patterson and Stone (1952), and Stebbins (1950) for plants, and almost daily in current cytological literature.

With the exception of polyploid plants, all species and genera of a group may have different karyotypes, and the karyotypes may be used as a taxonomic criterion of value. To a certain extent this is true also for the subgenera of *Drosophila.* However, such differences are not general and are not sufficiently orderly to give them a definite phylogenetic meaning in terms of chromosomal evolution. This means that in special cases we might well conclude that, say, a group with six chromosomes is derived from one with eight chromosomes by one or the other known or supposed processes; but no rule obtains which would permit endowing such processes with a genetic meaning, fitted to serve as a basis for evolutionary speculation. (Good examples in Babcock's 1947 *Crepis* monograph.) It is just this point which makes

Babcock and others embrace the Neo-Darwinian doctrine as the only way out, as they see it.

It is possible that all these facts on the evolution of the karyotype have no meaning at all, and are just chance happenings. When the sauropsids originated (not considering such details as the aberrant type of Crocodilia) the karyotype was there by chance and, not having any significance, persisted even to the almost mammalian Monotremata. But why did it change when the marsupials originated? In the same way the different configurations in the drosophilids may be the product of the chance alone that the first ancestor of each species carried an otherwise meaningless translocation, and so on. It is certainly possible to defend such a negative point of view, though it will not appeal to many geneticists. The alternative is that these features have a definite genetic meaning. What could this be?

Within the classic theory of the gene a chromosome is a linkage group, and a change in the karyotype means establishment of different linkage groups. This might have an evolutionary meaning if by this change groups of genes are kept together which for some reason are needed as an intact group. In this case, however, inhibition of crossing over would be needed. In addition, such an interpretation would have a meaning only if genes concerned with similar or related functions had an orderly distribution on the chromosome, which cannot be asserted as a general fact. There is another possibility apparent. If genes produce their primary products *in loco* and the first reactions between them take place on the chromosomal surface, and if, further, the reaction products diffuse along the surface of the chromosome to enter into new reactions, all of which has been claimed, as we saw before, the conclusion could be drawn that the establishment of new linkage groups allows new primary reactions along the chromosome. If such were the case, we should expect to find definite laws for the change of the karyotype from species to genus to family, and so on, and not the complete irregularity actually found. While it might be very difficult to prove or even to make plausible such an interpretation, it is equally difficult to disprove it, except by showing that the basic assumptions regarding primary reactions are wrong. We discussed this point previously and mentioned the obstacles to the acceptance of this theory of genic action.

If we renounce the classic gene and accept the theory of the hierarchical pattern of the genic material, the changes in the karyotype would mean the introduction or removal of some of the categories of concerted action, especially the higher ones. But up to the point of discussion reached so far, not much is gained by this interpretation, because it would also lead to the postulate of some order in the observed facts of phylogeny of the karyotype. However, the situation is different when we proceed from the karyotype to the structural pattern of the chromosome itself. Here the salivary chromosomes of *Drosophila* give very pertinent information, most of it owing to Dobzhansky and students (see Dobzhansky's book, 1952) and the Patterson group (see Patterson and Stone, 1952). In species crosses, as far as they succeed, it appears that more or less extensive parts of the salivary chromosomes are normally synapsed and therefore are structurally and genetically identical. In other regions smaller or larger inversions and sometimes translocations can be traced; still other regions do not synapse at all and seem structurally completely different. Though only a few species can be crossed successfully (see Patterson and Stone, 1952), it is probable that the dissimilarity of the structural pattern increases with decreasing taxonomic relation. The patterns of these chromosomes between (uncrossable) species are so different that they cannot be compared directly, and if we take different genera, or even families of Diptera, the comparability of pattern ceases to exist (e.g., *Drosophila* → *Sciara* → *Chironomus*). Whatever the details, at least one definite fact is visible, namely, that the intimate structural pattern of the chromosomes changes, diversifies with taxonomic distance. There is no reason to deny that this is a general feature, though only the giant salivary chromosomes of Diptera permit observing it.

How can this structural diversification, which must have taken place with evolution, be understood? I cannot see how the classic theory of the gene could answer this question. The only answer it has for the evolution of the genic material in the chromosomes is found in the explanation of the origin of new genes: if a protozoan chromosome is organized like any other one, this is only a matter of externa. The decisive difference is that it has fewer genes, which, then, means that evolution, beyond the reshuffling of mutant genes, consists of the addition of new genes at each step. As a spontaneous generation of genes is improbable, the new genes must be derived from old ones. Bridges introduced the idea that a duplicated gene, first in tandem duplication, later located anywhere else by translocation, may in time transform into a completely new gene. The presence of the old one permits such a development of a new one without harm to the organism.

I have always felt that this idea is very crude and, in addition, contrary to all we know about the action of the gene, if we argue now within the classic theory of the gene. Genes change only by mutation into one or more types of alleles, which all have the same general type of action. All alleles at the scute locus change the bristle pattern; and all at the white locus, the eye color. Nobody has ever found a scute allele affecting eye color. If we accept the explanation of pseudoalleles as duplicated genes, the theory would require that they become diversified. In all cases known, the assumed duplicate has generally the same action, and is different only in detail, but different only to the same extent as another allele. Actually, the pseudoalleles were always described first as ordinary multiple alleles and, in addition, as producing their own alleles of similar action. What dissimilarities there are, occur within the limits of multiple allelic action. For example, one group of the white alleles (see I 3 C *c ee ccc*) affects eye color with different expression in the female and in the male; the other group affects eye color with identical expression in the two sexes. The believers in new genes via duplication could say that in pseudoallelism we are witnessing only the beginning of an origination of new genes, and in a million years one of them will become a gene for the production of a new structure, not yet known today. I cannot be satisfied with such an argument, which sounds like Haeckel's type of phylogeny.

Another argument in favor of the theory could be derived from Lewis' views regarding the functioning of pseudoalleles (see III 4 A). As we have seen, Lewis assumed (as Pontecorvo had done tentatively with great caution) that in a series of pseudoalleles the new duplicate gene takes over the next synthetic step in a series of synthetic actions of which the original gene produced one step. The idea behind this assumption is, it seems, that an observed orderliness in the action of multiple alleles should be laid down in a similar orderliness in chromosomal structure. Previously Serebrovsky and Dubinin had used this approach when they concluded that the step arrangement of scute phenotypes (see I 3 C *a*) requires a stepwise arrangement of subunits of a gene. Both conclusions are rather unconvincing, actually a revival of the preformist error in chemical guise. But even accepting Lewis' ideas for argument's sake, we still face the general difficulty just discussed: How can the new gene get out of its connection with consecutive steps of a synthetic reaction to catalyze a completely new chain of reactions, as we must expect when a new gene for completely new evolutionary steps originates? Such an event seems to me to be much more miraculous than a repatterning within supermolecules for which we have known chemical models and, in addition, actually see the result in the known chromosomal patterns. Thus the classic theory of the gene seems to lead into a blind alley in regard to the possibilities of explaining evolution.

Though these difficulties have been realized occasionally by others (e.g., Mather, 1953*a*), I am aware of only one proposal that was intended to overcome them within the classical theory of the gene. Weir (1953) notes that there is a lack of correlation between chromatin content of the nucleus and complexity of the species, which is the same point given in our former (1940) and present discussions. Thus evolutionary progress apparently does not depend on an increase in gene number. Hence the question arises, How can an organism acquire new functions without an increase in gene number? Ordinary mutation and recombination do not create new variations, and there is no knowledge of an essential gene mutating to new functions. For these and other reasons, a species is faced with the problem either of acquiring additional gene loci, which are not restricted from the standpoint of their immediate usefulness, or of sparing existing genes from their essential roles. According to Weir, "neutral genes" bridge this gap. The action of such "neutral genes" is not necessary, because, for example, their products are already supplied from outside (like vitamins contributed by food). A neutral gene is a spare gene, available as potential material for fŭture evolution. Genes for bristle pattern are mentioned as examples of such "frivolous" genes, which can be present because the yeast supplies important gene products in the food. Neutral genes, then, can acquire new essential functions, perhaps working in a completely new reaction chain.

I am unable to see that these ideas help us to understand the origin of new genes within the classic concept of the gene (with the addition of the one gene—one action idea). The neutral genes in this concept play the same role as the duplicated genes in the one discussed before, and we still do not know why a gene, contrary to all knowledge, starts doing something quite new.

All these difficulties disappear when we accept the theory of the genic material which dispenses with the corpuscular gene and replaces it by the hierarchy of organizational (molecular) patterns in the chromosome. If small changes of pattern underlie the origin of the typical mutations, any degree of repatterning of the chromosomal material on the level of any of the segments of the hierarchy is possible, leading to different grades of change of the hierarchical pattern, which may increase in complication in numerous different ways. In a crude way, this is what is actually visible when the salivary chromosomes of *Drosophila* species of different taxonomic diversity are compared, and there is no reason why the crude visible diversity of pattern should not reflect the intimate diversity of the chemical pattern of the genic material. Evolution, in this case, would not require the origin of new genes, but only shifts in the hierarchy of patterns and sub- or super-patterns, which may be small and affect only minor characters, or may be large and affect major parts of the organization. In this picture the chromosomes of Protozoa do not have fewer genes but a simpler, less diversified and less hierarchical pattern of the genic material, which may be essentially the same as in all higher organisms. Evolution of the genic material, then, is internal diversification, not addition of new atomistic units.

Considerations like these have led me to postulate (1940), as a hypothesis, that scrambling and repatterning of the polarized sequences of chromosomal sections may occur occasionally in a single event, which I called "systemic mutations." Such repatternings in all grades, from small inversions or transpositions in one chromosome to a complete repatterning of all chromosomes, may lead, if viable, to a large over-all effect changing major features of development and producing in one step (or a few successive ones) a major evolutionary deviation. If the centromere region remains unchanged, synaptic pairing in the heterozygote is still possible; and a homozygote can be produced in time. As I said, this is a hypothesis only, and such a happening may never be observable. But it is good to keep in mind, when criticizing this hypothesis, that nobody has ever succeeded in producing a new species, not to mention the higher categories, by selection of micromutations. The critics of our hypothesis overlook that it is derived directly from the undeniable facts of increasing differences of intrachromosomal pattern with taxonomic distance, where it can be observed, namely, in the salivary gland chromosomes of *Drosophila* species. Either this is a product of chance and without any meaning, or it has an evolutionary meaning. If the latter, it leads logically to a hypothesis like that of systemic mutation (see Goldschmidt, 1940). This hypothesis involves, of course, the idea that evolution, except on the lowest intraspecific level, proceeds by saltations rather than by slow accumulation of small differences. The reasons that compel me to give preference to this view have been repeatedly given and do not belong to the present discussion. But one aspect of the hypothesis of evolution by saltation is linked to the theory of genic action and will therefore be discussed briefly.

3

EVOLUTION AND GENIC ACTION

I have been reproached for not having made it clear in my book *The Material Basis of Evolution* whether I was speaking of systemic mutation (scrambling of the chromosomal pattern) or of ordinary mutations of a macroevolutionary type, and of being confused myself on what I meant. Such criticism is based upon misunderstanding of the logic of the argument. We just derived the meaning of systemic mutation and its origin. In the extremest case, it would mean a complete repatterning of the genome in one or a few steps. In a less extreme case, it might mean a partial repatterning of one or two chromosomes of the type found in the differences between two still crossable species of *Drosophila.* But there is no clear delimitation of such a lower grade of repatterning from still lower ones. The lowest grade is an ordinary "genic mutation" which I consider to be a tiny repatterning on a submicroscopic level. From the point of view of action of the genic material there is so far no possibility of studying the differences brought about by a hypothetical systemic mutation; but we can study the difference at the lower end of the series, the simple mutation. Such a study can give us a model for the action of a systemic mutation, if we find mutants, macromutants, which produce such a large deviation from normal that they show in their limited action upon a part of the body (but sometimes also the entire organism, e.g., corn grass) what can be accomplished within the framework of viable development in regard to huge deviations, accomplishing in one step a real saltation of the kind we would expect to be produced by a systemic mutation. The argument is to show, with the model of the macromutant, that big saltatory deviations from normal are possible within the normal potentialities of development. If this can be shown, the facts not only serve as a model of macroevolutionary changes but demonstrate the possibility, in principle, of saltations in evolution, which might be due to systemic mutations, leading, in rare cases, to a viable whole. It is regrettable that many evolutionists forget that the developmental potencies are a necessary partner of genetic change in the understanding of evolution.

Demonstrating the possibility of saltations in principle means, of course, to show that developmental processes can be shifted by one mutant to such an extent that a structural departure appears which is of the order of magnitude of macroevolutionary differences. This must mean, in terms of development, that the mutant action affects one of the early determinative processes which decide the fate of a developing organism. We discussed such processes earlier (III 5 D *e*). A good example which may serve as a model (see figs. 21, 22) for any others is the *Drosophila* mutant tetraltera (one of the podoptera types). Here it can be seen that definite sections of the wing anlage are redetermined: one part into a leg or haltere-like structure by separating it from the rest and transforming it into a whole by adding a mirror image half; other parts of the wing anlage being redetermined into dorsum and scutellum, with their typical bristles, and incorporated into the thorax. In the same example we have seen the very important fact (figs. 21, 22) that the redetermined part subsequently becomes subjected to the power of integrating new and old structures in an appropriate way into a whole; this is one of the least understood properties of animal development, but it is an undeniable fact which is of the greatest importance for evolution. In the present example the transformed wing anlage was fitted in a perfect way into a completely reconstructed dorsal mesothorax, while the transformed scutellum with the normal one was crowded out and disappeared in the new architecture. This is a perfect example of how a macromutant (or a few successive ones) can produce in one step a major structural change, in itself perfect, integrated into the organism and changing it in general order of magnitude at least (of course for the one structure only in the observed example) to the extent of a generic difference or even more.

The number of such macromutants in animals and plants which could serve as similar models is steadily increasing. Stubbe and Wettstein (1941) and Stubbe (1952) described a number of them in *Antirrhinum* flowers, all reminiscent of the type of different genera. Stubbe showed also how they can easily acquire the necessary modifiers (meaning readjustment of the genetic system) for normal vitality. Burgeff (1943) found similar macromutants in liverworts; Andersson-Kottö and Gairdner (1936) in ferns; Gustafsson (1947, 1951*a*) in wheats; Lamprecht (1948) in peas; the most extreme case in plants is probably that of corn grass (Singleton, 1951), in which not only a part but the entire plant is affected extremely. An especially good example in plants has been studied by Gustafsson (1954) and D. von Wettstein (1954). In golden barley erectoides, a single mutant step, led to drastic change in morphology and anatomy, an altered ecological response, the origin of a sterility barrier, and (in one case) a new karyotype distinguishable cytologically. Further, these mutants form a basis for a new polymorphy, since secondary mutants appear rather frequently in outcrosses (Hagberg, 1954). Though Gustafsson is not yet ready to follow me completely in my conclusions upon macroevolution, he meets me at least halfway. In *Drosophila* the homoeotic mutants are examples; in the guinea pig, the polydactyl monsters (Wright, 1934); and in the mouse, mutants like luxated (see Grüneberg, 1952), in which early embryonic determination is shifted in regard to the location of some processes, with effects, such as change of vertebral number, which can be considered as models for known macroevolutionary features (see Forsthoefel, 1953). Thus there can be no doubt that single mutants can produce new effects upon embryonic determinative processes, leading to great departures in a direction which under proper conditions would lead to macroevolutionary divergence, especially so when the embryonic power of regulative integration fits the new structure harmoniously into the whole without need for special selective modification. If simple mutants can have an avalanche of consequences, a major repatterning of the genic material, as contemplated in the hypothesis of systemic mutation, could produce immense changes in one or a few steps. There is nothing in this idea which cannot be derived in an orderly way from the known facts of chromosomal evolution and the newer theory of the constitution and action of the genic material. It is therefore to be regretted that Dobzhansky called this point of view a cataclysmic theory, a designation which Stebbins even used for the title of a paper. There is nothing cataclysmic in a postulated process that occurs or is assumed to occur in a way that requires only known basic processes of chromosomal and genetic behavior. If cataclysms enter this theorizing at all, it is the cataclysm of the orthodox and extreme Neo-Darwinism.

We have not discussed evolution as such, but only its relation to genetic theory. As a matter of fact, evolution should again be appraised in the way I see it on the basis of all the material that has been added since my book of 1940 was written. It would then be seen that the number of evolutionists is increasing who take these views seriously and try to combine them with their own ideas (e.g., S.

Wright, 1950). It would also be seen that leading taxonomists in their respective fields, like Petrunkewitsch for spiders and scorpions (1952) and Zimmermann (*Insects of Hawaii,* 1948, see 1:151 ff., 2:342 ff.), find facts which force them to consider seriously my point of view. The same is true of the paleontologist Schindewolf (1950) in his remarkable volume. Perhaps some day an objective appraisal of all this will be made, together with a critical consideration of the failure of Neo-Darwinism to explain evolution beyond the level of mixed interbreeding populations.

BIBLIOGRAPHY

BIBLIOGRAPHY

Alexander, H. E., and G. Leidy
1953. Induction of streptomycin resistance in sensitive *Hemophilus influenzae* by extracts containing desoxyribonucleic acid from resistant *Hemophilus influenzae*. J. Exp. Med., 97:17–31.

Alfert, M.
1954. Composition and structure of giant chromosomes. Int. Rev. Cytol., 3:131–175.

Alfert, M., and H. Swift
1953. Nuclear DNA constancy: a critical evaluation of some exceptions reported by Lison and Pasteels. Exp. Cell Res., 5:455–460.

Allen, C. E.
1917. A chromosome difference correlated with sex differences in *Sphaerocarpos*. Science, 46:466–467.
1940. The genotypic basis of sex-expression in angiosperms. Bot. Rev., 6:227–300.

Ammann, H.
1954. Die postembryonale Entwicklung der weiblichen Geschlechtsorgane in der Raupe von *Solenobia triquetrella* F. R. (Lep.) mit ergänzenden Bemerkungen über die Entwicklung des männlichen Geschlechtsapparates. Zool. Jahrb. (Abt. 2, Anat.), 73:337–394.

Ancel, P.
1950. *La Chimiotératogenèse*. Paris: G. Doin. 397 pp.

Anders, F.
1953. Ueber die carotinoiden Körperpigmente und die Geschlechtsbestimmung von *Gammarus pulex* L. (Crust. Amphib.). Naturwissenschaften, 40:127.

Anderson, E. G.
1923. Maternal inheritance of chlorophyll in maize. Bot. Gaz., 76:411–418.
1935. Chromosomal interchanges in maize. Genetics, 20:70–83.
1938. Translocations in maize involving chromosome 9. *Ibid.*, 23:307–313.
1941. Translocations in maize involving the short arm of chromosome 1. *Ibid.*, 26:452–459.

Anderson, N. G.
1953. On the nuclear envelope. Science, 117:517–521.

ANDERSSON-KOTTÖ, I.
1930. Variegation in three species of ferns (*Polystichum angulare, Lastraea atrata,* and *Scolopendrium vulgare*). Z. indukt. Abstamm.- u. Vererb.-Lehre, 56:115–201.

ANDERSSON-KOTTÖ, I., and A. E. GAIRDNER
1936. The inheritance of apospory in *Scolopendrium vulgare.* J. Genet., 32:189–228.

ASTAUROFF, B. L.
1929. Studien über die erbliche Veränderung der Halteren bei *Drosophila melanogaster* Schin. Arch. Entw.-Mech. Org., 115:424–447.

ASTBURY, W. I.
1939. X-ray study of proteins and related substances. Sci. Progress, 34:1–19.

ATWOOD, K. C. and F. MUKAI
1953. Indispensable gene functions in *Neurospora.* Proc. Nat. Acad. Sci. Wash., 39:1027–1035.

AUERBACH, C.
1949*a*. Chemical induction of mutations. Proc. 8th Int. Congr. Genet. (Stockholm), 1948. Hereditas, 1949, Suppl., pp. 128–147.
1949*b*. Chemical mutagenesis. Biol. Rev., 24:355–391.
1950. Differences between effects of chemical and physical mutagens. Pubbl. Staz. zool. Napoli, 22, Suppl., pp. 1–21.
1951. Problems in chemical mutagenesis. Cold Spring Harbor Sympos. Quant. Biol., 16:199–214.

AUSTRIAN, R.
1952. Bacterial transformation reactions. Bact. Rev., 16:31–50.

AVERY, O. T., C. M. MACLEOD, and M. MCCARTY
1944. Studies on the chemical nature of the substance inducing transformation of pneumococcal types. J. Exp. Med., 79:137–158.

BABCOCK, E. B.
1947*a*. Cytogenetics and speciation in *Crepis.* Advanc. Genet., 1:69–93.
1947*b*. The genus *Crepis.* Univ. Calif. Publ. Bot., 21:1–197.

BAKER, W. K.
1953. V-type position effects of a gene in *Drosophila virilis* normally located in heterochromatin. Genetics, 38:328–344.

BAKER, W. K., and C. W. EDINGTON
1952. The induction of translocations and recessive lethals in *Drosophila* under various oxygen concentrations. Genetics, 37:665–677.

BAKER, W. K., and E. S. VON HALLE
1953. The basis of the oxygen effect on X-irradiated *Drosophila* sperm. Proc. Nat. Acad. Sci. Wash., 39:152–161.

BALTZER, F.
1920. Ueber die experimentelle Erzeugung und die Entwicklung von *Triton*-Bastarden ohne mütterliches Kernmaterial. Verh. schweiz. naturf. Ges., 101:217–220.
1933. Ueber die Entwicklung von *Triton*-Bastarden ohne Eikern. Verh. deutsch. zool. Ges., 1933:119–126.
1940. Ueber erbliche letale Entwicklung und Austauschbarkeit artverschiedener Kerne bei Bastarden. Naturwissenschaften, 28:177–206.

BALTZER, F. (*Continued*)

1952. Experimentelle Beiträge zur Frage der Homologie. Experientia, 8:285–297.

BARIGOZZI, C.

1942. Nuovo contributo alla conoscenza del fenomeno Notch. Riv. Biol., 34:3–16.

1949. On the role of the heterochromatin in the Y-chromosome in the determination of quantitative characters. Proc. 6th Int. Congr. Exp. Cytol. (Stockholm). Exp. Cell Res., 1, Suppl., pp. 149–152.

1950*a*. A general survey on heterochromatin. Portugal. Act. Biol., Sér. A, Volume R. B. Goldschmidt, pp. 593–620.

1950*b*. Le rôle du chromosome Y chez *Drosophila melanogaster*. Arch. Klaus-Stift. Vererb.-Forsch., 25:28–33.

1951. The influence of the Y-chromosome on quantitative characters of *D. melanogaster*. Heredity, 5:415–432.

1952. La struttura microscopica del nucleo durante il riposo. Experientia, 8:133–136.

BARIGOZZI, C., and A. DI PASQUALE

1953. Heterochromatic and euchromatic genes acting on quantitative characters, in *D. melanogaster*. Heredity, 7:389–399.

BATESON, W.

1914. Inaugural address. Nature, 93:635–642.

BATESON, W., and A. E. GAIRDNER

1921. Male sterility in flax, subject to two types of segregation. J. Genet., 11:269–275.

BAUER, H.

1939. Röntgenauslösung von Chromosomenmutationen bei *Drosophila melanogaster*. I. Chromosoma, 1:343–390.

1942. Röntgenauslösung . . . II. *Ibid.*, 2:407–458.

1952. Die Chromosomen im Soma der Metazoen. Verh. deutsch. zool. Ges. (Freiburg), 1952: 252–268.

BAUER, H., and W. BEERMANN

1952*a*. Der Chromosomencyclus der Orthocladiinen (Nematocera, Diptera). Z. Naturf., 7*b*:557–563.

1952*b*. Die Polytänie der Riesenchromosomen. Chromosoma, 4:630–648.

BAUR, E.

1909. Das Wesen und die Erblichkeitsverhältnisse der "Varietates albomarginatae hort." von *Pelargonium zonale*. Z. indukt. Abstamm.- u. Vererb.-Lehre, 1:330–351.

1925. Die Bedeutung der Mutationen für das Evolutionsproblem. *Ibid.*, 37:107–115.

BEADLE, G. W.

1932. A gene for sticky chromosomes in *Zea mays*. Z. indukt. Abstamm.- u. Vererb.-Lehre, 63:195–217.

1945. Biochemical genetics. Chem. Rev., 37:15–96.

1949. Genes and biological enigmas. Sci. Progress, 6:184–249, 313–317.

BEADLE, G. W., and B. EPHRUSSI

1936. The differentiation of eye pigments in *Drosophila* as studied by transplantation. Genetics, 21:225–247.

BEADLE, G. W., and E. L. TATUM
1941*a*. Genetic control of biochemical reactions in *Neurospora*. Proc. Nat. Acad. Sci. Wash., 27:499–506.
1941*b*. Genetic control of developmental reactions. Biol. Sympos., 4:173–182.
BEALE, G. H.
1951. Nuclear and cytoplasmic determinants of hereditary characters in *Paramecium aurelia*. Nature, 167:256–258.
1952. Antigen variation in *Paramecium aurelia*, variety 1. Genetics, 37:62–74.
BEAUCHAMP, P. DE
1910. Sur l'existence et les conditions de la parthénogenèse chez *Dinophilus*. C. R. Acad. Sci. Paris, 150:739–741.
BEERMANN, W.
1952. Chromomerenkonstanz und spezifische Modifikationen der Chromosomenstruktur in der Entwicklung und Organdifferenzierung von *Chironomus tentans*. Chromosoma, 5:139–198.
BELGOVSKY, M. L.
1938. Influence of inert regions of chromosomes on the frequency of occurrence and type of changes in the adjacent active sections. Izv. Akad. Nauk S.S.S.R. (Otd. mat.-est., ser. biol.), pp. 1017–1036.
1944. On the causes of mosaicism associated with heterochromatic chromosome regions. Zh. obsh. Biol., 5:325–356.
1946. On the causes of mosaicism . . . Amer. Nat., 80:180–183.
BEZEM, J. J., and F. H. SOBELS
1953. Penetrance and expressivity in the genotype Abnormal Abdomen of *Drosophila melanogaster*. Verh. Kon. nederl. Akad. Wetensch., Ser. C, 56:48–61.
BILLINGHAM, R. E., and B. P. MEDAWAR
1948. Pigment spread and cell heredity in guinea-pigs' skin. Heredity, 2:29–48.
1950. Pigment spread in mammalian skin: serial propagation and immunity reactions. *Ibid.*, 4:141–164.
BLANC, R.
1946. Dominigenes of the vestigial series in *Drosophila melanogaster*. Genetics, 31:395–420.
BODENSTEIN, D.
1943. Hormones and tissue competence in the development of *Drosophila*. Biol. Bull., 84:35–58.
1953*a*. Endocrine control of metamorphosis with special reference to holometabola. Trans. 9th Int. Congr. Ent., 2:58–62.
1953*b*. Studies on the humoral mechanisms in growth and metamorphosis of the cockroach *Periplaneta americana*. I. J. Exp. Zool., 123:189–232.
BODENSTEIN, D., and A. ABDEL-MALEK
1949. The induction of aristapedia by nitrogen mustard in *Drosophila virilis*. J. Exp. Zool., 111:95–115.
BOIVIN, A.
1947. Directed mutation in colon bacilli, by an inducing principle of desoxyribonucleic nature: its meaning for the general biochemistry of heredity. Cold Spring Harbor Sympos. Quant. Biol., 12:7–17.
BOIVIN, A., A. DELAUNAY, R. VENDRELY, and Y. LEHOULT
1945. L'acide thymonucléique polymérisé, principe paraissant susceptible de

Boivin, A., A. Delaunay, R. Vendrely, and Y. Lehoult (*Continued*)
déterminer la spécificité sérologique et l'équipement enzymatique des bactéries. Experientia, 1:334–335.

Bonner, D. M.
1946. Biochemical mutations in *Neurospora.* Cold Spring Harbor Sympos. Quant. Biol., 11:14–24.
1950. The Q-locus of *Neurospora.* Genetics, 35:655–656.
1951. Gene-enzyme relationships in *Neurospora.* Cold Spring Harbor Sympos. Quant. Biol., 16:143–158.

Bonnevie, K.
1907. Untersuchungen über Keimzellen. II. Physiologische Polyspermie bei Bryozoen. Jena. Z. Med. Naturw., 42:567–598.

Bonnier, G.
1951. Gynandromorph sex-combs in *Drosophila melanogaster.* Ark. Zool., ser. 2, 3:53–68.

Bonnier, G., and K. G. Lüning
1951. Spontaneous and X-ray induced gynandromorphs in *Drosophila melanogaster.* Hereditas, 37:469–487.

Bonnier, G., K. G. Lüning, and A. M. Perje
1949. Studies on X-ray mutations in the white and forked loci of *Drosophila melanogaster.* II. Hereditas, 35:31–336.

Bonnier, G., R. Rasmuson, and M. Rasmuson
1947. "Gene divisibility" as studied by differences in Bar facet numbers in *Drosophila melanogaster.* Hereditas, 33:348–366.

Boveri, Th.
1887. Ueber Differenzierung der Zellkerne während der Furchung des Eies von *Ascaris megalocephala.* Anat. Anz., 2:688–693.

Boycott, A. E., C. Diver, S. L. Garstang, and F. M. Turner
1930. The inheritance of sinistrality in *Limnaea peregra* (Mollusca, Pulmonata). Phil. Trans. Roy. Soc., B, 219:51–131.

Brachet, J.
1933. Recherches sur la synthèse de l'acide thymonucléique pendant le développement de l'oeuf d'oursin. Arch. Biol., 44:519–576.
1940. Étude histochimique des protéines au cours du développement embryonnaire des poissons, des amphibiens et des oiseaux. *Ibid.*, 51:167–202.
1944. *Embryologie chimique.* Paris: Masson. 509 pp. 2d ed., 1947.
1947. The metabolism of nucleic acids during embryonic development. Cold Spring Harbor Sympos. Quant. Biol., 12:18–26.
1949. L'hypothèse des plasmagènes dans le développement et la différenciation. Pubbl. Staz. zool. Napoli, 21, Suppl., pp. 77–105.
1950*a*. *Chemical Embryology.* New York: Interscience Publ. 533 pp.
1950*b*. Le rôle du noyau et du cytoplasme dans les synthèses de la morphogenèse. Ann. Soc. Roy. Zool. Belg., 81:185–209.

Brachet, J., and H. Chantrenne
1952. Incorporation de $C^{14}O_2$ dans les protéines des chloroplastes et des microsomes de fragments nuclées et anucléées d'*Acetabularia mediterranea.* Arch. Int. Physiol., 60:547–549.

BRAUN, W.

1940. Experimental evidence on the production of the mutant "aristapedia" by a change of developmental velocities. Genetics, 25:143–149.

1942. The effect of changes in time of development on the phenotypes of mutants of *Drosophila melanogaster.* Univ. Calif. Publ. Zoöl., 49:61–84.

BREHME, K. S.

1939. A study of the effect on development of "Minute" mutations in *Drosophila melanogaster.* Genetics, 24:131–161.

1941. Development of the Minute phenotype in *Drosophila melanogaster.* A comparative study of the growth of three Minute mutations. J. Exp. Zool., 88:135–160.

BREHME, K. S., and M. DEMEREC

1942. A survey of Malpighian tube color in the eye color mutants of *Drosophila melanogaster.* Growth, 6:351–355.

BREUER, M., and C. PAVAN

1955. Behavior of polytene chromosomes of *Rhynchosciara angelae* at different stages of larval development. Chromosoma. (In press.)

BRIDGES, C. B.

1917. Deficiency. Genetics, 2:445–465.

1922. The origin of variations in sexual and sex-limited characters. Amer. Nat., 56:51–63.

1925. Sex in relation to chromosomes and genes. *Ibid.,* 59:127–137.

1935. Salivary chromosome maps. J. Hered., 26:60–64.

1936. The Bar "gene" a duplication. Science, 83:210–211.

1939. Cytological and genetic basis of sex. In: *Sex and Internal Secretions.,* ed. by E. Allen. 2d ed., Baltimore: Williams and Wilkins. Pp. 15–63.

BRIDGES, C. B., and K. S. BREHME

1944. The mutants ot *Drosophila melanogaster.* Carnegie Inst. Wash. Publ. 552. 257 pp.

BROWN, S. W.

1949. Endomitosis in the tapetum of tomato. Amer. J. Bot., 36:703–716.

BRUNER, I. A.

1952. Further quantitative studies on the effects of androgens on sex-determination of *Ambystoma.* Anat. Rec., 113:58.

BUCHNER, P.

1953. *Endosymbiose der Tiere mit pflanzlichen Mikroorganismen.* Basel: Birkhäuser. 772 pp.

1954. Endosymbiosestudien an Schildläusen. I. Z. Morph. Oekol. Tiere, 43:262–312.

BUCK, J. B.

1942. Micromanipulation of salivary gland chromosomes. J. Hered., 33:3–10.

BURGEFF, H.

1943. *Genetische Studien an Marchantia.* Jena: G. Fischer. 296 pp.

BUTENANDT, A.

1952. The mode of action of hereditary factors. Endeavour, 11:188–192.

1953. Biochemie der Gene und Genwirkungen. Naturwissenschaften, 40:91–100.

BUTLER, J. A. V.

1952. The nucleic acid of the chromosomes. Endeavour, 11:154–158.

BUTTNER, A.
1950. Labilité particulière du sexe chez *Schistosoma mansoni* (Plathelminthe, Trematode). Essai d'interprétation. Ann. Parasit., 25:297–307.
CALLAN, H. G.
1952. A general account of experimental work on amphibian oocyte nuclei. Sympos. Soc. Exp. Biol., 6:243–255.
CAROTHERS, E. E.
1936. Components of the mitotic spindle with special reference to the chromosomal and interzonal fibers in the Acrididae. Biol. Bull., 71:469–491.
CASPARI, E.
1933. Ueber die Wirkung eines pleiotropen Gens bei der Mehlmotte *Ephestia kühniella* Zeller. Arch. Entw.-Mech. Org., 130:353–381.
1936. Zur Analyse der Matroklinie der Vererbung in der a-Serie der Augenfarbenmutationen bei der Mehlmotte *Ephestia kühniella* Z. Z. indukt. Abstamm.- u. Vererb.-Lehre, 71:546–555.
1946. On the effects of the gene a on the chemical composition of *Ephestia kühniella* Zeller. Genetics, 31:454–474.
1948. Cytoplasmic inheritance. Advanc. Genet., 2:1–66.
1949*a*. On the action of genes in development. Portugal. Act. Biol., Sér. A, Volume R. B. Goldschmidt, pp. 147–160.
1949*b*. Physiological action of eye color mutants in the moths *Ephestia kühniella* and *Ptychopoda serrata*. Quart. Rev. Biol., 24:185–199.
1952. Pleiotropic gene action. Evolution, 6:1–18.
CASPERSSON, T.
1939. Ueber die Rolle der Desoxyribosenukleinsäure bei der Zellteilung. Chromosoma, 1:147–156.
1940. Die Eiweissverteilung in den Strukturen des Zellkerns. *Ibid.*, 1:562–609.
1947. The relations between nucleic acid and protein synthesis. Sympos. Soc. Exp. Biol., 1:127–151.
1950. *Cell Growth and Cell Function*. New York: W. W. Norton. 185 pp.
CASPERSSON, T., and J. SCHULTZ
1938. Nucleic acid metabolism of the chromosomes in relation to gene reproduction. Nature, 142:294–295.
1940. Ribonucleic acids in both nucleus and cytoplasm, and the function of the nucleolus. Proc. Nat. Acad. Sci. Wash., 26:507–515.
CATCHESIDE, D. G.
1939. A position effect in *Oenothera*. J. Genet., 38:345–352.
1947. The P-locus position effect in *Oenothera*. *Ibid.*, 48:31–42.
1948. Genetic effects of radiations. Advanc. Genet., 2:271–349.
1951. *The Genetics of Micro-organisms*. London: I. Pitman. 223 pp.
CATSCH, A.
1948. Versuche an *Drosophila* über die Dosisabhängigkeit strahleninduzierter Chromosomenmutationen. Z. indukt. Abstamm.- u. Vererb.-Lehre, 82:155–163.
CAULLERY, M.
1951. *Organisme et sexualité*. 2d ed., Paris: G. Doin. 489 pp. 1st ed., 1941.
CAVALLI, L. L., and J. LEDERBERG
1953. Genetics of resistance to bacterial inhibitors. Sympos. Growth Inhib. and Chemother. Publ. Ist. Sup. di Sanità (Rome), pp. 108–142.

Chevais, S.
1943. Déterminisme de la taille de l'oeil chez le mutant Bar de la Drosophile. Bull. biol., 77:295–364.
Chèvremont, M., and H. Firket
1953. Alkaline phosphatase of the nucleus. Int. Rev. Cytol., 2:261–288.
Child, C. M.
1941. *Patterns and Problems of Development.* Chicago: University Press. 811 pp.
Child, G. P., R. Blanc, and H. H. Plough
1940. Somatic effects of temperature on development. I. Phenocopies and reversal of dominance. Physiol. Zool., 13:57–64.
Chovnick, A., and A. S. Fox
1953. Immunogenetic studies of pseudoallelism in *Drosophila melanogaster.* I. Proc. Nat. Acad. Sci. Wash., 39:1035–1043.
Clark, A. M.
1953. The mutagenic activity of dyes in *Drosophila melanogaster.* Amer. Nat., 87:295–306.
Claude, A., and J. S. Potter
1943. Isolation of chromatin threads from the resting nucleus of leukemic cells. J. Exp. Med., 77:345–354.
Cock, A. G.
1953. The interpretation of autosexing. J. Genet., 51:421–433.
Cooper, D. C.
1952. The transfer of desoxyribose nucleic acid from the tapetum to the microsporocytes at the onset of meiosis. Amer. Nat., 86:219–229.
Correns, C.
1900. Ueber Levkojenbastarde. Zur Kenntnis der Grenzen der Mendel'schen Regeln. Bot. Zbl., 84:97–113.
1907. *Die Bestimmung und Vererbung des Geschlechtes, nach neuen Versuchen mit höheren Pflanzen.* Berlin: Borntraeger. 81 pp.
1908. Die Rolle der männlichen Keimzellen bei der Geschlechtsbestimmung der gynodioecischen Pflanzen. Ber. deutsch. bot. Ges., 26*a*:686–701.
1928. Bestimmung, Vererbung und Verteilung des Geschlechts bei den höheren Pflanzen. Handbuch der Vererbungswissenschaften, II, C:1–138. Berlin: Borntraeger.
1937. Nicht mendelnde Vererbung. In: *Ibid.,* ed. by F. von Wettstein, II, H:1–159.
Correns, C., and R. Goldschmidt
1913. *Die Vererbung und Bestimmung des Geschlechtes.* Berlin: Borntraeger. 149 pp.
Crew, F. A. E.
1927. *The Genetics of Sexuality in Animals.* Cambridge: University Press. 188 pp.
Crick, F. H. C.
1954. The structure of the hereditary material. Sci. Amer., 151:54–61.
Csik, L.
1934. Die Zusammenarbeit einiger Gene bei der Determination der Flügelgrösse von *Drosophila melanogaster.* Biol. Zbl., 54:614–645.

CSIK, L. (*Continued*)

1936. Die Zusammenarbeit einiger Gene bei der Determination der Borstenlänge von *Drosophila melanogaster,* nebst einigen Bemerkungen über Epistasie. *Ibid.,* 56:338–355.

CUGNAC, A. DE

1939. Conséquences génétiques et phylétiques du croisement de deux graminées. C. R. Acad. Sci. Paris, 209:696–698.

DALCQ, A.

1941. *L'oeuf et son dynamisme organisateur.* Paris: A. Michel. 582 pp.

D'AMATO, F., and A. GUSTAFSSON

1948. Studies on the experimental control of the mutation process. Hereditas, 34:181–192.

DARLINGTON, C. D.

1937. *Recent Advances in Cytology.* 2d ed., London: J. and A. Churchill. 671 pp.

1939. *The Evolution of Genetic Systems.* Cambridge: University Press. 149 pp.

1942. Chromosome chemistry and gene action. Nature, 149:66–69.

1944. Heredity, development and infection. *Ibid.,* 154:164–169.

1947. Nucleic acid and the chromosomes. Sympos. Soc. Exp. Biol., 1:252–269.

1949. The working units of heredity. Proc. 8th Int. Congr. Genet. (Stockholm), 1948. Hereditas, 1, 1949, Suppl., pp. 189–200.

1953. The problem of chromosome breakage. In: Symposium on Chromosome Breakage. Heredity, 6, Suppl., pp. 5–8.

DARLINGTON, C. D., and L. LA COUR

1938. Differential reactivity of the chromosomes. Ann. Bot., 2:615–625.

1940. Nucleic acid starvation in *Trillium.* J. Genet., 40:185–213.

1947. *The Handling of Chromosomes.* 2d ed., New York: Macmillan. 180 pp.

DARLINGTON, C. D., and K. MATHER

1949. *The Elements of Genetics.* London: Allen and Unwin. 446 pp.

DARLINGTON, C. D., and P. T. THOMAS

1941. Morbid mitosis and the activity of inert chromosomes in *Sorghum.* Proc. Roy. Soc., B., 130:127–150.

DARLINGTON, C. D., and M. B. UPCOTT

1941. The activity of inert genes in *Zea mays.* J. Genet., 41:275–296.

DE BEER, G. R.

1951. *Embryos and Ancestors.* Rev. ed., Oxford: Clarendon Press. 159 pp.

DEKKER, C. A., and H. K. SCHACHMAN

1954. On the macromolecular structure of desoxyribonucleic acid: an interrupted two-strand model. Proc. Nat. Acad. Sci. Wash., 40:894–908.

DELAMATER, E. D.

1951. A new cytological basis for bacterial genetics. Cold Spring Harbor Sympos. Quant. Biol., 16:381–412.

DELBRÜCK, M.

1940. Radiation and the hereditary mechanism. Amer. Nat., 74:350–362.

1941. A theory of autocatalytic synthesis of polypeptides and its application to the problem of chromosome reproduction. Cold Spring Harbor Sympos. Quant. Biol., 9:122–126.

DELLINGSHAUSEN, M. VON
1935. Entwicklungsgeschichtlich-genetische Untersuchungen an *Epilobium.* V. Planta, 23:604–622.
1936. Entwicklungs. . . . VI. *Ibid.,* 25:282–301.
DEMARINIS, F.
1952. Action of the Bar series in relation to temperature studied by means of Minute-n mosaic technique. Genetics, 37:75–89.
DEMARINIS, F., and A. H. HERSH
1943. A further study of bar-eyed mosaics in *Drosophila.* Growth, 7:1–9.
DEMEREC, M.
1927. A second case of maternal inheritance of chlorophyll in maize. Bot. Gaz., 84:139–155.
1937. Frequency of spontaneous mutations in certain stocks of *Drosophila melanogaster.* Genetics, 22:469–478.
1941*a*. The nature of the gene. University of Pennsylvania Bicent. Conf., 1941: 1–11. In: *Cytology, Genetics, and Evolution.* Philadelphia: University of Pennsylvania Press.
1941*b*. Unstable genes in *Drosophila.* Cold Spring Harbor Sympos. Quant. Biol., 9:145–149.
1943. Gene deficiencies as cell lethals in *Drosophila melanogaster.* Amer. Nat., 68:165.
1949*a*. Chemical mutagens. Proc. 8th Int. Congr. Genet. (Stockholm), 1948. Hereditas, 1949, Suppl., pp. 201–209.
1949*b*. Patterns of bacterial resistance to penicillin, aureomycin and streptomycin. J. Clin. Invest., 28:891–893.
DEMEREC, M., *et al.*
1949. The gene. Carnegie Inst. Yearbook, 48:154–166.
1950*a*. The gene. *Ibid.,* 49:144–157.
DEMEREC, M. (ed.)
1950. *Biology of Drosophila.* New York: J. Wiley. 632 pp.
DEMEREC, M., and H. SLIZYNSKA
1937. Mottled white 258–18 of *Drosophila melanogaster.* Genetics, 22:641–649.
DESSAUER, F.
1954. *Quantenbiologie.* Heidelberg: J. Springer. 178 pp.
DOBZHANSKY, TH.
1930*a*. The manifold effects of the genes Stubble and Stubbloid in *Drosophila melanogaster.* Z. indukt. Abstamm.- u. Vererb.-Lehre, 54:427–457.
1930*b*. Studies on the intersexes and supersexes in *Drosophila melanogaster* (in Russian). Izv. Bur. Genet. (Leningrad), 8:91–158.
1930*c*. Genetical and environmental factors influencing the type of intersexes in *Drosophila melanogaster.* Amer. Nat., 64:261–271.
1932. The baroid mutation in *Drosophila melanogaster.* Genetics, 17:369–392.
1933. On the sterility of the interracial hybrids in *Drosophila pseudoobscura.* Proc. Nat. Acad. Sci. Wash., 19:397–403.
1952. *Genetics and the Origin of Species.* 3d ed., New York: Columbia University Press. 364 pp.

DOBZHANSKY, TH., and C. B. BRIDGES
1928. The reproductive system of triploid intersexes in *Drosophila melanogaster*. Amer. Nat., 62:425–434.
DOBZHANSKY, TH., and M. HOLZ
1943. A re-examination of the problem of manifold effects of genes in *Drosophila melanogaster*. Genetics, 28:295–303.
DOBZHANSKY, TH., and J. SCHULTZ
1934. The distribution of sex-factors in the X-chromosome of *Drosophila melanogaster*. J. Genet., 28:349–386.
DOBZHANSKY, TH., and C. C. TAN
1936. Studies on hybrid sterility. III. Z. indukt. Abstamm.- u. Vererb.-Lehre, 72:88–114.
DODSON, E. O.
1948. A morphological and biochemical study of lampbrush chromosomes of the vertebrates. Univ. Calif. Publ. Zoöl., 53:281–314.
DOERMANN, A. H.
1953. The vegetative state in the life cycle of bacteriophage: evidence for its occurrence and its genetic characterization. Cold Spring Harbor Sympos. Quant. Biol., 18:3–11.
DUBININ, N. P.
1932. Step allelomorphism and the theory of centres of the gene, achaete-scute. J. Genet., 26:37–58.
1936*a*. Experimental alteration of the number of chromosome pairs in *Drosophila melanogaster*. Biol. Zh. (Moscow), 5:833–850.
1936*b*. A new type of the position effect of genes. *Ibid.*, 5:851–874.
DUBININ, N. P., and B. N. SIDOROV
1934. Relation between the effect of a gene and its position in the system. Amer. Nat., 68:377–381.
DUBININ, N. P., and E. N. VOLOTOV
1936. Mutations arising at the Bar locus in *Drosophila melanogaster*. Nature, 137:869.
1940. Karyotype phylogeny in connection with the role played by linear repetitions. Zh. obsh. Biol., 1:205–232.
DUBUY, H. G., M. W. WOODS, and M. D. LACKEY
1950. Enzymatic activities of isolated normal and mutant mitochondria and plastids of higher plants. Science, 111:572–574.
DUNN, L. C., and E. CASPARI
1945. A case of neighboring loci with similar effects. Genetics, 30:543–568.
DUNN, L. C., and J. COYNE
1935. The relationship between the effects of certain mutations on developmental rate and on adult characters. Biol. Zbl., 55:385–389.
DUNN, L. C., and S. GLUECKSOHN-WAELSCH
1953. Genetic analysis of seven newly discovered mutant alleles at locus T in the house mouse. Genetics, 38:261–271.
DUNN, L. C., and J. C. MOSSIGE
1937. The effects of the Minute mutations of *Drosophila melanogaster* on developmental rate. Hereditas, 23:70–90.
DURYEE, W. R.
1937. Isolation of nuclei and non-mitotic chromosome pairs from frog eggs. Arch. exp. Zellforsch., 19:171–176.

1941. The chromosomes of the amphibian nucleus. University of Pennsylvania Bicent. Conf., 1941: 129–141. In: *Cytology, Genetics, and Evolution.* Philadelphia: University of Pennsylvania Press.

1950. Chromosomal physiology in relation to nuclear structure. Ann. N. Y. Acad. Sci., 50:920–953.

EAST, E. M.

1936. Genetic aspects of certain problems of evolution. Amer. Nat., 70:143–158.

ELSON, D., and E. CHARGAFF

1952. On the desoxyribonucleic acid content of sea urchin gametes. Experientia, 8:143–145.

EMERSON, R. A.

1914. The inheritance of a recurring somatic variation in variegated ears of maize. Amer. Nat., 48:87–115.

1921. Genetic evidence of aberrant chromosome behavior in maize endosperm. Amer. J. Bot., 8:411–424.

1929. The frequency of somatic mutation in variegated pericarp of maize. Genetics, 14:488–511.

1932. The present status of maize genetics. Proc. 6th Int. Congr. Genet. (Ithaca), 1:141–152.

EMERSON, R. A., and E. G. ANDERSON

1932. The A series of allelomorphs in relation to pigmentation in maize. Genetics, 17:503–509.

EMERSON, S.

1945. Genetics as a tool for studying gene structure. Ann. Missouri Bot. Garden, 32:243–249.

1949. Competitive reactions and antagonisms in the biosynthesis of amino acids by *Neurospora.* Cold Spring Harbor Sympos. Quant. Biol., 14:40–47.

EMMENS, C. W.

1937. Salivary gland cytology of roughest [3] inversion and reinversion, and roughest.[2] J. Genet., 34:191–202.

EPHRUSSI, B.

1934. The absence of autonomy in the development of the effects of certain deficiencies in *Drosophila melanogaster.* Proc. Nat. Acad. Sci. Wash., 20:420–422.

1942. Chemistry of "eye color hormones" of *Drosophila.* Quart. Rev. Biol., 17:327–338.

1950. Induction par l'acroflavine d'une mutation spécifique chez la levure. Pubbl. Staz. zool. Napoli, 22, Suppl., pp. 1–16.

1951. Remarks on cell heredity. In: *Genetics in the Twentieth Century,* ed. by L. C. Dunn. New York: Macmillan. Pp. 241–262.

1953. *Nucleo-Cytoplasmic Relations in Micro-Organisms.* Oxford: Clarendon Press. 127 pp.

EPHRUSSI, B., and H. HOTTINGUER

1951. On an unstable state in yeast. Cold Spring Harbor Sympos. Quant. Biol., 16:75–86.

EPHRUSSI, B., and P. P. SLONIMSKI

1950. La synthèse adaptive des cytochromes chez la levure de boulangerie. Biochem. Biophys. Acta, 6:256–267.

EPHRUSSI, B., and E. SUTTON
1944. A reconsideration of the mechanism of position effect. Proc. Nat. Acad. Sci. Wash., 30:183–197.
EPHRUSSI-TAYLOR, H.
1951*a*. Genetic aspects of transformations of pneumococci. Cold Spring Harbor Sympos. Quant. Biol., 16:445–456.
1951*b*. Transformations allogènes du pneumocoque. Exp. Cell Res., 2:589–607.
FABERGÉ, A. C.
1942. Homologous chromosome pairing: the physical problem. J. Genet., 43:121–144.
FEDERLEY, H.
1913. Das Verhalten der Chromosomen bei der Spermatogenese der Schmetterlinge *Pygaera anachoreta, curtula* und *pigra* sowie einiger ihrer Bastarde. Z. indukt. Abstamm.- u. Vererb.-Lehre, 9:1–110.
FERNANDES, A., and J. A. SERRA
1944. Euchromatine et hétérochromatine dans leurs rapports avec le noyau et le nucléole. Bol. Soc. Brot., ser. 2, 19:67–117.
FINCK, E. VON
1942. Die Allelenserie des Gens ss (spineless) bei *Drosophila melanogaster*. Biol. Zbl., 62:379–400.
FISHER, R. A.
1930. *The Genetical Theory of Natural Selection*. Oxford: Clarendon Press. 272 pp.
1935. Dominance in poultry. Phil. Trans. Roy. Soc., B, 225:195–226.
1946. The fitting of gene frequencies to the data on rhesus reactions. Ann. Eugen., 13:150–155.
FÖRSTER, H., and L. WIESE
1954*a*. Untersuchungen zur Kopulationsfähigkeit von *Chlamydomonas eugametos*. Z. Naturf., 9*b*:470–471.
1954*b*. Gamonwirkung bei *Chlamydomonas eugametos*. *Ibid.*, 9*b*:548–550.
FORSTHOEFEL, P. F.
1953. Developmental genetics of luxoid, a new skeletal variation in the house mouse, *Mus musculus*. Rec. Genet. Soc. Amer., 1953: 71–72.
FREIRE-MAIA, N., and A. FREIRE-MAIA
1953. O fenômeno de Pavan-Breuer no gênero *Drosophila*. V. Reun. Anual da S.B.P.C., Curitiba, 1953. 1 p.
FREIRE-MAIA, N., I. F. ZANARDINI, and A. FREIRE-MAIA
1953. Chromosome variation in *Drosophila immigrans*. Dusenia, 4:303–311.
FREY-WYSSLING, A.
1938. Submikroskopische Morphologie des Protoplasmas und seiner Derivate. Berlin: Borntraeger. 317 pp. 2d English ed., Amsterdam: Houston, Elsevier, 1953. 411 pp.
FRIEDRICH-FREKSA, H.
1940. Bei der Chromosomenkonjugation wirksame Kräfte und ihre Bedeutung für die identische Verdoppelung von Nucleoproteinen. Naturwissenschaften, 28:376–379.
FUKUDA, S.
1944. The hormonal mechanism of larval molting and metamorphosis in the silkworm. J. Fac. Sci. Tokyo Imp. Univ., 6:477–532.

1952. Function of the pupal brain and suboesophageal ganglion in the production of non-diapause and diapause eggs in the silkworm. Annot. zool. jap., 20:149–155.

1953. Determination of voltinism in the univoltine silkworm. Determination of voltinism in the multivoltine silkworm. Alteration of voltinism in the silkworm following transection of pupal oesophageal connectives. Proc. Japan. Acad., 29:381–391.

GAIRDNER, A. E.

1929. Male-sterility in flax. J. Genet., 21:117–124.

GALAN, F.

1951. Analyse génétique de la monoecie et de la dioecie zygotiques et de leur différences dans *Ecballium elaterium.* Acta Salamanticensia, Univ. de Salamanca (sec. biol.), 1951. 15 pp.

GALL, J. G.

1954. Lampbrush chromosomes from oocyte nuclei of the newt. J. Morph., 94:283–352.

GALLIEN, L.

1954. Hormones sexuelles et différenciation du sexe chez les Amphibiens. Rev. suisse Zool., 61:349–374.

GAMOW, G.

1954. Possible mathematical relation between deoxyribonucleic acid and proteins. Dansk Vidensk. Selsk. Biol. Medd., 22:1–13.

GARDNER, E. J.

1942. A further study of genetic modification of dominance, especially by position effect. Univ. Calif. Publ. Zoöl., 49:85–101.

GARROD, A. E.

1909. *Inborn Errors of Metabolism.* Oxford University Press. 2d ed., London: H. Frowde and Hadder and Stoughton, 1923. 216 pp.

GEIGY, R.

1931. Erzeugung rein imaginaler Defekte durch ultraviolette Eibestrahlung bei *Drosophila melanogaster.* Arch. Entw.-Mech. Org., 125:406–447.

GEITLER, L.

1938. Ueber den Bau des Ruhekerns mit besonderer Berücksichtigung der Heteropteren und der Dipteren. Biol. Zbl., 58:152–179.

1940*a*. Neue Ergebnisse und Probleme auf dem Gebiet des Chromosomenbaus. Naturwissenschaften, 28:649–656.

1940*b*. Die Polyploidie der Dauergewebe höherer Pflanzen. Ber. deutsch. bot. Ges., 58:131–142.

1941. Das Wachstum des Zellkerns in tierischen und pflanzlichen Geweben. Ergebn. Biol., 18:1–54.

1954. Endomitose und endomitotische Polyploidisierung. Protoplasmatologia, VI, C:1–89.

GERSCH, E. S.

1949. Influence of temperature on the expression of position effects in the scute-8 stock of *Drosophila melanogaster* and its relation to heterochromatization. Genetics, 34:701–707.

1952. Pigmentation in a mottled white eye due to position effect in *Drosophila melanogaster. Ibid.,* 37:322–338.

GIARDINA, A.
1901. Origine dell'oocite e delle cellule nutrici nel *Dytiscus*. Int. Mschr. Anat. Physiol., 18:1–68.
GIERKE, E. VON
1932. Ueber die Häutungen und die Entwicklungsgeschwindigkeit der Larven der Mehlmotte *Ephestia kühniella* Zeller. Arch. Entw-Mech. Org., 127:387–410.
GILES, N. H.
1951. Studies on the mechanism of reversion in biochemical mutants of *Neurospora crassa*. Cold Spring Harbor Sympos. Quant. Biol., 16:283–313.
1952. Recent evidence on the mechanism of chromosome aberration production by ionizing radiations. In: *Symposium on Radiobiology*, ed. by J. J. Nickson. New York: J. Wiley. Pp. 267–284.
GILES, N. H., and C. W. PARTRIDGE
1953. The effect of a suppressor on allelic inositolless mutants in *Neurospora crassa*. Proc. Nat. Acad. Sci. Wash., 39:479–495.
GILES, N. H., and H. P. RILEY
1949. The effect of oxygen on the frequency of X-ray-induced chromosomal rearrangements in *Tradescantia microspores*. Proc. Nat. Acad. Sci. Wash., 35:640–646.
GLOOR, H.
1944. Phänokopie einer Letalmutante (crc) von *Drosophila melanogaster*. Rev. suisse Zool., 51:394–402.
1947. Phänokopie-Versuche mit Aether an *Drosophila*. *Ibid.*, 54:637–712.
GLUECKSOHN-SCHOENHEIMER, S.
1943. The morphological manifestations of a dominant mutation in mice affecting tail and urogenital system. Genetics, 28:341–348.
1949*a*. Causal analysis of mouse development by the study of mutational effects. 9th Sympos. Growth, 13, Suppl., pp. 163–176.
1949*b*. The effects of a lethal mutation responsible for duplications and twinning in mouse-embryos. J. Exp. Zool., 110:47–76.
GLUECKSOHN-WAELSCH, S.
1951. Physiological genetics of the mouse. Advanc. Genet., 4:1–51.
1953. Lethal factors in development. Quart. Rev. Biol., 28:115–135.
GOLDSCHMIDT, R.
1903. Histologische Untersuchungen an Nematoden. I. Zool. Jahrb. (Anat.), 18:1–57.
1904. Der Chromidialapparat lebhaft funktionierender Gewebezellen. *Ibid.*, 21:1–100.
1908. Das Nervensystem von *Ascaris lumbricoides* und *megalocephala*. I. Z. wiss. Zoöl., 90:73–136.
1911*a*. Die Artbildung in Licht der neueren Erblichkeitslehre. In: *Die Abstammungslehre*. Jena: G. Fischer. Pp. 22–60.
1911*b*. Ueber die Vererbung der sekundären Geschlechtscharaktere. Münch. med. Wochenschr., 49. 4 pp.
1912. Erblichkeitsstudien an Schmetterlingen. Z. indukt. Abstamm.- u. Vererb.-Lehre, 7:1–62.
1915. Vorläufige Mitteilung über weitere Versuche zur Vererbung und Bestimmung des Geschlechts. Biol. Zbl., 35:565–570.

1916*a*. Genetic factors and enzyme reaction. Science, 43:98–100.
1916*b*. A preliminary report on further experiments in inheritance and determination of sex. Proc. Nat. Acad. Sci. Wash., 2:53–58.
1916*c*. Experimental intersexuality and the sex problem. Amer. Nat., 50:705–718.
1917*a*. A further contribution to the theory of sex. J. Exp. Zool., 22:593–611.
1917*b*. Crossing-over ohne Chiasmatypie? Genetics, 2:82–95.
1918. A preliminary report on some genetic experiments concerning evolution. Amer. Nat., 52:28–50.
1920*a*. *Die quantitativen Grundlagen von Vererbung und Artbildung*. Vorträge und Aufsätze über Entwicklungsmechanik. Heft 24. Berlin: J. Springer. 163 pp.
1920*b*. *Mechanismus und Physiologie der Geschlechtsbestimmung*. Berlin: Borntraeger. 251 pp.
1920*c*. Untersuchungen über Intersexualität. I. Z. indukt. Abstamm.- u. Vererb.-Lehre, 23:1–199.
1921*a*. Erblichkeitsstudien an Schmetterlingen. III. Der Melanismus der Nonne, *Lymantria monacha* L. *Ibid.*, 25:89–163.
1921*b*. Ein Beitrag zur Analyse der Doppelmissbildungen. Arch. Entw.-Mech. Org., 47:654–667.
1922. Untersuchungen über Intersexualität. II. Z. indukt. Abstamm.- u. Vererb.-Lehre, 29:145–185.
1923*a*. Untersuchungen über Intersexualität. III. *Ibid.*, 31:100–133.
1923*b*. Kleine Beobachtungen zur Zellenlehre. IV. Die Sammelchromosomen der Schmetterlinge. Arch. Zellforsch., 17:167–184.
1923*c*. Das Mutationsproblem. Sitz.-Ber. deutsche Ges. Vererbwiss. Z. indukt. Abstamm.- u. Vererb.-Lehre, 30:260-268.
1923*d*. Einige Materialien zur Theorie der abgestimmten Reaktionsgeschwindigkeiten. Arch. mikr. Anat., 98: 292–313.
1924. Untersuchungen zur Genetik der geographischen Variation. I. Arch. Entw.-Mech. Org., 101:92–337.
1927. *Physiologische Theorie der Vererbung*. Berlin: J. Springer. 247 pp.
1929*a*. Geschlechtsbestimmung im Tier- und Pflanzenreich. Biol. Zbl., 49:641–648.
1929*b*. Experimentelle Mutation und das Problem der sogenannten Parallelinduktion. *Ibid.*, 49:437–448.
1929*c*. Untersuchungen zur Genetik der geographischen Variation. II. Arch. Entw.-Mech. Org., 116:136–201.
1929*d*. Untersuchungen über Intersexualität. IV. Z. indukt. Abstamm.- u. Vererb.-Lehre, 49:168–242.
1930. Untersuchungen über Intersexualität. V. *Ibid.*, 56:275–301.
1931. *Die sexuellen Zwischenstufen*. Monog. Gesamtgeb. Pflanzen, Tiere, 23. Berlin: J. Springer. 528 pp.
1932*a*. Bemerkungen zur Kritik der quantitativen Natur multipler Allele. Bull. Lab. Genet. Leningrad, 9:129–135.
1932*b*. *Les problèmes de la sexualité*. 2d ed., Paris: G. Doin. 193 pp.
1932*c*. Untersuchungen zur Genetik der geographischen Variation. III. Abschliessendes über die Geschlechtsrassen von *Lymantria dispar* L. Arch. Entw.-Mech. Org., 126:227–324.

Goldschmidt, R. (*Continued*)

1932*d*. Untersuchungen zur Genetik . . . IV. Cytologisches. *Ibid.*, 126:591–612.

1932*e*. Untersuchungen zur Genetik . . . V. Analyse der Ueberwinterungszeit als Anpassungscharakter. *Ibid.*, 126:674–768.

1933*a*. Untersuchungen zur Genetik . . . VI. Die geographische Variation der Entwicklungsgeschwindigkeit und des Grössenwachstums. *Ibid.*, 130:266–339.

1933*b*. Untersuchungen zur Genetik . . . VII. *Ibid.*, 130:562–615

1933*c*. Die Genetik der geographischen Variation. Bull. Proc. 6th Int. Congr. Genet. (Ithaca), 1:173–184.

1934*a*. Untersuchungen über Intersexualität. VI. Z. indukt. Abstamm.- u. Vererb.-Lehre, 67:1–40.

1934*b*. The influence of the cytoplasm upon gene-controlled heredity. Amer. Nat., 68:5–23.

1934*c*. *Lymantria*. Bibl. Genet., 11:1–180.

1935*a*. Gen und Ausseneigenschaft. I (Untersuchungen an *Drosophila*). Z. indukt. Abstamm.- u. Vererb.-Lehre, 69:38–69.

1935*b*. Gen und Ausseneigenschaft. II. *Ibid.*, 69:70–131.

1935*c*. Gen und Aussencharakter. III. Biol. Zbl., 55:534–554.

1937. Gene and character. IV–VIII. Univ. Calif. Publ. Zoöl., 41:277–342. IV, Further data on the development of wing mutants in *Drosophila*, pp. 277–282; V, Further data on the vg dominigenes in *Drosophila melanogaster*, pp. 283–296; VI, (with E. Höner) Dominigenes and vg allelomorphs, pp. 297–312; VII, The "nonhereditary" kn effect in *Drosophila*, pp. 313–326; VIII, A selection experiment with dominigenes, pp. 327–342.

1938*a*. *Physiological Genetics*. New York: McGraw-Hill. 338 pp.

1938*b*. A *Lymantria* like case of intersexuality in plants. J. Genet., 36:531–535.

1938*c*. The time law of intersexuality. Genetica, 20:1–50.

1938*d*. The theory of the gene. Sci. Monthly, 46:1–6.

1939. Mass mutation in the Florida stock of *Drosophila melanogaster*. Amer. Nat., 73:547–559.

1940. *The Material Basis of Evolution*. New Haven: Yale University Press. 436 pp.

1942*a*. The structure of the salivary gland chromosomes and its meaning. Amer. Nat., 76:529–551.

1942*b*. Sex determination in *Melandrium* and *Lymantria*. Science, 95:120–121.

1943. A mutant of *Drosophila melanogaster* resembling the so-called unstable genes of *Drosophila virilis*. Proc. Nat. Acad. Sci. Wash., 29:203–206.

1944. On some facts pertinent to the theory of the gene. In: *Science in the University*. Berkeley and Los Angeles: University of California Press. Pp. 183–210.

1945*a*. A study of spontaneous mutation. Univ. Calif. Publ. Zoöl., 49:291–550.

1945*b*. Mimetic polymorphism, a controversial chapter of Darwinism. Quart. Rev. Biol., 20:147–164, 205–230.

1945*c*. Evolution of mouth parts in Diptera. Pan-Pacif. Ent., 21:41–47.

1945*d*. Additional data on phenocopies and genic action. J. Exp. Zool., 100:193–201.

1945*e*. The structure of podoptera, a homoeotic mutant of *Drosophila melanogaster*. J. Morph., 77:71–103.

1945*f*. A note on the action of the Bar series in *Drosophila*. Growth, 9:259–264.

1946*a*. The interpretation of the structure of triploid intersexes in *Solenobia*. Arch. Klaus-Stift. Vererb.-Forsch., 21:269–272.

1946*b*. Position effect and the theory of the corpuscular gene. Experientia, 2:197–203, 250–256.

1947. New facts on dependent, successive and conjugated spontaneous mutation. J. Exp. Zool., 104:197–222.

1948*a*. Neue Tatsachen zur Analyse der Geschlechtsbestimmung bei *Drosophila melanogaster*. Arch. Klaus-Stift. Vererb.-Forsch., 23:539–549.

1948*b*. A note on industrial melanism in relation to some recent work with *Drosophila*. Amer. Nat., 81:474–476.

1948*c*. Ecotype, ecospecies and macroevolution. Experientia, 4:465–472.

1949*a*. The Beaded-Minute intersexes in *Drosophila melanogaster* Meig. J. Exp. Zool., 112:233–302.

1949*b*. The interpretation of the triploid intersexes of *Solenobia*. Experientia, 5:417–424.

1949*c*. Heterochromatic heredity. Proc. 8th Int. Congr. Genet. (Stockholm), 1948. Hereditas, 1949, Suppl., pp. 244–255.

1950*a*. A remarkable structure in the ovocytes of a fish. In: *Moderne Biologie, Festschrift Nachtsheim*. Berlin: F. W. Peters. Pp. 39–42.

1950*b*. Marginalia to McClintock's work on mutable loci in maize. Amer. Nat., 84:437–455.

1950*c*. Repeats and the modern theory of the gene. Proc. Nat. Acad. Sci. Wash., 36:365–368.

1951*a*. Evolution as viewed by one geneticist. Amer. Scientist, 40:84–98.

1951*b*. The maternal effect in the production of the Beaded-Minute intersexes in *Drosophila melanogaster*. J. Exp. Zool., 117:75–110.

1951*c*. The theory of the gene. Cold Spring Harbor Sympos. Quant. Biol., 16:1–11.

1952*a*. A further study of homoeosis in *Drosophila melanogaster*. J. Exp. Zool., 119:405–460.

1952*b*. Homoeotic mutants and evolution. Act. Biotheor., 10:87–104.

1953*a*. Heredity within a sex-controlled structure of *Drosophila*. J. Exp. Zool., 122:53–96.

1953*b*. Experiments with a homoeotic mutant bearing on evolution. *Ibid.*, 123:79–114.

1954. Different philosophies of genetics. Science, 119:703–710.

Goldschmidt, R., and E. Fischer

1922. *Argynnis · paphia-valesina,* ein Fall geschlechtskontrollierter Vererbung. Genetica, 4:247–278.

Goldschmidt, R., and E. Gardner

1942. A further contribution to the analysis of scalloped wings in *Drosophila melanogaster*. Univ. Calif. Publ. Zoöl., 49:103–125.

Goldschmidt, R., E. Gardner, and M. Kodani

1939. A remarkable group of position effects. Proc. Nat. Acad. Sci. Wash., 25:314–317.

Goldschmidt, R., and A. Hannah

1944. One band inversion. *Ibid.*, 30:299–301.

GOLDSCHMIDT, R., A. HANNAH, and L. PITERNICK
1951. The podoptera effect in *Drosophila melanogaster.* Univ. Calif. Publ. Zoöl., 55:67–294.
GOLDSCHMIDT, R., and E. HÖNER. *See* Goldschmidt, R., 1937. VI.
GOLDSCHMIDT, R., and K. KATSUKI
1927. Erblicher Gynandromorphismus und somatische Mosaikbildung bei *Bombyx mori.* Biol. Zbl., 47:45–54.
1928*a*. Zweite Mitteilung. *Ibid.,* 48:39–42.
1928*b*. Cytologie des erblichen Gynandromorphismus von *Bombyx mori. Ibid.,* 48:685–699.
GOLDSCHMIDT, R., and M. KODANI
1942. The structure of the salivary gland chromosomes and its meaning. Amer. Nat., 76:529–551.
GOLDSCHMIDT, R., and T. P. LIN
1947. Chromatin diminution. Science, 105:619.
GOLDSCHMIDT, R., and H. POPPELBAUM
1914. Erblichkeitsstudien an Schmetterlingen. II. Z. indukt. Abstamm.- u. Vererb.-Lehre, 11:280–316.
GOTTSCHEWSKI, G.
1937. Das Notch-Phänomen bei *Drosophila melanogaster.* I. Z. indukt. Abstamm.- u. Vererb.-Lehre, 73:131–142.
GREEN, M. M.
1946. A study in gene action using different dosages and alleles of vestigial in *Drosophila melanogaster.* Genetics, 31:1–20.
1953*a*. The Beadex locus in *Drosophila melanogaster:* on the nature of the mutants Bx^r and Bx^1. *Ibid.,* 38:91–105.
1953*b*. The Beadex locus in *Drosophila melanogaster:* genetic analysis of the mutant Bx^{r49k}. Z. indukt. Abstamm.- u. Vererb.-Lehre, 85:435–449.
1954. Pseudoalleles at the vermilion locus in *Drosophila melanogaster.* Proc. Nat. Acad. Sci. Wash., 40:92–99.
GREEN, M. M., and K. C. GREEN
1949. Crossing-over between alleles at the lozenge locus in *Drosophila melanogaster.* Proc. Nat. Acad. Sci. Wash., 35:586–591.
GREEN, M. M., and C. P. OLIVER
1940. The action of certain mutants upon the penetrance of heterozygous vestigial wing in *Drosophila melanogaster.* Genetics, 25:584–592.
GRIFFEN, A. B.
1941. The B^s translocation in *Drosophila melanogaster* and modification of the Bar effect through irradiation. Genetics, 26:154–155.
GRIFFEN, A. B., and W. S. STONE
1938. Reverse mutation and the position effect. Rec. Genet. Soc. Amer., 7:73.
1940. The w^{m5} and its derivatives. Univ. Texas Publ. 4032:190–200.
GRIFFITH, F.
1928. The significance of pneumococcal types. J. Hyg. (London), 27:113–159.
GRÜNEBERG, H.
1937. The position effect proved by a spontaneous reinversion of the X-chromosome in *Drosophila melanogaster.* J. Genet., 34:169–189.
1938. An analysis of the pleiotropic effects of a new lethal mutation in the rat (*Mus norvegicus*). Proc. Roy. Soc. London, B, 125:123–144.
1943*a*. *The Genetics of the Mouse.* Cambridge: University Press. 412 pp.

1943*b*. Congenital hydrocephalus in the mouse, a case of spurious pleiotropism. J. Genet., 45:1–21.
1952*a*. Genetical studies on the skeleton of the mouse. IV. Quasi-continuous variation. *Ibid.*, 51:95–114.
1952*b*. *The Genetics of the Mouse*. The Hague: M. Nijhoff. 650 pp.

GUSTAFSSON, A.
1947. Mutations in agricultural plants. Hereditas, 33:1–100.
1951*a*. Some aspects of variation and evolution in plants. Evolution, 5:180–184.
1951*b*. Mutations, environment and evolution. Cold Spring Harbor Sympos. Quant. Biol., 16:263–282.
1954. Mutations, viability and population structure. Act. agric. scand., 4:601–632.

GUTHERZ, S.
1907. Zur Kenntnis der Heterochromosomen. Arch. mikr. Anat., 69:491–514.

GUYÉNOT, E., and M. DANON
1953. Chromosomes et ovocytes de Batraciens. Rev. suisse Zool., 60:1–129.

GUYÉNOT, E., M. DANON, E. KELLENBERGER, and J. WEIGLÉ
1950. Les chromosomes des ovocytes quiescentes de Batraciens, étudiés au microscope électronique. Arch. Klaus-Stift. Vererb.-Forsch., 25:47–53.

HABERLANDT, G.
1935. Beiträge zum *Crataegomespilus*-Problem. Sitz.-Ber. preuss. Akad. Wiss. (Phys.-Math. Kl.), 28:2–22.

HADORN, E.
1936. Uebertragung von Artmerkmalen durch das entkernte Eiplasma beim merogonischen *Triton* Bastard, *palmatus- Plasma* × *cristatus* Kern. Verh. deutsch. zool. Ges., 1936: 97–104.
1945. Zur Pleiotropie der Genwirkung. Arch. Klaus-Stift. Vererb.-Forsch., 20, Erg.-Bd.: 82–95.
1948. Genetische und entwicklungsphysiologische Probleme der Insektenontogenese. Folia Biotheor., 3:109–126.
1950. Physiogenetische Ergebnisse der Untersuchungen an *Drosophila*-Blastemen aus letalen Genotypen. Rev. suisse Zool., 57:115–128.
1951*a*. Developmental actions of lethal factors in *Drosophila*. Advanc. Genet., 4:53–85.
1951*b*. Beeinflussung der *Drosophila* Entwicklung durch Mutation und Experiment. Verh. deutsch. zool. Ges. Wilhelmshaven, 1951: 29–42.

HADORN, E., and H. GLOOR
1946. Transplantationen zur Bestimmung des Anlagemusters in der weiblichen Genital-Imaginalscheibe von *Drosophila*. Rev. suisse Zool., 53:495–501.

HAECKER, V.
1918. *Entwicklungsgeschichtliche Eigenschaftsanalyse* (Phänogenetik). Jena: G. Fischer. 344 pp.
1925. Aufgaben und Ergebnisse der Phänogenetik. Bibl. Genet., 1:1–314.

HÄMMERLING, J.
1946. Ueber die Symbiose von *Stentor polymorphus*. Biol. Zbl., 65:52–61.
1947. Neue Untersuchungen über die physiologischen und genetischen Grundlagen der Formbildung. Naturwissenschaften, 33:337–342, 361–365.
1953. Nucleo-cytoplasmic relationships in the development of *Acetabularia*. Int. Rev. Cytol., 2:475–498.

HAGBERG, A.
1954. Cytogenetic analysis of erectoides mutations in barley. Act. agric. scand., 4:472–490.
HAGBERG, A., and J. H. TJIO
1950. Cytological localization of the translocation point for the barley mutant erectoides 7. Hereditas, 36:487–491.
HAGEDOORN, A. L.
1911. Autocatalytical substances the determinants for the inheritable characters. Vorträge und Aufsätze über Entwicklungsmechanik, 12. Leipzig: W. Engelmann. 35 pp.
HALDANE, J. B. S.
1924. A mathematical theory of natural and artificial selection. Proc. Cambridge Phil. Soc., 23:19–41, 158–163, 363–372, 607–615, 838–844.
1932. The time of action of genes, and its bearing on some evolutionary problems. Amer. Nat., 66:5–24.
1935. Les contributions de la génétique à la solution de quelques problèmes physiologiques. Soc. Biol. Paris, Réun. plen., 1935. 14 pp.
1942. *New Paths in Genetics.* New York and London: Harper Bros. 206 pp.
1954. *The Biochemistry of Genetics.* London: G. Allen and Unwin. 144 pp.
HANNAH, A.
1951. Localization and function of heterochromatin in *Drosophila melanogaster.* Advanc. Genet., 4:87–125.
1953. Non-autonomy of yellow in gynandromorphs of *Drosophila melanogaster.* J. Exp. Zool., 123:523–560.
HANSON, F. B., and F. HEYS
1928. The effects of radium in producing lethal mutations in *Drosophila melanogaster.* Science, 68:115–116.
HARDER, R.
1927. Zur Frage nach der Rolle von Kern und Protoplasma im Zellgeschehen und bei der Uebertragung von Eigenschaften. Z. Bot., 19:337–407.
HARLAND, S. C.
1935. Homologous genes for anthocyanin pigmentation in New and Old World cottons. J. Genet., 30:465–476.
HARNLY, M. H.
1942. Wing form and gene function in nine genotypes of *Drosophila melanogaster.* Biol. Bull., 82:215–232.
HARRIS, H.
1954. *An Introduction to Human Biochemical Genetics.* Galton Lab. Monog. (In press. Quoted from Haldane.)
HARRISON, R. G.
1937. Embryology and its relations. Science, 85:369–374.
HARTMANN, M.
1929. Verteilung, Bestimmung und Vererbung des Geschlechts bei den Protisten und Thallophyten. *Handbuch der Vererbungswissenschaften,* II, E:1–115. Berlin: Borntraeger.
1943. *Die Sexualität.* Jena: G. Fischer. 426 pp.
1952. Polyploide (polyenergide) Kerne bei Protozoen. Arch. Protistenk., 98:125–156.
HAUENSCHILD, C.
1953. Die phänotypische Geschlechtsbestimmung bei *Grubea clavata* Clap.

(Annel. Polych.) und vergleichende Beobachtungen an anderen Sylliden. Zool. Jahrb. (Allg. Abt.), 64:14–54.

HAUROWITZ, F.

1950. *Chemistry and Biology of Proteins.* New York: Academic Press. 374 pp.

HAYDEN, B., and L. SMITH

1949. The relation of atmosphere to biological effects of X-rays. Genetics, 34:26–43.

HAYES, W.

1953. The mechanism of genetic recombination in *Escherichia coli.* Cold Spring Harbor Sympos. Quant. Biol., 18:75–93.

HEITZ, E.

1929. Heterochromatin, Chromocentren, Chromomeren. Ber. deutsch. bot. Ges., 47:274–284.

1933. Die somatische Heteropyknose bei *Drosophila melanogaster* und ihre genetische Bedeutung. Z. Zellforsch., 20:237–287.

HELD, H.

1916. Untersuchungen über den Vorgang der Befruchtung. I. Der Anteil des Protoplasmas an der Befruchtung von *Ascaris megalocephala.* Arch. mikr. Anat. (Abt. 2), 89:59–224.

HENKE, K.

1935. Entwicklung und Bau tierischer Zeichnungsmuster. Verh. deutsch. zool. Ges., 1935:176–244.

1947. Einfache Grundvorgänge in der tierischen Entwicklung. I. Naturwissenschaften. 34:149–157, 180–186.

1948*a*. Einfache Grundvorgänge . . . II. *Ibid.*, 35:176–181, 203–211.

1948*b*. Ueber Ordnungsvorgänge in der Spätentwicklung der Insekten. Rev. suisse Zool., 55:319–337.

1953. Die Musterbildung der Versorgungssysteme im Insektenflügel. Biol. Zbl., 72:1–51.

HENKE, K., E. VON FINCK, and S. Y. MA

1941. Ueber sensible Perioden für die Ausbildung von Hitzemodifikationen bei *Drosophila* und die Beziehungen zwischen Modifikationen und Mutationen. Z. indukt. Abstamm.- u. Vererb.-Lehre, 79:267–316.

HENKE, K., and H. J. POHLEY

1952. Differentielle Zellteilungen und Polyploidie bei der Schuppenbildung der Mehlmotte *Ephestia kühniella* Z. Z. Naturf., 7:65–79.

HENKE, K., and G. RÖNSCH

1951. Ueber Bildungsgleichheiten in der Entwicklung epidermaler Organe und die Entstehung des Nervensystems im Flügel der Insekten. Naturwissenschaften, 38:335–336.

HERBST, C.

1901. *Formative Reize in der tierischen Entwicklung.* Leipzig: A. Georgi. 125 pp.

HERSH, A. H.

1929. The effect of different sections of the X-chromosome upon bar eye in *Drosophila melanogaster.* Amer. Nat., 68:378–382.

1930. The facet temperature relation in the bar series of *Drosophila.* J. Exp. Zool., 57:283–306.

1941. Allometric growth: the ontogenetic and phylogenetic significance of differential rates of growth. 3d Sympos. Growth, 5, Suppl., pp. 113–141.

HERSHEY, A. D.

1953. Functional differentiation within particles of bacteriophage T2. Cold Spring Harbor Sympos. Quant. Biol., 18:135–139.

HERSHEY, A. D., and M. CHASE

1951. Genetic recombination and heterozygosis in bacteriophage. Cold Spring Harbor Sympos. Quant. Biol., 16:471–480.

HERSKOWITZ, I. H.

1946. The relationship of X-ray induced recessive lethals to chromosomal breakage. Amer. Nat., 80:588–592.

1950. An estimate of the number of loci in the X-chromosome of *Drosophila melanogaster*. *Ibid.*, 84:255–260.

1951. The genetic basis of X-ray induced recessive lethal mutations. Genetics, 36:356–363.

HERTWIG, G., and P. HERTWIG

1922. Die Vererbung des Hermaphroditismus bei *Melandrium*. Z. indukt. Abstamm.- u. Vererb.-Lehre, 28:259–294.

HERTWIG, R.

1889. Ueber die Conjugation der Infusorien. Abh. bayer. Akad. Wiss., 17:151–233.

HINTON, T.

1950. A correlation of phenotypic changes and chromosomal rearrangements at the two ends of an inversion. Genetics, 35:188–205.

HINTON, T., and F. DIBBLE

1947. Negative evidence on reverse mutations. D. I. S., 21:86.

HINTON, T., and J. ELLIS

1950. A nucleic acid requirement in *Drosophila* correlated with a position effect. Rec. Genet. Soc. Amer., 19:104–105.

HINTON, T., and W. GOODSMITH

1950. An analysis of phenotypic reversions at the brown locus in *Drosophila*. J. Exp. Zool., 114:103–114.

HIRSCHLER, J.

1942. Osmiumschwärzung perichromosomaler Membranen in den Spermatocyten der Rhynchotenart *Palomena viridissima*. Poder. Naturw., 30:105–106.

HOERSTADIUS, S.

1936. Studien über heterosperme Seeigelmerogone nebst Bemerkungen über einige Keimblattchimären. Mem. Mus. Roy. Hist. Nat. Belg., 2, ser. 3, pp. 801–880.

HOFF-JØRGENSEN, E., and E. ZEUTHEN

1952. Evidence of cytoplasmic deoxyribosides in the frog's egg. Nature, 169: 245–246.

HOFMANN, F. W.

1927. Some attempts to modify the germ plasm of *Phaseolus vulgaris*. Genetics, 12:284–294.

HOLLAENDER, A., W. K. BAKER, and E. H. ANDERSON

1951. Effect of oxygen tension and certain chemicals on the X-ray sensitivity of mutation production and survival. Cold Spring Harbor Sympos. Quant. Biol., 16:315–326.

HOLLAENDER, A., G. E. STAPLETON, and W. I. BURNETT, JR.

1951. The modification of X-ray sensitivity by chemicals. In: *Isotopes in Biochemistry*, ed. by G. W. E. Wolstenholme. London: Churchill, Ltd. Pp. 96–113.

HOLTER, H.
1949. Problems of enzyme localization and development. Pubbl. Staz. zool. Napoli, 21, Suppl., pp. 60–76.
HOLTFRETER, J.
1951. Orientaciones modernas de la embriologia. Publ. Apartado Inst. Invest. Cienc. Biol., 1:285–349.
HOROWITZ, N. H.
1950. Biochemical genetics of *Neurospora.* Advanc. Genet., 3:33–71.
HOROWITZ, N. H., and U. LEUPOLD
1951. Some recent studies bearing on the one gene—one enzyme hypothesis. Cold Spring Harbor Sympos. Quant. Biol., 16:65–74.
HOTCHKISS, R. D.
1951. Transfer of penicillin resistance in pneumococci by the desoxyribonucleate derived from resistant cultures. Cold Spring Harbor Sympos. Quant. Biol., 16:457–462.
1954. Cyclical behavior in pneumococcus growth and transformability occasioned by environmental changes. Proc. Nat. Acad. Sci. Wash., 40:49–55.
HOTCHKISS, R. D., and J. MARMUR
1954. Double marker transformations as evidence of linked factors in desoxyribonucleate transforming agents. Proc. Nat. Acad. Sci. Wash., 40:55–60.
HUGHES-SCHRADER, S.
1953. The nuclear content of desoxyribonucleic acid and interspecific relationships in the Mantid genus *Litorgousa* (Orthoptera, Mantoidea). Chromosoma, 5:544–554.
HULTIN, T.
1953. Metabolism and determination. Arch. néerland. Zool., 1, Suppl., pp. 76–91.
HUMPHREY, R. R.
1942. Sex reversal and the genetics of sex determination in the axolotl (*Amblystoma mexicanum*). Anat. Rec., 84, Suppl., p. 465.
1945. A study of the progeny of females experimentally converted into males. Amer. J. Anat., 76:33–66.
HUSKINS, C. L., and L. M. STEINITZ
1948. The nucleus in differentiation and development. I. Heterochromatic bodies in energic nuclei of *Rhoeo* roots. J. Hered., 39:35–43.
HUXLEY, J. S.
1935. Chemical regulation and the hormone concept. Biol. Rev., 10:427–441.
IRWIN, M. R.
1951. Genetics and immunology. In: *Genetics in the Twentieth Century,* ed. by L. C. Dunn. New York: Macmillan. Pp. 173–219.
IVES, P. T.
1949. Non-random production of visible mutations by the Florida high mutation rate gene in *Drosophila.* Rec. Genet. Soc. Amer., 18:96.
JACOBJ, W.
1925. Ueber das rhythmische Wachstum der Zellen durch Verdopplung ihres Volumens. Arch. Entw.-Mech. Org., 106:124–192.
JEHLE, H.
1952. Specific van der Waals forces of biological significance. (Printed as MS. Owned by C. Stern.)

JOHNSTON, O., and A. M. WINCHESTER
1934. Studies on reverse mutations in *Drosophila melanogaster.* Amer. Nat., 68:351–358.
JOLLOS, V.
1913. Experimentelle Untersuchungen über Infusorien. Biol. Zbl., 33:222–236.
1921. Experimentelle Protistenstudien. I. Arch. Protistenk., 43:1–222.
JONES, D. F.
1934. Unisexual maize plants and their bearing on sex-differentiation in other plants and in animals. Genetics, 19:552–567.
1944. Growth changes in maize endosperm associated with the relocation of chromosome parts. *Ibid.*, 29:420–427.
JUCCI, C.
1949. Physiogenetics in silkworms (*Bombyx mori* L.). Proc. 8th Int. Congr. Genet. (Stockholm), 1948. Hereditas, 1949, Suppl., pp. 286–297.
KAPLAN, R. W.
1951. Chromosomen und Faktormutationsraten in Gerstenkörnern. Z. indukt. Abstamm.- u. Vererb.-Lehre, 83:347–382.
1952. Genetics of microorganisms. Ann. Rev. Microbiol., 6:49–76.
KAUFMANN, B. P.
1939. Distribution of induced breaks along the X-chromosome of *Drosophila melanogaster.* Proc. Nat. Acad. Sci. Wash., 25:571–577.
1941. Induced chromosomal breaks in *Drosophila.* Cold Spring Harbor Sympos. Quant. Biol., 9:82–91.
1946. Organization of the chromosome. I. J. Exp. Zool., 102:293–320.
1948*a*. Radiation induced chromosome aberrations. Brookhaven Conference, Biological Applications of Nuclear Physics, Report BNL-C-4, pp. 27–35.
1948*b*. Chromosome structure in relation to the chromosome cycle. II. Bot. Rev., 14:57–126.
KAUFMANN, B. P., *et al.*
1951. Patterns of organization of cellular materials. Carnegie Inst. Wash. Yearbook, 50:203–215.
1952. Patterns of organization . . . *Ibid.*, 51:220–227.
KHVOSTOVA, V. V.
1939. The role played by the inert chromosome regions in the position effect of the cubitus interruptus gene in *Drosophila melanogaster.* Izv. Akad. Nauk S.S.S.R. (Otd. mat.-est., ser. biol.), pp. 541–574.
KIHARA, H.
1953. Genetics of *Bombyx* and *Drosophila:* a comparison of materials, methods and results. Seiken Zihô, Rep. Kihara Inst. Biol. Res., 6:15–29.
KIKKAWA, H.
1938. Studies on the genetics and cytology of *Drosophila ananassae.* Genetica, 20:458–516.
1953. Biochemical genetics of *Bombyx mori* (silkworm). Advanc. Genet., 5:107–140.
KIMBALL, R. F.
1953. The structure of the macronucleus of *Paramecium aurelia.* Proc. Nat. Acad. Sci. Wash., 39:345–347.
KLATT, B.
1919. Keimdrüsentransplantationen beim Schwammspinner. Z. indukt. Abstamm.- u. Vererb.-Lehre, 22:1–50.

KLEBS, G.
1907. Studien über Variationen. Arch. Entw.-Mech. Org., 24:29–113.
KNAPP, E.
1936. Heteroploidie bei *Sphaerocarpus*. Ber. deutsch. bot. Ges., 54:346–361.
KNAPP, E., and I. HOFFMANN
1939. Geschlechtsumwandelung bei *Sphaerocarpus* durch Verlust eines Stückes des X-chromosomes. Chromosoma, 1:130–146.
KODANI, M.
1942. The structure of the salivary gland chromosomes of *Drosophila melanogaster*. J. Hered., 33:115–133.
1947. Variations in the terminal bands of the salivary X-chromosome of *Drosophila melanogaster*. Genetics, 32:18–28.
KOLMARK, G., and N. H. GILES
1954. Studies on chemical mutagens using the *Neurospora*-back-mutation test. Rec. Genet. Soc. Amer., 22:84.
KOLTZOFF, N. K.
1928. Physikalisch-chemische Grundlage der Morphologie. Biol. Zbl., 48:345–369.
1939. *Les molécules héréditaires*. Paris: Hermann. 60 pp.
KOMAI, T.
1950. Semi-allelic genes. Amer. Nat., 84:381–392.
KONOPACKI, M.
1936. Le rôle de l'épithélium folliculaire et des cellules du test pendant l'oogenèse des Ascidies (*Clavelina lepadiformis*, Mull.). C. R. Soc. Biol. Paris, 122:139–142.
KOOPMANS, A.
1952. Changes in sex in the flowers of the hybrid *Solanum Rybinii* × *S. Chacoense*. Genetica, 26:359–380.
KOSMINSKY, P. A.
1909. Einwirkung äusserer Einflüsse auf Schmetterlinge. Zool. Jahrb. (Syst.), 27:361–390.
1927. Intersexualität im männlichen Kopulationsapparat von *Lymantria dispar* L. unterm Einfluss der Temperatur. Biol. Zbl., 47:323–326.
1930. Untersuchungen über Intersexualität bei *Lymantria dispar* L. Zool. Zh. (Russian), 10:1–50.
1935. Analysis of intersexuality in the gipsy moth. II. *Ibid.*, 14:113–158, 271–310, 439–464, 621–635.
KOSMINSKY, P. A., and X. GOLOWINSKAJA
1930. Untersuchungen über die sogenannten Scheinzwitter des Schwammspinners (*Lymantria dispar* L.). Z. indukt. Abstamm.- u. Vererb.-Lehre, 53:287–309.
KOSSWIG, C.
1931. Die geschlechtliche Differenzierung bei den Bastarden von *Xiphophorus helleri* und *Platypoecilus maculatus* und deren Nachkommen. Z. indukt. Abstamm.- u. Vererb.-Lehre, 57:226–305.
1935. Genotypische und phänotypische Geschlechtsbestimmung bei Zahnkarpfen. VI. Arch. Entw.-Mech. Org., 133:140–155.
1939. Die Geschlechtsbestimmung in Kreuzungen zwischen *Xiphophorus* und *Platypoecilus*. C. R. Fac. Sci. Univ. Istanbul, 4:1–54.

KRUGELIS, E.
1946. Distribution and properties of intracellular alkaline phosphatases. Biol. Bull., 90:220–233.
KÜHN, A.
1927. Die Pigmentierung von *Habrobracon juglandis* Ashmed, ihre Prädetermination und ihre Vererbung durch Gene und Plasmon. Nachr. Ges. Wiss. Göttingen (Math.-Phys. Kl.), 1927: 407–421.
1948. Ueber die Determination der Form- Struktur- und Pigmentbildung der Schuppen bei *Ephestia kühniella* Z. Arch. Entw.-Mech. Org., 143:408–487.
KÜHN, A., and H. PIEPHO
1936. Ueber hormonale Wirkungen bei der Verpuppung der Schmetterlinge. Nachr. Ges. Wiss. Göttingen (Fachgruppe VI), N.F., 2:141–154.
KUHN, R., and F. MOEWUS
1940*a*. Ueber die chemische Wirkungsweise der Gene Mot, M_D und gathe bei *Chlamydomonas*. Ber. deutsch. chem. Ges., 73:547–559.
1940*b*. Wie kommen die Verhältniszahlen der cis-:trans-Crocetindimethylester bei den getrenntgeschlechtlichen Rassen von *Chlamydomonas* zu Stande? *Ibid.*, 73:559–562.
KURNICK, N. B., and I. H. HERSKOWITZ
1952. The estimation of polyteny in *Drosophila* salivary gland nuclei based on determination of desoxyribonucleic acid content. J. Cell. Comp. Physiol., 39:281–299.
KUSHNIR, T.
1952. Heterochromatic polysomy in *Gryllotalpa gryllotalpa* L. J. Genet., 50:361–383.
KUWADA, Y.
1939. Chromosome structure. A critical review. Cytologia, 10:213–256.
1940. Studies of mitosis and meiosis in comparison. I. A morphological analysis of meiosis. *Ibid.*, 11:217–244.
LAMPRECHT, H.
1945. Intra- and interspecific genes. Agri. hort. genet., 3:45–60.
1948. The genetic basis of evolution. *Ibid.*, 6:83–145.
1949. Systematik auf genischer und zytologischer Grundlage. *Ibid.*, 7:1–28.
LANDAUER, W.
1945. Rumplessness of chicken embryos produced by the injection of insulin and other chemicals. J. Exp. Zool., 98:65–77.
1947. Insulin-induced abnormalities of the beak, extremities and eyes in chickens. *Ibid.*, 105:145–172.
1948*a*. The phenotypic modification of hereditary polydactylism of fowl by selection and by insulin. Genetics, 33:133–157.
1948*b*. The effect of nicotinamide and α-ketoglutaric acid on the teratogenic action of insulin. J. Exp. Zool., 109:283–290.
1952*a*. Malformation of chicken embryos produced by boric acid and the probable role of riboflavin in their origin. *Ibid.*, 120:469–508.
1952*b*. The genetic control of normal development in the chicken embryo. Ann. N. Y. Acad. Sci., 55:172–176.
1953*a*. On teratogenic effects of pilocarpine in chick development. J. Exp. Zool., 122:469–483.
1953*b*. Genetic and environmental factors in the teratogenic effects of boric acid on chicken embryos. Genetics, 38:216–228.

1953c. The effect of time of injection and of dosage on absolute and relative length of femur, tibiotarsus and tarsometatarsus in chicken embryos treated with insulin or pilocarpine. Growth, 17:87–109.

LANDAUER, W., and M. B. RHODES

1952. Further observations on the teratogenic nature of insulin and its modification by supplementary treatment. J. Exp. Zool., 119:221–261.

LANGHAM, D. G.

1940. The inheritance of intergeneric differences in *Zea-Euchlaena* hybrids. Genetics, 25:88–107.

LATTIN, G.

1952. Ueber die Bestimmung und Vererbung des Geschlechts einiger Oniscoideen (Crust. Isop.). II. Z. indukt. Abstamm.- u. Vererb.-Lehre, 84:536–567.

LAUGHNAN, J. R.

1949. The action of the allelic forms of the gene A in maize. II. Proc. Nat. Acad. Sci. Wash., 35:167–178.

1952a. The A^b components as members of a duplication in maize. Genetics, 37:598.

1952b. On the designation of closely linked genes with similar effects. Amer. Nat., 86:109–111.

LAWRENCE, W. J. C., and J. R. PRICE

1940. The genetics and chemistry of flower colour variation. Biol. Rev., 15:35–58.

LAWRENCE, W. J. C., and R. SCOTT-MONCRIEFF

1935. The genetics and chemistry of flower colour in *Dahlia;* a new theory of specific pigmentation. J. Genet., 30:155–226.

LEA, D. A.

1947. *Actions of Radiations on Living Cells.* New York: Macmillan. 402 pp.

LEA, D. A., and D. G. CATCHESIDE

1942. Induction by radiation of chromosome aberrations in *Tradescantia.* J. Genet., 44:216–245.

1945. The bearing of radiation experiments on the size of the gene. *Ibid.,* 47:41–50.

LEBEDEFF, G. A.

1939. A study of intersexuality in *Drosophila virilis.* Genetics, 24:553–586.

LEDERBERG, E. M.

1952. Allelic relationships and reverse mutation in *Escherichia coli.* Genetics, 37:469–483.

LEDERBERG, J.

1947. Gene recombination and linked segregations in *Escherichia coli.* Genetics, 32:505–525.

1952. Cell genetics and hereditary symbiosis. Physiol. Rev., 32:403–430.

LEDERBERG, J., and P. R. EDWARDS

1953. Serotypic recombination in *Salmonella.* J. Immunol., 17:232–240.

LEDERBERG, J., E. M. LEDERBERG, N. D. ZINDER, and E. R. LIVELY

1951. Recombination analysis of bacterial heredity. Cold Spring Harbor Sympos. Quant. Biol., 16:413–443.

LEDERBERG, J., and E. L. TATUM

1953. Sex in bacteria: genetic studies 1945–1952. Science, 118:169–175.

LEFEVRE, G. (JR.), F. J. RATTY, JR., and G. D. HANKS
1953. Frequency of Notch mutations induced in normal, duplicated and inverted X-chromosomes of *Drosophila melanogaster*. Genetics, 38:345–359.
LEHMANN, E.
1925. Die Gattung *Epilobium*. Bibl. Genet., 1:363–418.
LEHMANN, F. E.
1945. *Einführung in die physiologische Embryologie*. Basel: Birkhäuser. 414 pp.
LEUCHTENBERGER, C., and F. SCHRADER
1951. Relationship between nuclear volumes, amount of intranuclear proteins and desoxyribose nucleic acid (DNA) in various rat cells. Biol. Bull., 101:95–98.
LEWIS, D.
1951. Structure of the incompatibility gene. III. Types of spontaneous and induced mutation. Heredity, 5:399–414.
LEWIS, E. B.
1941. The Star and asteroid loci in *Drosophila melanogaster*. Genetics, 27:153–154.
1945. The relation of repeats to position effect in *Drosophila melanogaster*. *Ibid.*, 30:137–166.
1950. The phenomenon of position effect. Advanc. Genet., 3:75–115.
1951. Pseudoallelism and gene evolution. Cold Spring Harbor Sympos. Quant. Biol., 16:159–174.
1952. The pseudoallelism of white and apricot in *Drosophila melanogaster*. Proc. Nat. Acad. Sci. Wash., 38:953–961.
1954. The theory and application of a new method of detecting chromosomal rearrangements in *Drosophila melanogaster*. Amer. Nat., 88:225–239.
L'HÉRITIER, P.
1951. The CO_2 sensitivity problem in *Drosophila*. Cold Spring Harbor Sympos. Quant. Biol., 16:99–112.
L'HÉRITIER, P., and G. TEISSIER
1937. Une anomalie physiologique héréditaire chez la Drosophile. C. R. Acad. Sci. Paris, 205:1099–1101.
LIMA-DE-FARIA, A.
1952. Chromomere analysis of the chromosome complement of rye. Chromosoma, 5:1–68.
LIN, T. P.
1954. The chromosomal cycle in *Parascaris equorum* (*Ascaris megalocephala*): oogenesis and diminution. Chromosoma, 6:175–198.
LINDNER, E.
1914. Ueber die Spermatogenese von *Schistosomum haematobium Bilh.* (*Bilharzia haematobia* Cobb.) mit besonderer Berücksichtigung der Geschlechtschromosomen. Arch. Zellforsch., 12:516–538.
LISON, L., and J. PASTEELS
1951. Études histophotométriques sur la teneur en acide désoxyribonucléique des noyaux au cours du développement embryonnaire chez l'oursin *Paracentrotus lividus*. Arch. Biol., 62:1–64.
LUCE, W. M.
1926. The effect of temperature on infrabar, an allelomorph of Bar eye in *Drosophila*. J. Exp. Zool., 46:301–316.

1941. Effects of formalin upon facet number in the bar alleles of *Drosophila melanogaster.* Genetics, 27:154–155.
LUCE, W. M., H. QUASTLER, and H. B. CHASE
1951. Reduction in facet number in Bar-eyed *Drosophila* by X-rays. Genetics, 36:488–499.
LÜNING, K. G.
1952*a*. X-ray induced chromosome breaks in *Drosophila melanogaster.* Hereditas, 38:321–338.
1952*b*. Studies on the origin of apparent gene mutations in *Drosophila melanogaster.* Act. Zool., 33:193–207.
LÜSCHER, M.
1953. Kann die Determination durch eine monomolekulare Reaktion ausgelöst werden? Rev. suisse Zool., 60:524–528.
LURIA, S. E.
1953. *General Virology.* New York: J. Wiley. 427 pp.
LWOFF, A.
1949. Les organites doués de continuité génétique chez les protistes. Ed. Centre Nat. Rech. Sci. Paris, pp. 7–23.
1950*a*. La synthèse de l'amidon chez les leucophytes et la valeur morphologique du réseau de Volkonsky. New Phytol., 49:72–80.
1950*b*. *Problems of Morphogenesis in Ciliates.* New York: J. Wiley. 103 pp.
MA, S. Y.
1943. Experimentelle Untersuchungen über Hitzemodifikationen des Flügels von *Drosophila melanogaster.* Arch. Entw.-Mech. Org., 142:508–618.
MCCARTY, M., and O. T. AVERY
1946. Studies on the chemical nature of the substance inducing transformation of pneumococcal types. II. J. Exp. Med., 83:89–96.
MCCLINTOCK, B.
1941. The stability of broken ends of chromosomes in *Zea mays.* Genetics, 26:234–282.
1942. The fusion of broken ends of chromosomes following nuclear fusion. Proc. Nat. Acad. Sci. Wash., 28:458–463.
1944. The relation of homozygous deficiencies to mutation and allelic series in maize. Genetics, 29:478–502.
1950*a*. The origin and behavior of mutable loci in maize. Proc. Nat. Acad. Sci. Wash., 36:344–355.
1950*b*. Mutable loci in maize. Carnegie Inst. Wash. Yearbook, 49:157–167.
1951. Chromosome organization and genic expression. Cold Spring Harbor Sympos. Quant. Biol., 16:13–48.
MCELROY, W. D., and C. P. SWANSON
1951. The theory of rate processes and gene mutation. Quart. Rev. Biol., 26:348–363.
MCKENDRICK, E., and G. PONTECORVO
1952. Crossing over between alleles at the w locus in *Drosophila melanogaster.* Experientia, 8:390–392.
MAINX, F.
1938. Analyse der Genwirkung durch Faktorencombination. Versuche mit den Augenfarbenfaktoren von *Drosophila melanogaster.* Z. indukt. Abstamm.- u. Vererb.-Lehre, 75:256–276.

MAMPELL, K.
1945. Analysis of a mutator. Genetics, 30:496–505.
1946. Genic and non-genic transmission of mutator activity. *Ibid.*, 31:589–597.
MANGELSDORF, P. C., and G. S. FRAPS
1931. A direct quantitative relationship between vitamin A in corn and the number of genes for yellow pigmentation. Science, 73:271–272.
MARSHAK, A.
1948. Evidence for a nuclear precursor of ribo- and desoxyribonucleic acid. J. Cell. Comp. Physiol., 32:381–406.
1950. Comparison of the base composition of nucleic acids of nuclei and cytoplasm of different mammalian tissues. Biol. Bull., 99:332–333.
MARSHAK, A., and C. MARSHAK
1953. Desoxyribonucleic acid in *Arbacia* eggs. Exp. Cell Res., 5:288–300.
MARTINI, E.
1924. Die Zellkonstanz und ihre Beziehung zu anderen zoologischen Vorwürfen. Z. Anat., 70:179–259.
MATHER, K.
1941. Variation and selection of polygenic characters. J. Genet., 41:159–193.
1943*a*. Polygenic balance and the canalization of development. Nature, 51:68–71.
1943*b*. Polygenic inheritance and natural selection. Biol. Rev., 18:32–64.
1944. The genetical activity of heterochromatin. Proc. Roy. Soc. London, B, 132:308–332.
1946. Genes. Sci. J. Roy. Coll. Sci., 16:64–71.
1948. Nucleus and cytoplasm in differentiation. Sympos. Soc. Exp. Biol., 2:196–216.
1953*a*. Genetical control of stability in development. Heredity, 7:297–336.
1953*b*. The genetical structure of populations. Sympos. Soc. Exp. Biol., 7:66–95.
MATHER, K., and B. J. HARRISON
1949. The manifold effects of selection. Heredity, 3:1–52.
MATTHEY, R.
1949. *Les chromosomes des vertébrés.* Lausanne: F. Rouge. 356 pp.
1951. The chromosomes of vertebrates. Advanc. Genet., 4:159–180.
MAYR, E.
1951. Speciation in birds. Proc. 10th Int. Ornithol. Congr. (Uppsala), pp. 91–131.
MAZIA, D.
1941. Enzyme studies on chromosomes. Cold Spring Harbor Sympos. Quant. Biol., 9:40–46.
1952. Physiology of the cell nucleus. In: *Modern Trends in Physiology and Biochemistry,* ed. by E. S. Barron. New York: Academic Press. Pp. 77–122.
1954. The particulate organization of the chromosome. Proc. Nat. Acad. Sci. Wash., 40:521–527.
MAZIA, D., and H. I. HIRSHFIELD
1951. Nucleus-cytoplasm relationships in the action of ultraviolet radiation on *Amoeba proteus.* Exp. Cell Res., 2:58–72.
MAZIA, D., and D. M. PRESCOTT
1955. The role of the nucleus in protein synthesis. Biochem. Biophys. Acta. (In press.)

Mechelke, F.
1953. Reversible Strukturenmodifikationen der Speicheldrüsenchromosomen von *Acricotopus lucidus*. Chromosoma, 5:511–543.
Melchers, G.
1951. Einige Probleme der Virusforschung. Ber. deutsch. bot. Ges., 63:18–23.
1952. The physiology of flower initiation. Lectures given October 13, 15, and 17, 1952, at Research Institute of Plant Physiology of Imperial College of Science and Technology, South Kensington, University of London. (Als Manuskript vervielfältigt von der Dokumentationsstelle der Max Plank-Gesellschaft zur Förderung der Wissenschaften e. V. Göttingen.)
Metz, C. W.
1938. Chromosome behavior, inheritance and sex determination in *Sciara*. Amer. Nat., 72:485–520.
Metzner, H.
1952. Cytochemische Untersuchungen über das Vorkommen von Nukleinsäuren in Chloroplasten. Biol. Zbl., 71:257–272.
Michaelis, P.
1933/1935. Entwicklungsgeschichtlich-genetische Untersuchungen an *Epilobium*. I, Z. indukt. Abstamm.- u. Vererb.-Lehre, 65:1–71; III, Planta, 32:486–500; IV, Ber. deutsch. bot. Ges., 53:143–150.
1940/1948. Ueber reziprok verschiedene Sippenbastarde bei *Epilobium hirsutum*. I, Z. indukt. Abstamm.- u. Vererb.-Lehre, 78:187–222; III, 78:295–337; V, 80:429–453; VI, 80:454–499; VII, 82:343–383.
1951. Interactions between genes and cytoplasm in *Epilobium*. Cold Spring Harbor Sympos. Quant. Biol., 16:121–130.
1954. Cytoplasmic inheritance in *Epilobium* and its theoretical significance. Advanc. Genet., 6:287–401.
Michaelis, P., and M. von Dellingshausen
1935. Entwicklungsgeschichtlich-genetische Untersuchungen an *Epilobium*. VII. Jahrb. wiss. Bot., 82:45–64.
1942. Ueber reziprok verschiedene Sippenbastarde bei *Epilobium hirsutum*. IV. Z. indukt. Abstamm.- u. Vererb.-Lehre, 80:373–428.
Mirsky, A. E.
1947. Chemical properties of isolated chromosomes. Cold Spring Harbor Sympos. Quant. Biol., 12:143–146.
Mirsky, A. E., and A. W. Pollister
1946. Chromosin, a desoxyribose nucleoprotein complex of the cell nucleus. J. Gen. Physiol., 30:117–148.
Mirsky, A. E., and H. Ris
1947*a*. Isolated chromosomes. J. Gen. Physiol., 31:1–6.
1947*b*. The chemical composition of isolated chromosomes. *Ibid.*, 31:7–18.
1951. The composition and structure of isolated chromosomes. *Ibid.*, 34:475–492.
Moewus, F.
1936. Faktorenaustausch, insbesondere der Realisatoren bei *Chlamydomonas*-Kreuzungen. Ber. deutsch. bot. Ges., 54:45–57.
1938. Vererbung des Geschlechts bei *Chlamydomonas eugametos* und verwandten Arten. Biol. Zbl., 58:516–536.

Moewus, F. (*Continued*)

1940*a*. Die Analyse von 42 erblichen Eigenschaften in der *Chlamydomonas eugametos* Gruppe. I, Z. indukt. Abstamm.- u. Vererb.-Lehre, 78:418–462; II, 78:363–500; III, 78:501–527.

1940*b*. Ueber Mutationen der Sexualgene bei *Chlamydomonas*. Biol. Zbl., 60:597–626.

1951. Die Sexualstoffe von *Chlamydomonas eugametos*. Ergebn. Enzymforsch., 12:1–37.

Mohr, O. L.

1923*a*. Das Deficiency-Phänomen bei *Drosophila melanogaster*. Z. indukt. Abstamm.- u. Vererb.-Lehre, 30:279–283.

1923*b*. A genetic and cytological analysis of a section deficiency involving four units of the X-chromosome in *Drosophila melanogaster*. *Ibid.*, 32:108–232.

1929. Exaggeration and inhibition phenomena encountered in the analysis of an autosomal dominant. *Ibid.*, 50:113–200.

1932. On the potency of mutant genes and wild type allelomorphs. Proc. 6th Int. Congr. Genet. (Ithaca), 1:190–212.

Monod, J.

1947. The phenomenon of enzymatic adaptation. Growth, 11:223–289.

Monod, J., and M. Cohn

1952. La biosynthèse induite des enzymes. (Adaptation enzymatique.) Advanc. Enzymol., 13:67–119.

Moore, A. R.

1910. A biochemical conception of dominance. Univ. Calif. Publ. Physiol., 4:9–15.

1912. On Mendelian dominance. Arch. Entw.-Mech. Org., 34:169–175.

Moore, C. R.

1944. Gonad hormones and sex differentiation. Amer. Nat., 78:97–130.

Moore, R. C.

1952. Desoxyribose-nucleic acid in embryonic diploid and haploid tissues. Chromosoma, 4:563–576.

Morgan, L. V.

1947. A variable phenotype associated with the fourth chromosome of *Drosophila melanogaster* and affected by heterochromatin. Genetics, 32:200–219.

Morgan, T. H., J. Schultz, and V. Curry

1940/1941. Investigations on the constitution of the germinal material in relation to heredity. Carnegie Inst. Wash. Yearbook, 39:251–255; 40:282–287.

Mothes, K.

1952. Die stoffliche Organisation der Pflanze. Nova Acta Leopold, N.F., 15:63–75.

Muller, H. J.

1918. Genetic variability, twin hybrids and constant hybrids, in case of balanced lethal factors. Genetics, 3:422–499.

1928*a*. The measurement of gene mutation rate in *Drosophila*, its high variability, and its dependence upon temperature. *Ibid.*, 13:279–357.

1928*b*. The problem of genic modification. Verh. 5th Int. Congr. Genet. (Berlin). Z. indukt. Abstamm.- u. Vererb.-Lehre, 1, Suppl., pp. 234–260.

1930. Types of visible variations induced by X-rays in *Drosophila*. J. Genet., 22:299–334.

1932. Further studies on the nature and causes of gene mutation. Proc. 6th Int. Congr. Genet. (Ithaca), 1:213–255.
1935*a*. On the incomplete dominance of the normal allelomorphs of white in *Drosophila*. J. Genet., 30:407–414.
1935*b*. The position effect as evidence of the localization of the immediate products of gene activity. Proc. 15th Int. Physiol. Congr. (Leningrad), 21:587–589.
1936. Bar duplication. Science, 83:528–530.
1947. The gene. Proc. Roy. Soc. London, B, 134:1–37.
1949. Presidential address. Proc. 8th Int. Congr. Genet. (Stockholm), 1948. Hereditas, 1949. Suppl., pp. 96–127.
1950*a*. Some present problems in the genetic effect of radiation. J. Cell. Comp. Physiol., 35:9–70.
1950*b*. Evidence of the precision of genetic adaptations. Harvey Lect., 1947–1948, ser. 43, 53:165–229. Springfield, Ill.: Chas. C. Thomas.
1952. Gene mutations caused by radiation. In: *Symposium on Radiobiology*, ed. by J. J. Nickson. New York: J. Wiley. Pp. 296–332.

MULLER, H. J., and E. ALTENBURG
1930. The frequency of translocations produced by X rays in *Drosophila*. Genetics, 15:283–311.

MULLER, H. J., and T. S. PAINTER
1932. The differentiation of the sex-chromosomes of *Drosophila* into genetically active and inert regions. Z. indukt. Abstamm.- u. Vererb.-Lehre, 62:316–365.

MULLER, H. J., and A. A. PROKOFYEVA
1935. The individual gene in relation to the chromomere and the chromosome. Proc. Nat. Acad. Sci. Wash., 21:16–26.

NABOURS, R. K., and F. M. STEBBINS
1950. Cytogenetics of the grouse locust *Apotettix eurycephalus*, Hancock. Agric. Exp. Sta., Kansas State Agric. Coll., Bull. 67. 116 pp.

NANNEY, D. L.
1953*a*. Nucleo-cytoplasmic interaction during conjugation in *Tetrahymena*. Biol. Bull., 105:133–148.
1953*b*. Mating type determination in *Paramecium aurelia*, a model of nucleo-cytoplasmic interaction. Proc. Nat. Acad. Sci. Wash., 39:113–119.

NEEL, J. V.
1942*a*. The polymorph mutant of *Drosophila melanogaster*. Amer. Nat., 76:630–634.
1942*b*. A study of a case of high mutation rate in *Drosophila melanogaster*. Genetics, 27:519–536.

NEUHAUS, M. E.
1939. A cytogenetic study of the Y-chromosome of *Drosophila melanogaster*. J. Genet., 37:229–254.

NIU, M. C., and V. C. TWITTY
1953. The differentiation of gastrula ectoderm in medium conditioned by axial mesoderm. Proc. Nat. Acad. Sci. Wash., 29:985–989.

NOUJDIN, N. I.
1936. Influence of the Y-chromosome and of the homologous region of the X on mosaicism in *Drosophila*. Nature, 137:319–320.

OEHLKERS, F.
1938. Bastardierungsversuche in der Gattung *Streptocarpus* Lindley. I. Z. Bot., 32:305–393.
1940. Bastardierungsversuche . . . III. Neue Ergebnisse über die Genetik von Wuchsgestalt und Geschlechtsbestimmung. Ber. deutsch. bot. Ges., 58:76–91.
1941. Bastardierungsversuche . . . IV. Weitere Untersuchungen über Plasmavererbung und Geschlechtsbestimmung. Z. Bot., 37:158–182.
1943/1949. Ueber Erbträger ausserhalb des Zellkerns. Ber. naturf. Ges. Freiburg i. B., 39:83–121.
1952*a*. Neue Ueberlegungen zum Problem der ausserkaryotischen Vererbung. Z. indukt. Abstamm.- u. Vererb.-Lehre, 84:213–250.
1952*b*. Chromosome breaks influenced by chemicals. Heredity, 6:95–105.

OFFERMANN, C. A.
1935. The position effect and its bearing on genetics. Izv. Akad. Nauk S.S.S.R., ser. 7, pp. 129–152.

OGURA, S.
1931. Erblichkeitsstudien am Seidenspinner *Bombyx mori* L. II. Ueber die Koppelung zwischen dem Häutungsfaktor und dem Faktor F. Z. indukt. Abstamm.- u. Vererb.-Lehre, 58:403–421.

OLIVER, C. P.
1932. An analysis of the effect of varying the duration of X-ray treatment upon the frequency of mutations. Z. indukt. Abstamm.- u. Vererb.-Lehre, 61:447–488.
1937. Evidence indicating that facet in *Drosophila* is due to a deficiency. Amer. Nat., 71:560–566.
1938. A reversion in *Drosophila melanogaster* which affected the dominant eye color punch and its recessive lethal. Rec. Genet. Soc. Amer., 7:82.

ONO, T.
1935. Chromosomen und Sexualität von *Rumex acetosa*. Sci. Rep. Tohoku Imp. Univ. Sapporo, 10:41–210.

OSCHMANN, A.
1914. Beitrag zum Studium der Zellverschmelzung und der cellulären Erscheinungen. I. Teil: Die Ovogenese von *Tubifex* (Ilyodrilus) *bavaricus*. Arch. Zellforsch., 12:299–358.

PAINTER, T. S.
1945. Chromatin diminution. Trans. Connecticut Acad., 36:443–448.

PAINTER, T. S., and E. C. REINDORP
1939. Endomitosis in the nurse cells of the ovary of *Drosophila melanogaster*. Chromosoma, 1:276–283.

PALAY, S. L., and A. CLAUDE
1949. An electron microscope study of the salivary gland chromosomes by the replica method. J. Exp. Med., 89:431–438.

PANSHIN, I. B.
1941. The role of heterochromatin in the position effect of the white (mottled) and cubitus interruptus genes. D. I. S., 15:33.

PATTERSON, J. T., and W. S. STONE
1952. Evolution in the genus *Drosophila*. New York: Macmillan. 610 pp.

PAULING, L., and R. B. COREY
1953. A proposed structure for the nucleic acids. Proc. Nat. Acad. Sci. Wash., 39:84–97.

Pauling, L., and M. Delbrück
1940. The nature of the intermolecular forces operative in biological processes. Science, 92:585–586.

Pauling, L., H. A. Itano, S. J. Singer, and I. C. Wells
1949. Sickle cell anemia, a molecular disease. Science, 110:543–548.

Pease, D. C., and R. F. Baker
1949. Preliminary investigations of chromosomes and genes with the electron microscope. Science, 109:8–10, 22.

Petrunkewitsch, A.
1952. Macroevolution and the fossil record of Arachnida. Amer. Scientist, 40:99–122.

Piepho, H.
1942. Untersuchungen zur Entwicklungsphysiologie der Insektenmetamorphose. Arch. Entw.-Mech. Org., 141:500–583.

Pinto-Lopes, J., and F. Resende
1949. The role of the chromatic agglutination in the origin of mutations. Portugal. Act. Biol., 2:325–336.

Pipkin, S. B.
1940. Multiple sex genes in the X-chromosome of *Drosophila melanogaster.* Univ. Texas Publ. 4032:126–156.
1942. Intersex modifying genes in wild strains of *Drosophila melanogaster.* Genetics, 27:286–298.
1947. A search for sex-genes in the second chromosome of *Drosophila melanogaster* using the triploid method. *Ibid.,* 32:592–607.

Piternick, L. K.
1949. Reverse mutations in *Drosophila melanogaster.* D. I. S., 23:96–97.

Plagge, E.
1936. Der zeitliche Verlauf der Auslösbarkeit von Hoden- und Imaginalaugenfärbung durch den A-Wirkstoff bei *Ephestia* und die zur Ausscheidung einer wirksamen Menge nötige Zeitdauer. Z. indukt. Abstamm.- u. Vererb.-Lehre, 72:127–137.

Plough, H. H., G. P. Child, and R. Blanc
1936. The effect of high temperature on the expression of heterozygotes in *D. melanogaster.* Rec. Genet. Soc. Amer., 5:203–204.

Plough, H. H., and C. F. Holthausen
1937. A case of high mutation frequency without environmental change. Amer. Nat., 71:185–187.

Plough, H. H., and P. T. Ives
1935. Induction of mutations by high temperature in *Drosophila.* Genetics, 20:42–69.

Plunkett, C. R.
1932. A contribution to the theory of dominance. Rec. Genet. Soc. Amer., 1:84–85.

Pollister, A. W., and P. F. Pollister
1943. The relation between centriole and centromere in atypical spermatogenesis of viviparid snails. Ann. N. Y. Acad. Sci., 45:1–48.

Pollister, A. W., and H. Ris
1947. Nucleoprotein determination in cytological preparations. Cold Spring Harbor Sympos. Quant. Biol., 12:147–154.

POLLISTER, A. W., H. SWIFT, and M. ALFERT
1951. Studies on the desoxypentose nucleic acid content of animal nuclei. J. Cell. Comp. Physiol., 38, Suppl. 1, pp. 101–120.
PONSE, K.
1949. *La différenciation du sexe et l'intersexualité chez les vertébrés. Facteurs héréditaires et hormones.* Lausanne: F. Rouge. 366 pp.
PONTECORVO, G.
1943. Meiosis in the striped hamster (*Cricetulus griseus* Milne-Edw.) and the problem of heterochromatin in mammalian sex chromosomes. Proc. Roy. Soc. Edinb., B, 62:32–42.
1944. Structure of heterochromatin. Nature, 153:365–367.
1952*a*. The genetical formulation of gene structure and action. Advanc. Enzymol., 13, 121–149.
1952*b*. Genetical analysis of cell organisation. Sympos. Soc. Exp. Biol., 6:218–229.
PONTECORVO, G., *et al.*
1953. The genetics of *Aspergillus nidulans.* Advanc. Genet., 5:141–238.
POPPELBAUM, H.
1914. Studien an gynandromorphen Schmetterlingsbastarden aus der Kreuzung von *Lymantria dispar,* L. mit *Japonica* Motsch. Z. indukt. Abstamm.- u. Vererb.-Lehre, 11:317–354.
POULSON, D. F.
1940. The effects of certain X-chromosome deficiencies on the embryonic development of *Drosophila melanogaster.* J. Exp. Zool., 83:271–327.
1945. Chromosomal control of embryogenesis in *Drosophila.* Amer. Nat., 79:340–364.
PREER, J. R.
1950. Microscopically visible bodies in the cytoplasm of the "killer" strains of *Paramecium aurelia.* Genetics, 35:344–362.
PROKOFYEVA-BELGOVSKAYA, A. A.
1935. The structure of the chromocenter. Cytologia, 6:438–443.
1939. Inert regions in the inner part of the X chromosome of *Drosophila melanogaster.* Izv. Akad. Nauk S.S.S.R. (Otd. mat.-est., ser. biol.), 1939 (2): 362–370.
1947. Heterochromatization as a change of chromosome cycle. J. Genet., 48:80–98.
PUNNETT, R. C.
1915. *Mimicry in Butterflies.* Cambridge: University Press. 188 pp.
RAFFEL, D., and H. J. MULLER
1940. Position effect and gene divisibility considered in connection with three strikingly similar scute mutations. Genetics, 25:541–583.
RAINIO, A. J.
1927. Ueber die Intersexualität bei der Gattung *Salix.* Ann. Zool. Soc. Zool.-Bot. Fenn. (Helsinki), 5:165–275.
RAPOPORT, J. A.
1936. Quadruple-Bar in *Drosophila melanogaster.* Bull. Biol. Méd. exp. U.R.S.S., 2:242–244.
1941. Multiple linear repetitions of the Bar gene. D. I. S., 15:36.
1942. Genetic analysis of dependent differentiation in the embryogeny of

Diptera. Izv. Akad. Nauk S.S.S.R. (Otd. mat.-est., ser. biol.), 1942: 254–282.
1947. On the synthesis of gene products in equimolecular quantities. Amer. Nat., 81:30–37.

RASMUSON, M.
1952. Variation in bristle-number of *Drosophila melanogaster*. Act. Zool., 33:277–307.

REEVE, E. C. R., and F. W. ROBERTSON
1953. Studies in quantitative inheritance. II. J. Genet., 51:276–316.

RENNER, O.
1922. Eiplasma und Pollenschlauchplasma als Vererbungsträger bei den Oenotheren. Z. indukt. Abstamm.- u. Vererb.-Lehre, 27:235–237.
1924. Die Scheckung der Oenotherenbastarde. I. Biol. Zbl., 44:309–336.
1934. Die pflanzlichen Plastiden als selbständige Elemente der genetischen Konstitution. Ber. sächs. Akad. Wiss. (Math.-Phys. Kl.), 86:241–266.
1936. Zur Kenntnis der nichtmendelnden Buntheit der Laubblätter. Flora, N.F., 30:218–290.
1942. Ueber das crossing-over bei *Oenothera*. *Ibid.*, N.F., 36:117–214.

RENNER, O., and W. KUPPER
1921. Artkreuzung bei der Gattung *Epilobium*. Ber. deutsch. bot. Ges., 39:201–206.

RENSCH, B.
1929. *Das Princip geographischer Rassenkreise und das Problem der Artbildung.* Berlin: Borntraeger. 206 pp.

RESENDE, F.
1945. Hétérochromatine. Portugal. Act. Biol., 1:137–173.

RHOADES, M. M.
1933. The cytoplasmic inheritance of male sterility in *Zea mays*. J. Genet., 27:71–93.
1936. The effect of varying gene dosage on aleurone colour in maize. *Ibid.*, 33:347–354.
1938. Effect of the Dt gene on the mutability of the a_1 allele in maize. Genetics, 23:377–397.
1941. The genetic control of mutability in maize. Cold Spring Harbor Sympos. Quant. Biol., 9:138–144.
1943. Genic induction of an inherited cytoplasmic difference. Proc. Nat. Acad. Sci. Wash., 29:327–329.
1945. On the genetic control of mutability in maize. *Ibid.*, 31:91–95.
1946. Plastid mutations. Cold Spring Harbor Sympos. Quant. Biol., 11:202–207.
1950. Gene induced mutation of a heritable cytoplasmic factor producing male sterility in maize. Proc. Nat. Acad. Wash., 36:634–635.

RIS, H.
1945. The structure of meiotic chromosomes, bearing on the nature of "chromomeres" and "lamp brush chromosomes." Biol. Bull., 89:242–257.

RIS, H., and H. CROUSE
1945. Structure of the salivary gland chromosomes of Diptera. Proc. Nat. Acad. Sci. Wash., 31:321–327.

RIS, H., and R. KLEINFELD
1952. Cytochemical studies on the chromatin elimination in *Solenobia* (Lepidoptera). Chromosoma, 5:363–371.

RIS, H., and A. E. MIRSKY

1949*a*. Quantitative cytochemical determination of desoxyribonucleic acid with the Feulgen nucleal reaction. J. Gen. Physiol., 33:125–146.

1949*b*. The state of the chromosomes in the interphase nucleus. *Ibid.*, 32:489–502.

RIZET, G.

1952. Les phénomènes de barrage chez *Podospora anserina*. I. Rev. cyt. biol. végét., 13:51–91.

ROBERTS, L. M.

1942. The effects of translocation on growth in *Zea mays*. Genetics, 27:584–603.

ROBERTSON, F. W., and REEVE, E.

1952. Studies in quantitative inheritance. I. The effects of selection on wing and thorax length in *Drosophila melanogaster*. J. Genet., 50:414–448.

ROPER, J. A.

1950. Search for linkage between genes determining a vitamin requirement. Nature, 166:956–957.

ROSE, S. M.

1952. A hierarchy of self limiting reactions as the basis of cellular differentiation and growth control. Amer. Nat., 86:337–354.

ROSEN, G. VON

1944. Artkreuzungen in der Gattung *Pisum,* insbesondere zwischen *P. sativum* L. and *P. abyssinicum* Braun. Hereditas, 30:261–400.

ROSS, H.

1939. Ueber die physiologischen Ursachen der Verschiedenheiten einiger reziproker *Epilobium*-Bastarde, insbesondere die Beteiligung von Wuchsstoff. Ber. deutsch. bot. Ges., 57:(114)–(127).

1941. Ueber die Verschiedenheit des dissimilatorischen Stoffwechsels in reziproken *Epilobium*-Bastarden und die physiologisch-genetische Ursache der reziproken Unterschiede. Z. indukt. Abstamm.- u. Vererb.-Lehre, 79:503–529.

ROUX, W.

1883. *Ueber die Bedeutung der Kerntheilungsfiguren.* Leipzig: W. Engelmann. 19 pp.

RUDKIN, G. T., H. TEMIN, and J. SCHULTZ

1953. Evidence for the equality of chromosomal material in white and wild-type bearing sections of salivary gland chromosomes of *Drosophila melanogaster*. Genetics, 38:686–687.

SAX, K.

1938. Induction by X-rays of chromosome aberrations in *Tradescantia* microspores. Genetics, 23:494–566.

1941. Types and frequencies of chromosomal aberrations induced by X-rays. Cold Spring Harbor Sympos. Quant. Biol., 9:93–103.

SCHINDEWOLF, O. H.

1950. *Grundfragen der Paläontologie*. Stuttgart: Schweizerbarth. 507 pp.

SCHLEIP, W.

1929. Die Determination der Primitiventwicklung. Leipzig: Akademische Verlagsgesellschaft. 914 pp.

SCHLÖSSER, L. A.

1935. Beitrag zu einer physiologischen Theorie der plasmatischen Vererbung. Z. indukt. Abstamm.- u. Vererb.-Lehre, 69:159–192.

SCHMIDT, W. I.
1937. Doppelbrechung von Chromosomen und Kernspindel und ihre Bedeutung für das kausale Verständnis der Mitose. Arch. exp. Zellforsch., 19:352–362.
1941. Einiges über optische Anisotropie und Feinbau von Chromatin und Chromosomen. Chromosoma, 2:86–110.

SCHRADER, F.
1951. The extrusion of desoxyribose nucleic acid from the nucleus in the formation of nutritive materials in the egg. Science, 114:486.
1953. *Mitosis. The Movements of the Chromosomes in Cell Division.* 2d ed., Columbia University Press: New York. 170 pp.

SCHRADER, F., and C. LEUCHTENBERGER
1952. The origin of certain nutritive substances in the eggs of Hemiptera. Exp. Cell Res., 3:136–146.

SCHREINER, K. E.
1916. Zur Kenntnis der Zellgranula. Untersuchungen über den feineren Bau der Haut von *Myxine glutinosa.* Arch. mikr. Anat. (Abt. 1)., 89:79–188.

SCHRÖDINGER, E.
1944. *What Is Life?* Cambridge: University Press. 91 pp.

SCHULTZ, J.
1929. The Minute reaction in the development of *Drosophila melanogaster.* Genetics, 14:366–419.
1936. Variegation in *Drosophila* and the inert chromosome regions. Proc. Nat. Acad. Sci. Wash., 22:27–33.
1941. The evidence of the nucleoprotein nature of the gene. Cold Spring Harbor Sympos. Quant. Biol., 9:55–65.
1947. The nature of heterochromatin. *Ibid.,* 12:179–191.
1952. Interrelations between nucleus and cytoplasm: problems at the biological level. Exp. Cell Res., Suppl. 2, pp. 17–43.

SCHULTZ, J., R. C. MACDUFFEE, and T. F. ANDERSON
1949. Smear preparations for the electron microscopy of animal chromosomes. Science, 110:5–7.

SCHULTZ, J., and H. REDFIELD
1951. Interchromosomal effects on crossing over in *Drosophila.* Cold Spring Harbor Sympos. Quant. Biol., 16:175–198.

SCHWARTZ, D.
1952. The effect of oxygen concentration on X-ray induced chromosome breakage in maize. Proc. Nat. Acad. Sci. Wash., 38:490–494.
1954. Studies on the mechanism of crossing over. Genetics, 39:692–700.

SCHWEMMLE, J.
1932. Review of: Wettstein, F. v., Ueber plasmatische Vererbung, sowie Plasma- und Genwirkung, II; and of: R. E. Cleland and F. Oehlkers, Erblichkeit und Zytologie verschiedener Oenotheren und ihrer Kreuzungen. Z. Bot., 25:189–194.
1941. Weitere Untersuchungen an Eu-Oenotheren über die genetische Bedeutung des Plasmas und der Plastiden. Z. indukt. Abstamm.- u. Vererb.-Lehre, 79:321–335.

SCHWEMMLE, J., E. HANSTEIN, G. STURM, and M. BINDER
1938. Genetische und zytologische Untersuchungen an Eu-Oenotheren. Teil I bis VI. Z. indukt. Abstamm.- u. Vererb.-Lehre, 75:358–800.

SCOTT-MONCRIEFF, R.

1936. A biochemical survey of some Mendelian factors for flower-colour. J. Genet., 32:115–170.

1939. The genetics and biochemistry of flower colour variation. Ergebn. Enzymforsch., 8:277–306.

SEIDEL, F.

1936. Entwicklungsphysiologie des Insektenkeims. Verh. deutsch. zool. Ges., 1936:291–336.

SEILER, J.

1914. Das Verhalten der Geschlechtschromosomen bei Lepidopteren, nebst einem Beitrag zur Kenntnis der Eireifung, Samenreifung und Befruchtung. Arch. Zellforsch., 13:159–269.

1920. Geschlechtschromosomenuntersuchungen an Psychiden. I. Experimentelle Beeinflussung der geschlechtsbestimmenden Reifeteilung bei *Talaeporia tubulosa* Retz. *Ibid.,* 15:249–268.

1949. Das Intersexualitätsphänomen. Experientia, 5:425–438.

1951. Analyse des intersexen Fühlers von *Solenobia triquetrella* (Psychidae, Lepid.). Rev. suisse Zool., 58:489–495.

SEILER. J., and C. B. HANIEL

1921. Das verschiedene Verhalten der Chromosomen in Eireifung und Samenreifung von *Lymantria monacha* L. Z. indukt. Abstamm.- u. Vererb.-Lehre, 27:81–103.

SENGÜN, A.

1948. Vergleichend-ontogenetische Untersuchungen über die Riesenchromosomen verschiedener Gewebe der Chironomiden. I. Comm. Fac. Sci. Univ. Ankara, 1:187–248.

SENGÜN, A., and C. KOSSWIG

1947. Weiteres über den Bau der Riesenchromosomen in verschiedenen Geweben von *Chironomus*-Larven. Chromosoma, 3:195–207.

SEREBROVSKY, S.

1930. Untersuchungen über Treppenallelomorphismus. IV. Arch. Entw.-Mech. Org., 122:88–104.

SERRA, J. A.

1947. Composition of chromonemata and matrix and the role of nucleoproteins in mitosis and meiosis. Cold Spring Harbor Sympos. Quant. Biol., 12:192–210.

1949. A cytophysiological theory of the gene, gene mutation and position effect. Portugal. Act. Biol., Sér. A, Volume R. B. Goldschmidt, pp. 401–562.

SHEN, T. H.

1932. Zytologische Untersuchungen über Sterilität beim Männchen von *Drosophila melanogaster.* Z. Zellforsch., 15:547–580.

1936. Beiträge zum Studium der Geschlechtsbestimmung bei *Dinophilus apatris.* Zool. Jahrb. (Physiol.), 56:219–238.

SINGLETON, R. W.

1951. Inheritance of corn grass a macromutation in maize, and its possible significance as an ancestral type. Amer. Nat., 85:81–96.

SIRKS, M. J.

1937. Plasma-Aenderung als Ursache einer Knospenvariation. Z. indukt. Abstamm.- u. Vererb.-Lehre, 73:367–373.

1938. A case of bud variation in *Phaseolus* caused by a transitory plasmatic change. Genetica, 20:121–158.

SIVERTZEV-DOBZHANSKY, N. P., and TH. DOBZHANSKY

1933. Deficiency and duplications for the gene bobbed in *Drosophila melanogaster*. Genetics, 18:173–192.

SKOVSTEDT, A.

1943. Successive mutations in *Nadsonia Richteri* Kostka. C. R. Lab. Carlsberg (ser. physiol.), 23:409–453.

SLIZYNSKI, B. M.

1945. "Ectopic" pairing and the distribution of heterochromatin in the X-chromosome of the salivary gland nuclei of *Drosophila melanogaster*. Proc. Roy. Soc. Edinb., B, 62:114–119.

SLONIMSKI, P. P.

1952. Recherches sur la formation des enzymes respiratoires chez la levure. Thesis, Paris. Quoted by Ephrussi in: *Nucleo-Cytoplasmic Relations in Micro-Organisms*. Oxford: Clarendon Press, 1953. 127 pp.

SMITH, S. G.

1952. The evolution of heterochromatin in the genus *Tribolium* (Tenebrionidae, Coleoptera). Chromosoma, 4:585–610.

SOBEL, F. H.

1952. Genetics and morphology of the genotype "Asymmetric." Genetica, 26: 117–279.

SONNEBORN, T. M.

1943*a*. Gene and cytoplasm. I. The determination and inheritance of the killer character in variety 4 of *Paramecium aurelia*. Proc. Nat. Acad. Sci. Wash., 29:329–338.

1943*b*. Gene and cytoplasm. II. The bearing of the determination and inheritance of characters in *Paramecium aurelia* on the problems of cytoplasmic inheritance, pneumococcus transformations, mutations and development. *Ibid.*, 29:338–343.

1947. Recent advances in the genetics of *Paramecium* and *Euplotes*. Advanc. Genet., 1:263–358.

1949. Beyond the gene. Amer. Scientist, 37:33–59.

1950. The cytoplasm in heredity. Heredity, 4:11–36.

1951*a*. The role of genes in cytoplasmic inheritance. In:*Genetics in the Twentieth Century*, ed. by L. C. Dunn. New York: Macmillan. Pp. 291–314.

1951*b*. Some current problems of genetics in the light of investigations on *Chlamydomonas* and *Paramecium*. Cold Spring Harbor Sympos. Quant. Biol., 16:483–503.

1954. Patterns of nucleocytoplasmic integration in *Paramecium*. Proc. 9th Int. Congr. Genet. (In press. Quoted from mimeographed MS.)

SPEMANN, H. C.

1938. *Embryonic Development and Induction*. New Haven: Yale University Press. 401 pp.

SPIEGELMAN, S.

1948. Differentiation as the controlled production of unique enzymatic patterns. Sympos. Soc. Exp. Biol., 2:286–325.

SPIEGELMAN, S., and M. D. KAMEN

1947. Some basic problems in the relation of nucleic acid to protein synthesis. Cold Spring Harbor Sympos. Quant. Biol., 12:211–222.

STADLER, L. J.

1928. The rate of induced mutation in relation to dormancy, temperature and dosage. Anat. Rec., 41:97.

1932. On the genetic nature of induced mutations in plants. Proc. 6th Int. Congr. Genet. (Ithaca), 1:274–294.

1941. The comparison of ultraviolet and X-ray effects on mutation. Cold Spring Harbor Sympos. Quant. Biol., 9:168–178.

1946/1950. Spontaneous mutation at the R-locus in maize. I, Genetics, 31:377–394; II, Amer. Nat., 82:289–314; III, *ibid.*, 83:5–30; IV, Portugal. Act. Biol., Ser. A, Volume R. B. Goldschmidt, pp. 785–797.

1951. Spontaneous mutation in maize. Cold Spring Harbor Sympos. Quant. Biol., 16:49–64.

1954. The gene. Science, 120:811–819.

STANDFUSS, M.

1914. Mitteilungen zur Vererbungsfrage. Mitt. schweiz. ent. Ges., 12:238–308.

STAUDT, G.

1952. Cytogenetische Untersuchungen an *Fragaria orientalis* Los. und ihre Bedeutung für Artbildung und Geschlechtsdifferenzierung in der Gattung *Fragaria,* L. Z. indukt. Abstamm.- u. Vererb.-Lehre, 84:361–416.

STEBBINS, G. L.

1950. *Variation and Evolution in Plants.* New York: Columbia University Press. 643 pp.

STEDMAN, E., and E. STEDMAN

1943. Chromosomin, a protein constituent of chromosomes. Nature, 152:267–269.

1947. The function of desoxyribose-nucleic acid in the cell nucleus. Sympos. Soc. Exp. Biol., 1:232–251.

STEIN, E.

1939. Ueber einige Pfropfversuche mit erblichen, durch Radiumbestrahlung erzeugten Varianten von *Antirrhinum majus, Antirrhinum siculum,* und *Solanum lycopersicum.* Biol. Zbl., 59:59–78.

STEINBERG, A. G.

1941. A reconsideration of the mode of development of the Bar eye of *Drosophila melanogaster.* Genetics, 26:325–346.

1943. The development of the wild type and Bar eyes of *Drosophila melanogaster.* Canad. J. Res., 21:277–283.

STEPHENS, S. C.

1948. A biochemical basis of the pseudoallelic anthocyanin series in *Gossypium.* Genetics, 33:191–214.

1951*a*. "Homologous" genetic loci in *Gossypium.* Cold Spring Harbor Sympos. Quant. Biol., 16:131–142.

1951*b*. Possible significance of duplication in evolution. Advanc. Genet., 4:247–265.

STERN, C.

1929*a*. Ueber die additive Wirkung multipler Allele. Biol. Zbl., 49:261–290.

1929*b*. Untersuchungen über Aberrationen des Y-chromosoms von *Drosophila melanogaster*. Z. indukt. Abstamm.- u. Vererb.-Lehre, 51:253–353.
1930. *Multiple Allele*. Handb. Vererbungswiss. I, G. Berlin: Borntraeger. 147 pp.
1935. The effect of yellow-scute gene deficiency on somatic cells of *Drosophila*. Proc. Nat. Acad. Sci. Wash., 21:374–379.
1936. Somatic crossing over and segregation in *Drosophila melanogaster*. Genetics, 21:625–730.
1938. During which stage in the nuclear cycle do the genes produce their effects in the cytoplasm? Amer. Nat., 72:350–357.
1939. Recent work on the relation between genes and developmental processes. Growth, 1, Suppl., pp. 19–36.
1940. The prospective significance of imaginal discs in *Drosophila*. J. Morph., 67:107–122.
1943. Genic action as studied by means of the effects of different doses and combinations of alleles. Genetics, 28:441–475.
1948. The effects of change in quantity, combination and position of genes. Science, 108:615–621.
1954. Two or three bristles. Amer. Scientist, 42:213–247.

STERN, C., and E. HADORN
1938. The determination of sterility in *Drosophila* males without a complete Y-chromosome. Amer. Nat., 72:42–52.

STERN, C., and A. HANNAH
1950. The sex combs in gynanders of *Drosophila melanogaster*. Portugal. Act. Biol., Sér. A, Volume R. B. Goldschmidt, pp. 798–812.

STERN, C., and G. HEIDENTHAL
1944. Material for the study of the position effect of normal and mutant genes. Proc. Nat. Acad. Sci. Wash., 30:197–205.

STERN, C., R. H. MACKNIGHT, and M. KODANI
1946. The phenotypes of homozygotes and hemizygotes of position alleles and of heterozygotes between alleles in normal and translocated positions. Genetics, 31:598–619.

STERN, C., and S. OGURA
1931. Neue Untersuchungen über Aberrationen des Y-chromosoms von *Drosophila melanogaster*. Z. indukt. Abstamm.- u. Vererb.-Lehre, 58:81–121.

STERN, C., and E. W. SCHAEFFER
1943. On wild type isoalleles in *Drosophila melanogaster*. Proc. Nat. Acad. Sci. Wash., 29:361–367.

STERN, C., E. W. SCHAEFFER, and G. HEIDENTHAL
1946. A comparison between the position effects of normal and mutant alleles. Proc. Nat. Acad. Sci. Wash., 32:26–33.

STICH, H., and J. HÄMMERLING
1953. Der Einbau von ^{32}P in die Nucleolarsubstanz des Zellkernes von *Acetabularia mediterranea*. Z. Naturf., 8*b*:329–333.

STONE, W. S., F. HAAS, J. B. CLARK, and O. WYSS
1948. The rôle of mutation and of selection in the frequency of mutants among microörganisms grown on irradiated substrate. Proc. Nat. Acad. Sci. Wash., 34:142–149.

STONE, W. S., O. WYSS, and F. HAAS
1947. The production of mutations in *Staphylococcus aureus* by irradiation of the substrate. Proc. Nat. Acad. Sci. Wash., 33:59–66.

STORMONT, C.
1950. Additional gene controlled antigenic factors in the bovine erythrocyte. Genetics, 35:76–94.

STORMONT, C., R. D. OWEN, and M. R. IRWIN
1951. The B and C systems of bovine blood groups. Genetics, 36:134–161.

STUBBE, H.
1952. Ueber einige theoretische und praktische Fragen der Mutationsforschung. Abh. sächs. Akad. Wiss. Leipzig, 47:1–23.

STUBBE, H., and F. VON WETTSTEIN
1941. Ueber die Bedeutung von Klein- und Grossmutationen in der Evolution. Biol. Zbl., 61:265–297.

STURTEVANT, A. H.
1925. The effects of unequal crossing-over at the Bar locus in *Drosophila*. Genetics, 10:117–147.
1939. High mutation frequency induced by hybridization. Proc. Nat. Acad. Sci. Wash., 25:308–310.
1945. A gene in *Drosophila melanogaster* that transforms females into males. Genetics, 30:297–299.
1946. Intersexes dependent on a maternal effect in hybrids between *Drosophila repleta* and *D. neorepleta*. Proc. Nat. Acad. Sci. Wash., 32:84–87.

STURTEVANT, A. H., and G. W. BEADLE
1936. The relations of inversions in the X-chromosome of *Drosophila melanogaster* to crossing-over and disjunction. Genetics, 21:554–604.

STURTEVANT, A. H., and E. NOVITSKI
1941. The homologies of the chromosome elements in the genus *Drosophila*. Genetics, 26:517–541.

SÜFFERT, F.
1924. Bestimmungsfaktoren des Zeichnungsmusters beim Saisondimorphismus von *Araschnia levana-prorsa*. Biol. Zbl., 44:173–188.

SUMNER, F. B.
1915. Genetic studies of several geographic races of California deer-mice. Amer. Nat., 49:688–701.
1932. Genetic, distributional and evolutionary studies of the subspecies of deer-mice (*Peromyscus*). Genetica, 9:1–106.

SUTTON, E.
1940. Terminal deficiencies in the X-chromosome of *Drosophila melanogaster*. Genetics, 25:628–635.
1941. The structure of euchromatic and heterochromatic translocations in the salivary gland chromosomes of *Drosophila melanogaster*. Proc. 7th Int. Congr. Genet. (Edinburgh). Cambridge: issued as Suppl. to J. Genet., p. 279.
1943*a*. Bar eye in *Drosophila melanogaster:* a cytological analysis of some mutations and reverse mutations. Genetics, 28:97–107.
1943*b*. A cytogenetic study of the yellow-scute region of the X-chromosome in *Drosophila melanogaster*. *Ibid.*, 28:210–217.

SWIFT, H.
1953. Quantitative aspects of nuclear nucleoproteins. Int. Rev. Cytol., 2:1–76.
SYMPOSIUM ON CHROMOSOME BREAKAGE
1953. Heredity, 6, Suppl. Springfield, Ill.: C. C. Thomas. 315 pp.
SYMPOSIUM ON BIOCHEMISTRY OF NUCLEIC ACIDS
1951. J. Cell. Comp. Physiol., 38, Suppl. 1. Oak Ridge, Tenn., 1950. 245 pp.
TANAKA, Y.
1924. Maternal inheritance in *Bombyx mori* L. Genetics, 9:479–486.
1953. Genetics of the silkworm, *Bombyx mori*. Advanc. Genet., 5:239–317.
TATUM, E. L.
1946. Induced biochemical mutations in bacteria. Cold Spring Harbor Sympos. Quant. Biol., 11:278–284.
TATUM, E. L., and D. D. PERKINS
1950. Genetics of microorganisms. Ann. Rev. Microbiol., 4:129–150.
TAYLOR, H. E.
1950. Biochemical significance of the transforming principles of *Pneumococcus*. Pubbl. Staz. zool. Napoli, 22, Suppl., pp. 1–14.
TAZIMA, Y.
1943. Studies on chromosomal aberrations in the silkworm. I (in Japanese). Bull. Imp. Sericult. Exp. Sta. Tokyo, 11:525–604.
1944. Studies on chromosomal aberrations in the silkworm. II (with English summary). *Ibid.*, 12:109–181.
THIMANN, K. V.
1952. Plant growth hormones. In: *Action of Hormones in Plants and Invertebrates*, ed. by K. V. Thimann. New York: Academic Press. 228 pp.
THODAY, J. M., and J. READ
1947. Effect of oxygen on the frequency of chromosome aberrations produced by X-rays. Nature, 160:608.
THOMAS, P. T., and S. H. REVELL
1946. Secondary association and heterochromatic attraction. I. *Cicer arietinum*. Ann. Bot., N.S., 10:159–164.
TIMOFÉEFF-RESSOVSKY, H.
1927. Studies on the phenotypic manifestation of hereditary factors. I. Genetics, 12:128–198.
1931. Ueber phänotypische Manifestierung der polytopen (pleiotropen) Genovariation Polyphaen von *Drosophila funebris*. Naturwissenschaften, 19:765–768.
1934. Ueber den Einfluss des genotypischen Milieus und der Aussenbedingungen auf die Realisation des Genotyps. Nachr. Ges. Wiss. Göttingen (Math.-Phys. Kl., Biol.), N.F., 1:53–104.
TIMOFÉEFF-RESSOVSKY, H., and K. G. ZIMMER
1947. *Das Trefferprinzip in der Biologie*. Leipzig: Hirzel. 317 pp.
TIMOFÉEFF-RESSOVSKY, H., K. G. ZIMMER, and M. DELBRÜCK
1935. Ueber die Natur der Genmutation und der Genstruktur. Nachr. Ges. Wiss. Göttingen (Math.-Phys. Kl., Biol.), N.F., 1:189–245.
TOBGY, H. A.
1943. A cytological study of *Crepis fuliginosa, C. neglecta* and their F_1 hybrid, and its bearing on the mechanism of phylogenetic reduction in chromosome number. J. Genet., 45:67–111.

TOYAMA, K.

1913. Maternal inheritance and Mendelism. J. Genet., 2:351–404.

TROLAND, L.

1917. Biological enigmas and the theory of enzyme action. Amer. Nat., 51:321–350.

TSCHERMAK-WOESS, E., and G. HASITSCHKA

1954. Ueber die endomitotische Polyploidisierung im Zuge der Differenzierung von Trichomen und Trichozyten bei Angiospermen. Oest. bot. Z., 101:79–117.

UBISCH, L. VON

1943. Ueber die Bedeutung der Diminution von *Ascaris megalocephala.* Act. Biotheor., 7:163–182.

1952. Die Entwicklung der Monascidien. Verh. Kon. nederl. Akad. Wetensch., 2d ser., 49:1–56.

1953. *Entwicklungsprobleme.* Jena: Fischer. 196 pp.

1954. Ueber Seeigelmerogone. Pubbl. Staz. zool. Napoli, 25:246–340.

VANDEL, A.

1931. *La parthénogenèse* (Encyclopédie scientifique). Paris: G. Doin. 412 pp.

1938. Recherches sur la sexualité des Isopodes. III. Bull. Biol. France, Belg., 72:147–186.

1941. Recherches . . . VI. *Ibid.,* 75:316–368.

1945. Recherches . . . IX. *Ibid.,* 79:168–216.

1947. Recherches . . . X. *Ibid.,* 81:154–176.

VANDERHAEGHE, F.

1952. Mesure de croissance de fragments nucléees et énucléees d'*Acetabularia mediterranea.* Arch. int. Physiol., 60:190–191.

VILLEE, C. A.

1943. Phenogenetic studies of the homoeotic mutants of *Drosophila melanogaster.* I. J. Exp. Zool., 93:75–98.

1944. Phenogenetic studies . . . II. *Ibid.,* 96:85–102.

1945*a*. Phenogenetic studies . . . III. Amer. Nat., 79:246–258.

1945*b*. Developmental interactions of homoeotic and growth rate genes in *Drosophila melanogaster.* J. Morph., 77:105–118.

1946. Phenogenetic studies of homoeotic mutants of *Drosophila melanogaster.* IV. Genetics, 31:428–437.

VIRKKI, N.

1951. Zur Zytologie einiger Scarabaeiden (Coleoptera). Ann. Zool. Soc. Zool.-Bot. Fenn. (Helsinki), 14:1–99.

VISCONTI, N., and M. DELBRÜCK

1953. The mechanism of genetic recombination in phage. Genetics, 38:5–33.

VOGT, M.

1946/1947. Zur labilen Determination der Imaginalscheiben von *Drosophila.* I, Biol. Zbl., 65:223–238; II, *ibid.,* 65:238–254; III, *ibid.,* 66:81–105; V, *ibid.,* 66:388–395; IV, Z. Naturf., 1:469–475.

WADDINGTON, C. H.

1940*a*. The genetic control of wing development in *Drosophila.* J. Genet., 41:75–139.

1940*b*. *Organisers and Genes.* Cambridge: University Press. 160 pp.

1948. The genetic control of development. Sympos. Soc. Exp. Biol., 2:145–154.

1950. Genetic factors in morphogenesis. Rev. suisse Zool., 57:153–168.

1953*a*. Epigenetics and evolution. Sympos. Soc. Exp. Biol., 7:186–199.
1953*b*. The interactions of some morphogenetic genes in *Drosophila melanogaster*. J. Genet., 51:243–258.
1954. The cell physiology of early development. Colston Papers, 7:105–119.

WAGNER, R. P.
1949. The in vitro synthesis of pantothenic acid by pantothenicless and wild type *Neurospora*. Proc. Nat. Acad. Sci. Wash., 35:185–189.

WAGNER, R. P., and C. H. HADDOX
1951. A further analysis of the pantothenicless mutants of *Neurospora*. Amer. Nat., 85:319–330.

WAGNER, R. P., R. FUERST, and W. S. STONE
1950. The effect of irradiated medium, cyanide and peroxide on the mutation rate in *Neurospora*. Genetics, 35:237–248.

WARDLAW, C. W.
1952. *Phylogeny and Morphogenesis*. New York: St. Martins Press. 536 pp.

WATSON, D., and F. H. CRICK
1953*a*. Genetical implications of the structure of deoxyribonucleic acid. Nature, 171:964–967.
1953*b*. Molecular structure of nucleic acids. *Ibid.*, 171:737–739.

WEIER, T. E., and C. R. STOCKING
1952. The chloroplast: structure, inheritance and enzymology. II. Bot. Rev., 18:14–75.

WEIR, J. A.
1953. Sparing genes for further evolution. Iowa Agric. Exp. Sta., Journal paper I-1370:313–319.

WEISMANN, A.
1875. Studien zur Descendenz-Theorie. Leipzig: W. Engelmann. 431 pp.

WEISS, P.
1947. The problem of specificity in growth and development. Yale J. Biol. Med., 19:235–278.
1950. Perspectives in the field of morphogenesis. Quart. Rev. Biol., 25:177–198.

WEISZ, P. B.
1951. A general mechanism of differentiation based on morphogenetic studies in ciliates. Amer. Nat., 85:293–311.

WENT, F. W., and K. V. THIMANN
1937. *Phytohormones*. New York: Macmillan. 249 pp.

WESSING, A.
1953. Histologische Untersuchungen zu den Problemen der Zellkonstanz. Zool. Jahrb. (Anat)., 73:69–102.

WESTERGAARD, M.
1948. The relation between chromosome constitution and sex in the offspring of triploid *Melandrium*. Hereditas, 34:257–279.
1953. Ueber den Mechanismus der Geschlechtsbestimmung bei *Melandrium album*. Naturwissenschaften, 40:253–260.

WETTSTEIN, D. VON
1954. The pleiotropic effect of erectoides factors and their bearing on the property of straw-stiffness. Act. agric. scand., 4:491–506.

Wettstein, F. von

1924. Morphologie und Physiologie des Formwechels der Moose auf genetischer Grundlage. I. Z. indukt. Abstamm.- u. Vererb.-Lehre, 33:1–236.

1928*a*. Morphologie . . . II. Bibl. Genet., 10:1–216.

1928*b*. Ueber plasmatische Vererbung und das Zusammenwirken von Genen und Plasma. Ber. deutsch. bot. Ges., 46:32–49.

1936. Gesichertes und problematisches zur Geschlechtsbestimmung. *Ibid.*, 54:23–38.

1946. Untersuchungen zur plasmatischen Vererbung. I. *Linum*. Biol. Zbl., 65:149–166.

White, M. J. D.

1945. *Animal Cytology and Evolution.* Cambridge: University Press. 375 pp. 2d ed., 1954.

1950. Cytological studies of gall midges (Cecidomyidae). Univ. Texas Publ. 5007:1–80.

1951. Cytogenetics of orthopteroid insects. Advanc. Genet., 4:267–330.

Whiting, P. W.

1943. Multiple alleles in complementary sex determination of *Habrobracon.* Genetics, 28:365–382.

1945. The evolution of male haploidy. Quart. Rev. Biol., 20:231–260.

Whittaker, E.

1952. Eddington's principle in the philosophy of science. Amer. Scientist, 40:45–60.

Wigglesworth, V. B.

1934. The physiology of ecdysis in *Rhodnius prolixus.* II. Quart. J. Micr. Sci., 77:191–222.

1940. The determination of characters at metamorphosis in *Rhodnius prolixus* (Hemiptera). J. Exp. Biol., 17:201–222.

1952. Hormone balance and the control of metamorphosis in *Rhodnius prolixus* (Hemiptera). *Ibid.*, 29:620–631.

1953. Determination of cell function in an insect. J. Embr. Exp. Morph., 1:269–277.

Williams, C. R.

1945. Prolongation of larval-pupal development in *Drosophila melanogaster* and its effect on facet number. Amer. Nat., 79:259–270.

Winge, Ø.

1937. Goldschmidt's theory of sex determination in *Lymantria.* J. Genet., 34:81–89.

Winge, Ø., and O. Laustsen

1940. On a cytoplasmatic effect of inbreeding in homozygous yeast. C. R. Lab. Carlsberg (ser. physiol.), 23:17–40.

Winkler, H.

1924. Ueber die Rolle von Kern und Protoplasma bei der Vererbung. Z. indukt. Abstamm.- u. Vererb.-Lehre, 33:238–253.

1930. *Die Konversion der Gene. Eine vererbungstheoretische Untersuchung.* Jena: G. Fischer. 186 pp.

Witschi, E.

1914*a*. Experimentelle Untersuchungen über die Entwicklungsgeschichte der Keimdrüsen von *Rana temporaria.* Arch. mikr. Anat., 85:9–113.

1914*b*. Studien über die Geschlechtsbestimmung bei Fröschen. *Ibid.*, 86:1–50.
1929. Bestimmung und Vererbung des Geschlechts bei Tieren. Handb. Vererbungswiss., II, D. Berlin: Borntraeger. 116 pp.
1939. Modification of development of sex. In: *Sex and Internal Secretions*, ed. by E. Allen. 2d ed., Baltimore: Williams and Wilkins. Pp. 145–226.
1950. Génétique et physiologie de la différenciation du sexe. Arch. d'Anat. micr. et morph. expér., 39:215–246.

WOLTERECK, R.
1942. Neue Organe, durch postembryonale Umkonstruktion aus Fischflossen entstehend. Rev. ges. Hydrobiol., 42:317–355.

WRIGHT, S.
1916. An intensive study of the inheritance of color and other coat characters in guinea pigs, with special reference to graded series. In: Studies of inheritance in guinea pigs and rats, by W. E. Castle and S. Wright. Carnegie Inst. Wash. Publ. 241:59–160.
1925. The factors of the albino series of guinea pigs and their effects on black and yellow pigmentation. Genetics, 10:223–260.
1927. The effects in combination of the major color-factors of guinea pigs. *Ibid.*, 12:530–569.
1931. Evolution in Mendelian populations. *Ibid.*, 16:97–159.
1934*a*. Physiological and evolutionary theories of dominance. Amer. Nat., 68:24–53.
1934*b*. An analysis of variability in number of digits in an inbred strain of guinea pigs. Genetics, 19:506–536.
1934*c*. On the genetics of subnormal development of the head (otocephaly) in the guinea pig. *Ibid.*, 19:471–505.
1935. A mutation of the guinea pig, tending to restore the pentadactyl foot when heterozygous, producing a monstrosity when homozygous. *Ibid.*, 20:84–107.
1941. The physiology of the gene. Physiol. Rev., 21:487–527.
1942. The physiological genetics of coat color of the guinea pig. Biol. Sympos., 6:337–355.
1945*a*. Physiological aspects of genetics. Ann. Rev. Physiol., 7:75–106.
1945*b*. Genes as physiological agents. Amer. Nat., 79:289–303.
1949. Adaptation and selection. In: *Genetics, Paleontology, and Evolution*, ed. by G. L. Jepsen. Princeton: University Press. Pp. 365–389.
1950. Population structure as a factor in evolution. Moderne Biologie, Festschrift H. Nachtsheim. Berlin: F. W. Peters. Pp. 275–287.
1953. Gene and organism. Amer. Nat., 87:5–18.

WRIGHT, S., and K. WAGNER
1934. Types of subnormal development of the head from inbred strains of guinea pigs and their bearing on the classification and interpretation of vertebrate monsters. Amer. J. Anat., 54:383–447.

WRINCH, D. M.
1936. On the molecular structure of chromosomes. Protoplasma, 25:550–569.

ZELENY, C.
1920. A change in the bar gene of *Drosophila melanogaster* involving further decrease in facet number and increase in dominance. J. Exp. Zool., 30:293–324.

ZIMMERMAN, E. C.
1948. *Insects of Hawaii.* Honolulu: University of Hawaii Press. 5 vols.
ZINDER, N. D.
1953. Infective heredity in bacteria. Cold Spring Harbor Sympos. Quant. Biol., 18:261–269.
ZINDER, N. D., and J. LEDERBERG
1952. Genetic exchange in *Salmonella.* J. Bact., 64:679–699.
ZWILLING, E., and J. T. DEBELL
1950. Micromelia and growth retardation as independent effects of sulfanilamide in chick embryos. J. Exp. Zool., 115:59–81.

INDICES

INDEX OF AUTHORS

SUBJECT INDEX